The Role of Products of the Histocompatibility Gene Complex in Immune Responses

ACADEMIC PRESS RAPID MANUSCRIPT REPRODUCTION

*Proceedings of an International Conference Held at
Brook Lodge, Augusta, Michigan
November 3-7, 1975*

The Role of Products of the Histocompatibility Gene Complex in Immune Responses

Edited by
DAVID H. KATZ, M.D.
BARUJ BENACERRAF, M.D.

Department of Pathology
Harvard Medical School
Boston, Massachusetts

ACADEMIC PRESS INC.
New York   San Francisco   London   1976
A Subsidiary of Harcourt Brace Jovanovich, Publishers

ACADEMIC PRESS, INC.
111 Fifth Avenue, New York, New York 10003

United Kingdom Edition published by
ACADEMIC PRESS, INC. (LONDON) LTD.
24/28 Oval Road, London NW1

Library of Congress Cataloging in Publication Data

Main entry under title:

The Role of products of the histocompatibility gene
    complex in immune responses.

        Bibliography: p.
        Includes index.
        1.   Histocompatibility–Congresses.   2.   Immune
response–Congresses.   3.   H-2 locus–Congresses.
I.   Katz, David H.   II.   Benacerraf, Baruj,   (date)
[DNLM: 1.   Immune tolerance–Congresses.   2.   His-
tocompatibility antignes–Congresses.   QW504 R745 1975]
QR184.3.R64   616.07'9   76-4854
ISBN 0–12–401660–X

PRINTED IN THE UNITED STATES OF AMERICA

Contents

CONTENTS

CONTENTS

SESSION IV: GENETIC CONTROL OF CELL INTERACTIONS
WILLIAM PAUL, CHAIRMAN

SESSION V: IDIOTYPIC DETERMINANTS ON T CELL
RECEPTORS
DAVID H. KATZ, CHAIRMAN

Participants

D. Bernard Amos
Department of Microbiology and
  Immunology
Duke University Medical Center
Durham, North Carolina 27710

Dieter Armerding
Department of Pathology
Harvard Medical School
Boston, Massachusetts 02115

Fritz H. Bach
Immunobiology Research Center
University of Wisconsin
Madison, Wisconsin 53706

Baruj Benacerraf
Department of Pathology
Harvard Medical School
Boston, Massachusetts 02115

Kathleen Bechtol
Department of Zoology
University of Oxford
South Parks Road
Oxford OX 1 3PS England

Bruce A. Cunningham
Rockefeller University
New York, New York 10021

Jean Dausset
Université de Paris VII
Hospital St. Louis
Place du Docteur-Fournier
Paris, France

Martin E. Dorf
Department of Pathology
Harvard Medical School
Boston, Massachusetts 02115

Bo Dupont
Memorial Sloan-Kettering Cancer Center
1275 York Avenue
New York, New York 10021

David L. Gasser
Department of Human Genetics
University of Pennsylvania
Philadelphia, Pennsylvania 19174

Richard Gershon
Department of Pathology
Yale Medical School
New Haven, Connecticut 06510

Ira Green
Laboratory of Immunology
National Institute of Allergy and
  Infectious Diseases
National Institutes of Health
Bethesda, Maryland 20014

Howard Grey
National Jewish Hospital and Research
  Center
Denver, Colorado 80206

Günter Hämmerling
Institut für Genetik
  der Universität zu Köln
5 Köln-Lindenthal
Weyertal 121 Germany

Leroy Hood
Department of Biology
California Institute of Technology
Pasadena, California 91109

Bernard W. Janicki
Extramural Programs
National Institute of Allergy &
    Infectious Diseases
National Institutes of Health
Bethesda, Maryland 20014

Judith Kapp
Department of Pathology
Harvard Medical School
Boston, Massachusetts 02115

David H. Katz
Department of Pathology
Harvard Medical School
Boston, Massachusetts 02115

Rolf Kiessling
Department of Tumor Biology
Karolinska Institutet
S-104 01 Stockholm 60
Sweden

George Klein
Department of Tumor Biology
Karolinska Institutet
S-104 01 Stockholm 60
Sweden

Jan Klein
Department of Microbiology
University of Texas
Southwestern Medical School
Dallas, Texas 75235

Henry G. Kunkel
Rockefeller University
New York, New York 10021

Rose Lieberman
Laboratory of Immunology
National Institute of Allergy and
    Infectious Diseases
National Institutes of Health
Bethesda, Maryland 20014

Paul H. Maurer
Department of Biochemistry
Jefferson Medical College
Philadelphia, Pennsylvania 19107

Hugh O. McDevitt
Department of Medicine
Stanford University Medical Center
Stanford, California 94305

Tommaso Meo
Department of Genetics
Washington University School of
    Medicine
St. Louis, Missouri 63110

J.F.A.P. Miller
The Walter and Eliza Hall Institute
    of Medical Research
Royal Melbourne Hospital
Victoria 3050, Australia

Erna Möller
Division of Immunobiology
Karolinska Institute
Wallenberg Laboratory
104 05 Stockholm 50, Sweden

Edna Mozes
Department of Chemical Immunology
Weizmann Institute of Science
Rehovoth, Israel

Alan J. Munro
Immunology Division
Department of Pathology
Tennis Court Road
Cambridge, England

Stanley G. Nathenson
Dept. Microbiology and Immunobiology
Albert Einstein College of Medicine
Bronx, New York 10461

G.J.V. Nossal
The Walter and Eliza Hall Institute of
    Medical Research
Royal Melbourne Hospital
Victoria 3050, Australia

William E. Paul
Laboratory of Immunology
National Institute of Allergy and
    Infectious Diseases
National Institutes of Health
Bethesda, Maryland 20014

Carl W. Pierce
Department of Pathology
Harvard Medical School
Boston, Massachusetts 02115

Klaus Rajewsky
Institut für Genetik der
    Universität zu Köln
5 Köln-Lindenthal
Weyertal 121, Germany

Alan Rosenthal
Laboratory of Clinical Investigation
National Institute of Allergy and
    Infectious Diseases
National Institutes of Health
Bethesda, Maryland 20014

David H. Sachs
Immunology Branch
National Cancer Institute
National Institutes of Health
Bethesda, Maryland 20014

Michael Sela
Department of Chemical Immunology
Weizmann Institute of Science
Rehovoth, Israel

Gene M. Shearer
Immunology Branch
National Cancer Institute
National Institutes of Health
Bethesda, Maryland 20014

Ethan M. Shevach
Laboratory of Immunology
National Institute of Allergy and
    Infectious Diseases
National Institutes of Health
Bethesda, Maryland 20014

Donald C. Shreffler
Department of Genetics
Washington University School of
    Medicine
St. Louis, Missouri 63110

Morten Simonsen
University of Copenhagen
Nørre Alle 71
DK 2100 Copenhagen Ø
Denmark

Jack H. Stimpfling
McLaughlin Research Institute
Columbus Hospital
Great Falls, Montana 59401

Jack L. Strominger
Department of Biochemistry and
    Molecular Biology
Harvard University
Cambridge, Massachusetts 02138

Tomio Tada
Immunology Research Laboratories
School of Medicine
Chiba University
Chiba, Japan

Michael Taussig
Basel Institute for Immunology
478, Grenzacherstrasse CH 4058
Basel, Switzerland

Jonathan W. Uhr
Department of Microbiology
University of Texas
Southwestern Medical School
Dallas, Texas 75235

Emil R. Unanue
Department of Pathology
Harvard Medical School
Boston, Massachusetts 02115

Harald von Boehmer
Basel Institute for Immunology
487 Grenzacherstrasse CH 4058
Basel, Switzerland

Jon J. van Rood
Department of Immunohematology
University Hospital
Leiden, The Netherlands

Ellen Vitetta
Department of Microbiology
University of Texas
Southwestern Medical School
Dallas, Texas 75235

Hans Wigzell
Department of Immunology
Uppsala University
Uppsala, Sweden

Darcy B. Wilson
Department of Pathology
University of Pennsylvania
School of Medicine
Philadelphia, Pennsylvania 19174

Edmond J. Yunis
University of Minnesota Hospital
Minneapolis, Minnesota 55455

Rolf M. Zinkernagel
Department of Immunopathology
Scripps Clinic and Research
    Foundation
La Jolla, California 92037

Preface

In the past few years, many crucial discoveries have placed the major histo-compatibility gene complex (MHC) and gene products of the MHC on a much broader and higher level of biologic importance than was heretofore generally considered. Several factors have been responsible for advancing our knowledge and understanding of the MHC, and providing increasingly sophisticated technology which inevitably makes new discoveries possible.

First, in the mouse the availability of different inbred strains and, more importantly, the development of congenic-resistant strains differing only at the MHC or *H-2* gene complex, and of *H-2* recombinant mice identical or different at one or more intra-*H-2* gene regions; this has resulted from the pioneering efforts of Gorer, Snell, and their students and colleagues, and has opened the avenue to exploration of what at present is clearly the most thoroughly defined complex genetic system among vertebrate species. Studies in this species have laid the groundwork and provided invaluable insights into the system, and thereby hastened comparable analyses and discoveries in other species, in particular the *HLA* system of man. Second, in contrast to constitutents of other organ systems, the relative ease with which cells of the immune system can be obtained, identified, and fractionated by cell surface markers and analyzed functionally, has permitted development of complex assay systems, both *in vivo* and *in vitro*, by which classes and subclasses of immunocompetent lymphocytes and accessory lymphoid cells can be studied for independent and collaborative functional capacities. Third, the development of antisera specific for gene products of defined loci in the MHC has resulted in the identification on lymphocytes and macrophages of diverse surface macromolecules that are concerned with various aspects of recognitive and regulatory mechanisms in the immune system. Finally, the phenomenal burst of experimentation, made possible to a large extent by the aforementioned points, utilizing refined technological advances to isolate and characterize biochemically the molecular products of MHC genes on or in surface membranes of lymphoid cells.

Originally recognized and studied as that portion of the genome coding for the major transplantation antigens, it is now abundantly clear that the MHC genes code for a variety of molecules which are integrally involved in control mechanisms of immune responses. The relationships of these various molecules to one another and the degree of functional and chemical heterogeneity among them will provide fundamental clues to the genetic mechanisms involved in controlling lymphocyte functions. In the broader sense, delineation of the nature of these genetic mechanisms and the exciting possibility that these systems will permit the discovery of gene–gene interactions in eukaryotic cells may provide fundamental knowledge of enormous relevance to all of cell biology. It is also conceivable that further knowledge on the functions of histocompatibility gene products might reveal a fundamental and general involvement of these cell surface proteins in the regulation and control of cell differentiation processes in mammalian organ systems.

As we consider the relationship of the MHC with disease, there is an increasing awareness, which has been derived from experimental systems and also from clinical observations, that the products of the major histocompatibility gene complex, distinct from the classical histocompatibility molecules as serologically defined, play a crucial role in the pathogenesis of many important disease processes. For instance, genes in the *I* region concerned with specific immune responsiveness are intimately involved in (1) the response to tumor-specific transplantation antigens, (2) the development of experimental autoimmune conditions, (3) the susceptibility to virus diseases, and (4) susceptibility to develop specific allergies. In addition, gene products of various regions of the MHC appear to become associated with products of invading microorganisms (e.g., viruses) ultimately to regulate the specificity and/or effectiveness of immune recognition. Finally, it has recently become clear that the MHC codes for certain of the complement components and regulates the activity of others. Looking prospectively, one cannot escape the feeling that we are but at the threshold of our knowledge, and that in future years we will understand this fascinating multigene system in a manner that is impossible to foresee at the present time.

Recognizing the increasing complexity of discoveries being made in such rapid fashion pertaining (directly or indirectly) to the MHC, we conceived of organizing a conference which would bring together an international group of scientists spanning three independent disciplines, namely genetics and immunogenetics, molecular biochemistry, and immunobiology, with clinical medicine overlapping these disciplines. On November 3–7, 1975, it was indeed our privilege to witness and participate in the product of our efforts in this regard. As the contents of the book attest, this conference was in many ways remarkable, for it permitted a candid and critical interchange of data and concepts and suggestions between investigators from different areas of specialty interest who, far too often in this era of monumental pace in basic research, otherwise have little or no opportunity to communicate directly with one another.

Among other noteworthy highlights, the partial amino acid sequences of certain of the gene products of *H-2* in mouse and *HLA* in man were presented for the first time, which prompted a very cogent discussion on the evolutionary and genetic significance of these data (see Session VII). To summarize briefly the other many accomplishments of the conference would itself take many pages of print, but clearly a level of communication was attained among geneticists, biochemists, immunobiologists, and clinicians that we, as organizers, could have never planned or predicted. The credit for this belongs entirely to the conferees who were willing to work hard, and in many instances to struggle to digest concepts, technologies, and even vocabularies that were not a routine part of their everyday investigation. Unfortunately, the limitations of space at the Brook Lodge facilities made it impossible to include many investigators active in the field in one or more of the disciplines mentioned, and certain other prominent members of the scientific community were invited but unable to attend for various reasons, in particular Dr. George Snell who has played such a pioneering role in the genetics of *H-2* for many years.

In closing, we wish to acknowledge the capable efforts of Charlene Small in the organization and planning of the conference, and Lee Katz and Annette Benacerraf for their secretarial assistance during the conference. This conference was made possible by the support and sponsorship of the Special Program and Projects Division of the National Institute of Allergy and Infectious Diseases, the Edward P. Mallinckrodt, Jr. Foundation, and the Upjohn Company, which also made available to us the beautiful and serene setting of Brook Lodge.

David Katz and Baruj Benacerraf

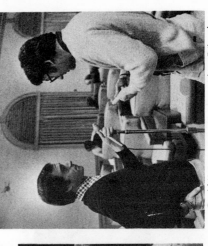

Hugh McDevitt

Alan Munro

Klaus Rajewsky

David Katz

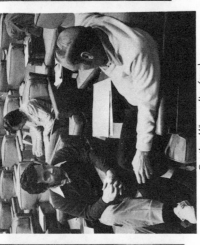

Gunther Hämmerling (rear)
Henry Kunkel
Fritz Bach

Charlene Small

Dick Gershon   Lee Katz

Fritz Bach

Mike Taussig (rear)
Jean Dausset   Jon van Rood
Baruj Benacerraf

Annette Benacerraf

Jack Strominger

Hugh McDevitt

Morten Simonsen

Tomio Tada

David Katz

Erna Möller

Baruj Benacerraf

Jon van Rood

Michael Sela

Ira Green

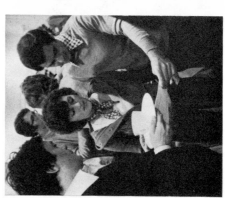

Tommy Meo

Lee Katz

David Katz

Lee Hood

George Klein   Rolf Kiessling

David Sachs

Baruj Benacerraf

Katie Bechtol

Harald von Boehmer

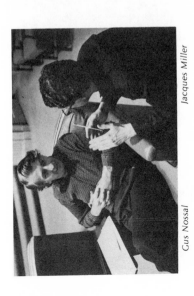

Jacques Miller

Gus Nossal

Conference in session, Bill Paul (standing)

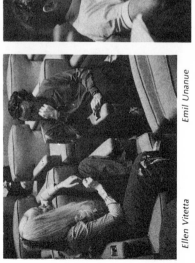

Bo Dupont

Jon Uhr

Emil Unanue

Ellen Vitetta

Bruce Cunningham   Bernard Janicki

David Gasser

Jan Klein

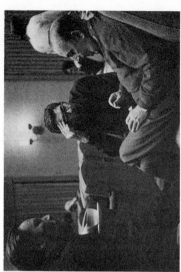

Jon van Rood   Jacques Miller   Baruj Benacerraf

First Row: Donald Shreffler, Alan Munro, Harald von Boehmer, Tommy Meo, Hugh McDevitt and Rose Lieberman. Second Row: Jacques Miller, Ellen Vitetta, Edmond Yunis, and Michael Bach.

Dick Gershon   Baruj Benacerraf

Genetics of the Major Histocompatibility Complex

JEAN DAUSSET, CHAIRMAN

GENETIC RESOLUTION OF THE PRODUCTS AND FUNCTIONS OF I AND S REGION GENES OF THE MOUSE H-2 COMPLEX

DONALD C. SHREFFLER, TOMMASO MEO AND CHELLA S. DAVID

Department of Genetics
Washington University School of Medicine

Abstract: The mouse major histocompatibility complex (H-2) encompasses a short segment of chromosome 17 which includes multiple genetic loci controlling a variety of discrete products and functions. Two subdivisions of the complex, the S and I regions, have been under intensive study for the past few years. The nature and functions of their products are now becoming understood to some degree. The S region controls variations in several serum proteins that have recently been found to be related to the complement system. Evidence is presented which indicate that the principal marker for the S region, the Ss protein, is the mouse homologue of the complement component C4 defined in human serum. The I region controls a variety of traits that relate to histocompatibility and to certain fundamental functions of T lymphocytes in the immune response. A set of serologically defined products of genes in the I region (the Ia antigens) has been defined during the past three years. A review of the serological, genetic and biochemical data on the Ia antigens indicate that the antigens detected by anti-Ia sera in the lymphocytotoxicity test can be ascribed primarily to two structural genes located in the I-A and I-C subregions of the I region. However, it is quite possible that these antisera also contain antibodies to other molecules not yet so clearly defined serologically. The use of anti-Ia sera to inhibit a variety of assays of lymphocyte function show very clearly that the Ia antigens play a key role in the cellular interactions that are involved in all immune responses, although the specific role(s) of the Ia antigens in these processes are not yet conclusively determined. The possible functional and genetic relationships of the Ia molecules to the various known I region traits and their implications for the genetic organization of the entire H-2 complex are discussed.

INTRODUCTION

The mouse major histocompatibility complex (MHC), the H-2 system, was originally defined as a set of cell-surface alloantigens detectable by transplant rejection and by serological techniques. During the past 12 years, it has become apparent that a variety of other traits are determined by the H-2 complex and by the MHC's of other species (1). The availability of intra-H-2 recombinants, resulting from genetic crossing-over between the multiple genes of the H-2 complex has made it possible to resolve and map some of the genetic loci that control these various traits (1). During the past five years, following the simplifying hypothesis that the classical H-2 alloantigens are determined by two duplicate loci, H-2K and H-2D (1,2), substantial progress has been made in the definition of the genetic polymorphism, the molecular properties and the functions of the MHC gene products that determine these associated traits. The first of the associated traits to be defined was the Ss (serum substance) protein variant (3). Very soon, H-2-associated differences in susceptibility to oncogenic viruses (4) and in capacity to respond to specific antigens (5), controlled by Ir (immune response) genes, were described. Pursuit of these early findings led to the recognition that the serum variation defines a discrete set of genes within the complex (the S region), while the immune response differences define a second series of multiple genes in a separate region called the I region (cf. 1). In the past two to three years, these two regions have emerged as two of the most interesting and significant segments of any mammalian chromosome to both geneticists and immunologists.

GENETIC ORGANIZATION OF THE H-2 COMPLEX

The currently accepted genetic map of the H-2 complex is shown in Figure 1. Each genetic region, defined by recombination, is marked by a specific genetic locus controlling a discrete genetic trait. Most regions have multiple traits associated with them. It remains to be determined, in most cases, whether these multiple traits reflect different phenotypic expressions of the same gene or expres-

4

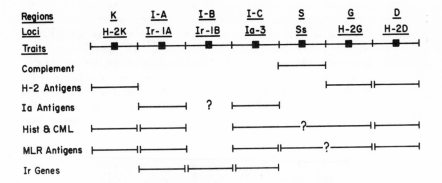

Figure 1. A map of the genetic subdivisions and associated traits of the mouse major histocompatibility complex (H-2).

---

sions of multiple genes (in addition to the "marker" gene) that all map in the same genetic region. This is an important question with respect to the genetic resolution of the MHC's of all higher vertebrates. The current map has been derived from analyses of numerous intra-H-2 recombinants and some mutants. However, it appears that many additional recombinants and mutants will be required for the most detailed resolution. A recent screening effort in our laboratory has yielded 8 new recombinants that are currently being established on inbred strain backgrounds in preparation for further analyses (see Meo et al., this volume).

The traits of the MHC can be divided into three broad groups: 1) the classical transplantation antigens of the K and D regions; 2) the complement-related traits of the S region; and 3) the immune response phenomena of the I region. At least some of the gene products in all three groups can be detected serologically. In this paper we will undertake to review the genetic organization of the S and I regions and the molecular properties and possible functions of the serologically detected products of these two regions.

THE ROLE OF THE S REGION IN COMPLEMENT FUNCTIONS

Immunochemically detected quantitative variation in the Ss protein was first described in 1963 (3). A sex-limited, testosterone-regulated, allotypic variant of the Ss protein, called Slp, was described in 1970 (6). These variants proved to be extremely useful markers within the

H-2 complex (7) and exhibit some very interesting genetic
regulatory phenomena (8). However, the function of the Ss
protein remained obscure until 1973, when Demant et al. (9)
showed that H-2-linked differences in total hemolytic complement activity are correlated with quantitative differences in Ss levels and are controlled by the S region. Experiments showing that antibodies to the Ss protein can
specifically deplete complement activity from mouse serum
(8,9,10) strongly implicated the Ss protein as a component
of the complement system.

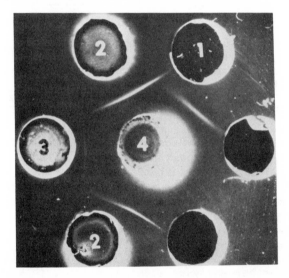

Figure 2. Reaction on immunodiffusion of partial identity between mouse Ss protein and a cross-
reactive human serum protein. Contents of wells:
1. Human serum; 2. B10.D2 male mouse serum (Ss-High);
3. C3H male mouse serum (Ss-Low); 4. Anti-mouse Ss.
Other two wells were empty. From Meo et al. (11).

Recent results by Meo et al. (11) have identified the
Ss protein as the fourth component of complement, $C4$. This
was accomplished through identification of the human homologue of Ss by cross-reaction of a rabbit anti-mouse Ss
serum (Figure 2). When polyethylene glycol (PEG) was added
to the medium in an Ouchterlony immunodiffusion test to
enhance precipitation of marginally soluble complexes, a
reaction of partial identity was observed between the Ss
protein and a human serum protein. During fractionations
of human plasma to isolate this cross-reacting protein, it

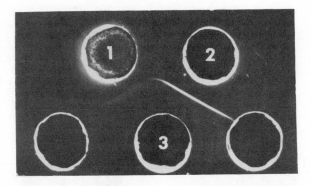

Figure 3. Comparative immunodiffusion showing reaction of complete identity between anti-mouse Ss (well 1) and anti-human C4 (well 2) versus human serum (well 3). From Meo et al. (11).

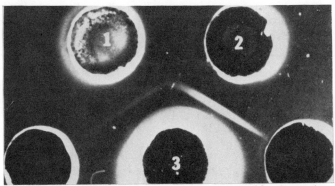

Figure 4. Comparative immunodiffusion showing reaction of complete identity between anti-human C4 (well 1) and anti-mouse Ss (well 2) versus DBA/2J male mouse serum (well 3). From Meo et al. (11).

was observed that Ss-positive fractions were always also positive with anti-human C4, and vice versa. An immuno-diffusion test in PEG showed reactions of identity between anti-mouse Ss and rabbit anti-human C4 antibodies when tested against human serum (Figure 3) and mouse serum (Figure 4). (These results have now been observed with several different anti-Ss and anti-C4 reagents.)

As further proof of the reactivity of anti-human C4 with Ss protein, anti-C4 and anti-Ss were tested in parallel against a panel of sera from different mouse strains in a

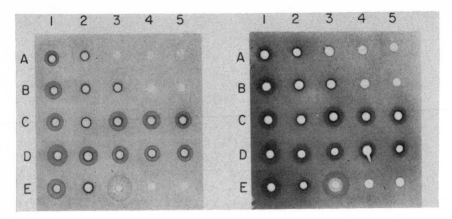

Figure 5. Comparative radial immunodiffusion results with anti-mouse Ss (left plate) and anti-human C4 (right plate) tested against 18 different mouse sera. Sera in wells A-2, B-2, B-3, C-2 and E-2 were Ss-Low, others were Ss-High, except A-3,4,5, B-4,5 and E-4,5, which were empty. From Meo et al. (11).

quantitative radial immunodiffusion technique (Figure 5). A correlation of 0.99 was obtained between the quantitative levels detected by the two sera. In addition, absorptions of anti-Ss with sera from this same panel removed its reactivity with human serum in proportion to the observed quantitative levels of Ss protein in the absorbing sera. Thus it is rather firmly established that the mouse Ss protein is structurally homologous to human C4.

A similar cross-reactivity has recently been demonstrated by Petersen et al. (12), who showed inhibition by purified human C4 in a radioimmunoassay against labeled mouse Ss, and <u>vice versa</u>. These authors have also reported that chain separations of reduced, purified Ss on SDS polyacrylamide gel electrophoresis yield two polypeptides with apparent molecular weights in the range of 70,000 to 80,000 daltons and a third of 23,000 daltons, from an intact molecule of slightly less than 200,000 daltons. Our own data (T. Meo and T. Krasteff, unpublished) on purified Ss protein reveal a molecular weight of approximately 180,000 daltons, with two discrete polypeptide chains centered about 70,000 daltons and one of about 30,000 daltons. The reported values for human C4 (13) are 204,000 for the intact molecule and 93,000, 78,000 and 33,000 for the three chains. Further evidence that Ss is mouse C4 has been presented by Lachmann

8

et al. (14). They prepared (by treatments which inactivate C1 and C2) EAC4 (erythrocyte-antibody-C4 complexes), which should have carried only the C4 component, and demonstrated agglutination of this complex by anti-Ss.

These data differ in several respects from those recently published by Capra et al. (15), who reported an Ss molecular weight of 120,000 and two polypeptides with molecular weights of 23,000 and 14,000 daltons. These authors implied that Ss might be the C2 component. We find no evidence relating Ss to C2 in our own data. Possibly the Ss protein purified was proteolytically degraded, or possibly the Ss "family" of molecules detected by some anti-Ss sera could include both C2 and C4. However, our own anti-Ss sera fail to detect at least human and guinea pig C2. In immuno-diffusion tests of anti-Ss against human sera from geneti-cally C2- and C4- deficient individuals, we have found a normal reaction with the C2-deficient serum (which has a normal C4 level) and no reaction with the C4-deficient serum (which has normal C2 activity). The data of Lachmann et al. (14) also failed to reveal any reactivity with C2.

Thus we cannot at present explain these inconsisten-cies. However, there is certainly some basis for expecting association between the S region and variations, not only in C2, but in several complement components. Goldman and Goldman (16) have reported S region control of quantitative variations in C1, C2 and C4. Ferreira and Nussenzweig have found S region-determined quantitative variations in C3 levels (17,18), and Gelfand et al. (19) found strain dif-ferences in numbers of lymphocyte C3 receptors, linked to the D end of the complex. This complement-MHC association also extends to other species. C4-deficiency is linked to the guinea pig MHC (20). Both C2 (21) and C4 (22) deficien-cies are linked to HL-A. Structural variations in properdin factor B are linked to HL-A (23) and to the MHC of the rhesus monkey (24).

Thus it is clear that the MHC plays a major role in the control of the complement system. Because of these associations, a more functionally descriptive genetic nomenclature may eventually be desirable. When the molecu-lar basis for this variation has been more clearly defined, we would suggest adoption, at least for the mouse, of the designation Cc (complement component) for the controlling genes. For example, Cc-4 would indicate control of C4, or Cc-4a would designate the structural gene for the α subunit of C4, etc.

One can at present only speculate about the significance of the close chromosomal association between the complement genes and the I region genes, which control functions
that are also immunologic but not otherwise very obviously
related to complement. Whether the linkage has an evolutionary or a functional basis, or both, cannot be determined
as yet. With respect to the apparent clustering within the
MHC of genes controlling different complement components,
the obvious implication is that these genes arose by duplication of a common ancestral gene. Duplication was previously invoked to account for observations on the Ss and Slp
traits (25). The functional homology of the C$\overline{42}$ complex
and Factor B has been pointed out (26) and it has been
suggested that this might reflect control by duplicate
structural genes for certain of the polypeptide subunits
of these proteins (11). One might, therefore, rather con-
fidently predict that the relationship by gene duplication
already established for the H-2K and H-2D products will
also be found to obtain for products of the S region and
its homologues in other species.

THE SEROLOGICALLY DETECTED I REGION PRODUCTS: GENETIC CONTROL, PROPERTIES, FUNCTIONS

The fundamental importance of I region function and
expression in the immune response and in histocompatibility
relationships is underscored by the diversity of the traits
that have been mapped to it. These include resistance to
oncogenic viruses and a great variety of immune response
differences (reviewed in 1). They also include the major
factors that stimulate in the mixed lymphocyte reaction
(MLR) and the graft versus host reaction (GVH) (cf. 1). In
addition to this role in histocompatibility, the I region
also determines alloantigens that are responsible for a
strong skin graft rejection (H-2I) (27) and that serve as
targets for cell-mediated lympholysis (CML) (28). Further,
the I region determines structures that are involved in
cell-cell interactions, between T and B lymphocytes (29)
and between macrophages and T lymphocytes (30). These
structures may be related to the I region-determined soluble T cell helper and suppressor factors described by
several investigators (reviewed in 31) and the B cell
acceptor for such factors described by Munro and Taussig
(32). Finally, the I region controls a set of serologically
detected lymphocyte alloantigens, the Ia antigens (cf. 1).

The search for the Ia antigens was stimulated by the findings that immune response differences and MLR stimulating factors could be mapped to the I region by specific combinations of intra-H-2 recombinants that differed only in the I (and S) region. Since these traits were thought to involve genetically variant cell-surface structures, cross-immunizations with lymphoid tissues were carried out between these strains to produce antisera that might detect such structures. This approach was successful and a new class of I region associated (Ia) antigens was defined by several laboratories (cf. 1).

The details of the Ia system and the other I region traits have been extensively reviewed elsewhere (1,31,33,42) and will be considered by other contributors to this volume. Obviously, the anti-Ia sera constitute a potentially powerful tool for definition of the I region gene products and thereby the controlling genes. Our purpose in this section will be to briefly summarize our view of the current status of definition of the Ia antigens and to raise a number of specific points and questions concerning the relationship of the Ia antigens to other I region traits and their bearing on the genetic organization of the I region.

The current chart of defined Ia specificities is presented in Table 1. Several points are worth noting. The definition of Ia specificities has proceeded rapidly; the present data suggest a serological complexity comparable to that of the H-2 antigens. One change from previous tables should be noted -- Ia.15 has now also been assigned to the H-2^b haplotype. This change is discussed in more detail below. All specificities in the table have been mapped to the I region by analyses of intra-H-2 recombinants, except 20 and 21, for which no appropriate recombinants are available. These are therefore given provisional "W" designations.

The results of the analyses to map these specificities are summarized in Figure 6. Note that three specificities have been localized on the grounds that in sequential immunoprecipitation experiments they are found to be associated with specificities that have been genetically mapped, i.e. 13 with 5, W20 with 8 and 9, and W21 with 7 (39,40,41). An important point to be noted here is that none of these specificities have so far been definitively mapped to the I-B subregion. Ia.3, which was previously tentatively mapped to I-B (1), and Ia.15, which previously appeared to perhaps require a new subregion between I-B and I-C (42),

11

Table 1. Distribution of Ia Specificities in Haplotypes of Independent Origin

H-2 Haplotype	Type Strain	Ia Specificities*																				
		1	2	3	4	5	6	7	8	9	10	11	12	13	14	15	16	17	18	19	W20	W21
b	C57BL/10	–	–	–	–	–	–	–	8	9	–	–	–	–	–	15	–	–	–	–	W20	–
d	B10.D2	–	–	–	–	–	6	7	8	–	–	11	–	–	–	15	16	–	–	–	–	–
f	B10.M	1	–	–	–	5	–	–	–	–	–	–	–	–	14	–	–	17	18	–	–	–
k	B10.K	1	2	3	–	–	–	7	–	–	–	–	–	–	–	15	–	17	18	19	–	–
p	B10.P	–	–	–	–	5	6	7	–	–	–	–	–	13	–	–	–	–	–	–	–	W21
q	B10.G	–	–	3	–	5	–	–	–	9	10	–	–	13	–	–	16	–	–	–	–	–
r	B10.RIII	1	–	3	–	5	–	7	–	–	–	–	12	–	–	–	–	17	–	19	–	–
s	B10.S	–	–	–	4	5	–	–	–	9	–	–	12	–	–	–	–	17	18	–	–	–

*References to specificity assignments: Ia.1–10 (1), 11 (34), 12–14 (35), 15 (36), 16 (37), 17–19 (38), W20 and W21 (39).

12

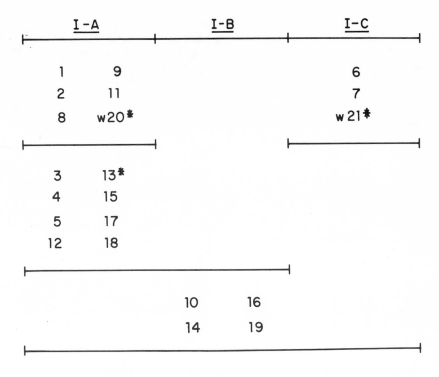

Figure 6. Localization of Ia specificities to the I region and subregions. Specificities marked by an asterisk (*) have been localized by molecular associations.

now could be mapped in either I-A or I-B.

Ia.3 was originally defined by the cross-reaction of antiserum A.TH anti A.TL with H-2^b targets (1). This serum also reacted with H-2^d targets, due to specificity Ia.7 (1). Since neither target significantly absorbed reactivity for the other, it was concluded that they shared no specificity recognized by this serum. Since intra-I recombinant haplotype H-2^{g2}, thought to be K^{d}A^{d}B^{b}C^{b}S^{b}D^b, was positive with this antiserum, and the reaction was absorbed by H-2^b cells, the reaction was attributed to Ia.3, which seemed therefore to be positioned in the B subregion (1). Because of the weakness of the reaction, this assignment was considered tentative. Analyses of serum (A.TH x B10.HTT) anti A.TL, a combination which excludes anti Ia.7 production, defined Ia.15 by its reaction with H-2^d targets. Initial analyses of recombinants suggested a position for Ia.15 between the

13

B and C subregions (42). This serum also contains anti-Ia.3 and reacts with $H-2^b$ targets. However, recent absorption analyses (David et al., in preparation) have shown that $H-2^b$ cells remove the reaction with $H-2^d$ targets, indicating that $H-2^b$ also determines Ia.15. Further analysis of the $H-2^{g2}$ haplotype now indicates that it is actually Ia.3-negative, Ia.15-positive. Therefore, Ia.3 may map in either the A or B subregion. Further analyses of recombinants with a higher-titered anti-15 indicate that it also could map in either A or B.

The crossover in $H-2^{g2}$ was thought to be between A and B because of a separation of responses to the RE (ragweed extract) and GLT (glutamic acid, lysine, tyrosine polymer) antigens, demonstrated by Dorf et al. (43). At that time, GLT response was mapped to the B subregion. Recent data of Dorf et al. (44) on the very closely related response to antigen GLØ, showing control of response by two genes, now suggest that the relevant controlling gene is in the C region. Thus, both of the previous grounds for positioning the $H-2^{g2}$ crossover between A and B have been found not to hold. On the basis of present data, the crossover could have been either between A and B or between B and C.

We have two reasons for introducing this very complex situation in this paper: 1) It demonstrates the pitfalls that are inherent in all attempts to map such complex traits with limited numbers of recombinants; 2) It leaves us with the $H-2^{h4}$ recombinant haplotype as the sole basis for the definition of a B subregion. This point will be further discussed below. Immunizations have been done in a number of strain combinations that differ only in the B subregion, without detectable antibody production (unpublished data). The B subregion also seems to be silent with respect to MLR stimulation (1). Thus it appears that the B subregion determines no currently detectable Ia antigens.

It is also important to note that only three speci-ficities have been definitively mapped to the I-C subregion and that these are associated with only three haplotypes, $H-2^d$, $H-2^k$ and $H-2^p$, all of which have specificity Ia.7 (1). Numerous attempts to produce antibodies to the expected allelic products of the $H-2^b$ and $H-2^s$ haplotypes have failed (David et al., unpublished). It is also noteworthy in this regard that no MLR stimulation can be obtained with differ-ences in the $I-C^b$ and $I-C^s$ subregions (1,45,46).

14

A very important adjunct to the serological approach to definition of the Ia antigens has been the application of immunoprecipitation techniques by Cullen et al. (40,41, 47,48). The conclusions that, in our opinion, have come out of this work are summarized in Table 2. The molecules detected by this approach are clearly distinct from the H-2 molecules (47,49). They apparently have a two-chain structure; the chain carrying the Ia determinants has not yet been conclusively defined (47,48). The antigenic differences very probably reside in the polypeptide part of the molecule, rather than the carbohydrate (49,50).

Table 2.   Properties of Ia Molecules
Detected by Immunoprecipitation

1. A single glycoprotein molecule of 58,000 daltons; reduces to two polypeptides, 33,000 and 25,000 daltons.

2. No association with H-2K or H-2D molecules or with immunoglobulins.

3. No evidence for association with β_2-microglobulin.

4. Glycosidase treatment indicates no antigenic role of carbohydrate; peptide mapping shows difference in protein structure.

5. Sequential precipitation shows I-A region specificities on one molecule, I-C region specificities on another. Only two molecules have been demonstrated.

6. All specificities demonstrated by cytotoxicity are detectable by immunoprecipitation, where tested.

7. Allelic specificities of I-A region expressed on separate molecules.

Genetically, the most interesting findings are that all serologically defined specificities tested have been detectable by this method (40,41,47,48), indicating a high degree of correlation between the two approaches, and that the specificities assort to two discrete Ia molecules according to their map positions in the I-A or I-C regions, providing a molecular confirmation of the genetic assignments (40,41,47,48). These results imply rather strongly

that the major Ia antigens thus far defined serologically
and biochemically comprise two discrete molecules (or possibly populations of related molecules) controlled by two
discrete structural genes, Ia-1 in the A subregion and Ia-3
in the C subregion. Since only two basic molecules have
been detected, there is once again no evidence for a B
region product of this type. It should be noted that heterogeneity within each class of molecules, as might be expected with a single constant region-multiple variable region
model, is not excluded. But if this is true, there would
appear to be only two types of constant regions.

As indicated in Table 3, the two defined Ia antigen
molecules are represented strongly on B lymphocytes (cf. 1).

Table 3. Tissue Expression of Ia Antigens

1. Major specificities detected by cytotoxicity and immunoprecipitation are found on most B lymphocytes.

2. Same specificities are found on some T lymphocytes --
   cortisone-resistant, Con A thymus blasts, Con A-
   responsive cells.

3. No indication of genic exclusion of I-A vs. I-C region
   products, nor of allelic exclusion.

4. Anti-Ia sera also react with macrophages, epidermal
   cells, sperm, some tumors, and with soluble T cell
   helper and suppressor factors and macrophage
   helper-inducer factors.

5. No evidence whether latter reactions (#4) involve
   same antibodies as B cell reactions.

Reactivity of these antisera with T lymphocytes has been
much more difficult to demonstrate, however a number of
laboratories have presented evidence supporting some Ia
expression of T cells (52,53,54). Our own recent data have
shown weak and variable reactions with cortisone-resistant
thymocytes (55), but relatively strong reactions with
Con A-stimulated thymocytes (56). We have also found that
the Con A-responsive spleen cell is sensitive to anti-Ia
plus complement, while the PHA-responsive cell is not (57).
Serological analyses of Con A-stimulated thymocytes in the
cytotoxic test have revealed little, if any, difference in

expression of Ia specificities relative to B cells (LPS-stimulated splenocytes) (56). Thus it appears that at least the major Ia antigens detected by the cytotoxic test are shared by most B cells and a restricted subpopulation of T cells. There is no evidence for allelic exclusion of Ia antigens (55). Since antisera containing antibodies only to A region specificities or only to C region specificities give approximately the same level of kill in the cytotoxic test as antisera containing antibodies against both regions, it appears that products of both loci are expressed concordantly, i.e. there is no restriction in expression of these two loci to different lymphocyte populations.

Anti-Ia sera have also been shown to react in various assays with other tissues or with soluble products of certain cell types (32,49,58,59,60). It should be strongly emphasized, we believe, that in most cases it has not yet been established whether or not the antibodies involved in these reactions are the same antibodies defined by cytotoxicity and immunoprecipitation. It is quite possible that in at least some cases they are not -- for example, the reactivities with soluble factors or with epidermal cells might be due to distinct populations of antibodies. To properly test this, it is most important that cross-absorption or cross-inhibition analyses be performed.

In Table 4 are listed the various functions and products for which anti-Ia inhibition has been demonstrated. These findings will be developed in much more detail during this conference; we will make only two observations about them at this time: 1) They show very conclusively that the molecules that react with anti-Ia sera do play an important role in immune mechanisms -- therefore the antisera are useful tools for analysis of these mechanisms; 2) All of these results might be accounted for by two general classes of Ia antigen molecules. The MLR stimulating factors, Fc receptors, LPS binding sites and B cell acceptors are all structures that are predominantly represented on the B cell, as are the cytotoxicity-defined Ia antigens. Graft enhancement by anti-Ia sera could also be explained by an inhibition of the MLR-related recognition phase of graft rejection (69). On the other hand, the T cell and macrophage factors appear to be a different class of molecules, in terms of functions, molecular properties and tissue expression. These could, therefore, be reactive with a population of antibodies in anti-Ia sera that are not detectable, or are

Table 4.   Functions or Products
Inhibited by Anti-Ia Sera.

1.   MLR stimulating factors (61)

2.   In vitro PFC responses (62,63)

3.   In vitro antigen-induced proliferation (64,65)

4.   Fc receptor (66)

5.   B cell response to LPS (67)

6.   In vivo graft rejection (enhancement) (37)

7.   T cell helper and suppressor factors (32,59,60)

8.   B cell acceptor sites for factors (32)

9.   Macrophage-T cell interaction factors (68)

---

only marginally detectable, by cytotoxicity or immunoprecipitation. Anti-Ia inhibition of in vitro immune responses
and antigen-induced proliferation could occur at any of
several levels, which will doubtless be identified in time.
In any event, Ia molecules are clearly involved in these
processes, there is a strong correlation between the defined
Ia specificities and the B cell surface functions, and there
is some basis for suspecting that anti-Ia sera react with
at least a second class of molecules, the soluble effector
factors released by T cells and macrophages. Obviously,
since both types of molecules are detected by anti-Ia sera,
both must be controlled by the I region.

POSSIBLE PATTERNS OF GENETIC ORGANIZATION OF THE I REGION

Now, on the basis of these data, what conclusions can
we draw about the organization of genes in the I region?
Two discrete genes now seem rather clearly defined in terms
of polypeptide products. The biochemical similarities of
these products suggest that they might be determined by
duplicate genes. Data by Murphy (70) documenting serological cross-reactivity between the A and C region products
are consistent with that indication. Thus the picture with
respect to the major Ia antigens begins to look very much

like that of the H-2 antigens. The occurrence of such duplicate genes with cross-reactive products also raises the possibility of artifactual assignment of specificities to central regions, as occurred previously for the H-2 antigens -- a danger of which we should be aware, but which does not seem to have created difficulties so far.

The recognition of the existence of two principal Ia genes comes coincidently with the recognition that at least some H-2-linked immune responses are controlled by two discrete and complimentary (interacting) genes. This was first suggested by Zaleski et al. (71) for the Thy-1.1 antigen and has since been demonstrated for GLϕ by Dorf et al. (44), for (T,G)-A--L by Munro and Taussig (32) and for LDH$_B$ by Melchers and Rajewsky (71). This raises the obvious question whether the two Ir genes for a given response might correspond to the two Ia genes. In the case of GLϕ response, this might be possible since the two genes appear to map in the I-A and I-C subregions. However, the two genes for (T,G)-A--L response seem both to map in I-A, at least as evidenced by anti-Ia inhibition of the two products involved. Furthermore, the two genes postulated for control of (T,G)-A--L response include one controlling a soluble T cell factor and another controlling a B cell acceptor site, whereas the two principal Ia genes both appear to control structures that are primarily associated with B cells. (Those T cells that appear to express the same major Ia antigens as B cells might do so in order to accept soluble effector molecules from other T cells, or from macrophages.)

Another difficulty with the idea that the two Ia genes represent the two interacting Ir genes is that several responses map in the B subregion, which has no defined Ia gene -- at least thus far. This fact, plus the silence of the I-B region in MLR and the peculiar one-way MLR behavior of the H-2^{h4} haplotype (which defines the left boundary of the I-B region), in combination with H-2^{h2} (which differs in the I-B, I-C and S regions) (cf. 1), has led us, and others (72), to question whether the I-B subregion might be an artifactual consequence of joint control of an immune response by two Ir genes, one located in the I-A and one in the I-C subregion. Because a response requires interaction of two dominant genes, such a concept appears difficult to fit to the data on the IgG and LDH$_B$ responses that map in the B region, unless one assumes some complex pattern of asymmetric interactions between the various alleles at the two loci. The possibility that the immune response data are interpretable in this way will be dealt with in detail in a future paper. At present, however, there seems to be no simple, obvious way to eliminate the B subregion by this line of reasoning.

Another possibility which has been suggested to account for certain unexpected features of the H-2^{h4} haplotype, which solely defines the I-B subregion, is that this recombinant haplotype carries a deletion or deficiency (73). This is a possibility that must be considered, but it is difficult to explain how a deletion could lead to the acquisition of an immune response capacity (to IgG) not previously expressed, unless the IgG nonresponse were due to some mechanism not typical of the MHC-linked responses, e.g. dominant non-response due to cross-tolerance. Still another possibility could be that the H-2^{h4} recombinant is a double crossover and that the B region is actually located outside the K-D interval. However, an examination of the available recombination data suggests that this hypothesis creates more complexities than it resolves.

On the other hand, if the two immune response genes control interacting T cell and B cell molecules, as postulated by Munro and Taussig (32), it is possible that the H-2^{h4} crossover event may have defined a small segment of the I region that contains only genes for T cell factors that are not detectable in the cytotoxic test. A hypothetical model of such a situation is illustrated in Figure 7.

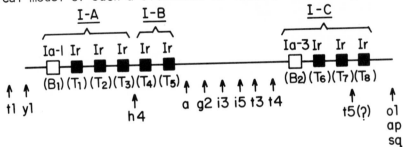

Figure 7. Hypothetical arrangement of I region genes. Ia-1 and Ia-3 refer to genes controlling major cytotoxicity-defined antigens. Ir's refer to postulated multiple genes controlling specific ——— immune responses. Arrows indicate positions of intra-H-2 crossovers defined by haplotypes H-2^{h4}, H-2^a etc. According to model of Munro and Taussig (32), Ia-1 and Ia-3 would control B cell acceptors (B$_1$ and B$_2$), Ir genes would control T cell effector factors (T$_1$-T$_8$).

This model envisions the two defined _Ia_ genes as controlling
B cell acceptors for the products of a series of genes for
different soluble T cell factors, as previously suggested
(32). Most intra-_I_ recombinants could be envisioned as
having occurred between two discrete B-T sets, while $\underline{H-2}^{h4}$
would be envisioned as having occurred within a T set.

Another point of concern about _I_ region organization
is the paucity of _C_ region specificities and our inability
to produce antibodies to the expected allelic products of
the _Ia-3_ locus. One might speculate whether this reflects
complete absence of the _I-C_ region in certain haplotypes,
null alleles of the _Ia-3_ locus, or poor immunogenicity of
certain _Ia-3_ allelic products. It will be most important
to determine whether all haplotypes determine two discrete
Ia molecules on B cells. The possibility of deletions or
deficiencies in certain haplotypes is one that should not
be overlooked in any considerations of what appears to be a
highly duplicated genetic region.

Another small concern about the current picture of the
entire _H-2_ complex is the apparent inconsistency in the order of the various functional types of genes relative to the
MHC's of man, the rhesus monkey and probably the guinea pig.
The most striking inconsistency is that in the mouse the _I_
and _S_ regions lie between the two loci controlling the
classical H-2 antigens while in the other species the _I_ and
_S_-homologous regions seem to lie outside that interval.
This should not be viewed as a serious problem, given the
multiple chromosomal rearrangements that must certainly
take place during evolution. The more remarkable fact is
that these different functional types of genes have remained
so closely linked, in whatever order. A very simple mechanism by which the mouse genes might have been reordered is
depicted in Figure 8. This is highly diagrammatic -- there
may be many more duplicates of certain types of genes, and
the specific orders for the human MLR and complement genes
are not yet precisely known -- but it does demonstrate how
simply a different order might be established.

Much of the preceding discussion has been speculative
and unspecific. Our objective was to emphasize that the
currently accepted _H-2_ genetic map is not necessarily final
or entirely accurate, that alternatives should be continuously considered and that occasional reordering should be
expected. Although there are now several interesting observations that may lead to future reevaluations, there

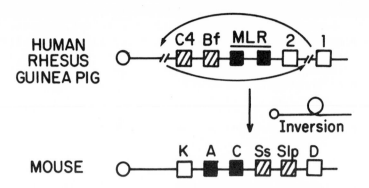

Figure 8. Hypothetical mechanism for origin of mouse MHC gene order by a simple chromosomal inversion. The pairs of loci are intended to represent clusters of two or more functionally related genes. The order shown for the human, rhesus or guinea pig complexes is hypothetical. No implications as to <u>specific</u> homologies of human and mouse genes are intended.

---

seem to be no compelling reasons for rearranging the map at this time.

ACKNOWLEDGMENTS

This work was supported by U.S.P.H.S. Grants GM15419 and AI11962 and by American Cancer Society Research Grants IM-74 and IM-80. We are grateful to Mrs. Carol Jones for her skillful assistance in preparation of the manuscript.

REFERENCES

(1) D.C. Shreffler and C.S. David. Adv. Immunol. 20 (1975) 125.

(2) D.C. Shreffler, C.S. David, H.C. Passmore and J. Klein. Transpl. Proc. 3 (1971) 176.

(3) D.C. Shreffler and R.D. Owen. Genetics. 48 (1963) 9.

(4) F. Lilly. Genetics. 53 (1966) 529.

(5) H.O. McDevitt and M. Tyan. J. Exp. Med. 128 (1968) 1.

(6) H.C. Passmore and D.C. Shreffler. Biochem. Genet. 4 (1970) 351.

(7) D.C. Shreffler, in Blood and Tissue Antigens. ed. D. Aminoff. (Academic Press, New York, 1970) p. 85.

(8) T.H. Hansen. Ph.D. Dissertation, University of Michigan, 1975.

(9) P. Demant, J. Capkova, E. Hinzova and B. Voracova. Proc. Nat. Acad. Sci. U.S. 70 (1973) 863.

(10) T.H. Hansen, H.S. Shin and D.C. Shreffler. J. Exp. Med. 141 (1975) 1216.

(11) T. Meo, T. Krasteff and D.C. Shreffler. Proc. Nat. Acad. Sci. U.S. (1975). In press.

(12) P.A. Peterson. Personal communication.

(13) R.D. Schreiber and H.J. Müller-Eberhard. J. Exp. Med. 140 (1974) 1324.

(14) P.J. Lachmann, D. Grennan, A. Martin and P. Demant. Nature. In press.

(15) J.D. Capra, E.S. Vitetta and J. Klein. J. Exp. Med. 142 (1975) 664.

(16) M.B. Goldman and J.N. Goldman. Fed. Proc. 34 (1975) 979.

(17) A. Ferreira and V. Nussenzweig. J. Exp. Med. 141 (1975) 513.

(18) A. Ferreira and V. Nussenzweig. Personal communication.

(19) M.C. Gelfand, D. Sachs, R. Lieberman and W.E. Paul. J. Exp. Med. 139 (1974) 1142.

(20) E. Shevach. Personal communication.

(21) S.M. Fu, H.G. Kunkel, H.P. Brusman, F.H. Allen and M. Fotino. J. Exp. Med. 140 (1974) 1108.

(22) G. Hauptmann. Personal communication.

(23) F.H. Allen. Vox Sanguinis. 27 (1974) 382.

(24) A.B. Zeigler, C.A. Alper, and H.Balner. Nature. 254 (1975) 609.

(25) D.C. Shreffler and H.C. Passmore. in Immunogenetics of the H-2 System. ed. M. Vojtiskova and A. Lengerova. (Karger, Basel, 1970) p. 58.

(26) D.T. Fearon, K.F. Austen and S. Ruddy. J. Exp. Med. 138 (1973) 1305.

(27) J. Klein, M. Hauptfeld and V. Hauptfeld. Immuno-genetics. 1 (1974) 45.

(28) M. Nabholz, H. Young, A. Rijnbeek, R. Boccardo, C.S. David, T. Meo, V. Miggiano and D. C. Shreffler. Eur. J. Immunol. (1975). In press.

(29) D.H. Katz, M. Graves, M.E. Dorf, H. Dimuzio and B. Benacerraf. J. Exp. Med. 141 (1975) 263.

(30) P. Erb and M. Feldmann. J. Exp. Med. 142 (1975) 460.

(31) B. Benacerraf and D.H. Katz, in Immunogenetics and Immunodeficiency. ed. B. Benacerraf. (Medical and Technical Publishers, London, 1975). In press.

(32) A.J. Munro and M.J. Taussig. Nature. 256 (1975) 103.

(33) H.O. McDevitt. Fed. Proc. (1975). In press.

(34) D.A.L. Davies and M. Hess. Nature. 250 (1974) 228.

(35) C.S. David, J. Colombani, M. Colombani and S.E. Cullen. In preparation.

(36) C.S. David. In preparation.

(37) N.A. Staines, K. Guy and D.A.L. Davies. Transplantation. 18 (1974) 192.

(38) J. Colombani, M. Colombani, D.C. Shreffler and C.S. David. Tissue Antigens. (1975). In press.

(39) S.E. Cullen. Personal communication.

(40) S.E. Cullen, D.H. Sachs and C.S. David. in Proc. Xth Leukocyte Culture Conference. (1975). In press.

(41) S.E. Cullen, C.S. David, J.L. Cone and D.H. Sachs. Submitted for publication.

(42) D.H. Sachs, C.S. David, D.C. Shreffler, S.G. Natheson and H.O. McDevitt. Immunogenetics. 2 (1974) 301.

(43) M.E. Dorf, F. Lilly and B. Benacerraf. J. Exp. Med. 140 (1974) 859.

(44) M.E. Dorf, J.H. Stimpfling and B. Benacerraf. J. Exp. Med. (1975). In press.

(45) T. Meo, J. Vives, A.M. Rijnbeek, V.C. Miggiano, M. Nabholz and D.C. Shreffler. Transpl. Proc. 5 (1973) 1339.

(46) M.E. Dorf, J.M.D. Plate, J.H. Stimpfling and B. Benacerraf. J. Immunol. 114 (1975) 602.

(47) S.E. Cullen, C.S. David, D.C. Shreffler and S.G. Nathenson. Proc. Nat. Acad. Sci. U.S. 71 (1974) 648.

(48) S.E. Cullen and B.D. Schwartz. Personal communication.

(49) E.R. Unanue, M. Dorf, C.S. David and B. Benacerraf. Proc. Nat. Acad. Sci. U.S. 71 (1974) 5014.

(50) S.E. Cullen, J.H. Freed, P.H. Atkinson and S.G. Nathenson. Transpl. Proc. 8 (1975) 237.

(51) J.H. Freed. Personal communication.

(52) J.H. Goding, E. White and J.J. Marchalonis. Nature. 257 (1975) 230.

(53) C.G. Fathman, J.L. Cone, S.O. Sharrow, H. Tyrer and D.H. Sachs. J. Immunol. 115 (1975) 584.

(54) D. Götze. Immunogenetics. 1 (1975) 495.

(55) J.A. Frelinger, J.E. Niederhuber, C.S. David and D.C. Shreffler. J. Exp. Med. 140 (1974) 1273.

(56) C.S. David, T. Meo and D.C. Shreffler. J. Exp. Med. (1976). In press.

(57) J.E. Niederhuber, J.A. Frelinger, M. Dine, E. Dugan, and D.C. Shreffler. Submitted for publication.

(58) T.L. Delovitch and H.O. McDevitt. Immunogenetics. 1 (1975) 39.

(59) T. Tada and T. Takemori. J. Exp. Med. 140 (1974) 239.

(60) D.H. Katz, M.E. Dorf, D. Armerding and B. Benacerraf. in Molecular Approaches to Immunology. eds. E.E. Smith and D.W. Ribbons. (Academic Press, New York, 1975).

(61) T. Meo, C.S. David, M. Nabholz, V. Miggiano and D.C. Shreffler. Transpl. Proc. 7 (1975) 127.

(62) C.W. Pierce, J.A. Kapp, S.M. Solliday, M.E. Dorf and B. Benacerraf. J. Exp. Med. 140 (1974) 921.

(63) J.A. Frelinger, J.E. Niederhuber and D.C. Shreffler. Science. 188 (1975) 268.

(64) E. Shevach, W.E. Paul and I. Green. J. Exp. Med. 136 (1972) 1207.

(65) R.H. Schwartz. Personal communication.

(66) H. Dickler and D.H. Sachs. J. Exp. Med. 140 (1974) 779.

(67) J.E. Niederhuber, J.A. Frelinger, E. Dugan, A. Coutinho and D.C. Shreffler. J. Immunol. (1975). In press.

(68) P. Erb, M. Feldmann and N. Hogg. in Proc. Xth Leukocyte Culture Conference. (1975). In press.

(69) V.P. Eijsvogel, M. du Bois, C. Melief, M. de
      Groot-kooy, C. Koning, J.J. van Rood, A. van Leeuwen,
      E. du Toit and P. Schellekens. in Histocompatibility
      Testing (Munksgaard, Copenhagen, 1972). p. 501.

(70) D.B. Murphy. Fed. Proc. 34 (1975) 1016.

(71) I. Melchers and K. Rajewsky. Personal communication.

(72) D.B. Murphy. Personal communication.

(73) E.D. Lozner, D.H. Sachs, G.M. Shearer and W.D. Terry.
      Science. 183 (1974) 757.

DISCUSSION FOLLOWING DONALD SHREFFLER

BENACERRAF: Do you conclude that the I-B sub-region only rests on the evidence of distinct Ir genes mapping in that region? How valid do you consider that data?

SHREFFLER: Since no other traits have been shown definitively to map to the I-B sub-region, its existence at present is defined <u>only</u> by the separation in the H-2^{h4} recombinant strain, B10.A(4R), of responses to IgG, LDH$_B$ and BGG from other responses that are mapped to the I-A sub-region. It is difficult to see at present how those responses can be accommodated to a map that does not include an I-B sub-region, without developing a complex scheme of differentially interacting alleles that would map in the I-A and I-C sub-regions. In the absence of more definitive data, I think we have to reserve judgment about the existence of the I-B sub-region.

BENACERRAF: What is the genetic definition of the D2.GD strain?

SHREFFLER: Based on the points I mentioned concerning the map positions of Ia.3 and the GLΦ-GLT response, we now cannot determine whether the cross-over in the H-2^{g2} haplotype occurred between I-A and I-B or between I-B and I-C. The constitution then becomes $K^d A^d B^d$ or $^b C^b S^b D^b$.

SHEVACH: Have you studied the effects of anti-Ss sera on an *in vitro* function associated with the MHC, such as the mixed lymphocyte reaction?

SHREFFLER: We are looking at this, but have nothing to report so far.

CUNNINGHAM: I wonder if Dr. Shreffler would comment on the peptide maps comparing I-A and I-C gene products, which were indicated on one of his slides.

SHREFFLER: The peptide map differences in the table referred to differences between products of two different alleles at the I-A region shown by John Freed and Stan Nathenson (personal communication). They found about 25% of the peptides to be different, implying that the difference in Ia antigenic activity is due to a

difference in polypeptide structure, rather than carbohydrate groups.

THE GENETICS OF THE MAJOR HISTOCOMPATIBILITY COMPLEX IN MAN, HLA.

J.J. VAN ROOD, A. VAN LEEUWEN, A. TERMIJTELEN
AND J.J. KEUNING

Department of Immunohaematology
University Hospital Leiden

Abstract: The HLA supergene is located in the 6th chromosome.
Its position to the centromere and the position of a
number of polymorphic isoenzymes has been elucidated.
The HLA supergene codes not only for determinants
present on all nucleated cells, but also for determinants present on B cells and absent from T cells and
platelets. These determinants can be recognized by serology and evidence is presented that some of them are
coded for by a hitherto unrecognized locus Ag, which is
very closely linked to the MLC or D locus. The determinants of the D locus can be recognized with the help
of the MLC test itself using unprimed cells, homozygous
for the MLC determinants, socalled typing cells, or
cells primed against one MLC determinant in the PLT
test. Sofar 8 MLC determinants have been recognized.
Significant disease associations have been found with
HLA. Disease association studies in different racial
groups appear to be especially informative. They already
indicate that the associations found sofar must rest on
different mechanisms. Whether some of them could be
caused by partial deficiency for one or more of the
complement factors remains to be proven.
Twin studies provide a useful model for the study of
the genetic control of the immune response and indicate
that this control is especially clear for diphteria and
measles of which the latter one might be linked to HLA.
Two case histories are presented of children suffering
from familial autosomal hypogammaglobulinaemia with B
cells. No HLA antigens could be detected on their
lymphocytes while β_2-microglobulin was absent as well.
Possible pathogenic mechanisms are discussed as well as
the implication for our understanding of the control of
immunoglobulin synthesis.

31

INTRODUCTION

The growing complexity of the genetics of the HLA region is of interest in itself and the highly significant evidence that genes in this region predispose for an array of different diseases adds only to this interest. In this presentation we will give first an orientation of the genetics of the HLA region and its relation to other markers on the 6th chromosome. Secondly the recognition of the determinants coded for by the MLC-s or D locus and other loci closely linked to the D locus will be discussed, while in the third part we will summarize studies which are relevant for our understanding of the association of HLA to disease predisposition and immune response.

THE HLA SUPERGENE AND THE 6TH CHROMOSOME

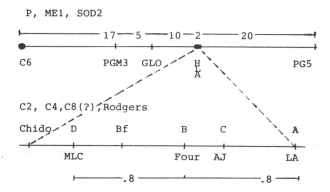

Figure 1. Schematic representation of the HLA supergene on the 6th chromosome.

Fig. 1 gives a summary of our present day knowledge of the HLA supergene. The evidence that the HLA supergene is located on the sixth chromosome is unequivocal and has been confirmed by several groups.(1,2,3) The centromere is positioned nearer to the HLA-B than to the HLA-A side of the supergene, but it is unknown whether the HLA supergene is on the long arm or the short arm of the 6th chromosome. (4) The presence of the locus coding for the P bloodgroup determinants on C6 is disputed by some workers (5,3),its position as well as that of the not polymorphic loci ME1 and SOD2 and thus also their linear sequence is as yet unknown. PGM3 is thought to lie 15 centimorgans and GLO 10 centimorgans to the left of HLA. (4) PG5 is on 20 centimorgans distance of HLA to the right. The Chido and Rodgers loci code for red blood cell

(and serum) antigens, the D locus for determinants which can
be recognized in the MLC test. We will refer to them as
lymphocyte defined or LD determinants. Bf codes for factor B
in the properdin system, C2, C4 and C8 for complement factors.
(6,7,8) The evidence that C8 is coded for by loci in the HLA
supergene is of a preliminary nature. The A(LA), B(Four) and
C(AJ) code for determinants present on all nucleated cells,
which can easily be detected by serology. We will refer to
them as serologically defined or SD determinants. Whether a
MLC locus leading to weak MLC reactivity exists near the A
locus is still under dispute. The distance between the A and
Chido loci is about 2 centimorgans and is called the HLA
supergene. It is in this context of special relevance that we
are now able to recognize the products of two polymorphic
loci outside HLA, GLO to the left and PG5 to the right. This
enables us to determine whether a crossover outside HLA has
taken place. As a consequence of such a crossover incompatibility for as yet undetected loci could occur between HLA
identical siblings. Incompatibility for loci outside HLA
could explain for instance severe rejection in HLA identical
sibling kidney transplant combinations, severe GVH disease
after bone marrow transplantation etc.

The finding that some of the complement factors are
coded for by genes in the HLA region is especially relevant
for our topic. There appears to be a significant linkage disequilibrium between a C2 defective gene, the SD determinants
HLA-A10-BW18 and DW2. (8,9) C4 appears to be the human
analogue of Ss in the mouse and crossreacts with it. (10,11)
There has been, of course, substantial speculation on the
existence of Ir genes in the HLA region. Claims have been
made only for genes controlling the IgE response to allergens
but some of these claims have been disputed. (12,13) The
only hard evidence in primates comes from Balner who studied
with Dorf, Benacerraf and others the immune response against
glutamic-acid alanine (GA) and the DNP conjugate of glutamic
acid and lysine (GL) which both mapped in the RhLA region.
(14,15,16) It seems likely that Balner's finding in the
Rhesus monkey will prove to be relevant for the situation in
man.
Because the similarity of the MHC regions in the different mammal (and non mammal) species is so striking, it is
common usage to extrapolate from one species to another. This
has most frequently been done between mouse and man, although
it was known during many years that in the mouse the MLC
stimulating locus was between the SD loci while in man it was
outside these loci. This disparity has received recently

extra emphasis when it became clear that in the rat the
order of the MLC stimulating and SD loci appears to be equal
to that in man and not to the mouse.(17)(Figure 2) It seems

CONCEPT OF THE M H - COMPLEX OF MAMMALIAN SPECIES

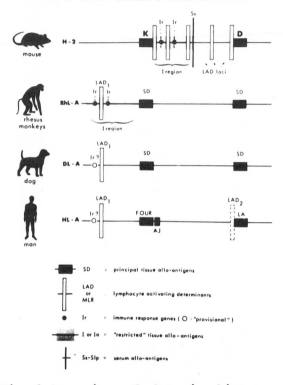

Fig. 2 Comparison of the major histocompatibility complexes of several mammalian species. The
concept of an I region of the Rhesus monkey (as
analogue to the murine I region) is postulated on
the basis of the preliminary data described. For
"mapping" of the LAD₁ locus and the Ir genes in the
RhL-A complex see ref. 14. In ref. 14, an alternative location for one of the Ir genes (here depicted
to the left of the LAD₁ locus) is described. (16)

thus that not man but the mouse and the inbred mouse at that
is the "odd mouse out". Also the levels of C3 appears to be
linked to H2 but is not linked to HLA.(18) To which extent

this might interfere with the justification of the extrapolation of findings in the H2 genome to HLA remains to be seen, but it is obvious a point which one has to bear in mind.

THE GENETICS OF THE D(MLC-s) LOCUS

a) The recognition of MLC determinants with lymphocyte culture techniques.

The basic assumption in MLC typing using the MLC test itself is that if a MLC test between two individuals is negative this implies that they share a MLC determinant. To facilitate the interpretation of the test results of MLC typing socalled typing cells are used which are homozygous for both MLC determinants i.e. both chromosomes carry the same MLC determinant. Let us indicate such cells as a/a. If X is the cell of which we want to determine the MLC determinants and a/a is the typing cell, X will be used as responder and a/a as stimulator cell. If the MLC test is negative then this implies that X does not see anything foreign on the typing cell a/a, in other words X must be either a/a itself or a/b, a/c etc. If on the other hand the reaction is positive, X can carry any MLC determinant except the MLC determinant a. (19-22)

Following this approach Keuning from our group collected from more than 200 cousin-marriages 22 typing cells and tested them against a panel of 100 individuals selected at random. (23,24)(Figure 3)

Figure 3 shows you that the typing cells could be arranged in 8 clusters, vertical columns are the results obtained with each typing cell, horizontal rows the results of each cell of the panel. Black squares indicate typing results which were unequivocal, open squares typing results of less certain interpretation. These data are compatible with the assumption that these 8 MLC determinants are alleles of one, single locus. Seven of the 8 determinants were studied in an international workshop: 6 of these 7 got an official WHO nomenclature: DW1 to DW6, the total gene frequency is almost 60%. (25)

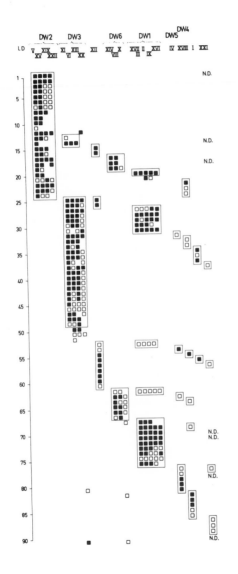

=negative MLC
reaction or
typing cell
reaction.

=doubtful
typing cell
reaction

N.D.= not done
The reactions of the
leading cells are
outlined.
If left blank this
indicates that the
MLC reaction was
positive.

Figure 3. Reaction pattern of 91 random individuals against 21 typing cells. Nine individuals gave no
typing cell response and are not shown. See further
text.

An alternative approach to type for the MLC determinants by lymphocyte culture techniques has been suggested by Sheehy and Bach. (26) They primed responder cells against haplotype different stimulator cells. The so primed responder cells were restimulated by cells sharing or not sharing a MLC determinant with the original stimulator cell. Only in the first instance significant restimulation occurs. The advantage of this test is that it can give an answer within 24-36 hours (compared to the 6-7 days needed for the typing cells) and that a sharing of a MLC determinant results in increased thymidine uptake which is easier to interpret than the absence of such an uptake in the test using typing cells. Bradley et al.(27) have confirmed and extended Sheehy's findings and showed in a family with a crossover between the D and B locus that it was indeed the D locus determinants which are responsible for restimulation (Table I)

Table I. Correlation between typing for the MLC determinants with the typing cells and the PLT test

Unrelated individuals	MLC determinants recognized by typing cells		
	aa	ac,cc	ab,cb,bb
PLT pos.	0	3	13
PLT weak	5	14	5
PLT neg.	20	1	0

Family members	MLC determinants recognized by typing cells		
	aa	ac,cc	ab,cb,bb
PLT pos.	0	1	18
PLT weak	1	7	1
PLT neg.	13	1	0

(a = compatible and self, b = specific and c = third party)

b) The recognition of MLC determinants by serology.
That antibodies against MLC stimulating determinants might exist, has been a possibility which has been considered by many workers over the last years. (28,29,30) The difficulty however was, to identify sera which might contain such anti-

bodies. Generally speaking such sera will also contain antibodies against the SD determinants and these SD antibodies
will complicate the interpretation of the test results. To
circumvent this difficulty, we devised a modification of the
MLC inhibition test, used by many and championed in HLA
serology by Ceppellini (28). The test was modified in the
following manner. In the first place lymphocytes from the
serum donor were used as the responder cells. In this manner
if an inhibition of the MLC test is found, it is less likely
that this inhibition is due to a reaction of the antibody
with the responder cells. If that would be the case one had
to assume that the antibody was an auto-immune antibody, and
this is unlikely when the serumdonor is healthy. Next stimulator cells were selected which were SD identical with the
responder cell. Again if inhibition of the MLC test is found
this is less likely to be due to SD antibodies because responder and stimulator carry the same SD determinants. Of
course the test was done in parallel using the serum to be
investigated and an AB serum, without antibodies. (31) An
example of the results which one can obtain with this test
is shown in Table II.

Table II. Identification of anti MLC antibodies by MISIS
and immunofluorescence

	AB serum cpm	Serum Sch. cpm	AB/Sch.	Fluorescence pos. cells(%)
Sch. + B$_m$	3300	400	8.3	17
C$_m$	14000	8000	1.8	4
D$_m$	9700	1100	8.8	17
E$_m$	10000	6400	1.6	9
F$_m$	4200	2800	1.5	7
G$_m$	5200	700	7.4	7
H$_m$	13500	1300	10.4	16
I$_m$	26500	1100	24.1	17
K$_m$	1800	200	9.0	-

MISIS stands for MLC inhibition test using SD identical
stimulator cells. For discussion see text.

It shows the results obtained with the serum of a parous
woman Mrs. Sch. with the HLA type 2,3,7, W40. Mrs. Sch.'s
lymphocytes were used as responder cells and 10 unrelated

individuals were selected as stimulator cells which were all
SD identical to Mrs. Sch. In AB serum the MLC reaction varied
from 1800 to over 20.000, but when the AB serum was replaced
by the serum of Mrs. Sch. in some instances significant
inhibition was found while in others this was not the case.
The one but last column indicates the inhibition ratio:
$\dfrac{\text{(AB cpm)}}{\text{(Sch.cpm)}}$ Significant values have been underlined and indicate the stimulator cells which carry the determinant with
which the presumptive anti MLC antibody reacts. With this
test we can thus detect sera which might contain anti MLC-s
antibodies while we are not confused by anti SD antibodies.
These sera were then used for absorption studies and it could
be shown that lymphocytes were able to absorb these antibodies but platelets could not. This is in contrast to anti
SD antibodies which can be absorbed by platelets and lymphocytes both.

Next Aad van Leeuwen succeeded in detecting these antibodies also by immunofluorescence (Table II). This technique
enables us to show that these antibodies reacted with B cells
and not with T cells (or platelets) and we will refer further
to these antibodies as B cell antibodies. (31, 32)
Hereafter it became possible to modify the two stage complement dependent cytotoxicity test in such a manner that it
could be used to detect these B cell antibodies. In the first
place sera were absorbed with platelets. In this manner the
SD antibodies are removed while anti B cell antibodies are
retained. Next lymphocytes were isolated and the B cell
fractions of these lymphocytes were enriched. This was done
by sheep erythrocyte rosetting and centrifugation over a
ficoll-isopaque gradient. Incubation times were prolonged to
obtain greater sensitivity and the kill was expressed as the
percentage of the B cells present in the suspension.(33)When
several sera were studied in this manner we found indeed some
which after extensive absorption with platelets (one has to
use twice the volume of the serum of packed platelets)
appeared to recognize the B cell determinants. Sofar 5 antibodies have been studied in some detail.(34) When studied a-
gainst a panel of lymphocytes obtained from over 60 donors
which had been typed for LD by typing cells and for SD by
HLA antibodies it became clear that these sera showed in each
instance a better fit with the LD or MLC determinants than
with the SD determinants. However none of the sera showed a
complete fit, a pattern of identity, with any of the MLC
determinants.
Although suggestive these data were certainly no proof that

these anti B cell antibodies were recognizing the MLC determinants. To study this more critically the sera were tested
against the typing cells collected by Keuning. (Table III)

Table III. <u>Reaction pattern of anti B cell sera with typing</u>
<u>cells</u>

MLC(D) determ.	Typing cell	anti B cell sera				
		Mo	Be	Po	Si	Ag
DW1	XVII,III,II,IX	−	−	−	−	+++++
DW2	V,XV,XIX,XXII	−	−	++++	−	−
DW3	XI,VI,XIII,(XX)	++++	++++	−	−	−
DW4	XVIII	−	−	−	−	−
DW5	IV	−	−	ND	−	−
DW6	XIV,VIII,X	−	−	ND	−	−
	I	−	−	ND	−	++++
	XII	++++	++++	−	++++	−

At the top you find the anti B cell sera, at the left the
typing cells in clusters recognizing the MLC determinants.
If each serum would recognize one MLC determinant only, we
would expect to find as positive reactions only the ones
which are enclosed by lines. Except for Po,which was only
tested against apart of the typing cells and Si, all other
sera showed extra reactions.
Next crossabsorption studies were done. Only for Mo (and
Be which is virtually identical to Mo) it is likely that it
contained two antibodies, one a monospecific anti DW3 antibody reacting sofar with all cells carrying DW3 and with none
lacking it and a weaker, contaminating anti LD XII. The discrepancies with the other sera when tested against the panel
selected at random could not be explained in this manner. The
absorbed antibody Mo might thus recognize the MLC determinant
DW3. (34)
These sera were then tested against families selected at
random (to confirm their segregation with HLA) and selected
because a crossover between the MLC and Four loci had occurred. Table IV shows you an example, the family Br. in which
such a crossover had occurred in child 3. The MLC test between child 3 with the SD different child 2 was for instance
negative. This is also proven by the segregation pattern of
the typing cell LD V which segregates perfectly with the
maternal haplotype 2-7 except in child 3 where the crossover

is assumed to have occurred and where this determinant occurs together with the 1-8 SD antigens.

Table IV. <u>Fam. Br. with a maternal crossover between (D)MLC and (B)Four.</u>

| | | DW2 | B cell determ. | | |
			Po	Mo	Ag
Father	(1,8/2,13)	n.d.	n.d.	n.d.	n.d.
Mother	/1,8/2,7	++	++	−	−
Ch 1	2,13/1,8	−	−	−	−
Ch 2	1,8 / 2,7	++	++	++	++
Ch 3	1,8 /[1,8]	++	++	++	++
Ch 4	2,13/ 2,7	++	++	−	−
Ch 5	1,8 / 2,7	++	++	++	++
Ch 6	1,8 /1,8	−	−	++	++

When the anti B cell serum Po was tested in this family, it segregated not with the SD determinants 2-7 but with the MLC determinant DW2. Since the determinant for Po segregates with HLA in other families this is formal proof that this anti B cell antibody recognizes a determinant which is coded for by a locus which can be separated from the Four locus by a crossover. These data however do not tell us whether this locus is identical to or separate from the MLC locus. This same family was also studied with the other anti B cell sera. Mo and Ag were informative and showed an identical segregation pattern. However Mo and Ag have completely independent distribution patterns in the typing cell (Table III) and random panel and are thus neither similar to or inclusive in each other. These data force us to the conclusion that Ag and Mo must be coded for by not one but two different loci. As Mo might be coded for by the MLC or D locus DW3, the Ag locus must be the right or the left of that locus. Furthermore family and population data suggest that the B cell sera Ag, Po and the serum Si might recognize alleles of this new Ag locus. These findings have been published in extenso elsewhere (34) and are summarized in Fig. 4.

Of course we entertain the possibility that these sera are recognizing the human equivalent of the mouse Ia antibodies. However because so little is known about the presence, let alone the localization of Ir genes in the HLA system, we prefer to refer to these antibodies as "B-cell antibodies". Similar antibodies have also been described in the Rhesus monkey. The interesting point is that some of them appear to

HLA SUPERGENE

D	Ag	B	C	A
MLC		Four	AJ	LA
DW1	Ag	B7	C1	A1
DW2	Po	B8	C2	A2
DW3		B12	C3	A3
= Mo		etc.	etc.	etc.
DW4				
DW5				
DW6				
LD XII	Si			

Figure 4. The A, B and C loci code for determinants which are present on all nucleated cells.
Seven MLC or D locus determinants can be recognized
by typing cells, one of them (DW3) also by serology.
To the right or the left of the D locus, lies the Ag
locus coding for three determinants Ag,Po and Si which
which are in linkage disequilibrium with DW1,DW2 and
LD XII respectively. These determinants are preferentially expressed on B cells.

segregate with the equivalent of the A locus in the monkey.
(15) Amos has found also in man preliminary evidence for the
occurrence of B cell antibodies segregating with the A locus.
(This issue)

For the study of anti-B cell antibodies many technique
variations have been suggested. These include the use of
lymphoid cell lines or CLL cells to identify the presence of
these antibodies and the use of the lymphocyte dependent antibody (LDA) test to detect them. (35,36,37) An alternative
approach which could possibly eliminate the need for the
time-consuming platelet absorptions is the use of anti β_2-
microglobuline to cap the SD determinants on the lymphocyte
membrane after which the B cell determinants which are not
coupled to β_2-microglobulin can be detected by a standard
complement dependent lymphocytotoxicity test. (38) Other
techniques involve blocking of the Fc receptor, complement
fixation or combinations of those listed above. (39,40)
It is too early to assess the usefulness of these techniques
and a comparison of the results obtained with them will be
one of the major topics during the next histocompatibility
workshop.

HLA AND DISEASE ASSOCIATIONS

Extensive reviews on HLA and disease have recently been published and the interested reader is referred to them. (41)The data sofar available could be summarized as proving beyond doubt that predisposition for many different diseases, often of an autoimmune nature, is significantly associated with specific HLA antigens. The most significant association has been found for HLA-B27 and ankylosing spondylitis,while HLA-B8 is an antigen which shows an increased frequency in patients suffering from many different diseases. It is however of interest that in none of these diseases all patients carry the antigen in question: for instance although about 90% of the patients suffering from ankylosing spondylitis carry HLA-B27 (versus about 8% in controls) some patients suffering from the classical form of the disease lack HLA-B27. Similarly, 80% of the patients suffering from gluten enteropathy carry HLA-B8 versus 20% in the controls. Why this is so is as yet uncertain but the following information is relevant in this context and indicates that the association of disease with HLA might rest on more than one mechanism. In the first place HLA-B8 and HLA-B27 are virtually absent in Japanese but gluten enteropathy and ankylosing spondylitis do occur in that population. The interesting point is that also in Japanese there is a highly significant increase of HLA-B27 in ankylosing spondylitis patients. (43) If we combine these findings with what is known about the occurrence of ankylosing spondylitis in families, the following model emerges: two genes predispose for ankylosing spondylitis: one is the antigen HLA-B27 itself or a gene in extreme linkage disequilibrium with HLA. The other factor might be a recessive gene which can lead to the disease when it is present together with HLA-B27 or when it is present in a double dose. (42,44)
For gluten enteropathy the situation seems to be different: in Japanese the disease occurs although rarely but such patients do not carry HLA-B8 more frequently than in controls (the frequency of HLA-B8 is in both groups extremely low). This could indicate that it is not HLA-B8 which predisposes to gluten enteropathy but a gene which is in linkage disequilibrium with HLA-B8 in Caucasians. As such of course the B cell determinants qualify and it could indeed be shown that 27 out of 28 Caucasian patients suffering from gluten enteropathy carried the B cell determinant Mo and DW3. (45)

The recently observed linkage between C2 and possibly C4 deficiency with HLA might be another factor which could

43

lead to significant associations between certain diseases and
HLA. Because the HLA haplotype HLA-A10-BW18 is in significant
linkage disequilibrium with a C2 deficient gene (9) it might
be of interest as was recently suggested to us by Dr. James
Mowbray, to investigate whether this haplotype occurs more
frequently in patients suffering from complex-disease. Such
patients occur quite frequently among those afflicted with
end-stage renal disease. It was of considerable interest to
us that the frequency of HLA-A10-BW18 combinations was more
frequent in patients on the Eurotransplant waiting list than
in healthy controls. The differences did however not yet
attain statistical significance. Mowbray (personal communication) has found the same to be true in England.

HLA AND IMMUNE RESPONSE

Although there could thus be many reasons why disease
associations with HLA can occur the explanation which is
favoured by many is that immune response genes in the HLA
region either fail to produce immunity against disease
causing agents or overshoot. In the latter case they induce
the production of antibodies which not only react with the
disease causing agent, but crossreact with the patient's own
tissue as well and are thus of autoimmune nature. As has been
pointed out in the introduction pityingly little direct information is available on Ir genes in man. Haverkorn et al.
(46) have recently introduced a model by which such information can be collected. Monozygotic and dizygotic twins of
school going age were bled and antibody titres against a
number of viral and bacterial antigens were determined.
Next it was tested whether the difference in titre was
smaller in monozygotic than in dizygotic twins. It was argued
that if this would be the case it would indicate a strong
genetic influence in antibody titre response. To our surprise
only for diphteria and measles this appeared to be true.
(Table V)
Next the dizygotic twins were divided in HLA identical and
HLA non identical siblings. Now only the data for measles
were (of borderline) significance. These data are certainly
not sufficient to state that an Ir gene in the HLA supergene
controls the antibody response to measles, but they indicate
that this model is an useful approach to answer this
question.

Table V.
Antibody titre ratios
in twins

(Haverkorn et al. 1975)

	mono versus dizygotic twins	HLA identical versus HLA non-identical
Polio I	p = .043	p = .39
Polio II	p = .459	p = .85
Polio III	p = .944	p = .92
Diphteria	p = .001	p = .38
Measles	p = .02	p = .05
Rubella	p = .99	p = .99

The beautiful complex work of Benacerraf, Katz, Munro, Taussig and many others indicate that the major histocompatibility complex in the mouse and by inference also in other species including man, plays also an important role in T-B cell interactions. (47,48) The following case histories, presenting a experiment of nature in the classical sense might be relevant in this context.

Two Turkish children were admitted to the pediatric Sophia Hospital in Rotterdam (head Prof.Dr.H.K.A. Visser, resident Dr.R.K.B. Schuurman) with complaints of eczema, diarrhoea and upper respiratory infections. On physical examination pale but lively children were found with the skin-lesions mentioned above and a moderate hepato-megaly. Routine laboratory findings were within normal limits apart from a moderate anaemia, but an almost complete absence of all immunoglobulin classes except for IgM was observed. Light microscopy and fluorescence antibody studies (courtesy of Drs. J. Vossen) showed virtual absence of plasma cells and cytoplasmatic immunoglobulins except for IgM. Membrane fluorescence was normal for all classes. The percentage of T cells was normal, and of B cells and K cells low. PHA stimulation was within normal limits as were MLC tests in which the children's cells were used as stimulators. Sofar these two children present thus a syndrome of familial, autosomal a- (or hypo-) gammaglobulinaemia. The reason that they are presented here is that on the lymphocytes of both children none of the HLA antigens present in the parents could be detected.

The HLA antigens were also below the detection limit in the serum of the children. Furthermore β_2-microglobulin was absent on the lymphocytes of both children and present in about half of the normal amount in the parents. The MLC determinants appear to be present because the lymphocytes of the children were able to stimulate responder cells of normal donors in the MLC test. None of the available anti B cell sera reacted with the B cells of the children or the parents. It is for that reason still unclear whether B cell determinants are present in them or not. Their karyograms were normal.

These case histories lead at least to two questions: In the first place why are the HLA-A and B cell antigens lacking and has this something to do with the absence of β_2-microglobulin. Coating of the HLA antigens by an autoimmune antibody appears not to be the explanation. Lack of β_2-microglobulin production might have led to incomplete expression of the HLA antigens and hybridization studies might shed light on this.
The second question is of course: Is there a causal relationship between the absence of the HLA antigens and the absence of the immunoglobulins. Of the many hypotheses which can be formulated one suggested to us by Dr. A. Munro is of special relevance for our discussion today. Suppose that for the exchange of information from the T cell to the B cell the HLA-A and B antigens are necessary, then in the absence of the HLA-A and B antigens whatever the reason, one would get a block in the transfer of such information and B cells will remain dormant.

This work was in part supported by the National Institute of Health(contract NO1-AI-4-2508), the J.A. Cohen Institute of Radiopathology and Radiation Protection (IRS), the Dutch Foundation for Medical Research (FUNGO) which is subsidized by the Dutch Organization for the Advancement of Pure Research (ZWO) and the Dutch Organization for Health Research (TNO).

REFERENCES

(1)   H. van Someren, A. Westerveld, A. Hagemeyer, J.R.Mees, P. Meera Khan and O.B. Zaalberg. Proc.Nat.Acad.Sci.USA 71 (1974) 962.

(2)   L.U. Lamm, F. Kissmeyer-Nielsen, A. Svejgaard, G.B. Petersen, E. Thorsby, W. Mayr and C. Högman. Tissue Antigens 2 (1972) 205.

(3) W. Bodmer. Personal communication.

(4) Third Conference on Human Gene Mapping. Baltimore 1975.

(5) M. Fellous, C. Billardon, J. Dausset et J. Frezal. C.R.
     Acad.Sc., Paris 26 (1971) 3356.

(6) Ch. Rittner, H. Grosse Wilde, B. Rittner, B. Netzel,
     S. Scholz, H. Lorenz and E.D. Albert. Humangenetik 27
     (1975) 173.

(7) Histocompatibility Testing 1975. Ed. F. Kissmeyer-
     Nielsen. Copenhagen, Munksgaard, 1975 in press.

(8) S.M. Fu, H.G. Kunkel, H.P. Brusman, F.H. Allen and M.
     Fotino. J.exp.Med. 140 (1974) 1108.

(9) S.M. Fu, R. Stern, H.G. Kunkel, B. Dupont, J.A. Hansen,
     N.K. Day, R.A. Good, C. Jersild and M. Fotino.
     J.exp.Med. 142 (1975) 495.

(10) J. Capková and P. Démant. Folia Biol. 20 (1974) 101.

(11) T. Meo, T. Frasteff and D.C. Shreffler. Proc.Nat.Acad.
     Sci. USA in press.

(12) B.B. Levine, R.H. Stember and M. Fotino. Science 178
     (1972) 1201.

(13) D.G. Marsh, W.B. Bias, S.H. Hsu and L. Goodfriend.
     Science 179 (1973) 691.

(14) M.E. Dorf, H. Balner and B. Benacerraf. Transplant.
     Proc. VII (1975) 21.

(15) H. Balner. To be submitted to Nature.

(16) H. Balner and W. van Vreeswijk. Transplant.Proc. VII
     (1975) 13.

(17) T.J. Gill and H.W. Kunz. To be published.

(18) A. Ferreira and V. Nussenzweig. J.exp.Med. 141 (1975)
     513.

(19) B.A. Bradley, J.M. Edwards, D.C. Dunn and R.Y. Calne.
     Nature (New Biol.) 240 (1972) 54.

(20) W. Mempel, H. Grosse Wilde, E. Albert and S. Thierfelder. Transplant.Proc. V (1973) 401.

(21) F. Jørgensen, L.U.Lamm and F. Kissmeyer-Nielsen. Tissue Antigens 3 (1973) 323.

(22) J.G. van den Tweel, A. Blussé van Oud Alblas, J.J. Keuning, E. Goulmy, A. Termijtelen, M.L. Bach and J.J. van Rood. Transplant.Proc. V (1973) 1535.

(23) J.J.Keuning, A. Termijtelen, A. Blussé van Oud Alblas, J.G. van den Tweel, I. Schreuder and J.J. van Rood. Transplant.Proc. VII (1975) 35.

(24) J.J.Keuning, A. Termijtelen, A. Blussé van Oud Alblas, B.W. Gabb, J. D'Amaro and J.J. van Rood. Histocompatibility Testing 1975. Ed. F. Kissmeyer-Nielsen, Copenhagen, Munksgaard 1975 in press.

(25) E. Thorsby and A. Piazza. Joint Report from the Sixth International Histocompatibility Workshop Conference II. Typing for HLA-D (LD-1 or MLC) determinants. Histocompatibility Testing 1975. Ed. F. Kissmeyer-Nielsen. Copenhagen, Munksgaard 1975 in press.

(26) M.J. Sheehy, P.M. Sondel, M.L. Bach., R.Wank and F.H. Bach. Science 188 (1975) 1308.

(27) B.A.Bradley, M. Sheehy, J.J.Keuning, A. Termijtelen, D. Franks and J.J. van Rood. To be submitted.

(28) R. Ceppellini, G.D. Bonnard, F. Coppo, V.C.Miggiano, M. Pospisil, E.S. Curtoni and M. Pellegrino. Transplant.Proc. III (1971) 63.

(29) A.O. Carbonara. Personal communication.

(30) P. Wernet and H.G. Kunkel. Transplant.Proc. V (1973) 1975.

(31) A. van Leeuwen, H.R.E. Schuit and J.J. van Rood. Transplant.Proc. V (1973) 1539.

(32) A. van Leeuwen, R. Winchester and J.J. van Rood. Ann. N.Y.Acad.Sci. 254 (1975) 289.

(33)   J.J. van Rood, A. van Leeuwen, J.J. Keuning and A. Blussé van Oud Alblas. Tissue Antigens 5 (1975) 73.

(34)   J.J.van Rood, A. van Leeuwen, J. Parlevliet, A. Termijtelen and J.J. Keuning. Histocompatibility Testing 1975. Ed. F. Kissmeyer-Nielsen. Copenhagen, Munksgaard 1975 in press.

(35)   R.J. Winchester, S.M. Fu, P. Wernet, H.G. Kunkel, B. Dupont and C. Jersild. J.exp.Med. 141 (1975) 924.

(36)   R.L. Walford, T. Gossett, G.S. Smith, E. Zeller and J. Wilkinson. Tissue Antigens 5 (1975) 196.

(37)   T. Kovithavongs, L. Hyshka, P.R. McConnachie and J.B. Dossetor. Tissue Antigens 5 (1975) 165.

(38)   W. Bodmer. Histocompatibility Testing 1975. Ed. F. Kissmeyer-Nielsen. Copenhagen, Munksgaard 1975 in press.

(39)   P. Wernet. Histocompatibility Testing 1975. Ed. F. Kissmeyer-Nielsen. Copenhagen, Munksgaard 1975 in press.

(40)   J. Colombani. Personal communication.

(41)   H.O. McDevitt and W.F. Bodmer. Lancet i (1974) 1269.

(42)   J.J. van Rood, J.P. van Hooff and J.J. Keuning. Transplant.Reviews 22 (1975) 75.

(43)   H. Sonozaki, H. Seki, S. Chang, M. Okuyama and T.Juji. Tissue Antigens in press.

(44)   J.M.J.P. van der Linden, J.J. Keuning, J.H.C. Wuisman, A. Cats and J.J. van Rood. Lancet i (1975) 520.

(45)   A.S. Peña, A. van Leeuwen, J.J. Keuning, A.J.Ch.Haex and J.J. van Rood. Manuscript in preparation.

(46)   M.J.Haverkorn, B. Hofman, N. Masurel and J.J. van Rood. Transplant.Reviews 22 (1975) 120.

(47)   D.H. Katz and B. Benacerraf. Transplant.Reviews 22 (1975) 175.

(48)   A.J. Munro and M.J. Taussig. Nature 256 (1975) 103.

DISCUSSION FOLLOWING JON van ROOD

GREEN: Patients with progeria have been reported to have
absent HLA antigens as well. Do these patients have
any evidence of immunodeficiency?

van ROOD: To the best of my knowledge, this has not been
studied in any detail.

NOSSAL: We should not be surprised at your finding that it
was not possible to show a genetic influence in the
immune response to antigens such as rubella or polio
virus. After all, these are complex antigenic mosaics,
and nearly all of our information in the mouse on genetics of immune responses comes from studies of defined
antigens of restricted heterogeneity. The anti-viral
responses are certainly "pools" of a number of different
immune responses.

van ROOD: I agree with you. Furthermore, only a very
limited number of antigens were studied and then only
for humoral immune responses. A large variety of
"ethical" antigens is now studied by more techniques.

MUNRO: Do the immune deficient children express HLA antigens on cells other than lymphocytes?

van ROOD: So far, only the *HLA-A* antigens were found on
fibroblasts after culture for several days.

DAUSSET: The presence of the *P* locus on the sixth chromosome in human has been confirmed by Dr. Fellows. Each
time the sixth chromosome is lost, the cell lost also
the *P* reactivity.

van ROOD: There still seems to be contradictory data
around. For instance, that the *P* locus codes in a
linkage group outside the *HLA* linkage group. Perhaps
this indicates that for this expression of the *P* locus,
two genes have to cooperate, one of which is on the
sixth chromosome.

G. KLEIN: Do the *HLA*-deficient, immunodeficient children's
lymphocytes contain β_2-microglobulin?

van ROOD: No, they do not contain β_2-microglobulin.

G. KLEIN: What is the representation of your B cell antibodies, detected by the B cell cytotoxicity, on established lymphoid cell lines?

van ROOD: They are present on some, but not on all lymphoid
cell lines.

AMOS: The lack of reactions of the immunodeficient children
seem very similar to the situation with the cell DAUDI
which also lacks β_2-microglobulin and has little or no
HLA antigenicity.   The DAUDI cells do carry the HLA core
molecule apparently without the variable site.   Have you
had the opportunity of examining the cells with a xeno-
antibody to the core sequence of HLA.

van ROOD: No, but we have examined chimpanzee anti-human.

AMOS: This probably detects primarily alloantigens.

van ROOD: Yes.

AMOS: I suggest using antibody from Cresswell or from
Strominger for testing this point.   I would also like to
comment that the reactions that we and others found on
lymphoid lines, not present on the donor are almost
certainly B cell antigens.   Using anti-B cell antibodies
free from HLA activity, we can haplotype cultured cells
from families and obtain a close correlation between
cultured and fresh B lymphocytes.

BACH: Have you studied the cells of the children with the
lack of the HLA SD antigens for their ability to sensitize in cell-mediated lympholysis or to act as targets
in CML?

van ROOD: Vincent Eijsvoogel has attempted this, but the
experiments have not so far provided informative data.

51

MOLECULAR RELATIONSHIPS OF Ia ANTIGENS CONTROLLED BY THE SAME
AND BY DIFFERENT SUBREGIONS OF THE *I* REGION

JAN KLEIN, VĚRA HAUPTFELD, AND ELLEN S.VITETTA

Department of Microbiology, The University of Texas
Southwestern Medical School, Dallas, Texas   75235

Abstract: The technique of antibody-induced resistance to
cell lysis (lysostrip) was used to determine topographical relationships of Ia antigens in the cell membrane.
Data obtained thus far demonstrate that antigens controlled by the same subregion of the *I* region (IaA.1
and 2) behave as if present on the same molecule, whereas an antigen coded for by a different subregion (IaC.7)
is on a separate molecule.

The *I* region of the *H-2* complex codes for antigens that
can be detected by standard serological methods. These *I*
region associated (Ia) antigens are most easily demonstrated
on the surface of B lymphocytes (1,2), but are also present
on T lymphocytes as well as on other cells (3,4). By producing antisera in various strain combinations and testing them
against a panel of strains carrying independent and recombinant
H-2 haplotypes, one can define a large number of individual
Ia antigens. Nine Ia antigens have been defined in our
laboratory (ref. 5 and unpublished data), 15 in the laboratory
of D. C. Shreffler (6), 12 by D. Götze (7), and a few others
by other laboratories. The Ia antigens can be arranged into
an Ia chart listing individual *H-2* haplotypes and the Ia
antigens they control. This chart resembles the H-2 chart
in that it is complex and contains private antigens (i.e.,
those restricted to a single *H-2* haplotype of independent
origin), as well as public antigens (i.e., those shared by
several independent *H-2* haplotypes). On the basis of genetic
mapping studies, the loci coding for Ia antigens can be
assigned to one of two subregions of the *I* region, *IA* or *IC*.
In addition, David and Shreffler (6) described antigens
controlled by the *IB* and *IE* subregions, but in our laboratory
we have been unable to produce antibodies against IaB and IaE

antigens. More recently, Götze (7) described Ia antigens
whose loci he tentatively assigned to additional *I* subregions.

Most of the known Ia antigens seem to be coded for by
the *IA* subregion thus raising the question of how many Ia loci
this subregion contains. Serological complexity does not
a priori require a large number of loci; in fact, theoretically, all the antigens can be controlled by a single locus.
In an analogous situation, the classical H-2 antigens are
also extremely numerous, yet they all seem to be controlled
by one locus in the *K* region and another locus in the *D*
region (8). Since the question of the number of *Ia* loci has
an important bearing on the understanding of the relationship
of these loci to other loci in the *I* region, we have been
attempting to answer it by determining molecular relationships
of Ia antigens. The tests are based on the method of antibody-induced resistance to lysis (lysostrip) adapted by us
(9) to the *H-2* and *Ia* systems. The method is based on the
assumption that cell membrane antigens carried by separate
molecules can be redistributed independently, whereas antigens
carried by the same molecule redistribute together. The
redistribution is achieved by attaching two layers of antibodies to the antigen, in this case, the Ia alloantibody and
a xenogeneic (goat) antibody against mouse immunoglobulin
(GAMIG), and by warming the cells to 37°C. The redistribution
is then determined by a standard cytotoxic test. Only antigens
that have not been redistributed can bind antibodies and
complement with the ensuance of cell lysis; cells are resistant
to lysis by antibodies directed against the redistributed
antigens.

For the tests of the molecular relationship of Ia
antigens, we selected three antigens, Ia.1 and 2, both controlled by the *IA* subregion, and an antigen resembling
Shreffler's Ia.7 and controlled by the *IC* subregion. The
first two antigens are detected by antibodies in antiserum
(B10.HTT x A.SW)F_1 anti-A.TL (K-417). The unabsorbed antiserum reacts, among others, with haplotypes $H-2^k$ and $H-2^f$;
absorption by $H-2^f$ lymphocytes removes the reactivity of the
antiserum against $H-2^f$ but not against $H-2^k$ cells. Such a
reactivity pattern is usually interpreted as indicating the
presence of two antibodies, one against an antigen (Ia.1)
shared by $H-2^f$ and $H-2^k$, and another (Ia.2) specific for
$H-2^k$. The third antigen is defined by antiserum B10.D2(R106)
anti-B10.A(5R) (K-197) which reacts with all strains carrying
Shreffler's Ia.7 but in addition also crossreacts weakly with
$H-2^s$ cells; it may be, therefore, detecting a variant of the
Ia.7 antigen. The reactivity pattern of the three antisera is
summarized in Tables 1 and 2.

TABLE 1

REACTIVITY IN CYTOTOXIC TEST OF THREE ANTI-Ia SERA WITH SPLEEN
CELLS OF STRAINS CARRYING *H-2* HAPLOTYPES OF INDEPENDENT ORIGIN

Strain	*H-2* haplotype	K-417	K-417abs.	K-197
C57BL/10	*b*	0	0	0
B10.D2	*d*	0	0	64
B10lM or A.CA	*f*	32	0	0
B10.BR	*k*	128	64	128
C3H.NB	*p*	0	0	64
B10.Q	*q*	0	0	0
B10.RIII(71NS)	*r*	32	0	64
B10.S	*s*	0	0	8

K-417: (B10.HTT x A.SW)F$_1$ anti-A.TL.
K-417abs.: (B10. HTT x A.SW)F$_1$ anti-A.TL absorbed
by B10.M lymphocytes.
K-197: B10.D2(R106) anti-B10.A(5R).

TABLE 2

REACTIVITY IN CYTOTOXIC TEST OF THREE ANTI-Ia SERA WITH SPLEEN
CELLS OF STRAINS CARRYING *H-2* RECOMBINANT HAPLOTYPES

Strain	*H-2* haplo- type	Origin of *H-2* regions							Reciprocal of titre		
		K	IA	IB	IC	S	G	D	K-417	K-417abs.	K-197
B10.A	*a*	*k*	*k*	*k*	*d*	*d*	*d*	*d*	128	128	128
A.AL	*al*	*k*	*k*	*k*	*k*	*k*	*k*	*d*	128	128	128
A.TFR1	*anl*	*s*	*k*	*k*	*k*	*k*	*f*	*f*	64	128	64
HTG	*g*	*d*	*d*	*d*	*d*	*d*	.	*b*	0	0	64
D2.GD	*g2*	*d*	*d*	*b*	*b*	*b*	*b*	*b*	0	0	0
B10.A(2R)	*h2*	*k*	*k*	*k*	*d*	*d*	.	*b*	64	128	128
B10.A(4R)	*h4*	*k*	*k*	*b*	*b*	*b*	*b*	*b*	128	128	0
B10.A(5R)	*i5*	*b*	*b*	*b*	*d*	*d*	*d*	*d*	0	0	0
C3H.OH	*o2*	*d*	*d*	*d*	*d*	*d*	*d*	*k*	0	0	128
A.TL	*tl*	*s*	*k*	*k*	*k*	*k*	*k*	*d*	128	128	128
A.TH	*t2*	*s*	*s*	*s*	*s*	*s*	*s*	*d*	0	0	0
B10.HTT	*t3*	*s*	*s*	*s*	*d*	*d*	*d*	*d*	0	0	64
B10.AQR	*yl*	*s*	*k*	*k*	*d*	*d*	*d*	*d*	128	128	128
B10.T(6R)	*y2*	*q*	*q*	*q*	*q*	*q*	.	*d*	0	0	0

See footnote Table 1 for description of antisera.

Independence of the Ia.7-like antigen from the antigens
controlled by the *K* and *D* subregions is demonstrated in
Table 3.   Cells of an *H-2^d* strain can be made resistant to
antibodies (and complement) against one of three antigens,
IaC.7, H-2D.4, and U-2K.31, and at the same time retain
susceptibility to antibodies (and complement) against the
remaining two antigens.

TABLE 3

SUCEPTIBILITY OF DBA/2 SPLEEN CELLS TO LYSIS AFTER TREATMENT
WITH ANTI-Ia OR H-2 SERA AND GAMIG

Treated with As against Ag	Tested with As against Ag	% dead cells at dilution of As				
		1:2	1:4	1:8	1:16	1:32
-------	IaC.7	70	60	55	45	25
IaC.7		25	25	25	20	20
H-2D.4		65	60	60	45	30
H-2K.31		65	65	60	20	20
-------	H-2D.4	100	92	90	80	60
H-2D.4		30	30	25	25	25
IaC.7		90	88	80	70	60
H-2K.31		90	90	85	70	35
-------	H-2K.31	85	80	70	45	25
H-2K.31		30	20	20	20	20
IaC.7		85	75	70	40	25
H-2D.4		80	70	65	40	20
GAMIG	NMS + C'	20	22	25	20	20

IaC.7 = B10.D2(R106) anti-B10.A(5R) (K-197).
H-2D.4 = (A.BY x B10.AKM)F$_1$ anti-B10.A (K-304).
H-2K.31 = (A x B10)F$_1$ anti-B10.D2 (K-331).

The results of the experiment testing the relationship
of the three Ia antigens are summarized in Table 4.   Cells
that have become resistant to anti-Ia.2 are also resistant to
anti-Ia.1,2 and vice versa, but are still sensitive to anti-Ia.7.
Similarly, cells resistant to anti-Ia.7 are still sensitive to
either Ia.2 or anti-Ia.1,2.   With certain reservations discussed elsewhere (8), these results suggest that in the cell
membrane antigens IaA.1 and IaA.2, which are controlled by the
same subregion (IA), are carried by the same molecule, whereas
antigens IaA.1,2 and the IC-subregion controlled IaC.7 are on
separate molecules.   This conclusion is in agreement with
genetic mapping studies which show no recombination between
determinants for antigens Ia.1 and 2, but show several
recombinations between the determinantes for Ia.1,2 and Ia.7.

TABLE 4

SUSCEPTIBILITY OF CBA/J $(H-2^k)$ SPLEEN CELLS TO LYSIS AFTER
TREATMENT WITH ANTI-Ia SERUM AND GAMIG

Treated with As against Ag	Tested with As against Ag	% dead cells at dilution of AS				
		1:2	1:4	1:8	1:16	1:32
-------	IaA.1,2	68	60	58	40	25
IaA.1,2	↑	25	25	25	25	25
IaA.2		20	18	18	20	20
IaC.7	↓	50	40	45	40	30
-------	IaA.2	55	50	45	30	15
IaA.2	↑	15	15	12	12	15
IaA.1,2		15	15	15	15	15
IaC.7	↓	55	45	40	40	30
-------	IaC.7	65	60	50	50	40
IaC.7	↑	20	20	20	20	20
IaA.1,2		50	50	40	30	20
IaA.2	↓	50	45	40	30	20
GAMIG	NMS + C'	20	20	25	25	20

Anti-IaA.1,2 - (B10.HTT X A.SW)F_1 anti-A.TL (K-417).
Anti-IaA.2 = K-417 absorbed by B10.M lymphocytes.
Anti-IaC.7 = B10.D2(R106) anti-B10.A(5R) (K-197).

Experiments testing the relationships among other Ia
antigens are in progress and preliminary data indicate that
this behavioral pattern might be quite general. Furthermore,
coprecipitation experiments on isolated antigens (10) indicate
that other antigens controlled by different subregions are
also on separate molecules. All these data seem to be suggesting that the *Ia* loci are not as numerous as the serology might
seem to indicate. If the Ia antigens are coded for by the *Ir*
loci, as was suggested by one of us (11), then the paucity of
Ia loci would argue against the hypothesis of *Ir* loci coding
for molecules having an antigen receptor function (12).

ACKNOWLEDGEMENTS

We thank Ms. JoAnne Tuttle for her secretarial assistance.
This research was supported by grants AI11650 and AI12589 from
the National Institutes of Health.

REFERENCES

(1) G.J. Hämmerling, B.D. Deak, G. Mauve, U. Hämmerling, and H.O. McDevitt. Immunogenetics 1 (1974) 68.

(2) V. Hauptfeld, M. Hauptfeld, and J. Klein. J. Immunol. 113 (1974) 181.

(3) J.A. Frelinger, J.E. Niederhuber, C. S. David, and D.C. Shreffler. J. Exp. Med. 140 (1974) 1273.

(4) G.J. Hämmerling, G. Mauve, E. Goldberg, and H.O. McDevitt. Immunogenetics 2 (1975) 428.

(5) J. Klein. *Biology of the Mouse Histocompatibility-2 Complex.* (Springer-Verlag, New York, 1975).

(6) C.S. David and D.C. Shreffler. Transplantation 17 (1974) 462.

(7) D. Götze. Immunogenetics In Press.

(8) V. Hauptfeld and J. Klein. J. Exp. Med. 142 (1975) 288.

(9) V. Hauptfeld, M. Hauptfeld, and J. Klein. J. Exp. Med. 141 (1975) 1047.

(10) S.E. Cullen and S.G. Natheson. In *The Immune System: Genes, Receptors, Signals.* Proceedings of the 1974 I.C.N.-U.C.L.A. Symposium on Molecular Biology. Eds. E.E. Sarcarz, A.R. Williamson, and C.F. Fox, Academic Press, New York, 1974) p. 191.

(11) J. Klein. Comtemp. Topics Immunogiol. In Press.

(12) B. Benacerraf and H.O. McDevitt. Science 175 (1972) 273.

Br AND Wh, B CELL ANTIGENS IN GLUTEN SENSITIVE ENTEROPATHY
AND DERMATITIS HERPETIFORMIS

DEAN L. MANN[1], WARREN STROBER[1], STEPHEN I. KATZ[1],
SHYUAN HSIA[2], AND D. BERNARD AMOS[2]

[1]National Cancer Institute
National Institutes of Health
Bethesda, Maryland 20014

[2]Division of Immunology
Duke University Medical Center
Durham, North Carolina 27710

Abstract: Fc receptor cells (B cells) are separated from
    other lymphocytes by their ability to adhere to antibody-
    antigen complexes on microcytotoxicity plates, or in a
    batch procedure, on petri dishes. Sera defining B cell
    specificities are obtained from multiparous women or
    from mothers of children with disease. B cell antigens
    in differing degrees of linkage disequilibrium with HLA
    are described in Amish and in random subjects. New spe-
    cificities apparently present only on B cells from
    patients with dermatitis herpetiformis or gluten entero-
    pathy are presented. The possibility that anti-HLA sera
    giving occasional unexpected reactions are really reac-
    ting with T cell antigens is discussed in the context
    that the subpopulation antigens are differentiation
    antigens and can give a new insight into the genetics
    and etiology of disease.

INTRODUCTION

The association of HLA and disease has, until recently,
been a tantalizing one. The extraordinary relationship
between HLA-B27 and ankylosing spondylitis (AS) or Reiter's
syndrome has given a glimpse of the potential for diagnosis
and of a future base for an investigation of the etiology of
the diseases. The associations of HLA-B8 with gluten enteropathy, juvenile diabetes and other autoimmune type diseases
have been significant but clearly of a different order of magnitude from the B27 and AS combination, while associations

with Hodgkin's disease and with leukemia have been inconstant (1).

The most likely explanation for the differences between diseases and between individual series is that the structural genes for HLA are at varying distances from the genetic loci involved in the HLA associated diseases. Thus, a genetic locus responsible for the abnormality leading to AS may be in close proximity to the HLA-B genetic locus, while the genetic locus responsible for gluten sensitive enteropathy (GSE) or dermatitis herpetiformis (DH) may be at a greater distance though still in significant linkage disequilibrium with HLA-B alleles. Still further, presumably, would be genes associated with Hodgkin's disease or leukemia, and with the hypersensitive states, and here the differences between populations would be extreme.

We have been interested in detecting other genetic markers related to HLA (2). To emphasize our realization that a considerable segment of the C6 chromosome or haplotype is involved in a variety of immunological processes the designation HL-1 was introduced (3). HL-1 was defined as the genetic region coding for the HLA antigens, the lymphocyte stimulating MLR-S determinants (now HLA-D), and genes controlling immune responsiveness. At some distance from HLA and generally considered as part of HL-1 appears to be a locus or loci controlling spinal development and contributing to spina bifida occulta and other spinal defects (4). The WHO terminology committee has subsequently defined an "HLA region" which is essentially comparable to HL-1 (5). For this paper we will use both designations.

Until recently, we were only able to define many of the components of HL-1 by biologic testing. In 1973, van Leeuwen and her colleagues found that antibodies produced by deliberate immunization of unrelated HLA identical pairs were capable of recognizing antigenic determinants closely related to or identical to products of the HLA-D locus (6). Since then, a growing number of studies have concentrated on the serological definition and identification of the various specificities of B lymphocytes (7,8). Our own early studies were on the antigens of cultured lymphocytes (9), since one of the difficulties encountered by van Leeuwen and subsequent workers including ourselves was the isolation of B cells from peripheral blood. The formation of rosettes with antibody-sensitized erythrocytes has been widely used (10), but even when dextran is added to increase the tightness of binding of the rosettes (11), this procedure is time-consuming and not very efficient, since the rosettes may be disrupted during separation of rosetting and nonrosetting lymphocytes.

MATERIALS AND METHODS

A novel procedure for separating B cells reported to us at the 6th Histocompatibility Testing Workshop offered a considerable improvement over previous methods (12). In brief, microcytotoxicity plates were rinsed with fetal calf serum which formed a film on the plastic. The serum component adherent to plastic appears to be a heat-stable lipoprotein (13). Trinitrobenzene sulphonate was added to the tray, followed by antibody to DNP. Excess antibody and unattached complexes were removed by repeated washing. Peripheral blood lymphocytes (PBL) freed from macrophages by treatment with carbonyl iron, were added (2.5×10^4/well). The Fc receptor (B) cells attached to the antibody-antigen complexes, while non-Fc receptor (T) cells were washed off and tested separately. Antibody (5 μl) was added to the wells and the cells were again washed before the addition of complement. The supernatant was removed after 15 min. and excess complement again added. The method gives very satisfactory separation but necessitates the dispensing of alloantisera after the cells have been separated. Typically, between 10 and 15% of the cells introduced adhere by direct counting as determined by [51]Chromium labeling.

We have recently developed a procedure for batch separation of Fc receptor lymphocytes (14). In this procedure, 60 mm Falcon Petri dishes are coated with poly-L-lysine and a confluent monolayer of sheep red blood cells is prepared. The red blood cells are then sensitized with rabbit-anti-sheep antibody. The red cell monolayer is washed three times with PBS. Peripheral blood lymphocytes sedimented with Plasmagel, after purification by Ficoll-Hypaque centrifugation and exposure to carbonyl iron to remove macrophages, are then added in the proportion of between 5 and 10×10^6 cells/dish. The dishes are incubated at 37°C for 50 min., (30 min. rocking 8 x minute, 20 min. stationary). The nonadherent cells are pipetted off with washing. The red cell layer is disrupted by treatment with Tris-NH$_4$Cl. The Fc receptor cells are immediately removed by pipetting and the plates are gently scraped with a rubber policeman. The cell suspension is adjusted to a concentration of 2×10^6 cells/ml and dispensed in 1 μl quantities into preloaded trays. Testing is by the Amos modified 2 stage microcytotoxicity test (15). From fluorescence staining with goat anti-human globulin, 50-60% of the cells have surface immunoglobulin, while less than 10% of the nonadherent

cells stain. Values obtained by rabbit anti-B cell serum
(16) are slightly higher.

Using the plate method at Duke and the TNP tray method
at the NIH, we have screened some 600 sera. The most pro-
lific source of active antibodies has been Amish multipara.
However, Australian and New Guinean sera from Dr. H. Bashir
and local serum from Dr. F. Ward, selected to contain non-HLA
activity, have also been found to react. The Amish women
usually marry in their early twenties and frequently have
eight or more children, often at very short intervals. The
largest sibship we have encountered numbered 22 and one of
our highly cooperative donors has 15 children. The frequency
of anti-HLA antibodies is about the same as, or slightly
lower than, that in the general Caucasian multiparous population. One possible reason for the failure to produce antibodies to HLA despite so many pregnancies is antigenic similarity between husband and wife. The frequency of anti-B
cell antibodies is high; we have identified 38 positive sera
containing anti-B cell activity. These antisera are free
from detectable anti-HLA antibodies in conventional and in
the highly sensitive antiglobulin cytotoxicity procedure.
While these sera have provided excellent pilot reagents, it
is often impossible to collect large quantities of serum
from any of these individuals.

With the Amish sera we have readily been able to demonstrate the segregation of haplotypes in families. Sometimes
only one serum identifies a haplotype, sometimes 5 or more
sera react with the same haplotype. No two sera have given
identical reaction patterns and two sera reacting together in
one family may identify different haplotypes in another. The
sera can also distinguish between different haplotypes that,
when tested with conventional sera, are HLA identical. A
recombinant HLA-A2-B27 haplotype reacted with sera AM 35,76,
322,251 and 370; the normal paternal A2-B12 haplotype reacted
with sera Am 35,76 and 177, and the normal A9-B27 haplotype
with sera Am 570,67,322,251 and 370. We thus deduce that
sera 322,251 and 370 react with the B locus (B27) end of the
chromosome and sera 35 and 76 with the A locus (A2) end of
the recombinant haplotype (17). Two examples of haplotype
segregation in nonrecombinant Amish families are given in
Table 1. The fathers of the two families are haploidentical
brothers. The table gives an idea of the consistency of B
cell typing in different families. We do not as yet know how
many loci we are detecting. From the recombinant mentioned
above, we know that there are at least two. This assertion

is also supported by the detection of two distinct peaks by
precipitation with rabbit anti-human B cell antigen serum
(16). From the serology, we suspect at least 3 loci and,
since we have examples of 5 and 6 sera of different reactivity
identifying the same haplotype, we believe there are multiple
loci.

TABLE 1

B LYMPHOCYTE TYPING IN 2 AMISH FAMILIES

	Parents				Offspring			
	Da Mil		Id Mil		2 Children		1 Child	
HLA	3-W10	11-W27	9-W5	2-12	3-W10	9-W5	3-W10	2-12
B cell	192	359	244	52	192	244	192	52
sera	590				590		590	
	43				43		43	
	289				289		289	

	He Mil		Or Mil		1 Child		1 Child		1 Child	
HLA	3-W10	1-W5	1-8	2-5	1-W5	1-8	1-W5	2-5	3-W10	2-5
B cell	192	9	76		76	76	76		192	
sera	590	76	189		9	189	9		590	
	43	359			359		359		43	
	289	107			107		107		289	
		196			196		196			

Multiplicity of sites may explain some of the extraordinary results with patients with gluten sensitive enteropathy (GSE) and dermatitis herpetiformis (DH), where absence of
expected antigenicity and disease associated reactions have
both been observed. Data on reactions in DH and GSE are
given in Table 2. The patients have been tested with a bat-
tery of Amish sera and also with sera from mothers in families with one or more members with DH and GSE. Four of the
Amish sera (Table 2, Group A) recognize cells carrying HLA-B8
from the general population and react infrequently with cells
carrying other specificities. They also react with all Amish
A1-B8 carrying cells tested and with some cells from Amish
donors of different HLA types. Interestingly, these sera
react infrequently with HLA-B8 positive cells from DH and GSE
patients. The B cell specificity normally associated with B8
seems to be absent. Note that the patients, with 3 exceptions, are unrelated. The exceptions are in the Br family.

Table 2

B CELL TYPING IN HEALTHY RANDOM AND AMISH DONORS AND IN PATIENTS WITH
DERMATITIS HERPETIFORMIS (DH) AND GLUTEN SENSITIVE ENTEROPATHY (GSE)

Identification	Random		Amish		DH		GSE	
	with 8	without 8	with 8	without 8	with 8	without 8	with 8	without 8
A. Amish Maternal Sera Detecting Cells with HLA-B8 from Normal Subjects								
Am 43	8/8	0/34	12/12	9/24	1/9	0/3	0/14	0/4
Am 52	8/8	0/34	a	11/24	0/9	0/3	0/14	0/4
Am 124	8/8	0/34	12/12	4/14	1/9	0/3	0/14	0/4
Am 9	8/8	3/34	--b	6/21	0/9	0/3	0/14	0/4
(Anti HLA-B8)	(8/8)	(0/34)	(12/12)	(0/24)	(9/9)	(0/3)	(14/14)	(0/4)
B. Amish Sera Showing No Association with HLA-B8c								
Am 291	0/8	2/34	0/12	0/15	1/9	2/34	2/14	0/4
Am 505	0/8	7/42	0/12	2/17	0/9	0/3	0/14	0/4
C. Amish Maternal Sera Detecting Amish 1-8 Haplotypes But Not the Random 1-8 Donors								
Am 76	2/8	5/29	12/12	7/25	1/9	0/3	0/14	0/4
Am 386	0/8	2/34	12/12	1/14	0/9	0/3	0/14	0/4
Am 640	0/8	4/34	12/12	2/15	0/9	0/3	0/14	0/4
D. Reactions of Maternal Sera from Mothers in DH Families								
Wh	0/3	0/13	---	---	4/5	3/3	0/14	0/4
Sol	0/3	0/13	---	---	4/5	3/3	0/14	0/4
New	0/3	0/13	---	---	0/5	0/5	0/14	0/4
E. Reactions of Maternal Sera from Mothers of GSE Offspring								
Br	0/3	0/13	---	---	6/9	2/3	13/14	3/4
Ri	0/3	0/13	---	---	0/5	0/5	0/14	0/4
Mik	0/3	0/13	---	---	0/5	0/5	0/14	0/4

aThis serum appears to detect the 2-7 and the 2-12 haplotype in the Amish; bNot tested; cMany sera, not shown, fall into this category; dThese antisera may give reactions with other Amish haplotypes.

A grandmother and two affected children are included and all are recognized by Br serum.

Group B (Table 2) includes two of the numerous sera that showed no association with HLA-B8 in any of the populations. It is of interest that, in contrast to unselected anti-HLA sera which are most frequently broadly reactive, anti-B cell sera from Amish multipara have relatively low frequencies of reactivity.

A second group of 3 sera (Table 2, Group C) react with low frequency in the random population and with high frequency in the Amish. Those cells react with all 1-8 Amish cells and also with some non 1-8 cells. They too are almost unreactive with DH and GSE cells.

Group D includes three sera from mothers in DH families. Serum Wh has detectable activity. The mother has 3 normal children and an affected husband. Her serum reacts with B cells from her husband but with none of the children. This serum, like serum Sol, mother of the affected child, gives high frequency reactions with DH patients regardless of HLA type (but does not react with GSE cells). Serum New and 3 other sera from mothers of DH children failed to react.

Group E includes 3 sera from mothers of GSE patients. Serum Br is exceptional. It is from the mother of 2 affected children and, to date, has reacted only with cells from GSE and DH patients (24/30 compared to 0/16 normal individuals) regardless of haplotype. This serum appears to recognize some factor shich is different from that recognized by van Rood's sera Be and Mo (7). Sera from two other mothers of affected children failed to react.

DISCUSSION

This is obviously a very preliminary account. It is presented now because the findings are exciting and because we think the results, incomplete as they are, will be of interest to others. In particular, the use of the serum of mothers of affected children as a source of reagents for the detection of unrelated persons with the disease has great potential, although it is already clear that not all mothers respond.

In some of the studies presented here, we are clearly defining new regions of HL-1. How close they may be to the

HLA markers we do not know, and linkage to HLA has not yet been demonstrated for the markers on cells from DH and GSE patients. Some anti-B cell sera detect the HLA-B8 antigen, or the 1-8 haplotype in Amish or other normal individuals but not in DH or GSE patients. This is a fascinating finding and raises the interesting question as to the integration in functional terms of the alleles that constitute a haplotype. Some of the recombinant H-2 haplotypes in the mouse appear to undergo further recombination rather frequently (18). Some apparent H-2 mutants or recombinants have been sterile (Amos, D.B. and Cohen, C., unpublished). The recombinant haplotype may itself contribute to immune responsiveness and, therefore, perhaps, to disease. Dorf <u>et al</u>. have demonstrated that some Ir loci, for example, function only when the appropriate alleles are assembled on the same chromosome (19). Alternatively, a mutation producing GSE may, in the past, have affected an ancestor with the HLA-B8 allele and the reported association between HLA-B8 and GSE may be a reflection of linkage disequilibrium in the progeny. Our present studies do, of course, reinforce the association of HLA-B8 with both GSE and DH. Additional family studies, now in progress (20), will establish whether the new antigenic markers detected on B cells from GSE and DH subjects are HLA-linked or whether they are identifying a separate entity.

It is also interesting that the Amish should show three different forms of linkage disequilibrium between HLA-B8 and B cell markers. One set of 3 antisera recognize the HLA-B8 positive cells in the random and in the Amish populations but not in the patients with GSE or DH. One interesting serum, Am 52, reacted with all B8 random panel donors but reacts predominantly with the A2-B7 and A2-B12 haplotypes in the Amish. This serum is also nonreactive with the disease patients. Another set of 3 sera, Am 76, 386 and 640 (Group C) recognize the Amish A1-B8 haplotype but do not show any significant association with HLA-B8 in the other groups. These findings are compatible with those of Dossetor and his colleagues (21). In studies of the Hutterites, a distinctive religious and sociological isolate, Dossetor found very unusual linkage disequilibria between HLA-B and HLA-D specificities. While this association may be chance or a founder effect, it might also be a reflection of differing population fitness under varying selective pressure. Unlike the Amish who migrated through Western Europe, the Hutterites migrated into Russia and were thus subjected to a different environment at a time when the great infectious diseases were still endemic.

It is interesting that after some 15 years of intensive investigation and just when the first phase of HLA definition was nearing completion, such tremendous opportunities should present themselves. Progress in B and T cell genetics should be extremely rapid. In the early 1960's, the early days of the study of HLA, few laboratories were involved, technological inadequacies were very apparent and the complexities of cross reactivity greatly slowed progress. Now, thousands of sera, many of which are known to lack anti-HLA activity, are available for the typing of lymphocyte subpopulations. MLC and typing procedures are standardized and homozygous cells, although not plentiful, are available. It should be noted also that, besides identifying B cell antisera, we are also able to identify T cells. A number of anti-HLA sera have long been known to give occasional anomalous reactions that did not appear to be cross reactivities. Duke serum FS, an anti-4a serum, is one of these. It reacts with separated T cells but not with B cells from the same individual. Since T cells form the bulk of peripheral blood lymphocytes, anti-T cell sera, in contrast to anti-B cell antibodies, give strong reactions against unseparated lymphocyte populations. It will be of obvious interest to test other sera which give misfitting reactions, and also to test some of the third and fourth locus antisera on both T and B cells.

Recombinants, either between the A and B loci or between the B and D loci, have now become extremely valuable for the localization of the lymphocyte subpopulations. If antigens of HL-1 can discriminate between T cells and B cells, they surely qualify as differentiation antigens. If differentiation antigens exist on lymphoid cells, why should they not exist on other cell types, just as H-2 linked antigenic determinants define teratoma antigens (22). The antigens of kidney vascular endothelium and other differentiated tissues must be scrutinized using HLA identical transplant rejection sera and other special reagents. The next few years of immunogenetic research should indeed be fascinating and the results could revolutionize medical and genetic knowledge.

ACKNOWLEDGMENT

This work was supported in part by funds from the National Institutes of Health.

REFERENCES

(1) A. Svejgaard, P. Platz, L.P. Ryder, L. Staub Nielsen and M. Thomsen. Transplant. Rev. 22 (1975) 3.

(2) E.J. Yunis and D.B. Amos. Proc. Nat. Acad. Sci. 68 (1971) 3031.

(3) E.J. Yunis, H.F. Seigler, R.L. Simmons and D.B. Amos. Transplantation 15 (1973) 435.

(4) D.B. Amos, R. Ruderman, N.R. Mendell and A.H. Johnson. Transplant. Proc. 7 (1975) 93.

(5) WHO-IUIS Terminology Committee, in: Histocompatibility Testing 1975. ed. F. Kissmeyer-Nielsen. (Munksgaard, Copenhagen, 1976) In press.

(6) A. van Leeuwen, H.R.E. Schuit and J.J. van Rood. Transplant. Proc. 5 (1973) 1539.

(7) J.J. van Rood, A van Leeuwen, J.J. Keuning and A. Termijtelen. Transplant. Proc. 7 (1975) 31.

(8) R.J. Winchester, S.M. Fu, P. Wernet, H. Kunkel, B. Dupont and C. Jersild. J. Exp. Med. 141 (1975) 141.

(9) D.L. Mann, L. Abelson, S. Harris and B.D. Amos. J. Exp. Med. 142 (1975) 84.

(10) E. Kedar, M. Ortiz de Landazuri and B. Bonavida. J. Immunol. 112 (1974) 1231.

(11) C.D. Severson, J.W. Blaschke and J.S. Thompson. Transplantation (1976) In press.

(12) D.L. Mann, L. Abelson, S. Harris and D.B. Amos, in: Histocompatibility Testing 1975. ed. F. Kissmeyer-Nielsen. (Munksgaard, Copenhagen, 1976) In press.

(13) P. Vadnais, P.Cresswell and D.B. Amos. Cell. Immunol. (1975) In press.

(14) S. Hsia, F.E. Ward and D.B. Amos. To be published.

(15) D.B. Amos, R. Corley, D. Kostyu, Y. Delmas-Marsalet
      and M. Woodbury, in: Histocompatibility Testing 1972.
      eds. J. Dausset and J. Colombani. (Munksgaard,
      Copenhagen, 1973) p. 359.

(16) S. Geier and P. Cresswell. Nature 257 (1975) 147.

(17) D.L. Mann, L. Abelson, S. Harris and D.B. Amos.
      Submitted for publication.

(18) J. Klein, in: Contemporary Topics in Immunology.
      (Plenum Press, New York, 1975) In press.

(19) M.E. Dorf, P.H. Maurer, C.F. Merryman and B. Benacer-
      raf. J. Exp. Med. (1976) In press.

(20) D.L. Mann, L. Abelson, W. Strober, S.I. Katz and D.B.
      Amos. To be published.

(21) J.B. Dossetor, T. Kovithavongs, L. Marchuk, D.
      Butcher, G. St. Louis and J. Schlaut, in: Histocom-
      patibility Testing 1975. ed. F. Kissmeyer-Nielsen.
      (Munksgaard, Copenhagen, 1976) In press.

(22) D. Bennett and L.C. Dunn, in: Immunogenetics of the
      H-2 System. eds. A. Lengerova and M. Vojtiskova.
      (S. Karger, Basel, 1971) p. 90.

RECENT STUDIES OF Ia LIKE ANTIGENS AND COMPLEMENT COMPONENTS RELATING TO THE HUMAN HISTOCOMPATIBILITY SYSTEM

H. G. KUNKEL, R. J. WINCHESTER, S. M. FU AND B. DUPONT

THE ROCKEFELLER UNIVERSITY AND
SLOAN KETTERING INSTITUTE

Our laboratory has reported previously on the detection of an assortment of different antibodies in pregnancy sera which react preferentially with B cells (1,2). Considerable evidence is available that they represent the human equivalent of Ia antibodies in the mouse. For convenience we have termed them HL-B. These have been detected with similar results by fluorescent antibody analysis as well as by cytotoxicity. However, for the latter technique to be effective, it is essential that the B cells are concentrated. The low level in normal peripheral blood ($<$ 15%) represents the primary reason these antibodies were not detected earlier. In our experience approximately 20% of pregnancy sera show such antibodies but absorption studies are usually required to remove HL-A antibodies. Platelet absorption or absorption with appropriate lymphoid cell lines have proven effective. A rare serum has been encountered where no absorption is required. In each case the sera react strongly against the husband but are negative against the donor mother's cells.

Recent efforts have been concentrated on the utilization of B cell lines of specific types, preferentially homozygous B cell lines on the basis of MLC typing as well as homozygous cells. In fluorescent antibody studies $F(ab')_2$ reagents are employed to avoid Fc receptor problems and in studying individual bloods pokeweed mitogen stimulation has been employed to obtain clearer differentiation of positive and negative individuals. The stimulated cells are considerably brighter staining than the resting B lymphocyte.

Several of the sera in these as well as additional experiments clearly relate to the LD 7a and 8a systems. Serum 770 has become our standard 7a serum and 58, our standard 8a serum. Serum 111 is of special interest because it has an extremely broad reactivity and only a few cell lines and normal bloods are negative including the mother from which the serum was obtained. The high

TABLE I
TYPING PATTERN OF HL-B ANTISERA WITH A GROUP OF CELL LINES
AND WITH LD-HOMOZYGOUS NORMAL LYMPHOCYTES

Preg. Sera	B-type lymphoid cell lines					LD-Homozygous PBL			
	Daudi	7301	1788	8866	B35M	7a7a	8a8a	12a12a	15a15a
57	0	++++	0	++++	0	++++	0	0	++++
58	++++	0	0	0	++++	0	++++	0	0
277	++++	0	0	+	++++	0	++++	0	0
770	++++	0	0	0	0	++++	0	0	0
232	0	++++	++++	0	0	0	0	++++	++++
111	++++	++++	0	++++	++++	++++	++++	++++	++++

Table I illustrates results with 6 different B cell specific sera showing the reaction with several B cell lines and certain LD homozygous cells utilized for MLC typing.

---

frequency of positive results with serum 111 has made it difficult to carry out genetic studies; the accumulated evidence indicates that this is a single, non HL-A linked, B cell system. The other sera shown in Table I are still under study with regard to their exact HL-B specificity.

In both the 7a and 8a systems, utilizing the sera described above, all cells positive for these LD systems are also positive by serological typing. However, in each case some LD negative cells are positive by serological typing. In the 7a system the 7a antigen has been found on all of the approximately 33% of individuals of LD type 7a; this antigen also was found on an additional 18% of individuals that were not LD 7a. Thus far absorption studies indicate that only a single antigen is involved in this serological typing but further experiments in this direction are continuing.

It is clear that close relationship exists between LD typing by MLC reactions and the serological typing by the B cell antigens, and that the same antigens are involved at least in part. However, the relationship thus far is not

absolute and this does not appear to be simply due to difficulties in LD typing which certainly are real when different
homozygous cells are utilized.

COMPLEMENT-MHC RELATIONSHIPS

Two years ago it was observed in our laboratory (3)
that C2 deficiency in the heterozygous and homozygous form
was closely linked to HL-A. At approximately the same time
Allen (4) observed similar linkage for Factor B of the properdin system. Table II shows a listing of complement components that have been studied sufficiently to determine
whether they are or are not linked to the MHC.

Table II

HL-A or H2 Linked C Components	Non Linked
1. C2 (Human)	1. C3 (Human)
2. C3 (Mouse)	2. C1r (Human)
3. C4 (Human)	3. C5 (Mouse)
C4 (Guin.Pig)	
4. Factor B (Human)	

In our initial propositus with homozygous C2 deficiency
it was observed that he was also homozygous for the HL-A
haplotype 10,W18, even though his parents were clearly unrelated. This suggested a strong linkage disequilibrium
between C2 deficiency and this haplotype which has been amply
confirmed in studies of subsequent families (5,6). Table III
shows the results with six different families studied for
C2 deficiency by quantitative immunodiffusion and by HL-A
and MLC-LD typing. The vast predominance of 10,W18 is
readily apparent and six of the eleven haplotypes linked to
C2 deficiency were 10,W18 and a seventh 2,W18. The comparative gene frequency in the general population of the
10,W18 haplotype is approximately 1%. Table III also
shows the close correlation with the MLC type LD 7a. In
only one instance was the C2 deficiency associated with a
non LD 7a type. This correlation as well as that with
10,W18 is highly significant statistically (6).

73

Table III
MAJOR HISTOCOMPATIBILITY COMPLEXES IN ASSOCIATION WITH C2
DEFICIENCY

Family	HL-A		MLC	Disease Association
S (RU)	10,W18	(maternal)	LD7a	SLE,(Hodgkins Disease)
	10,W18	(paternal)	LD7a	
C (RU)	10,W18	(maternal)	LD7a	Discoid Lupus Erythe-
	9,5	(paternal)	LD7a	matosus
Gro(RU)	10,W18		LD7a	none
K (UM-SKI)	10,W18	(maternal)	LD7a	SLE
	2,4A2*	(paternal)	LD7a	
	2,W18		–	none
A (SKI)	9,W18	(paternal)	LD7a	Hodgkins Disease
	2,W18	(maternal)	LD7a	
Gri (RU)	10,W18		non LD7a	SLE

A number of crossovers have been encountered that provide suggestive evidence for the ordering of the genes for
the complement system. Table IV shows a preliminary map
encompassing this evidence. This ordering remains very

Table IV

MLC (Major) - - C4 - B - C2 - - HL-A (Four) - - HL-A (La)

7a - - - - - - - - - C2 - - W 18 - - - - - - 10

Preliminary mapping of the human histocompatibility system including complement components.The major
complex associated with C2 is also indicated.

tentative and is partially based on the results of others
on Factor B. No conclusive evidence is available that the
different complement genes are together as depicted and the
possibility that the C2 gene should be placed on the other
side of the MLC locus is not ruled out.

The striking feature of the studies of the complement-MHC relationship is the evidence for a strong linkage disequilibrium with other components of the MHC, particularly the HL-A genes, where evidence of separation by crossovers has been obtained.

REFERENCES

(1) P. Wernet, R. Winchester, H.G.Kunkel, D. Wernet, M. Giphart, A. van Leeuwen, J.J. van Rood. Transplant. Proc. Suppl. 1 7 (1975) 193.

(2) R. J. Winchester, S. M. Fu, P. Wernet, H.G.Kunkel, B. Dupont, C. Jersild. J. Exp. Med. 141 (1975) 924.

(3) S. M. Fu, H.G. Kunkel, H. P. Brusman, F. H. Allen Jr., M. Fotino. J. Exp. Med. 140 (1974) 1108.

(4) F. H. Allen Jr. Vox Sang. 27 (1974) 382.

(5) S. M. Fu, H. G. Kunkel. Transplantation 20 (1975) 179.

(6) S. M. Fu, R. Stern, H.G.Kunkel, B. Dupont, J.A. Hansen, N. K. Day, R. A. Good, C. Jersild, M. Fotino. J. Exp. Med. 142 (1975) 495.

NATURAL KILLER CELLS IN THE MOUSE

ROLF KIESSLING

Department of Tumor Biology

Karolinska Institute

Abstract: Non-immune lymphocytes from some mouse strains can
kill certain syngeneic, semisyngeneic and allogeneic
lymphoma cells in a ^{51}Cr release assay. The cytolytic
activity was selective, but the specificity unknown.
Spleen and peripheral blood from 1-2 month old mice
yielded highest activity. Spleen cells from nude mice
were highly active. This natural killer cell (abbreviated NK) appeared to be a small lymphocyte but could not
be classified as a T- or B-lymphocyte by various cell
fractionation procedures. The in vitro cytolytic
activity was genotype dependent. Genetic analysis
revealed that the responsible gene(s) were dominant,
with an H-2 linked factor(s). A high degree of concordance was seen when in vitro cytolytic activity
was compared to in vivo tumor resistance in different
genotypes, using a Moloney virus induced lymphoma.
Also in vivo resistance to the same lymphoma appeared
to be H-2 linked and thymus independent.

INTRODUCTION

Normal mice of several strains have been shown to produce natural antibody against virus associated cell surface
antigens (1) and against virus particles (2,3,4,5).

We and other investigators have recently shown that
also cell mediated immune reactions as measured by in vitro
killer cell activity occur naturally. Greenberg and Play-
fair, using old NZB mice, found spontaneous reactivity
against the P 815 mastocytoma cell line (6). Herberman
et al. found a cell mediated reactivity against a variety

of allogeneic and syngeneic target cells, expressing type-C viruses (7). Sendo et al. detected reactivity against the radiation induced leukemia RL♂1 (8). Zarling et al. found reactivity against the spontaneous AKR lymphoma K-36 (9).

We have found a natural reactivity against certain virus induced mouse lymphomas, and it is the purpose of the present article to summarize our present knowledge about the nature, the genetic regulation and the in vivo relevance of this natural killer cell (abbreviated NK).

SPECIFICITY OF NATURAL KILLER CELLS

We have reported that non-immune spleen cells from some mouse strains kill allogeneic, semisyngeneic and syngeneic mouse lymphoma cells in a ^{51}Cr release assay. The killer activity seemed to be specific, in the sense that only certain target cells were killed. Others, although highly sensitive for immune T-cell killing, were not affected. When a limited number of cell lines were studied, sensitivity for NK-cell lysis was restricted to some Moloney leukemia virus (MLV) induced lymphomas (10), although lately also other types of tumors have been found sensitive for NK-activity (unpublished results). Tissue cultured lymphomas were considerably more sensitive for lysis than the original in vivo maintained ascites tumors (10). In an in vitro inhibition assay, where non-labeled tumor cells competed for killer cell activity with isotope labeled target cells, a positive correlation was found between sensitivity for lysis and competing capacity (10).

In the natural killer cell system of Herberman et al. evidence was obtained for natural reactivity against several different antigens, each associated with expression of murine endogenous type-C virus (7).

There are obvious difficulties in discussing the specificity of NK-cells, since it is not known whether this activity is generated by an immunization in conventional meaning. We have considered the possibility that mice from our colony were "preimmunized" by horizontal infection with a microbiological agent. However, all mice tested so far soon after their arrival from other breeding units in Sweden, Denmark and USA were as efficient as mice from the same strain of our breeding. Also, wild mice from Sweden and California were highly active in this test (unpublished results). Furthermore, Herberman

et al. found mice raised in specific patogen free condition clearly reactive as natural killer cells (7).

AGE VARIATION OF NATURAL KILLER CELL ACTIVITY

A very pronounced age dependence of natural killer
cell activity was found by us (10) and other investigators
(7,8) with peak activity when lymphocytes from mice around
2 months of age were used. Spleen cells from newborn as
well as from older mice invariably showed lower if any
activity. This early onset and rapid decline of NK-activity
could be explained by exposure of newborn mice to the
relevant antigen, followed by an immune response which
would decrease in older mice. Herberman has suggested
as an explanation that latent endogenous type-C viruses
become activated soon after birth and produce sensitization
against the associated antigen(7) However, an early exposure
to horizontal infection by an ubiquitous agent must also
be considered.

EFFECTOR CELL ANALYSIS OF NATURAL KILLER CELLS

When studying the tissue distribution of NK-cells,
lymphocytes from spleen and peripheral blood invariably
showed high activity. Lymph node and bone marrow cells were
somewhat less active, and thymus cells were totally inactive
(11).

Various cell factionation procedures were performed
to analyse the nature of NK-cells. The result of this
analysis is summarized in Table 1, where also the effect of
similar treatments on the cytotoxicity of cytotoxic T-cells
and antibody-dependent cellular cytotoxicity (ADCC) is shown.
Spleen cells from "nude" mice were highly active as NK-cells,
which provided the first indication for a non-T cell nature
of the killer cell (11,12). Further strengthening its non-T
cell nature, the NK-cell proved to be resistant (11), or
almost resistant (12), to anti theta plus complement
treatment. However, it was not a B-cell since depletion of
Ig-positive cells increased the efficacy of the population
(11,12). EAC-rosette or EAC-monolayer depletion has failed
to decrease killer cell activity (11,12). Thus this cell
type lacks the conventional surface markers of lymphocytes.
Still, its low adhesive properties (11,12), as well as its
morphology (11) makes it highly probable that the NK-cell
is a lymphocyte of yet undefined type.

TABLE 1

EFFECT OF VARIOUS FRACTIONATION METHODS ON THE CYTOTOXICITY
IN DIFFERENT KILLER-CELL SYSTEMS

Treatment of spleen cells	NK	CTL[2]	ADCC[3]
anti θ serum + C'	——[4]	↓	——
anti-mouse-immunoglobulin column	↑[5]	↑	↓
nylon wool column	——	——	↓
iron-magnet method	——	——	↓
EAC-rosette depletion	——	n.d.	↓
addition of aggregated γ -globulin	——	——	↓
trypsin treatment	↓	↓	——

[1]For more exact results and experimental details see references 11 and 13.

[2]Cytotoxic T-lymphocyte in CBA anti P 815-system

[3]Antibody-dependent cellular cytotoxicity in CRBC-system

[4]—— = no effect on cytotoxicity

[5]↑ ↓ = indicates increase or decrease of cytotoxicity

Non T-cell dependent cytotoxicity is often ascribed to antibody-dependent cellular cytotoxicity (ADCC). As could be seen in Table 1, the NK-cells differ by several characteristics from the effector cell in ADCC. The "K-cell" in ADCC in our hands was almost or completely abolished by anti mouse immunoglobulin column passage and by nylon

column passage, as well as by EAC-rosette depletion (11,13).
Addition of aggregated gamma globulin strongly reduced ADCC
but did not affect NK-activity (12,13). Also, trypsin
treatment seemed to distinguish K-cell activity from natural
killer cell activity, since the K-cell was relatively trypsin resistant whereas the NK-cell was trypsin sensitive
(13).

GENETIC ANALYSIS OF NATURAL KILLER CELL ACTIVITY

Early in the course of this study it was found that
various mouse strains differ in NK activity. Some mouse
strains yielded spleen cells with high NK activity,
whereas spleen cells from other strains, preferentially
strain A, were low reactive (10). When the low reactive
A-strain was crossed to various other strains, and cells
from these F_1-hybrids were tested against a semisyngeneic
A lymphoma for NK activity, reactivity resembled the
high reactive parental strain (14), which showed that high
reactivity was dominant.

Linkage analysis of in vitro NK-activity was performed
in an (A x C57Bl) x A backcross population. A strong H-2
linked factor was found, although other factors appeared
to contribute as well (14). Recently this linkage analysis
was extended to involve several isozyme, Ig-1 allotype,
coat color and complement markers. In this study the strong
H-2 linkage was further confirmed and no linkage with any
other tested marker was seen (15).

IN VIVO RELEVANCE OF NATURAL KILLER CELLS

In order to assess the in vivo participation of the
natural killer cell in resistance to tumor cell growth,
we compared "low" and "high" responder strains with regard
to their ability to resist small numbers (10^3, 10^4) of
living lymphoma cells. The same strain A derived lymphoma
line (YAC) and the same semisyngeneic A F_1 hybrids were
used for the in vitro NK system and for the in vivo
resistance study. As can be seen in Table 2 and Figure 1
there was a concordance between in vitro cytotoxicity and in
vivo tumor resistance in all tested genotypes (16). The
in vitro "low" reactive A and A F_1-hybrids had a shorter
tumor latency period and a considerably higher cumulative
incidence of tumors than the in vitro "high" reactive
strains.

TABLE 2

KILLER ACTIVITY OF SPLEEN CELLS FROM A AND F$_1$ HYBRID MICE
AGAINST YAC-1[1]

Genotype	Number of mice tested	Mean corrected % lysis	± SE
A	33	0.0	1.24
A x A.SW	10	-0.6	2.15
A x A.BY	14	9.4	5.06
A x A.CA	14	0.4	1.86
A x C57Bl/6	28	20.8	1.83
A x C57 leaden	19	24.6	1.81
A x C3H	24	21.1	3.91
A x CBA	28	31.6	2.38
A x DBA/2	31	19.1	3.48

[1]The results from eight separate experiments. In each experiment 3-6 A spleens were included, and the mean percentage lysis from these spleens was subtracted from each individual value obtained from the tests of other spleens in the same experiment.

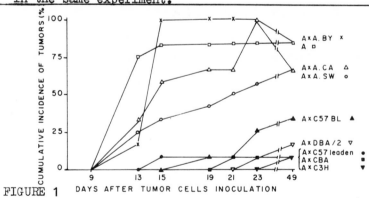

FIGURE 1

Cumulative incidence of tumors in two experiments following the inoculation of 10^3 YAC ascites cells. Each group consisted of a total of 12 mice.

The relationship between the in vitro and in vivo activities was also studied by us in an in vivo segregation analysis with the above mentioned (A x C57Bl) x A backcross population, to see if the previously reported in vitro linkage analysis was also valid for in vivo resistance. We found that in vivo resistance to living YAC tumor cells was H-2 linked, in line with the earlier backcross analysis of the in vitro cytotoxicity. No strong linkage was found between in vivo resistance and several other markers involved in this segregation analysis (16,15).

When individual backcross mice were tested both for tumor growth resistance and in vitro cytolytic activity, a positive correlation was found (15), although this correlation was not absolute and some mice showed low in vitro cytolytic activity and high tumor resistance, and vice versa.

In line with the non T-cell nature of the NK-cells, also in vivo resistance to the growth of a MLV-induced lymphoma appeared to be thymus-independent. Mice made "T-cell free" by thymectomization, irradiation and fetal liver reconstitution were at least as resistant to the growth of a semisyngeneic MLV-induced lymphoma as were their normal controls (17).

Also nude mice were highly resistant to the growth of the same lymphoma (17).

CONCLUSIONS

From the present data we conclude that the NK-cell probably contributes with one of the major protective mechanisms responsible for the primary resistance to certain MLV-induced lymphomas. This killer cell is unique, since it does not belong to the T-cell, B-cell or monocyte-macrophage type of cell shown to operate in other tumor-host systems. Still the possibility exists that it belongs to an immature precursor cell to one of these cell types, therefore lacking the surface characteristics representative for the mature celltype. Attempts are now made by us to find a positive surface marker on the NK-cell, using antisera directed against "differentiation" antigens of precursor T-cells.

The genetic study has revealed that both the in vitro NK activity and the in vivo resistance to certain MLV lymphomas is under polygenic control, but with a strong H-2 linked component. Therefore this might represent the first reported case of a non T-cell mediated reactivity influenced by anH-2 linked gene(s). It could be speculated that this is due to the fact that our target tumor cell in this system, the YAC cell, is of T-cell origin. May be a "surveillance" mechanism against a T-cell lymphoma has to operate through a non T effector cell, since T-cells otherwise themselves would risk to be transformed by the causative agent.

The low incidence of spontaneous tumors among "nude" mice has often been used as an argument against immunosurveillance (18). This argument is however based on the assumption that only T-cell dependent mechanisms are active in immunosurveillance. However, the present in vitro and in vivo data show that the non T NK-cells are highly active in nude mice and could be a functional alternative to T-cell mediated mechanisms.

ACKNOWLEDGEMENTS

This study was supported by Public Health Service Research Grant No. 5 R01 CA 14054-02, and by contract N01-CB-33859.

The skilled technical assistance of Miss M.Hansson is gratefully acknowledged.

REFERENCES

(1)   T.Aoki, E.A.Boyse and L.J.Old. Cancer Res. 26 (1966) 1415.

(2)   M.G.Hanna Jr., R.W.Tennant, J.M.Yuhas, N.K.Clapp, B.L. Batzig and M.J.Snodgrass. Cancer Res. 32 (1972) 2226.

(3)   J.N.Ihle, M.Yurconic Jr. and M.G.Hanna Jr. J.exp.Med. 138 (1973) 194.

(4)   R.C. Nowinski and S.L.Kaehler. Science 185 (1974) 869.

(5)   M.B.A.Oldstone, T.Aoki and F.J.Dixon. Proc.nat. Acad.Sci. (Wash) 69 (1972) 134.

(6)   A.H.Greenberg and J.H.L.Playfair. Clin.exp.Immunol.
       16 (1974) 99.

(7)   R.B.Herberman, M.E.Nunn and D.H.Lavrin. Int.J.
       Cancer 16 (1975) 216.

(8)   F.Sendo, T.Aoki, E.A.Boyse and C.K.Buafo. J.nat.
       Cancer Inst. in press (1975).

(9)   J.Z.Zarling, R.C.Nowinski and F.H.Bach. Proc.Natl.
       Acad.Sci. in press.

(10)   R.Kiessling, E.Klein and H.Wigzell. Eur.J.Immunol.
       5 (1975) 112.

(11)   R.Kiessling, E.Klein, H.Pross and H.Wigzell.
       Eur.J.Immunol. 5 (1975) 117.

(12)   R.B.Herberman, M.E.Nunn and D.H.Lavrin. Int.J.Cancer
       16 (1975) 230.

(13)   R.Kiessling, G.Petrányi, K.Kärre, M.Jondal, D.Tracey
       and H.Wigzell. Submitted to J.Exp.Med.

(14)   G.Petrányi, R.Kiessling and G.Klein. Immunogenetics
       2 (1975) 53.

(15)   G. Petrányi, R. Kiessling, S. Povey, G.Klein,
       L.Herzenberg and H.Wigzell. Submitted to Immuno-
       genetics.

(16)   R.Kiessling, G.Petrányi, G.Klein and H.Wigzell.
       Int.J.Cancer 15 (1975) 935.

(17)   R.Kiessling, G.Petrányi, G.Klein and H.Wigzell.
       Int.J.Cancer in press.

(18)   J.Rygaard and C.O.Poulsen. Transplantation 17
       (1974) 135.

EVIDENCE FOR THE ASSOCIATION OF SPECIFICITY Ia.3 WITH AN *I-A* REGION MOLECULE

T.L. DELOVITCH, D.B. MURPHY, H.O. McDEVITT

Department of Medicine
Stanford University School of Medicine

Three regions in the *H-2* complex have been postulated for the control of Ia antigens (1). It is clear that determinants controlled by the *I-A* and *I-C* regions are present on distinct glycoproteins. Since antigenic specificity appears to reside in the protein moiety, this is good evidence for the existence of two separate *Ia* genes (2). In this report, we have examined whether specificity Ia.3, which is purportedly determined by the *I-B* region, is present on a molecule distinct from that specified by the *I-A* region.

SDS–polyacrylamide gel electrophoretic analyses were performed on ^{125}I-labeled, NP-40 solubilized and anti-Ia immunoprecipitated lysates derived from B10 spleen cells (3). After initially removing labeled immunoglobulin from the extracts, the samples were treated with an anti-Ia serum and goat anti-mouse γG. The precipitate formed was discarded, and the supernatant further reacted with a second anti-Ia serum and goat anti-mouse γG. The latter precipitate was then solubilized and electrophoresed on 12.5% acrylamide gels.

Specificity Ia.3 is defined by the reactivity of an A.TH anti-A.TL serum with B10 target cells (1). In Figure 1A, a distinct Ia peak is observed in this test combination. A second antiserum, (B10.A(4R) x A.SW)F$_1$ anti-B10, contains H-2 antibody against k^b and Ia antibody against *I-A*^{b} (Fig. 1B). This antiserum cannot cross-react with determinants controlled by *I-B*^{b}, since the recipient and donor share this chromosomal segment. Treatment of B10 extracts with the A.TH anti-A.TL serum completely removes the Ia reactivity for the (B10.A(4R) x A.SW)F$_1$ anti-B10 serum, and vice versa (Fig. 1C, 1D). Two other antisera directed against K^b and $I\text{-}A^b$, (B10.A(4R) x B10.D2)F_1 anti-B10 and (B10.A(4R) x B10.HTT)F_1 anti-B10 yielded the same result in combination with the A.TH anti-A.TL serum.

These data clearly demonstrate that specificity Ia.3, as defined by the reactivity of an A.TH anti-A.TL serum with B10 targets, is on a molecule which is controlled by the $I\text{-}A$ region. No known Ia determinants therefore are controlled by the $I\text{-}B$ region.

*[EDITOR'S NOTE: The preceding text represents the data and its interpretation actually presented at the Conference. New information presented during the Conference, of which the authors were previously unaware, raises pertinent qualifications to the initial interpretation of the data which are discussed in the following addendum paragraph.]

Recently, a second specificity, Ia.15, has been defined which could be detected by the A.TH anti-A.TL serum. Initially, strain B10 was classified as lacking this specificity (4). Subsequent to the presentation of the manuscript above, it now appears that strain B10 expresses it (Shreffler, et al, this volume). Absorption analysis revealed that the reactivity of the serum used in this study against B10 cells involved Ia.15, and not Ia.3. Hence, the results presented here indicate that Ia.15 is associated with an $I\text{-}A$ region molecule. The possible association of Ia.3 with an $I\text{-}A$ region molecule cannot be evaluated.

REFERENCES

(1) D.C. Shreffler and C.S. David. Adv. Immunol. 20 (1974) 125

(2) S.E. Cullen, J.H. Freed, P.H. Atkinson, S.G., Nathenson. Transpl. Proc. 7 (1975) 237.

(3) T.L. Delovitch and H.O. McDevitt. Immunogenetics 2 (1975) 39.

(4) C.S. David, J.E. Neiderhuber, J.A. Frelinger, E. Dugan, T. Meo, D.C. Shreffler. Proceedings of the 10th Leukocyte Culture Conference. V.P. Eijsvoogel, D. Roos, and W.P. Zeylemaker, editors. Academic Press, New York, 1975.

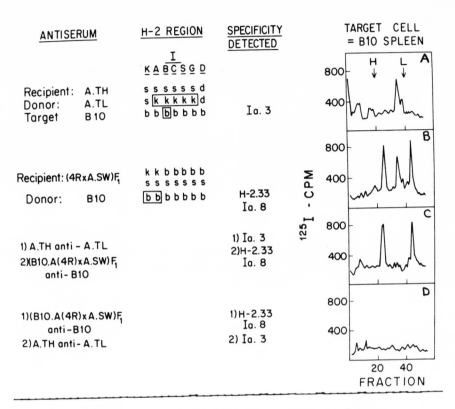

Figure 1. Electrophoretic analyses demonstrating the association of Ia.3 and I-A^b region determinants. The Ia specificity detected is predicted on the basis of the Ia chart presented by Shreffler and David (1). Reaction patterns of these antisera in direct cytotoxic tests are consistent with this assignment. However, formal absorption analyses have not been performed. The positions of migration of marker immunoglobulin heavy (H) and light (L) chains are indicated by arrows.

GENERAL DISCUSSION - SESSION I

GENETICS OF THE MAJOR HISTOCOMPATIBILITY COMPLEX

Jean Dausset - Chairman

BACH: Dr. Kiessling, in your presentation, you stated that
there is polygenic control, and yet the only significant
association was with *H-2*. What is your evidence for
polygenic control or is it possible that *H-2* genes are
only ones of import? Could your back-cross variation
be on the basis of technical variations?

KIESSLING: Yes.

McDEVITT: Dr. Kiessling, what is the normal incidence of
those θ negative, Ig-negative lymphocytes that you
described in your paper?

KIESSLING: This is difficult to judge, since we have no
markers for these cells.

PAUL: Although it has been pointed out that an apparent
difference exists between genetic control of C3 levels
in humans and mice, it should be pointed out that the
work of Nussenzweig and his colleagues indicates that
there are only quantitative differences in C3 levels
among mouse strains.* It seems possible that one might
have missed quantitative polymorpisms of this type in
the human. Furthermore, the Goldmans have reported
that quantitative variations in C1, C4 and C2 levels
are controlled by the *S* region of the mouse.* This
type of work obviously raises the question as to
whether some or all of these quantitative variations
may be the result of regulatory rather than structural
genes encoded in the mouse *S* region.

   *[*EDITOR'S NOTE:* For references to these points, see
   1) Ferreira, A. and Nussenzweig, V. J. Exp. Med. 141:
      513, 1975.
   2) Goldman, M.B. and Goldman, J.N. Fed. Proc. 34:979,
      1975 - DHK.]

SHREFFLER: It is true that most of the MHC-associated
complement differences involve quantitative differences
or deficiencies, which could be due to regulatory gene
differences. The factor B variation linked to *HLA* and

91

RhL-A involves electrophoretic differences, presumably defining a structural gene. It will be important to find structural variants of the other components to define the controlling structural genes definitively.

KUNKEL: This is an important question and the answer is not entirely available. The factor B is, of course, an electrophoretic polymorphism which favors a structural gene. The C2 cases we have studied are completely devoid of C2 which also favors a structural gene. We are doing some hybridization studies to answer this important question.

YUNIS: In collaboration with Dr. Peter Friend, we have made a genetic analysis of inheritance of C2 deficiency with *HLA* linkage groups. In this family (Fig. 1), the C2 total deficiency is found in one patient who is *A10-BW18-DW2* homozygous, but his *HLA*–different sibling had half values of C2 and lacked the *A10, BW18* and *DW2* determinants, suggesting that the C2-deficient gene was inherited from either parent without the *A10-BW18-DW2* linkage group. This, therefore, points to the occurrence of recombination outside of that group. The data supports the mapping of C2 outside of *HLA-D*. (See Fig. 1 on next page.)

SHEVACH: In the guinea pig linkage between C4 deficiency and *GPLA*, animals that lack C4 manifest absolute deficiency.* Earlier studies of Colten demonstrated that this is a structural gene defect, rather than a regulatory gene defect.*

*[*EDITOR'S NOTE:* For references to the above points, see:
1) Shevach, E.M., Frank, M.M. and Green, I. To be published, 1976
2) Colten, H. and Parkman, R. Science 176:1029, 1972 – DHK.]

MEO: A possible explanation for the discrepancy between mouse and man in the control of C3 is a non-genetic one. The observation that the Ss high strains have low levels of C3 and conversely Ss low strains, practically restricted only to the allele *K*, have higher levels of C3 could be accounted for by an activation and degradation of the early C components occurring perhaps during clotting. Then one would expect that the level of C3 might be unevenly correlated with the amount of Ss which we know now to be murine C4.

PEDIGREE OF THE H FAMILY

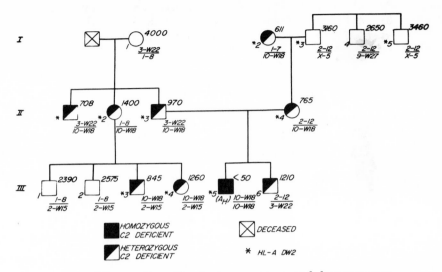

Figure 1. The heterozygous and homozygous
C2-deficient individuals are indicated by the solid
black symbols. C2 determination expressed in CH50
units and the HLA type are given in the adjoining
space. Mean C2 of normal family members = 2785
CH50 unit. III-6 did not inherit the specificity
DW2 from either parent and is heterozygote for C2
deficiency. It shows that C2 deficiency was
inherited in the absence of HLA-A, B and D
(Peter Friend and E.J. Yunis, unpublished).

McDEVITT: What are the molecular weights of the subunits
    of C1, C2 and C3?

MEO: C3 and C5 are characterized by a very similar struc-
    ture and molecular weight. They are composed of a
    heavy and light chain with an apparent molecular weight
    of, respectively, 120,000 and 75,000 daltons.*

    *[EDITOR'S NOTE: See Nilsson, U. and Mapes, J.
    J. Immunol. 111:293, 1973 - DHK.]

NATHENSON: What is the relationship of Ss to Slp? Are
    they the same molecule?

SHREFFLER: When the Ss-reactive molecules are removed from
an Ss-H, Slp-positive serum by precipitation with anti-
Ss, all Slp-reactivity is removed, indicating that the
Slp sites are associated with the Ss molecule. When an
Ss-H, Slp-positive serum is reacted with anti-Slp serum
to remove all Slp-reactivity, only about 50% of the Ss-
reactivity is removed. This implies two populations of
Ss molecules in such sera, one Slp-positive, one Slp-
negative. This is supported by the separation of two
peaks of Ss activity on Sephadex G-200 gel filtration
of such sera. One peak has a molecular weight > 200,000
daltons and is Slp-negative; the other has a molecular
weight of about 180,000 daltons and is Slp-positive.*

   *[EDITOR'S NOTE: See Hansen, T.H. et al. Biochem.
   Genetics   12:281, 1974 - DHK.]

DAUSSET: What is the relationship between sex and complement levels?   I don't know any relationship in human.

SHREFFLER: The only obvious effect of male hormone on complement levels is related to the male-female differences
in Ss levels. There is no higher level of complement
activity in Slp-positive, Ss-H serum than in Slp-
negative, Ss-H serum, unless the sera differ also in
total Ss levels. Females of all strains have lower Ss
levels than males (by about 50%) and have correspondingly
lower complement levels.

GREEN: I would like to ask Dr. Shreffer and/or Dr. Kunkel
the following question. Since many gene products of
HLA locus are found on cell surfaces, are Ss proteins
or complement components also found on cell surfaces?

SHREFFLER: Saunders and Edidin* have shown synthesis of
Ss protein in liver cells and macrophages but found no
association by immunofluorescence of Ss activity with
membranes of any normal cells including lymphocytes.

   *[EDITOR'S NOTE: See Saunders, D. and Edidin, M.
   J. Immunol. 112:2210, 1974 - DHK.]

KUNKEL: We have looked at C2 in detail and it is clearly
not on lymphocytes, at least by fluorescent and cytotoxicity assays. There is a rumor around that factor B
may be on lymphocytes; we have had no personal experience.*

*[*EDITOR'S NOTE:* See Halbwachs, L., McConnell, I. and Lachmann, P.J. The demonstration on lymphocytes of an activity resembling factor B of the alternative pathway of complement activation. In Membrane Receptors of Lymphocytes. M. Seligmann, J.L. Preud'homme and F.M. Kourilsky, editors. North-Holland, Amsterdam. 1975. p. 141 - DHK.]

SHEVACH: We could not find C4 on lymphoid cell surfaces by immunofluorescence in the guinea pig. C4 has been described on some human lymphoid cell lines.

NOSSAL: Before discarding the possibility that complement components reside on cell surfaces, one should explore methodologies other than immunofluorescence or sandwich immunofluorescence. Immunoradioautography using ^{125}I-labelled antisera is certainly more sensitive. Another technique which can give surprisingly good results is the lactoperoxidase-catalyzed surface radio-iodination technique, followed by immuno-coprecipitation. This technique, for example, has given the most unequivocal evidence for the presence of Ia antigens on T cells.

DAUSSET: Dr. Kunkel, the very strong disequilibrium between *A10, W18* and C2 should have an important meaning. Are you certain that there is no consanguinity between the families that you studied?

KUNKEL: This is indeed extraordinary, particularly in view of the high crossover frequency between C2 deficiency and the *HLA* loci. I have no real answer but perhaps you or Dr. van Rood can give us your thoughts sometime during the symposium.

DAUSSET: In the past year, we have been able to define two B lymphocyte systems (Lepraud and Dausset. Transpl. Proc. 7:5, 1975; Legraud and Dausset in Histocompatibility Testing, 1975; Munksgaard, Copenhagen, 1975. In press). The corresponding antibodies were both developed in fathers immunized against one *HLA* pheno-identical child. The detection of the antigens was made either directly using the lymphocytotoxicity technique on normal B cell suspensions or indirectly testing on a panel of chronic lymphocytic leukemia cells the serum previously absorbed on normal lymphocytes. The first system called Ly-Co is independent from *HLA*. Only one allele is known--*Ly-Co1* with a gene frequency of

0.212. The second system called Ly-Li is closely linked to *HLA*. In the father's serum, two antibodies were present recognizing two antigens. The narrowest, *Ly-Li* 2 (gene frequency 0.162), is completely "included" in the broadest, *Ly-Li* 1 (gene frequency 0.660). Both Ly-Co and Ly-Li specificities are absent from red cells, granulocytes, platelets, fibroblasts and T cells, at least with the resolution of our technique. Another specificity called Ly-Jav (Fellows *et al*, Histocompatibility Testing, 1975, Munksgaard, Copenhagen 1975. In press) was shown to be present on sperm and on epidermal cells.

The problem of whether or not these B lymphocyte specificities could be targets in organ transplantation has been approached by skin graft and primary cell-mediated lympholysis (CML) for the Ly-Co system. Before any immunization, the father received the skin of two *HLA*-identical sibs, one possessing the Ly-Co 1 and 2 antigens and the other not. The skin of the former was rejected in 15 days and that of the latter in 18 days suggesting a possible role of this system in transplantation. The CML test performed with the father's cells was positive only against the Ly-Co-positive sib (Mawas *et al*, Transplantation 18:256, 1974). In the Ly-Li system, no skin grafts were performed. But the secondary CML using the father lymphocytes primed by the immunizing Ly-Li-positive donor were shown to kill not only the members of the family possessing the Ly-Li antigens but also others, suggesting that the target is not the B lymphocyte antigens (Mawas *et al*, Immunogenetics 2:465, 1975). Likewise, the father's cells do not kill a control donor *HLA-D* (MLC) identical with a sib whose lymphocytes were killed, suggesting this time that the *HLA-D* products are not the target.

[*EDITOR'S NOTE:* At this point in the general discussion, Hugh McDevitt presented formal data obtained by Terry Delovitch and Donal Murphy with him on the association of specificity Ia.3 with a molecule coded by gene(s) in the *I-A* subregion, thereby arguing strongly against its previously purported intra-*H-2* localization in the *I-B* subregion. This appears as a short formal manuscript immediately preceding the general discussion of this session in these proceedings. This is pointed out because the following comments in the discussion pertain to this presentation - DHK.]

PAUL: In view of the new results mentioned by McDevitt and those alluded to earlier by Shreffler that the Ia.3 antigen is probably encoded within *I-A* rather than within *I-B*, the mapping of *Ir-IgG*, or more properly, *Ir-1b*, to *I-B*, indicates that Ia genes and *Ir* genes, although closely linked, are separate.

BENACERRAF: Bill Paul made a very pertinent comment. If, indeed, we come to the conclusion that there are only two <u>classes</u> of Ia molecules on B and T cells, the mapping of *Ir* genes in a region or regions where no Ia specificities are found is very critical. This data should be examined very carefully. In addition, even if two molecular classes of Ia are the only ones identified, the possibility exists that these classes of molecules may still be extremely heterogeneous within each class.

J. KLEIN: The fact that, thus far, antibodies have not been produced against the products of the *I-B* subregion (if it exists) does not mean much. It might simply signify that we have not tried hard enough, or that we have not struck the right immunizing combination.

SACHS: As I see it, the B10.A recombinant immune responses which led to the split of *I-A* and *I-B* (then called *Ir-1A* and *Ir-IgG*) remain as sound as they were when originally proposed. The serologic studies Dr. Shreffler has presented indicate <u>not</u> that there is no *I-B* subregion, but that we may not presently have an Ia specificity marking that region. They may indicate either that no such specificities exist or that we just have to look a bit harder.

In this regard, the sequential precipitation studies presented by Hugh McDevitt are all the more important since they imply that Ia.3 is on the same gene product as Ia.8; that is, the *I-A* subregion product. It is important to be sure, however, before closing the issue, that the reagents used in that study did not contain additional specificities to those shown on Hugh's slide. In the case of Ia.3, the A.TH anti-A.TL tested on $H\text{-}2^b$ may contain antibodies against other *I-A* subregion antigens which just have not yet been defined as Ia by mapping studies. In the other direction, I think the conclusions are on firmer grounds, unless, of course, the B10.A(4R) has had a deletion of a portion of *I-B* and therefore makes an anti-$I\text{-}B^b$ antibody as well as anti-Ia.8.

97

McDEVITT: The A.TH anti-A.TL on a B10 target could have
    antibodies other than Ia.3 and this needs to be
    checked. This combination was used because it is the
    standard combination which defines Ia.3

    The possibility that the (4R x A.SW) anti-B10 serum also
    has an antibody to an *I-B* coded molecule again has to be
    considered, but since 4R defines the split between *I-A*
    and *I-B*, this seems unlikely. This is thus the best
    combination available to test this hypothesis.

STROMINGER: I would like to ask the serologists who have
    worked with B cell-specific alloantisera whether any of
    these have been characterized with respect to type of
    polypeptide with which the antiserum reacts. I ask
    this because we have isolated from human B cells at
    least three groups of proteins which appear to be B
    cell-specific. These are a complex of 23,000 and 30,000
    daltons polypeptides (probably the human Ia antigen),
    one of 70,000 daltons and one of 13,500 daltons (see
    Strominger *et al*, this volume).

van ROOD: Can I ask Dr. Shreffler to refresh my memory as
    to the number and type of non-*H-2*-linked B cell deter-
    minants (other than surface Ig) are now known in the
    mouse?

SHREFFLER: McKenzie and Snell have described the Ly-4 anti-
    gens as B cell-specific antigens. There are also a
    number of newer "anti-Ly" sera under study in various
    laboratories, some of which may be specific for B cells.

    [*EDITOR'S NOTE:*   The references cited by Dr. Shreffler
    are:
    1) McKenzie, I.F.C. and Snell, G.D. J. Immunol. 114:
       848, 1975.
    2) McKenzie, I.F.C. J. Immunol. 114:856, 1975.
    3) McKenzie, I.F.C. and Plate, J.M.D. Cell. Immunol.
       14:376, 1974 - DHK.]

van ROOD: May I ask Bernard Amos to tell us how many dif-
    ferent loci your anti-B cell sera are recognizing?

AMOS: It would be premature to guess how many loci are
    involved. We know there must be two because we can
    distinguish them on the recombinant. We deduce there
    are at least three, but we have great sympathy with

people struggling with Ia in the mouse who know they have two products and may have more. We must identify additional informative recombinants.

The Biology of Mixed Lymphocyte Interactions and Cell-mediated Cytotoxicity Reactions

MORTEN SIMONSEN, CHAIRMAN

GENETIC AND CELLULAR ASPECTS OF MIXED LEUKOCYTE CULTURE AND
CELL MEDIATED LYMPHOLYSIS REACTIONS

FRITZ H. BACH

Immunobiology Research Center and
Departments of Medical Genetics and Surgery
the University of Wisconsin

Abstract: The antigenic systems determined by genes of the
    major histocompatibility complex can be divided into
    two sets: the LD (L determinants or lymphocyte defined)
    and SD (S determinants or serologically defined) anti-
    gens. These antigens function differentially in both
    the primary mixed leukocyte culture and cell-mediated
    lympholysis test and in the secondary proliferative
    cytotoxic test. There appears to be a collaborative
    response when allogeneic cells are confronted with both
    LD and SD antigens; this collaboration is based on the
    existence of two populations of T lymphocytes. The
    specificity of the secondary response may be based on
    both postive and negative selection in that a suppres-
    sive cellular mechanism appears to be generated in the
    MLC for the subsequent development of cytotoxicity.
    Preliminary results are presented suggesting that LD-SD
    collaboration takes place in vivo as well as in vitro.

Antigens controlled by genes of the major histocompatibility complex (MHC) can be divided into the LD (lymphocyte
defined or L determinant) and SD (serologically defined or S
determinant) systems. These antigens appear to play a differential role in activation of T lymphocytes, a phenomenon best
illustrated by studies using the in vitro models of the mixed
lymphocyte culture (MLC) and cell-mediated lympholysis (CML)
tests.

In this paper we will focus on the role of these antigenic systems in the primary and secondary responses of the
MLC and CML test. The MLC test is a measure of the proliferative response, a response that is primarily initiated by the
MHC LD antigens. The CML test is an assay of the effector

103

phase in which T lymphocytes are activated (primarily against the MHC SD antigens) and eventually kill target cells presumably by the recognition of those same SD determinants. We will in addition include some studies done in vivo that bear on the LD-SD problem. We have recently reviewed several aspects of this area in two articles (1,2) and several of the topics discussed here are taken from those publications.

On the basis of serological findings and the use of MLC and CML tests, it is possible to divide MHC determined cell surface antigens into at least three categories. First, the classical SD antigens that are present on the surface of essentially all cells (3). Second, there are antigens detected serologically that are present on only restricted cell types, among them B lymphocytes, macrophages, epidermal cells and sperm (4). These antigens are referred to as Ia (Ir-associated) in mouse and other designations (including B cell antigens) in man. (Although it has not been conclusively established that these mouse and human antigenic systems are homologous we shall make that assumption and, since the human terminology has not been unified, refer to both as Ia.) Third, the MHC antigens that, if different in two individuals, lead to an MLC proliferative response. We shall refer to these as LD antigens (5,6). Whereas genes determining the MHC SD antigens are genetically separable from those determining the Ia and LD antigens in both mouse and man, it is not clear whether to some degree there may be identity between Ia and LD determinants.

It must be stressed that the designations SD, Ia and LD are simply terms we use to allow one to differentiate between MHC determinants that may have different biological roles. Since the terminologies for these antigens and the loci coding for them are different in the several experimental species used for various studies, the terms allow simplified reference to and discussion of pertinent phenomenology related to what are presumably homologous systems in several species. In addition, in a single species several genetically separable loci coding for antigens all apparently subserving a single function can be conveniently referred to with a single term. The terms should in no way imply that a function associated with LD cannot also be associated with SD; for instance, that SD antigens cannot induce lymphocyte proliferation. The LD-SD notation in its original meaning may represent a terminological inexactitude; to avoid this, one could instead have the terms refer to the "L determinants" and "S determinants" respectively.

For convenience in further discussion, the word "locus" will be used to describe the genetic control of all antigens or determinants where it has not been shown that more than one cistron is involved. Two strains (individuals) designated as "LD different" differ for the strong LD locus and are identical for the SD loci; those designated as "SD different" differ for either the K and/or D regions in mouse or the SD loci in man but are identical for the strong LD locus. This focuses on only the MHC LD and SD loci; other MHC loci may well be involved in the reactions discussed.

GENETIC CONTROL OF MLC -- THE MHC LD SYSTEM

In figure 1 are shown the MHCs in man and mouse. In man, the HLA-D (LD-1) locus plays the predominant role in activating proliferative events in MLC; differences for the SD

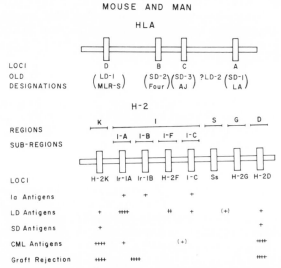

Figure 1. The H-2F locus given for the mouse has been detected by primed LD typing in human-mouse xenogeneic combination (7). The name for this locus is provisional and may be changed. Pluses refer to the presence of a given activity in mouse strain combinations differing by the locus in question. Pluses listed between loci cannot be ascribed to a single locus but rather to a region in that general area of the H-2 complex. The pluses listed in parentheses are not clearly established.

loci do not, by themselves, lead to strong MLC activation (reviewed in 8,9). Cells of siblings that are HLA-D identical
but differ for SD loci either do not stimulate each other at
all or only minimally (10,11); this low stimulation may be
due to SD antigenic differences themselves and/or to a weak
LD locus between HLA-A and HLA-C. It is not established
whether HL-A SD antigens provide a significant additional
proliferative stimulus in MLC in the presence of HLA-D disparity.

In mouse, a strong LD locus in the H-2 I region is primarily responsible for proliferative events in MLC; differences for the H-2 SD regions (K and/or D) given I region identity are also significantly stimulatory although to a lesser
extent. These latter proliferative responses, as in man, may
be caused by the SD antigens or by LD-type stimuli within the
K and D regions (e.g. there is evidence for an LD locus between S and D (12). In mouse, apparently unlike man, there
is a locus (Mls) alleles of which segregate independently of
H-2, and differences at which lead to an MLC proliferative response (13).

GENETIC CONTROL OF CML -- "LD-SD COLLABORATION"

Despite the finding that the MHC LD antigens are primarily responsible for activating the proliferative response
in MLC, and that cytotoxic T lymphocytes (CTLs) active in
CML are generated in MLC, the target antigens primarily recognized by CTLs are not LD. Rather the specific lytic effect
of CTLs is directed at either the MHC SD antigens themselves
or the phenotypic product of genes very closely linked to
those determining the SD antigens (14-18). This is, once
again, true even in xenogeneic combinations (19). We shall,
for simplicity, refer to them as the SD antigens.

These findings are most elegantly demonstrated in
"three-cell" experiments (20,21) in which cells of one strain
(individual) are simultaneously stimulated by mitomycin-C
treated cells of two other strains, one differing from the
responding cells by LD and the second differing by SD antigens (table 1). In addition these data give evidence for
"LD-SD collaboration". Cells of two LD different strains
(AQR-B10.T(6R)) stimulate each other significantly in MLC but
this leads to no cytotoxicity directed at B10.A target cells,
the SD target. Two SD region different strains (AQR-B10.A)
lead to a relatively weaker proliferative response (as compared with that caused by I region LD differences) and sig-

Table 1:   LD–SD Collaboration in a Three–Cell Experiment

Counts per minute ^{3}H-TdR incorporated ± SD*	Target Cell	% CML ± SD
10842 ± 236 AQR + 6R$_m$	B10.A	− 1.2 ± 3.1
4113 ± 190 AQR + B10.A$_m$	B10.A	21.8 ± 2.1
8292 ± 309 AQR + 6R$_m$ + B10.A$_m$	B10.A	40.4 ± 2.8

* The control culture AQR(AQR)$_m$ incorporated 2926 ± 254 cpm ^{3}H-TdR.

Table 1 Legend.   The strain B10.T(6R) is abbreviated as 6R.   The designation for the seven regions and subregions of H-2 (K, I-A, I-B, I-C, S, G and D) for the strains is as follows: AQR, qkkdddd; 6R, qqqqq?d; B10.A, kkkdddd. As such, AQR and 6R are H-2 SD identical but differ by LD, and AQR and B10.A are K region different but identical for the rest of H-2.   (D.J. Schendel and F.H. Bach, unpublished data.)

nificant cytotoxicity against B10.A (22,23).   The simultaneous presentation of LD and SD stimuli, however, leads to a markedly enhanced cytotoxic response against SD different target cells (LD–SD collaboration).   The percent CML is linearly related to the log of the number of CTLs; a difference from 21.8% to 40.4% thus represents much greater than a two–fold difference in terms of lytic potential (24).   It should be pointed out, however, that whereas the stimulation of AQR cells by B10.T(6R) does not lead to CML directed at B10.A, relatively low level but highly significant CML directed at B10.T(6R) does result (23,24).

These results demonstrate clearly the LD–SD cooperation, i.e. the presence of an LD difference in the stimulating mixture markedly enhances development of cytotoxicity against the SD region target even though the LD stimulus by itself does not generate cytotoxic cells against that the target. In contrast, the presence of the SD antigen does not enhance anti–LD (anti–I region) CML (23).

Experiments with human cells yield similar results with one exception: SD antigenic disparity "alone" (i.e. HLA-D i-

dentity) leads neither to a strong proliferative response nor
to a detectable cytotoxic response (10,14,15,21,25) contrasting with the MLC and CML associated with SD region differences in mouse. The high magnitude proliferative and cytotoxic responses seen in LD plus SD disparate human MLCs would
suggest that this difference is not due to insensitivity of
the human method although the culture technique cannot be
ruled out as the explanation. The contrariety could be based
on variation of human and mouse SD antigen presentation or
recognition. Alternatively, it may be explained by the evolutionary generation of somewhat different arrangements of
the genes of human and mouse MHCs (see Figure 1). In mouse,
the H-2K locus and loci of the I-A subregion are very closely
linked; recombinational events between them may in most cases
result in the inclusion of some relatively weak LD loci in
what we call the "SD region". In contrast the probably ten-
fold greater recombinational frequency between HLA-B and D
may prevent such LD loci from being included in the SD segment of most human recombinant chromosomes, thereby allowing
a more complete genetic separation of LD and SD antigens in
human recombinants.

CELLULAR RECOGNITION OF MHC ANTIGENS

The cells responding in MLC and CML are primarily T
cells. Based on evidence that functionally different subpopulations of T cells exist (26), we suggested in 1972 (27)
that the LD-SD dichotomy might be explained at the cellular
level by the existence of two separate subpopulations of T
cells, one responding primarily to LD (the proliferating helper cell - PHC) and another responding to SD (the cytotoxic T
lymphocyte - CTL). Results of experiments using cellular im-
munoadsorbants (28)(monolayers of allogeneic adherent cells)
were consistent with the existence of two separate populations of T lymphocytes, one responding to LD by proliferation
and not adhering to an allogeneic monolayer; the other, the
CTLs adhering to the monolayer. These two cell populations
can be separated prior to sensitization in MLC. An example
of such an experiment is shown in Figure 2. Cells of individual A are adsorbed onto either an A, B or C monolayer; one
hour later the nonadherent cells are removed from the monolayer and stimulated with cells of individual B and tested on
B target cells. The level of cytotoxicity generated against
B when the non-adherent A cells recovered from the B monolayer are stimulated with B_m is minimal as compared with similarly stimulated non-adherent cells from the A or C monolayers. In 12 experiments (28) the average reduction in cy-

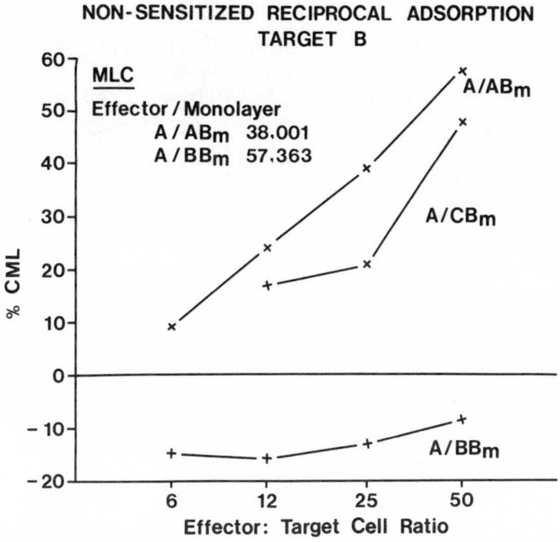

Figure 2. Cells of individual A (listed before the /) are adsorbed on either an autologous, A, monolayer or on allogeneic monolayers from individuals B or C (listed immediately after the /). The non-adherent cells from the monolayer are then stimulated with mitomycin-C treated cells from individual B, (designated B_m), and assayed 5 days later for their ability to lyse B target cells. The marked reduction in cytotoxic activity following adsorption on the D monolayer, as compared with the A or the C monolayer, is shown with no significant decrease in the proliferative activity. The reciprocal experiment stimulating the non-adherent cells with mitomycin-C treated cells of individual C and testing on C target cells in CML gave qualitatively similar results. (From K.S. Zier and F.H. Bach, unpublished data.)

totoxic activity (lytic units or potency) of non-adherent lymphocytes after pre-adsorption on allogeneic monolayers was 70% whereas only a 12% reduction in ^{3}H-TdR incorporation measured in MLC was observed. The adsorption experiments are consistent with the finding that the CTLs divide (29,30)(incorporate ^{3}H-TdR), although they appear to contribute only a relatively small percentage to the total ^{3}H-TdR incorporated

in a normal MLC -- the majority incorporated by the PHCs
(27,28).

The concept of two cell populations responding to LD
and SD antigens was strengthened by the findings of Cantor
and Boyse (31,32) using antisera against Ly cell surface antigens. These antigens are T cell differentiation markers
controlled by three loci, Ly-1, -2, and -3. It appears that
LD responsive PHCs are Ly-1+ and do not mediate cytotoxicity;
Ly-2,3+ cells divide and become CTLs. Support for ths dual T
cell concept has also come from studies of Wagner, Röllinghoff, et al. (33,34).

SECONDARY RESPONSES IN VITRO

Lymphocytes stimulated in MLC and left beyond their peak
proliferative and cytotoxic reactions revert to a status where
upon restimulation with the antigens to which they were originally "sensitized", there are both more rapid and strong
proliferative and cytotoxic reactions generated (35-40).
This has been referred to as a secondary response and the
lymphocytes responding can be referred to as "secondary" or
"primed" lymphocytes. We have used both the restimulation
of proliferative activity and the restimulation of the CML
response to gain a further understanding of the LD-SD dichotomy and collaboration. These studies provide further data on
both LD-SD dichotomy of function and collaboration.

PRIMED LD TYPING (PLT) TEST

Human lymphocytes primed in vitro to cells differing
by a single HLA haplotype and left for 9-14 days can be restimulated to respond in a secondary-type manner by cells
carrying the same HLA-D (LD-1) antigens present on the initial sensitizing cell (41,42). Most important to our present
discussion is the relative role of LD and SD antigens in the
restimulation of proliferation.

Several experimental approaches have been used to probe
this question. First, we have done studies in which cells of
the initial responding individual were sensitized to a given
haplotype carrying two foreign HLA SD antigens of the HLA-A
and B loci (figure 3). The PLT cells thus obtained were restimulated with cells from unrelated individuals carrying
those two SD antigens or other cells carrying neither one of
those two antigens and in fact no antigens cross-reactive
with those two antigens. Unrelated cells carrying both of

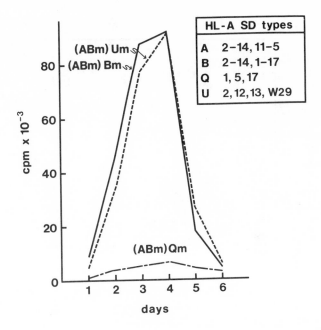

Figure 3. Kinetics of ^{3}H-TdR incorporation by cells of a person A that have been "primed" by cells of haploidentical brother B, and re-stimulated by cells of brother B and unrelated persons Q and U. Figure indicates assay time, in days after restimulation.

the SD antigens to which A was sensitized in some cases restimulate to only a minimal extent. Other unrelated cells carrying neither of the two SD antigens to which cells of individual A were sensitized, and no SD antigens that are cross-reactive with them, can restimulate almost as much as the initial sensitizing cell, suggesting strong LD sharing with the sensitizing haplotype. From studies such as this one we were able to conclude that the SD antigens on the sensitizing haplotype are neither essential nor sufficient for restimulation of the proliferative response (42).

If the LD antigens are primarily responsible for activating the proliferative secondary response, then two unrelated individuals matched by PLT testing for their LD antigens, should stimulate each other very little in a primary MLC. A large series of experiments in which this hypothesis

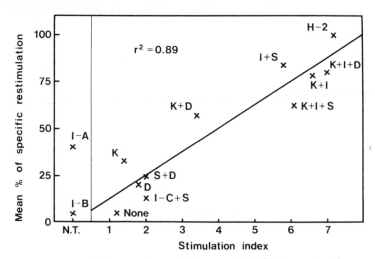

Primary allogeneic mouse MLC (Widmer et al.)

Figure 4. Demonstration of the similarity between the importance of different H-2 regions and sub-regions in allogeneic and xenogeneic lymphocyte proliferative stimulation.

was tested were also all consistent with the suggestion that the HLA LD antigens were for the most part responsible for restimulating the proliferative response (43). More recently, Bradley and his colleagues as well as studies in other laboratories (44,45) have used recombinant families to study this question. The conclusion regarding the relative roles of LD and SD has been the same. It would thus seem that the secondary proliferative response, like the primary, is largely dependent on differences for MHC LD antigens.

We have proposed PLT as a potential histocompatibility test for the definition of HLA LD antigens on the following basis: 1) differences for HLA are important in restimulation; products of genes segregating independently of HLA do not appear to initiate the proliferative response upon restimulation (41,42), 2) within the HLA system it is the LD differences that are responsible for the great majority of the proliferative responses (41,43; see figure 3), and 3) the amount of restimulation appears to be a reflection of the sharing by the restimulating cells of LD determinants recognized by the initial responding cell on the initial sensitizing cell. The value of this test as a histocompatibility assay have been discussed elsewhere (41-43). Data obtained in xenogeneic MLC combinations by Kirsten Lindahl and myself (7) using PLT testing also suggest that human lymphocytes are restimulated to divide by differences for the same regions (and subregions) of H-2 that are responsible for activating proliferative responses in the primary allogeneic mouse MLC (figure 4).

RESTIMULATION OF CYTOXICITY

If cells of an individual A are sensitized to both LD and SD antigens in a primary MLC, a secondary-type CML reaction can be evoked by restimulation with the same phenotype used for primary sensitization. Most interesting, with respect to MHC LD and SD components, restimulation of anti-SD cytotoxicity can be accomplished by adding only an LD stimulus for restimulation. Whereas the initial data suggesting this conclusion was obtained in studies in man (46), we will discuss data obtained in mouse (38,40) below since the genetic dissection can be done more cleanly.

Cells of strain 6R are sensitized to cells of B10.A, two strains differing for both H-2 LD-1 and H-2K. Secondary restimulation is accomplished either by restimulation with cells of B10.A, the original sensitizing strain, or cells of AQR, a strain carrying the same I region as B10.A. The data (table 2) clearly demonstrate that restimulation with the LD differences alone is sufficient to evoke the anti-B10.A cytotoxic response. The level of cytotoxicity generated is of

Table 2: CML Following B10.T(6R) Sensitization to B10.A

		Target cell - % CML			
Stimulus:	Day of Assay	6R qqqd	B10.A kkdd	AQR qkdd	B10.S ssss
Primary					
--	5	- 1	50	6	5
--	14	-20	5	- 6	- 3
Secondary					
B10.A	2	- 5	71	10	3
AQR	2	5	59	14	- 6

the same order of magnitude as that generated by restimulation with B10.A. Whether B10.A SD antigen has remained in the culture during this period and is playing a role in this restimulation process is not known.

That the SD antigens can play a role in restimulation of cytotoxicity is illustrated by results of experiments such as the following. Cells of strain A are stimulated with cells of strain B differing by both LD and SD antigens; maximal cytotoxicity is developed against the SD antigens of strain B. Two additional strains, C and D, are tested as cytotoxic targets and share SD antigens with strain B as indicated by the finding that target cells of strain C and D can be "cross-killed" to the same extent in a primary CML. If restimulation is done with cells of C, then, whereas maximal cytotoxicity will still be developed against cells of strain B, target cells of C will now be killed more than cells of D; if D is the restimulating donor, those cells will be killed more than C (38,40). We have referred to this as "deviation" of the secondary response by cross-reactive SD antigens.

Velocity sedimentation separation studies have shown that the blast cells produced in a primary MLC revert to small lymphocytes that rapidly differentiate into proliferating and/or cytotoxic T lymphocytes upon restimulation with the initial antigen (47). These findings demonstrate that positive selection for the responding population in primary MLC does exist and may account for at least part of the specificity of the secondary response. However this positive selection does not preclude possible involvement of a suppressor mechanism. In fact we (48) have detected suppressor activity in primary MLC sensitization cultures at a time when the proliferation responsible for positive selection is not yet significant, suggesting that suppression may be of overriding importance in the specificity of MLC activated secondary responses.

Direct evidence supporting a suppressive mechanism is presented in table 3. Fresh C_m stimulating cells were added to ongoing 2 day AB_m or AA_m cultures with or without fresh A lymphocytes. The AB_m cultures pre-empted the cytotoxic response to fresh C_m alone (row 5 compared to rows 4 and 6). If this pre-emption were merely selective in nature it would not be expected to influence fresh A lymphocytes from responding to C_m. However, the ongoing AB_m culture (row 8), but not the AA_m culture (row 7), markedly suppressed the expected development of cytotoxicity directed towards C (row 3)

114

Table 3: In vitro induced CML suppression.

		CTLs		Day 8 % Cytotoxicity B targets K/T Ratio		C targets K/T Ratio	
	Day 0	Day 2	Day 3	25/1	5/1	25/1	5/1
1	AB_m	–	–	58	33	5	– 1
2	AC_m	–	–	5	1	60	38
3	–	AC_m	–	5	3	73	39
4	$AB_m C_m$	–	–	51	27	62	33
5	AB_m	C_m	–	64	29	15	6
6	AA_m	C_m	–	1	1	52	32
7	AA_m	AC_m	–	2	0	64	34
8	AB_m	AC_m	–	74	42	32	15
9	AA_m	A	C_m	4	5	48	32
10	AB_m	A	C_m	68	43	20	8
11	–	A + med*	C_m	0	0	47	23
12	–	A + sup**	C_m	0	1	46	27

Table 3 legend. CML reactions were performed with CTLs obtained from sensitization flasks to which responding and stimulating cells were added on days 0, 2 or 3. Each flask received a total of 9×10^6 responding cells and 12×10^6 stimulating cells. Control values for each target:
B Targets: S.R. = 179, Max. = 1,441;
C Targets: S.R. = 379, Max. = 1,904.

* Fresh A lymphocytes were cultured on day 2 in medium that had been cultured since day zero in the absence of cells.

** Fresh A lymphocytes were cultured on day 2 in cell free supernatant from an AB_m culture established on day zero.

when fresh A plus C_m cells were added to them on day 2.

The combinations presented in the last four rows involved the addition of fresh A cells on day 2 and fresh C cells on day 3. Again, the ongoing AB_m response initiated on day zero suppressed the generation of CTLs directed against C. The observed suppressive effect required the responding AB_m cells since the cell-free supernatant from a 2 day AB_m culture did not suppress (row 12).

In other experiments, cells from an AB_m sensitization flask were removed and washed after 2 days of culture and added to fresh A plus C_m cells; suppression similar to the above was caused by these cells while the 2 day AB_m supernatant had no suppressing effect.

These experiments have demonstrated that a cell dependent suppression of CTL activation is generated in human MLC. Several distinct methods of generating and detecting suppressor activity have recently been described (49-58); aspects of this in vitro suppression in man appear to parallel certain qualities of in vitro induced murine suppression (59). However, more studies are required to determine the in vivo significance and the specific cellular mechanism of this suppression. Many complex models could be constructed to account for the phenomena, yet this seems unwarranted until more insight is provided. At present, two conclusions can be derived from these studies. First, cell mediated suppression of immune responses can be generated and studied in vitro using human lymphocytes responding to allogeneic cells. Second, the specificity of secondary responses to alloantigens following sensitization in MLC represents, at least in part, a "pre-emption" of third-party responsiveness by this suppression mechanism.

MODEL -- AN ATTEMPT AT SYNTHESIS

The LD-SD dichotomy can be summarized as follows.

(1) The SD antigens function as the prime CTL activating determinants and as targets for these cells. The weak proliferative response stimulated by SD region differences in mouse may reflect division of CTLs or PHCs in response to an SD antigenic molecule. Alternatively the proliferative response is due to PHCs responding to LD determinants included in the "SD region difference".

(2)   A strong MHC LD locus, separable from the SD loci, is primarily responsible for stimulating the strong proliferative response in MLC and presumably for inducing the PHC-CTL helper effect. One or more weaker MHC LD loci probably exist. Weak but significant cytotoxicity is often associated with I region differences; it is not established whether this is directed against LD as opposed to other I region antigens.

(3)   There is very substantial and clear evidence for LD-SD collaboration based on both genetic and cellular studies. The presence of an LD stimulus in the sensitizing MLC markedly enhances the development of cytotoxicity aimed at the SD region targets (unless maximum CML is already present (60) in vitro due to the presence of a strong signal two such as may be provided by heterologous serum or conditioned medium) even though stimulation by LD alone does not generate cytotoxicity against the SD target. It is not known whether the LD helper effect is essential and the CML generated in SD region different strains is due to an LD-like stimulus determined by gene(s) in that region, or that LD simply influences the quantitative amount of CML induced by SD alone.

We have discussed above data supporting the contention that LD and SD antigens are functionally distinct and that there are two separable populations of T lymphocytes responsive to these antigens. We shall now attempt to expand on our previous model to explain how LD and SD antigens and their respective responding lymphocyte populations interact to result in the generation of a specific cytotoxic response. The elaboration is based on the Bretscher-Cohn model for B cell activation (61) and is in general agreement with Crichton and Lafferty (62). It would suggest that the CTL receives two signals for activation: "signal one", the SD antigen, and "signal two" given by the PHC following its stimulation by LD. It is quite likely that many stimuli will, either via the PHC or by acting directly on the CTL, be able to provide signal two. This model is illustrated in figure 5.

The suggestion that the SD antigens actually initiate (signal 1) a differentiative response that is expanded, or allowed to differentiate further, by the presence of cells responding to the LD stimulus (signal 2) is based on kinetic experiments in which SD and LD stimuli are added to responding cell populations at different times. The basic findings (23), are quite similar to T-B cell collaboration. If the SD different stimulus (in a "three-cell" protocol) is added at time zero and the LD stimulus is delayed for 24

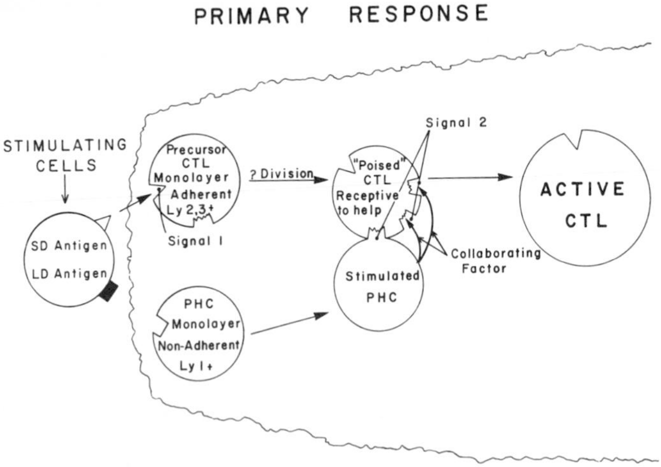

PRIMARY RESPONSE

Figure 5. See text for discussion.

hours, the CML against B10.A target cells is in fact increased, although the kinetics of the development of the cytotoxic response aimed at the SD antigens may differ. In the reciprocal direction, delay in adding the SD different cells, after adding the LD different cells on day zero, results in a similar delay in the development of CML. We have discussed this in detail elsewhere (1,23). Most importantly, the presence of the SD stimulus does not appear to potentiate "anti-LD" CML. This is in contrast to the potentiation of anti-SD CML by an LD stimulus, and further supports the LD-SD dichotomy.

Two findings might appear to contradict the need for signal two in the generation of CTLs. First, that Ly-2,3+ lymphocytes alone can respond to an entire MHC difference and become CTLs (32). This apparent circumvention of the PHC role could be explained by several models. (i) A relatively weak signal 2 can be given directly to the CTL by mechanisms other than PHC collaboration either by the SD antigens themselves or some other stimulus. (ii) The Ly 2,3+ cells may be a heterogeneous population, a portion of which can respond to the LD antigens and thereby provide the helper effect to allow CTLs within that population to develop. This is consistent with the finding in those same studies that an Ly-2,3+ population depleted of Ly-1+ cells still shows a highly significant proliferative response to strains differing for only the I and S regions (i.e. LD different-SD identical strains) without showing CML activity (31,32). The lack of cytotoxicity in this situation suggests that the proliferation seen is not due to division of CTLs. (iii) The Ly-1+ cells that proliferate in response to LD (proliferating "helper" cells) may not be required for the induction of CTLs but may simply expand an ongoing response and may be functionally distinct from Ly-2,3+ LD reactive cells. (iv) It may be that PHCs in the stimulating cell population respond to LD antigens on the responding cells and provide the helper effect to the responding CTLs. If help is provided via a factor, the observation that mitomycin-C treated cells do produce factors is important (63).

The second apparent contradiction is the finding that an SD region difference alone can stimulate both proliferative and CML responses in mouse. Ultraviolet (uv) irradiation of stimulating cells abrogates their ability to evoke a proliferative MLC response thus appearing to ablate LD expression; the SD antigens on uv treated cells can still be detected serologically (64). The SD region different stimulating cells are treated with uv irradiation rather than mitomycin-C (23). Under these circumstances the cells evoke minimal if any proliferative or cytotoxic response. However, the addition of an LD stimulus to the sensitizing mixture still leads to a very marked cytotoxic response against the SD different target cells. The three-cell experiments with uv treated stimulating cells show that an SD stimulus that is effective at activating CTLs is not capable of strongly stimulating the PHC and does not by itself lead to as great a cytotoxic reaction as in the presence of LD. At least four mechanisms could be evolved to explain the difference between the mitomycin-C treated (see table 1) and uv treated SD region disparate stimulating cells. (i) The same determinant on the SD molecule may be responsible for activating the PHC and CTL but the two cell populations have different requirements for activation (possibly due to molecularly different recognition molecules). Treatment with uv leaves a cell still capable of activating CTLs but not PHCs. For instance, the cell surface density of SD antigens may be reduced by uv treatment making the SD stimulus ineffective at stimulating PHCs or providing signal 2 directly to the CTL. (ii) Cellular contact initiated by recognition of surface SD antigen might allow a cell membrane interaction (possibly unrelated to antigen recognition) to provide a weak substitute for signal 2. Uv treated stimulating cells provide the SD stimulus (signal 1) but are unable to provide the substitute signal 2 and therefore require

an additional generation of signal 2 provided by the LD stimulus via the PHCs. (iii) A uv sensitive part of the SD molecule different from that triggering the CTL may activate the
PHC. This is similar to our initial analogy of a carrier-
hapten system to the LD-SD problem (5,20) and the reiteration
of that model applied to the SD antigen (65). (iv) There may
be LD-type loci in the K region separable from the SD loci (24).
Conceptually, in terms of phenotypic expression, models (iii)
and (iv) both suggest that the LD and SD antigens are determined by genetically separate sites; the question whether the
LD and SD stimuli are determined by separate genes or separate
subcistronic segments is not terribly important in this context.

Following a period of activity, CTLs as well as PHCs revert to become "secondary" CTLs and PHCs respectively. If at
this time the system is restimulated with only an LD stimulus
then the secondary CTL can now be reactivated to respond to
the specific SD antigen(s) against which it was "sensitized" in
the primary MLC. Whether there is a need for SD antigen to
remain in culture from the primary sensitization to allow this
restimulation by LD "alone" is not known. Whereas this signal
2 to the secondary CTL is sufficient to lead to differentiation
of the cell to cytotoxic activity, the simultaneous presentation
of signal 2, from the stimulated secondary PHC, and signal 1
to the secondary CTL appears to be a more effective stimulus
for the generation of cytotoxic activity. We base this conclusion on the finding of "deviation" of the cytotoxic response in the secondary restimulation system as discussed
above and elsewhere (38,40). The mechanism by which the two
stimuli are more effective than the simple introduction of
signal 2 requires further investigation.

Our model, depicted in figure 5, would seem valuable in
that many of the new steps added to the original model of two
T lymphocyte subpopulations responding to LD and SD can be
tested (27). Does a "poised" CTL different from the "precursor" CTL exist and, if so, does its deviation require cell
division? Does such a cell have increased numbers of "collaborating factor" receptors? Whereas the precursor CTLs apparently cannot be stimulated to become CTLs by an LD stimulus alone, as tested in PHA dependent CML (66), does a poised
CTL behave like a secondary CTL in this regard? At which
stages can a "factor" replace the PHC? What is the basis
of deviation at a cell population and individual cell basis?
And, perhaps most important, to what extent do the in vitro
results leading to this model fit the in vivo allograft rejection response?

IN VIVO LD-SD COLLABORATION

Dr. Hans Sollinger and I have recently done experiments to test whether LD-SD collaboration may also be demonstrable in vivo. We have used the thyroid transplantation system devised by Lafferty (67). One lobe of the thyroid is transplanted under the kidney capsule; at varying times between five to twenty-five days later radioactive iodine is injected into the recipient animal and 24 hours later the kidney containing the thyroid and the contralateral kidney are removed. If the thyroid is viable it will take up iodine, the magnitude of iodine uptake reflecting the relative function of the thyroid. If the thyroid has been rejected, no iodine will be taken up. Results can be expressed as a ratio of iodine incorporated into the thyroid-bearing kidney to that present in the contralateral kidney.

Studies by Lafferty (67) and Talmage and Lafferty (68) have demonstrated that if the thyroid is either cultured in vitro prior to transplantation or the donor animal is treated in a variety of ways, the thyroid will show prolonged survival upon transplantation. This prolonged survival can be abrogated (i.e. faster rejection induced) if, at the time of thyroid transplantation, peritoneal exudate cells of thyroid donor phenotype are injected intraperitoneally into the recipient. These authors have interpreted their data to indicate that the recipient is sensitized to the injected peritoneal exudate cells, and the recipient's sensitized cells then invade the thyroid and reject it. A further refinement of this hypothesis would suggest that either in addition to or as an alternative the LD antigens on the injected lymphoid cells sensitize the PHCs in the recipient and that these latter cells either themselves or via a secreted factor enhance the ability of CTLs in the transplanted thyroid to reject the graft.

We have done experiments to test this model by transplanting B10.A thyroid into AQR recipients (an SD region different thyroid)(see figure 6). Such thyroids show prolonged survival as compared with thyroids that differ for both SD and I region associated LD components. If, at the time of thyroid transplantation, 6R lymph node cells (which we have used instead of peritoneal exudate cells) are injected intraperitoneally into the recipient (cells differing from the recipient by I region LD factors), rejection of the thyroid is very rapid -- similar to that seen when an LD + SD different thyroid is transplanted. We have done a variety of con-

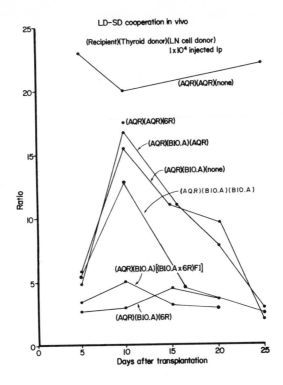

Figure 6. Thyroid transplantation has been performed as described by Lafferty, et al. (67). Twenty-four hours before the removal of the kidneys 0.5 C of ^{125}I was injected intraperitoneally. Both kidneys of each animal were counted in a gamma-counter. The counts of ^{125}I in the kidney containing the thyroid to those in the contralateral kidney were expressed as a ratio. All thyroids were examined histologically for signs of rejection; the results are consistent with those expected based on the ratio. We have injected 1 x 10^4 lymph node cells (instead of peritoneal exudate cells) intraperitoneally into thyroid graft recipients. The H-2 complex can be divided into four regions, K, I, S and D. The SD loci are in the K and D regions; the strong LD locus is in I. The MHC genotypes of these strains are the following: AQR (qkdd), B10.A (kkdd) and 6R (qqqd), where the lower case letter in parentheses refers to the H-2 haplotype from which each region for a given strain is derived.

122

trols to demonstrate that the collaborative effect of the injected lymph node cells and the transplanted SD different
thyroid is ascribable to the MHC; that the injected lymph
nodes do not, per se, participate in the rejection of the
thyroid, and that the injection of the 6R lymph node cells
does not generate a non-specific rejection mechanism. We
cannot rule out that the I region determined antigens on the
6R cells which are recognized by AQR are cross-reactive with
the SD target antigens on the B10.A thyroid. We hold this
to be very unlikely; AQR cells sensitized to 6R in vitro will
kill 6R target cells in CML but will not kill B10.A cells.
We thus interpret these results to indicate that LD-SD collaboration does exist in vivo.

SUMMARY

We have presented evidence in this paper regarding the
dichotomy of function of MHC LD and SD antigens in a variety
of test systems. The evidence for a dichotomy of function e-
licited in a primary MLC-CML system is very dramatic in man;
in mouse the primary relationship between LD stimulating the
proliferative events in MLC, and SD sensitizing the cytotoxic
T lymphocytes and acting as targets for these cells is also
very clear. The fact that there is proliferative activity associated with SD region differences and cytotoxic activity associated with I region disparity in mouse has been discussed.
The role of SD in xenogeneic CML as well as other test systems where the SD antigens have been modified by either chemical treatment of the cell surface, virus infection of the
cell, tumor transformation or other processes once again
speaks to the dichotomy of function.

In the secondary MLC-CML system, the LD and SD antigens
once again show a dichotomy of function. In terms of restimulating a proliferative response, only LD is able to do this
in any significant degree in man. In mouse, the allogeneic
situation is not well studied yet however in xenogeneic human-mouse combinations the same determinants that stimulate
the allogeneic primary MLC proliferative response are responsible for stimulating the secondary PLT response. We have
discussed the role of LD and SD antigens with respect to cytotoxicity. The in vivo experiments we have presented are consistent with LD-SD collaboration.

The model we have presented for the cellular events in
the primary and secondary in vitro responses is hopefully
valuable in leading to further experimentation. With the exception of the now proven existence of the two subpopulations

of T lymphocytes involved in the reaction, the model is highly speculative in many respects.

REFERENCES

(1) F.H. Bach, M.L. Bach and P.M. Sondel. Nature. Submitted.

(2) F.H. Bach, Proc. of the 10th Leukocyte Culture Conference. In press.

(3) J. Klein and D.C. Shreffler. Transpl. Rev. 6 (1971) 3.

(4) D.C. Shreffler and C.S. David. Adv. Immunol. 20 (1975) 125.

(5) F.H. Bach, M.B. Widmer, M.L. Bach and J. Klein. J. Exp. Med. 136 (1972) 1430.

(6) F.H. Bach, M.B. Widmer, M. Segall, M.L. Bach and J. Klein. Science. 176 (1972) 1024.

(7) K.F. Lindahl and F.H. Bach. In preparation.

(8) F.H. Bach and J.J. van Rood. New Engl. J. Med. In press.

(9) F.H. Bach, M.L. Bach, B.J. Alter, K.F. Lindahl, D.J. Schendel and P.M. Sondel, in: Immune Recognition. ed. A.S. Rosenthal. (Academic Press, New York, 1975) p. 175.

(10) E.J. Yunis and D.B. Amos. Proc. Natl. Acad. Sci. U.S.A. 68 (1971) 3031.

(11) V.P. Eijsvoogel, M.J.G.J. du Bois, C.H. Melief, M.L. DeGroot-Kooy, L. Koning, A. van Leeuwen, J.J. van Rood, E.D. duToit and P.Th.A. Schellekens, in: Histocompatibility Testing 1972. eds. J. Dausset and J. Colombani. (Munksgaard, Copenhagen, 1972) p. 501.

(12) M.B. Widmer, A.B. Peck and F.H. Bach. Transpl. Proc. V (1973) 1501.

(13) H. Festenstein. Transplantation. 18 (1974) 555.

(14) V.P. Eijsvoogel, R. DuBois, C.J.M. Melief and L. Kooy. Transpl. Proc. V (1973) 1301.

(15) G. Trinchieri, D. Bernoco, S.E. Curtoni, V.C. Miggiano and R. Ceppellini, in: Histocompatibility Testing 1972. eds. J. Dausset and J. Colombani. (Munksgaard, Copenhagen, 1972) p. 509.

(16) B.J. Alter, D.J. Schendel, M.L. Bach, F.H. Bach, J. Klein and J. Stimpfling. J. Exp. Med. 137 (1973) 1303.

(17) Nabholz, M., Vives, J., Young, H.M., Meo, T., Miggiano, V., et al. Eur. J. Immunol. 3 (1974) 378.

(18) K. Abbasi, P. Demant, H. Festenstein, J. Holmes, B. Huber and M. Rychlikova. Transpl. Proc. V (1973) 1329.

(19) K.F. Lindahl and F.H. Bach. Nature. 254 (1975) 607.

(20) D.J. Schendel, B.J. Alter and F.H. Bach. Transpl. Proc. V (1973) 1651.

(21) V.P. Eijsvoogel, M.J.G.J. duBois, A. Meinesz, A. Bierhorst-Eijlander, W.P. Zeylemaker and P.Th.A. Schellekens. Transpl. Proc. V (1973) 1675.

(22) A.B. Peck and F.H. Bach. Scand. J. Immunol. 4 (1975) 53.

(23) D.J. Schendel and F.H. Bach. Eur. J. Immunol. In press.

(24) D.J. Schendel and F.H. Bach. J. Exp. Med. 140 (1974) 1534.

(25) G.D. Bonnard, M. Chappuis, A. Glauser, W. Mempel, P. Baumann, H. Grosse-Wilde and E.D. Albert. Transpl. Proc. V (1973) 1679.

(26) H. Cantor and R. Asofsky. J. Exp. Med. 135 (1972) 764.

(27) F.H. Bach. Transpl. Proc. V (1973) 23.

(28) F.H. Bach. M. Segall, K.S. Zier, P.M. Sondel and B.J. Alter. Science. 180 (1973) 403.

(29) H. Cantor and J. Jandinski. J. Exp. Med. 140 (1974) 1712.

(30) B.J. Alter, F.H. Bach and R. Dutton. Unpublished observation.

(31) H. Cantor and E.A. Boyse. J. Exp. Med. 141 (1975) 1376.

(32) H. Cantor and E.A. Boyse. J. Exp. Med. 141 (1975) 1390.

(33) H. Wagner, M. Röllinghoff and G.J.V. Nosall. Transpl. Rev. 17 (1973) 3.

(34) H. Wagner, M. Röllinghoff and K. Shortmann, in: Prog. in Immunol. II. eds. L. Brent and J. Holoborow. (North Holland Publ. Co., Amsterdam, 1974) p. 111.

(35) L.C. Andersson and P. Häyry. Eur. J. Immunol. 3 (1973) 595.

(36) J.C. Cerottini, H.D. Engers, H.R. MacDonald and K.T. Brunner. J. Exp. Med. 140 (1974) 703.

(37) K.S. Zier and F.H. Bach. Scand. J. Immunol. In press.

(38) M.L. Bach, C. Grillot-Courvalin, K.S. Zier and B.J. Alter, in: Histocompatibility Testing 1975. ed. F. Kissmeyer-Nielsen. (Munksgaard, Copenhagen), in press.

(39) D. Fradelizi and J. Dausset. Eur. J. Immunol. 5 (1975) 295.

(40) B.J. Alter, C. Grillot-Courvalin, K.S. Zier and M.L. Bach, in: Proc. of the 10th Leukocyte Culture Conference, in press.

(41) M.J. Sheehy, P.M. Sondel, M.L. Bach, R. Wank and F.H. Bach. Science. 188 (1975) 1308.

(42) F.H. Bach, M.L. Bach, R. Wank, M.J. Sheehy and P.M. Sondel, in: Histocompatibility Testing 1975. ed. F. Kissmeyer-Nielsen. (Munksgaard, Copenhagen) in press.

(43) M.J. Sheehy, P.M. Sondel, F.H. Bach, M. Sopori and M.L. Bach, in: Histocompatibility Testing 1975. ed. F. Kissmeyer-Nielsen. (Munksgaard, Copenhagen) in press.

(44) B.H. Bradley, M. Sheehy, J.J. Keuning, et al., submitted to Immunogenetics.

(45) C. Mawas, M. Sasportes, D. Charmot, D. Fradelizi, M.
      Fellous and J. Dausset, in: Histocompatibility Test
      ing 1975. ed. F. Kissmeyer-Nielsen. (Munksgaard,
      Copenhagen) in press.

(46) K.S. Zier and F.H. Bach. Scand. J. Immunol. In
      press.

(47) H.R. MacDonald, H.D. Engers, J.C. Cerottini, and K.T.
      Brunner. J. Exp. Med. 140 (1974) 718.

(48) P.M. Sondel, M. Jacobson and F.H. Bach. J. Exp. Med.,
      In press.

(49) R.W. Dutton. J. Exp. Med. 136 (1972) 1445.

(50) R.K. Gershon., in: The Immune System, Genes, Receptors,
      Signals. eds. E.E. Sercarz, A.R. Williamson and C.F.
      Fox. (Academic Press, New York, 1974) p. 471.

(51) J.A. Kapp, C.W. Pierce and B. Benacerraf, in: Immune
      Recognition. ed. A.S. Rosenthal. (Academic Press,
      New York, 1975) p. 667.

(52) O. Kuperman, G.W. Fortner and Z.J. Lucas. J. of Immunol.
      In press.

(53) T.A. Waldmann, S. Broder, R.M. Blaese, M. Durm, M. Black-
      man and W. Strober. The Lancet. ii (1974) 609.

(54) G. Möller and N. Kashiwagi. Immunology. 22 (1972) 441.

(55) H. Folch and B.H. Waksman. J. of Immunol. 113 (1974)
      140.

(56) G.B. Mackaness and P.H. Lagrange. J. Exp. Med. 140
      (1974) 865.

(57) R. Elie and W.S. Lapp, in: Immune Recognition. ed. A.S.
      Rosenthal. (Academic Press, New York, 1975) p. 563.

(58) D.W. Thomas, W.K. Roberts and D.W. Talmage. J. of Im-
      munol. 114 (1975) 1616.

(59) R.R. Rich and S.R. Rich. J. of Immunol. 114 (1975)
      1112.

(60) M.B. Widmer, F.H. Bach, H.R. McDonald and J.C. Cerrot-
     ini. Unpublished data.

(61) P. Bretscher and M. Cohn. Science. 169 (1970) 1042.

(62) R. Crichton and J. Lafferty. Conference on Phytogeny,
     Hawaii (June, 1975) in press.

(63) M. Janis, R.J. Hartzman and F.H. Bach, in: Histocom-
     patibility Testing 1970. ed. P.I. Terasaki. (Munks-
     gaard, Copenhagen, 1970) p. 509.

(64) K. Lindahl-Kiessling and J. Safwenberg, in: Proc. of
     the VIth Leukocyte Culture Conference. ed. R. Schwarz.
     (Academic Press, New York, 1971) p. 623.

(65) J. Klein, V. Hauptfeld and M. Hauptfeld, in: Prog. in
     Immunol. II, Vol. 3. eds. L. Brent and J. Holborow.
     (North-Holland Publ. Co., Amsterdam, 1974) p. 197.

(66) B.J. Alter and F.H. Bach. J. Exp. Med. 140 (1974)
     1410.

(67) K.J. Lafferty, M.A. Cooley, J. Woolnough and K.Z.
     Walker. Science. 188 (1975) 259.

(68) D.W. Talmage, J. Radovich and K.J. Lafferty. In pre-
     paration.

ACKNOWLEDGEMENT

I thank my colleagues for permission to quote data
which is as yet unpublished.

This work has been supported by NIH grants AI-11576,
AI-08439, CA-14520 and CA-16836 and National Foundation
March of Dimes grant CRBS 246. This is paper no. 64 from
the Immunobiology Research Center and paper no. 1932 from
the Laboratory of Genetics, The University of Wisconsin,
Madison, Wisconsin 53706.

DISCUSSION FOLLOWING FRITZ BACH

GERSHON: When LD and SD are present, you get pre-emption by culturing for 48 hours alone. In other experiments you used LD alone and SD alone for 48 hours. Did either of these situations lead to similar pre-emption?

BACH: Most of the experience which Paul Sondel, Mark Jacobsen and I have had has been with humans differing by both LD and SD components. This is the data that I presented. We have very preliminary data in the mouse that would suggest that initial stimulation with SD or LD will pre-empt the later response to LD or SD, respectively. However, I would stress that our experience to date in the mouse is very preliminary.

DUPONT: Is the predictive value of LD typing by the PLT test equally good for all six *HLA-DW* specificity groups or is this primarily possible for best defined D-specificities as *DW2* (*LD8a*) or *DW3* (*LD7a*)?

BACH: I am afraid that we have only made comparisons with the homozygous typing cells in the case of *DW2* in collaboration with Dr. Arne Svegaard. There we obtained a very strong correlation. We have not yet tried to look at the LD determinants associated with the other clusters.

PAUL: In your study of re-stimulation of cytotoxicity of cells primed to B10.D2 with B10.BR or B10.G cells, is there evidence of shared LD and SD determinants in the priming and in the stimulating antigens?

BACH: We interpret the CML found on B10.BR and B10.G after the initial sensitization in the primary CML as evidence of cross-reactive SD target antigens. There may also be shared LD determinants (if the LD determinants are the targets); however, in the presence of SD differences, the amount of CML associated with the LD differences is minimal. From experiments, the results of which I did not present, it would seem that non-cross-reactive strains (i.e. those that are not cross-killed in CML) do not re-stimulate a response.

PAUL: In the use of PLT to identify LD antigens on lymphoid cells, what level of relative proliferation is accepted as indicating a sharing of LD antigens between the cells

129

used to prime PLT and those used to secondarily stimulate PLT. I ask this because in one slide you showed, different stimulated cells did not show a discrete break allowing simple segregation into high and low cross-reactants.

BACH: Let me first answer your question, but then comment on this problem in general. We used a level of 80% as the level at which we would consider a "match" between the LD antigens recognized by that PLT and the re-stimulating cell. What I would stress, however, is that a match does not give any idea to what degree the LD antigens on the initial stimulating cell and the re-stimulating cell are identical. If one thinks in terms of a number of LD determinants coded for by the *HLA-D* genes, then an 80% re-stimulation would simply indicate to me that some of those antigens are shared and perhaps all. However, I would not make a strong statement in this regard. I do not think that one can speak of LD identity unless there is a clear biphasic response in terms of a population of re-stimulating cells. I should add that we do have some PLT cells that show such a pattern.

van ROOD: We have been able to confirm Fritz's findings although our PLT results are not always as clear as his. (See Van Rood *et al*, this volume, Table L) Bradley and his colleagues in Oxford have developed a computer-aided analysis of this and similar data. The program divides the data without a bias into a positive, doubtful and negative group. If one analyzes the data this way, a good but not absolute correlation between PLT and typing results obtained with homozygous cells is obtained.

BACH: The question that I suppose will come up is whether the discordant results, those in which the homozygous typing cells and the PLT cells do not give the same answers, are due to the fact that the two tests really measure something different or whether there are still technical problems. I personally have the feeling that the homozygous typing cells actually carry several LD determinants; my hope is that the PLT cells will be able to measure individual determinants.

van ROOD: Have you found evidence with the PLT test for heterogeneity in the different MLC determinants which could indicate that the *DW1* to *DW6* determinants are not alleles coded by one locus, but pseudoalleles coded by several closely bonded loci?

BACH: We have data that we interpret to mean that there may be more than one LD determinant associated with a single *HLA-D* haplotype. The arguments are complex and rather than take time to go into them here, I would mention that they will be published in Histocompatibility Testing 1975.

BIFUNCTIONAL HISTOCOMPATIBILITY-LINKED REGULATION OF CELL MEDIATED LYMPHOLYSIS TO MODIFIED AUTOLOGOUS CELL SURFACE COMPONENTS

GENE M. SHEARER, ANNE-MARIE SCHMITT-VERHULST
AND TERRY G. REHN

Immunology Branch, National Cancer Institute

Abstract: Murine thymus-derived lymphocytes can be sensitized in vitro to trinitrophenyl-(TNP-) modified or N-
(3-nitro-4-hydroxy-5-iodophenylacetyl)-β-alanylglycyl-
glycyl-(N-) modified autologous lymphocytes. During
five days of culture, cytotoxic effector cells are
generated which specifically lyse only ^{51}Cr-labelled
spleen target cells which are modified with the same
agent and which share H-2K and/or H-2D alleles with the
cells of the sensitizing phase. Experiments using F_1
hybrid responding lymphocytes sensitized and assayed
with TNP-modified parental cells indicated that the
homology required for lympholysis was either between
modified stimulating and modified target cells, or
among responding, modified stimulating and modified
target cells. Furthermore, specificity was such that
effector cells generated by sensitization with TNP-modified stimulating cells were incapable of lysing N-modified, H-2-matched targets, and vice versa. Antisera
directed against serologically defined region products
of unmodified target cells inhibited lysis of TNP-modified target cells, whereas anti-Ia antibodies had no
detectable effect on lysis. Anti-TNP sera also blocked
the lysis of TNP-modified targets irrespective of
whether the effector cells were specific for TNP-modified autologous H-2 products or unmodified H-2 alloantigens. Such experiments indicate that the effector
cells are directed against specificities associated
with serologically-defined region products and that
some TNP groups are sterically close to the H-2K and
H-2D region antigens.

Sensitization of B10.A responding lymphocytes

with TNP-modified autologous spleen cells generated
effectors which lysed TNP-modified $\underline{K}$-end matched targets, but not TNP-modified $\underline{D}$-end matched target cells.
In contrast, B10.D2 effector cells generated by TNP-
autologous sensitization lysed TNP-modified $\underline{K}$-end and
$\underline{H-2D}$ region matched targets equally well. Experiments
using (B10.AxB10.D2)F_1 hybrid responding lymphocytes
sensitized with TNP-modified F_1, B10.A or B10.D2 stimulating cells and the response patterns observed in
other C57BL/10 congenic and recombinant mouse strains
indicate that cell-mediated lympholysis response potential to TNP-modified autologous components controlled
by genes mapping in or near $\underline{H-2D}$ are controlled by $\underline{Ir}$
genes mapping in or near $\underline{H-2K}$ and/or $\underline{I-A}$. These findings demonstrate bifunctional genetic regulation of
cellular immunity to modified autologous lymphocytes in
which genes mapping in or near the serologically defined regions of the major histocompatibility complex control new antigenic specificities formed, and genes mapping in or near the $\underline{I}$ region regulate response potential to these new self-antigens. A similar type of
bifunctional $\underline{H-2}$-linked control of immunity may be
relevant in autologous systems for surveillance against
viral-associated neoplasia and for autoimmunity.

INTRODUCTION

Among the immunological functions attributed to products of the histocompatibility gene complex, one of the most
recent discoveries has been the observation that a number of
thymus derived-(T-) cell mediated cytotoxic reactions induced
$\underline{in}$ $\underline{vivo}$ or $\underline{in}$ $\underline{vitro}$ and directed either against "altered self
antigens" (1-8) or weak natural antigens (9-12) appear to be
associated with the major histocompatibility complex (MHC).
This association with the MHC of cell-mediated lympholysis
(CML) to chemically-modified autologous lymphocytes has been
shown to occur at two functionally distinct levels: (a) generation of T-cell mediated cytotoxicity against modified MHC
products controlled by genes mapping in or near the serological regions which appear to serve as "altered self antigens"
(2); and (b) genetic control of the immunocompetent potential
of the responding lymphocytes, which maps in or near the $\underline{I}$
region of the murine MHC (13).

At the present time, the CML responses associated with
syngeneic MHC can be classified into three broad categories.
These are CML to: (a) viral-associated antigens (5-8);

(b) chemically-modified or "hapten-associated" specificities (1-4); and (c) certain weak cellular antigens (9-12). All of these models share in common the observation that lympholysis of target cells by T-effector cells occurs only when there is H-2K and/or H-2D homology between the cells involved in the sensitizing and lytic phases of the CML. The viral systems thusfar reported in which H-2 homology is required between in vivo infected cells and in vitro target cell lysis include lymphocytic choriomeningitis (5,6), ectromelia (7), and vaccinia (8). The weak murine antigens which appear to require some form of H-2 homology include: (a) primary in vitro CML to a non-H-2 alloantigen (possibly controlled by the M-locus) (11); (b) a secondary in vitro CML to the sex-linked H-Y antigen, which requires priming in vivo (9,10); and (c) the blocking of the lytic phase of an in vivo CML to tumor-associated antigens with antisera directed against either the H-2 type of the target cell or the tumor-associated antigen (12). The two examples of chemically or "hapten"-modified autologous CML which have been shown to require H-2 homology between the cells of the sensitizing and/or effector phases involve trinitrophenyl-(TNP-) modification (2,3) and N-(3-nitro-4-hydroxy-5-iodophenylacetyl)-β-analylglycylglycyl-(N-) modification of mouse spleen cells (4). These two models have potential advantages over some of the other natural models with respect to elucidation of the immune mechanisms involved since: (a) they can be generated and assayed in vitro (which makes them applicable to a human model); (b) the "haptens" themselves are chemically well characterized entities; and (c) information regarding the nature and specificity of the recognition unit can be obtained by introducing specific modification in the chemical structure of the "haptens".

The present report reviews recent developments in the chemically modified autologous CML in vitro models with respect to their relationship to products and functions of the major histocompatibility gene complex. These findings indicate that the MHC can play a role in the response potential to and in the formation of new antigenic specificities involving modified self components.

REQUIREMENT FOR H-2 HOMOLOGY OF MODIFIED TARGET CELLS WITH MODIFIED STIMULATING CELLS AND/OR RESPONDING LYMPHOCYTES

The observation that effector cells generated by sensitization of responding lymphocytes with TNP-modified autologous spleen cells specifically lyse only TNP-modified, H-2-

135

matched target spleen cells can be summarized by the examples
shown in Tables I and II, using cells from the B10.A and
B10.D2 mouse strains. Effector cells from B10.A donors lysed
spleen target cells which were TNP-modified and H-2 matched
with the cells of the sensitization phase at K or at K plus
I-A. No appreciable lysis was detected on H-2 matched, unmodified targets or on TNP-modified targets sharing the I-C,
S, D or I-A, I-B, D regions with the responding and stimulating cells. Thus, the B10.A effector cells preferentially
or exclusively lysed K-end matched TNP-modified targets, but
not D-end matched target cells. In contrast, B10.D2 effector
cells generated by TNP-modified autologous sensitization
lysed TNP-modified target cells sharing only D-region homology with B10.D2 (A.TL), as well as targets differing at D
but matched at the other H-2 regions (C3H.OH). Furthermore,
the magnitude of lysis detected using B10.D2 effector cells
(range, 12-20%) was always lower than that detected using
B10.A lymphocytes (range 25-40%). It should be noted that
lysis of B10.A-TNP targets was obtained using B10.D2 effector
cells, whereas B10.D2-TNP targets were not lysed by B10.A
effectors. Since these two strains differ in their I region,
the possibility was raised that a responding cell defect involving an immune response (Ir) gene is responsible for the
differential reactivities of B10.A and B10.D2 cells to TNP-
modified products of H-2D^d (14). This issue will be considered in more detail in a later section.

Another chemical modifying agent which has been recently found to elicit an in vitro CML when coupled to autologous
cell surfaces is the "hapten" N-(3-nitro-4-hydroxy-5-iodophen-
ylacetyl)-β-analyglycylglycyl-(N-) (15). This reagent was
synthesized with a tripeptide spacer between the hapten and
the cell, for the purpose of generating a non-H-2-associated,
hapten specific CML (16). Tables III and IV show data representative of those obtained by generating B10.A and B10.D2
effector cells by sensitization with N-modified autologous
spleen cells (4). As was seen in the TNP model, preferential
reactivity of B10.A effector cells was obtained against H-2
matched targets sharing K or K plus I-A with the cells of the
sensitization phase. Significant but weak lysis was obtained
using N-modified targets homologous with responding and stimulating cells at I-C, S, D or I-A, I-B, D. B10.D2 effector
cells exhibited equal lysis of N-modified targets sharing
I-C, S, D or all H-2 regions except D, but not I-C, S with
the cells of the sensitizing phase. Thus, the in vitro TNP-
and N-modification CML models are similar with respect to
their reactivity patterns in these two congenic mouse strains.

TABLE I

REQUIREMENT FOR H-2 HOMOLOGY OF TNP-MODIFIED TARGET CELLS WITH TNP-MODIFIED
STIMULATING CELLS AND/OR RESPONDING LYMPHOCYTES (B10.A)

Responding Cells	Stimulating Cells	Target Cells	% Specific Lysis ± S.E.	Target cell H-2 region common to responding and stimulating cells
B10.A kkkddd	B10.A-TNP kkkddd-TNP	B10.A kkkddd	-3.2+2.0	All of H-2
"	"	B10.A-TNP kkkddd-TNP	28.6+3.9	All of H-2
"	"	B10.A(4R)-TNP kkbbbb-TNP	37.3+2.5	K, I-A
"	"	B10.D2-TNP dddddd-TNP	3.9+2.0	I-C, S, D
"	"	A.TL-TNP skkkkd-TNP	3.9+4.8	I-A, I-B, D

Effector:target cell ratio = 20:1

TABLE II

REQUIREMENT FOR H-2 HOMOLOGY OF TNP-MODIFIED TARGET CELLS WITH TNP-MODIFIED STIMULATING CELLS AND/OR RESPONDING LYMPHOCYTES (B10.D2)

Responding Cells	Stimulating Cells	Target Cells	% Specific Lysis $\pm$ S.E.	Target cell H-2 region common to responding and stimulating cells
B10.D2 ddddd	B10.D2-TNP ddddd-TNP	B10.D2 ddddd	-2.4±2.8	All of H-2
"	"	B10.D2-TNP ddddd-TNP	19.2±2.4	All of H-2
"	"	B10.A-TNP kkkddd-TNP	17.6±3.6	I-C, S, D
"	"	B10.A(2R)-TNP kkkddb-TNP	0.8±2.1	I-C, S
"	"	A.TL-TNP skkkkd-TNP	15.6±3.7	D
"	"	C3H.OH-TNP ddddk-TNP	14.7±1.2	K, I-A, I-B, I-C, S

Effector:target cell ratio = 20:1

TABLE III

REQUIREMENT FOR H-2 HOMOLOGY OF N-MODIFIED TARGET CELLS WITH N-MODIFIED
STIMULATING CELLS AND/OR RESPONDING LYMPHOCYTES (B10.A)

Responding Cells	Stimulating Cells	Target Cells	% Specific Lysis $\pm$ S.E.	Target cell H-2 region common to responding and stimulating cells
B10.A kkkddd	B10.A-N kkkddd-N	B10.A kkkddd	0.5±0.6	All of H-2
"	"	B10.A-N kkkddd-N	19.1±5.3	All of H-2
"	"	B10.A(4R)-N kkbbbb-N	18.6±1.5	K, I-A
"	"	B10.D2-N ddddd-N	7.1±1.2	I-C, S, D
"	"	A.TL-N skkkkd-N	8.0±1.0	I-A, I-B, D
"	"	C57BL/10-N bbbbbb-N	1.9±1.1	None

Effector:target cell ratio = 40:1

TABLE IV

REQUIREMENT FOR H-2 HOMOLOGY OF N-MODIFIED TARGET CELLS WITH N-MODIFIED STIMULATING CELLS AND/OR RESPONDING LYMPHOCYTES (B10.D2)

Responding Cells	Stimulating Cells	Target Cells	% Specific Lysis ± S.E.	Target cell H-2 region common to responding and stimulating cells
B10.D2 ddddd	B10.D2-N dddddd-N	B10.D2 ddddd	-0.4±1.4	All of H-2
"	"	B10.D2-N dddddd-N	15.0±4.6	All of H-2
"	"	B10.A-N kkkddd-N	12.4±1.2	I-C, S, D
"	"	B10.A(2R)-N kkkddb-N	-2.2±0.9	I-C, S
"	"	C3H.OH-N dddddk-N	14.3±2.3	K, I-A, I-B, I-C, S
"	"	C57BL/10-N bbbbbb-N	2.5±1.3	None

Effector:target cell ratio = 40:1

140

SPECIFICITY OF CYTOTOXICITY AS A FUNCTION OF THE ✓ MODIFYING AGENT

The similarities obtained above for TNP- and N-modified autologous CML raised the possibility that both of the reagents modify the stimulating cells in a similar way such that the effector cells would recognize a common specificity. To test this possibility, responding lymphocytes from several C57BL/10 congenic lines were sensitized with autologous spleen cells modified with either TNP or N (4). The effectors generated were assayed separately on H-2 matched tumor targets modified with either TNP or N. The results, summarized in Table V using C57BL/10, demonstrate that the effector cells generated lyse only H-2 matched targets modified with the same reagent to which they were sensitized.

TABLE V

SPECIFICITY OF CYTOTOXICITY AS A FUNCTION OF TNP- OR
N-MODIFICATION OF THE AUTOLOGOUS SENSITIZING SPLEEN CELLS

Responding Cells	Stimulating Cells	Target Cells	% Specific Lysis ± S.E.
C57BL/10	C57BL/10-TNP	EL-4-TNP	47.6±1.5
"	"	EL-4-N	-1.8±1.1
"	C57BL/10-N	EL-4-TNP	1.8±2.1
"	"	EL-4-N	26.1±1.2

Effector:target cell ratio = 20:1

EFFECTOR CELL SPECIFICITY: MODIFIED AUTOLOGOUS H-2 PRODUCTS VS HAPTEN

Three interpretations can be envisioned for the H-2 homology required between modified target cells and the responding and modified stimulating cells. First, it can be postulated that the lysis of modified target cells is hapten specific, but that H-2 homology involving interaction between effector and target cells is required for this type of lysis to occur. An alternate possibility is that cell surface reactive agents such as trinitrobenzene sulfonate and N-azide react with cell surface components including products of the MHC, resulting in altered self-antigens (2,4). These new antigenic-specificities activate the relevant clones of

141

responding lymphocytes, resulting in the generation of cytotoxic effector cells which preferentially interact with target cells expressing the same altered self antigens. Similar
interpretations have been considered for the specificity of
H-2 associated CML directed against viral-infected cells
(6,7) and non-H-2 determinants (9-12). Experiments using F_1
responding and parental stimulating and target cells have
been performed to test these two possibilities for a number
of the H-2-associated CML (2-4,6,10,17). Such experiments
using TNP- and N-modified cells are shown in Table VI. For
both of these models, F_1 effector cells lysed modified parental target cells only if the sensitization had been against
the same modified parental target cells. Thus, H-2 homology
was required either between modified stimulator and modified
target cells or among all three groups of cells, i.e. responder, stimulator and target. Similar F_1 antiparental experiments have been reported for other H-2-associated CML
with identical results (6,10,17). If the lytic event were
hapten-specific and if the dependence on H-2 homology were
for efficient effector-target cell interaction leading to
hapten specific lysis, homology between stimulator and target
cells should not have been critical. If H-2 homology is postulated to be necessary among responding, stimulating, and
target cells (which the F_1 experiments do not exclude), then
this homology must be for the same haplotype throughout,
i.e., responding and stimulating cells cannot interact
through one haplotype and effector and target through the
other. The F_1 experiments do not rule out the possibility
that two structures are included in the recognition unit at
the sensitization and lytic phases: one involving the hapten
and the other involving unmodified H-2 of the stimulating
cells. If this model were valid, one might expect that the
effector phase of the CML could be blocked either by unmodified H-2-matched lymphoid cells or by TNP-modified non-H-2-
matched lymphoid cells. It was found that efficient blocking
of the effector phase of TNP-autologous CML could be obtained
only if the blocking cells were both TNP-modified and H-2-
matched with the ^{51}Cr-labelled targets (2). This suggests
that the specificity of this T-cell receptor includes both
hapten and H-2 gene products. The above results are most
compatible with the hypothesis that the antigenic unit consists of a chemically modified H-2 self product.

H-2 LINKED GENETIC CONTROL OF LYMPHOLYSIS RESPONSE POTENTIAL
    TO TNP-MODIFIED H-2 CONTROLLED CELL SURFACE PRODUCTS

As shown in Tables I-IV and in previous reports

TABLE VI

DEMONSTRATION THAT THE H-2 HOMOLOGY REQUIRED IS BETWEEN MODIFIED
STIMULATING AND MODIFIED TARGET CELLS

Responding Cells	Stimulating Cells	Target Cells	% Specific Lysis $\pm$ S.E.	Target cell homology with:	
				Responding Cells	Stimulating Cells
(B10xB10.A)F$_1$	B10.A-TNP	B10.A-TNP	26.0+2.2	Yes	Yes
"	B10.A-TNP	B10-TNP	5.5+1.8	Yes	No
"	B10-TNP	B10-TNP	38.1+3.4	Yes	Yes
"	B10-TNP	B10.A-TNP	4.6+2.7	Yes	No
(B10xB10.BR)F$_1$	B10-N	EL-4-N	18.7+1.3	Yes	Yes
"	B10-N	RDM-4-N	4.0+2.0	Yes	No
"	B10.BR-N	RDM-4-N	21.9+3.7	Yes	Yes
"	B10.BR-N	EL-4-N	8.0+1.0	Yes	No

143

(2,4,13), sensitization of B10.A responding lymphocytes, with modified autologous stimulating cells led to the generation of effector cells which exhibited stronger reactivity against TNP- or N-modified K-end products than to modified D-end products. In contrast, B10.D2 spleen cells sensitized in either the TNP- or N-modified autologous models generated equal reactivity to modified $\underline{K}$ or $\underline{D}$ products (2,4). This difference in response to $\underline{H-2D^d}$-TNP by B10.A and B10.D2 responding cells cannot be accounted for at the antigenic level, since (a) the same D-end products are involved in the new specificities found in both strains; and (b) B10.A-TNP target spleen cells were lysed by B10.D2 effectors generated in the TNP-autologous model. Thus, by replacing the $\underline{k}$ alleles (B10.A) at the $\underline{K}$ and $\underline{I}$ regions with the corresponding $\underline{d}$ alleles (B10.D2) a cytotoxic response was obtained. It is noteworthy that the $\underline{H-2}$ region differences are not those associated with the specificity of the modified $\underline{H-2D}$ region, but do include part of the $\underline{I}$ region. The $\underline{I}$ region is known to control immune response potential to many immunogens, and in most cases, responsiveness has been found to be dominant (18). In order to determine whether the negative or weak CML generated by B10.A lymphocytes to the TNP-modified cell surface components controlled by $\underline{H-2D^d}$ were due to a responding cell defect (possibly controlled by $\underline{H-2}$-linked $\underline{Ir}$ genes), two types of experiments have been performed (13,19).

Earlier studies have shown that the lytic phase of an allogeneic CML can be blocked by antisera directed against the serological region of the target cell to which the responding lymphocytes were sensitized (20). Similar blocking experiments with alloantisera directed against different $\underline{H-2}$ subregions were carried out using B10.A and B10.D2 effector cells generated by TNP-modified autologous sensitization to define the specificities involved. In Table VII, lympholysis by B10.A and B10.D2 effector cells sensitized by TNP modified autologous cells was assayed on TNP modified spleen target cells which were preincubated in the presence of either normal mouse serum or different $\underline{H-2}$ alloantisera. The $\underline{H-2}$ subregions expressed on the target cells to which the alloantisera are directed are underlined in Table VII. Section A demonstrates that the lympholysis by B10.A effector cells is significantly blocked only in the presence of the alloantisera directed against $\underline{K}$, $\underline{I-A}$, and $\underline{I-B}$ $\underline{H-2}$ subregions of the target. In contrast, the lympholysis by B10.D2 effector cells against the B10.A-TNP target was abolished only in the presence of serum directed against $\underline{I-C}$, $\underline{S}$, and $\underline{D}$ $\underline{H-2}$ subregions. Furthermore, section B demonstrates that only

144

TABLE VII

SELECTIVE EFFECT OF SPECIFICALLY DIRECTED ANTI-H-2 SERA AND ANTI-TNP-KLH SERUM ON THE LYSIS OF TNP-MODIFIED TARGET CELLS BY EFFECTOR CELLS GENERATED BY SENSITIZATION WITH TNP-MODIFIED AUTOLOGOUS STIMULATING CELLS

Responding Cells	Stimulating Cells	Target Cells	% Specific lysis ± S.E. of target cells preincubated in the presence of			
A			normal serum	B10.BRαB10.D2	B10.D2αB10.BR	
B10.A kkkddd	B10.A-TNP kkkddd-TNP	B10.A-TNP kkkddd-TNP	34.4±1.3	39.4±1.5 kkkddd	13.8±2.8 kkkddd	
B10.D2 ddddd	B10.D2-TNP ddddd-TNP	"	15.8±3.8	2.4±0.6 kkkddd	12.0±4.0 kkkddd	
B				A.TLαA.AL	A.THαA.TL	B10.BRαB10.D2
B10.A kkkddd	B10.A-TNP kkkddd-TNP	B10.A-TNP kkkddd-TNP	36.0±3.0	0.0±2.7 kkkddd	40.4±2.3 kkkddd	42.7±1.0 kkkddd
C				B10.BRαB10.D2	(B10xA)αB10.D2	B10.BRαB10.A
B10.D2 ddddd	B10.D2-TNP ddddd-TNP	B10.D2-TNP ddddd-TNP	21.4±3.7	3.2±4.2 ddddd	14.2±3.1 ddddd	6.6±2.7 ddddd
D				B10αB10.BR	B10.BRαB10	αTNP-KLH
B10.BR kkkkkk	B10.BR-TNP kkkkkk-TNP	B10.BR-TNP kkkkkk-TNP	42.4±1.0	23.9±4.5 kkkkkk	Not Tested	-2.1±2.4
"	C57BL/10 bbbbbb	C57BL/10-TNP bbbbbb-TNP	46.0±3.1	49.2±3.7 bbbbbb	Not Tested	4.8±2.7
"	C57BL/10 bbbbbb	C57BL/10 bbbbbb	54.0±9.0	Not Tested	14.7±2.9 bbbbbb	41.5±6.0

alloantisera directed against the K subregion of H-2 completely abolished the lysis by B10.A effectors, whereas alloantisera directed against I-A, I-B and I-C or I-C, S, and D
were without effect. When B10.D2 effector cells were assayed
on B10.D2-TNP target cells, complete blocking of lympholysis
was obtained only in the presence of serum directed against
the whole H-2 region, whereas a partial effect was observed
in the presence of sera against K, I-A and I-B and against
I-C, S and D. Serum directed against the Ia.8 (serum B10.A
against B10) (21) specificity expressed by the target cells
did not significantly affect lympholysis (19). Controls were
performed that showed that none of these sera, when directed
only against effector cell H-2 specificities, affected the
lysis by effector cells sensitized against alloantigens (19).

In section D, it is shown that the lysis of B10.BR
effector cells sensitized by TNP modified autologous cells
was partly inhibited in the presence of serum directed
against the H-2 region of the target cells and was completely
inhibited in the presence of anti-TNP-KLH serum. The lysis
by B10.BR effector cells sensitized against unmodified C57BL/
10 allogeneic cells when assayed on B10-TNP was also completely inhibited in the presence of serum directed against
TNP-KLH. A possible interpretation of this finding is that
some TNP groups are closely associated with H-2 alloantigens
in such a way that reacting the hapten with antibody prevents
the effector cells from efficiently recognizing the alloantigens. The independent behavior of H-2K versus H-2D alloantigens, as shown in sections A and B of Table VII, compared to
the apparent close association between some TNP groups and
H-2 alloantigens (section D-Table VII) suggests that the
association between some TNP groups and the serologically defined antigens is closer than that between H-2K and H-2D
specificities. The latter are known to be located on separate molecules (22) and to migrate independently on the cell
surface (23).

It was demonstrated here (section B) that B10.A effector cells generated by sensitization with B10.A-TNP have
preferential reactivity toward the modified K^k structure, in
contrast to the reactivity of B10.D2 effector cells sensitized by B10.D2-TNP stimulators, which was directed against
both K- and D-end TNP-modified products. In order to determine whether the weak CML generated by B10.A responding lymphocytes to the TNP-modified cell surface components controlled by H-2D^d was due to a responding cell defect under
dominant H-2 linked Ir gene control, spleen cells from

(B10.AxB10.D2)F_1 mice were sensitized with TNP-modified F_1, B10.A, or B10.D2 stimulating cells. The effectors generated were assayed on modified B10.A and B10.D2 target cells (13). The results of such an experiment are summarized and reviewed in Table VIII. In contrast to the results obtained using B10.A responding lymphocytes, spleen cells from F_1 donors generated appreciable lympholysis against modified H-2K^k and H-2D^d products (13). Hence, the failure of B10.A responding lymphocytes to generate in vitro CML to TNP-modified H-2D^d is probably due to the lack of expression of the proper dominant H-2-linked Ir gene(s). This gene(s) is, however, apparently expressed in both B10.D2 and (B10.AxB10.D2)F_1 mice.

It is also noteworthy from the data shown in Table VIII that the level of lympholysis detected against modified H-2K^k was higher than that detected against modified H-2D^d or against H-2D^d plus modified H-2K^d. This quantitative difference in cytotoxic level was observed when TNP-modified B10.D2 spleen cells were used as stimulator and/or target cells. By using (B10.AxB10.D2)F_1 responding and target cells sensitized against TNP-modified F_1, B10.A, or B10.D2 stimulating cells, results were obtained suggesting that the new specificities resulting from TNP-modification of H-2D^d and H-2D^k are not as immunogenic as those resulting from TNP-modification of H-2K^k (also see Table IX) (13).

Further studies are in progress using mouse strains exhibiting intra-H-2 recombination between the K and I regions in order to map the gene(s) responsible for the immune response potential differences observed between B10.A and B10.D2 mice. A partial listing of such experiments is shown in Table IX. Effector cells generated from TNP-modified autologous sensitization of C57BL/10 and B10.D2 responding lymphocytes lysed equally well TNP-modified targets H-2 matched with the stimulators at both the K- and D-ends. In these two strains no preferential reactivity was detected against TNP-modified products of the K-end. In contrast, effector cells from B10.BR, B10.A, B10.A(2R), and B10.A(4R) all exhibited a higher lympholytic reactivity against TNP-modified K-end products than against TNP-modified D-end products. It is noteworthy that the strains showing equal reactivity are those expressing b or d alleles in the I subregions. Furthermore, with regard to their respective I subregions, those strains exhibiting preferential reactivity against TNP-modified K-end products express k alleles in I-A, I-B, and I-C (B10.BR), I-A and I-B (B10.A and B10.A[2R]), or in I-A only (B10.A[4R]).

147

TABLE VIII

DOMINANT GENETIC EXPRESSION OF CYTOTOXICITY BY (B10.AxB10.D2)F_1 RESPONDING CELLS TO TNP-MODIFIED PRODUCTS OF <u>H-2D^d</u>

Responding Cells	Stimulating Cells	Target Cells	% Specific Lysis $\pm$ S.E.
(B10.AxB10.D2)F_1 <u>kkkddd</u> ddddd	(B10.AxB10.D2)F_1-TNP <u>kkkddd-TNP</u> ddddd-TNP	B10.A-TNP kkkddd-TNP	36.9+3.5
"	"	B10.D2-TNP ddddd-TNP	17.9+1.5
"	B10.A-TNP kkkddd-TNP	B10.A-TNP kkkddd-TNP	40.6+4.0
"	"	B10.D2-TNP ddddd-TNP	12.4+2.7
"	B10.D2-TNP ddddd-TNP	B10.A-TNP kkkddd-TNP	13.2+3.2
"	"	B10.D2-TNP ddddd-TNP	19.6+1.9

Effector:target cell ratio = 20:1

148

TABLE IX

INTRA-H-2 MAPPING OF CYTOTOXIC RESPONSE POTENTIAL TO TNP-MODIFIED SYNGENEIC K AND D SEROLOGICAL REGION SPECIFICITIES

Mouse Strain	I Region Alleles			Modified K end Products		Modified K end Products	
	I-A	I-B	I-C	Probable serologically defined allele	Response Range	Probable serologically defined allele	Response Range
C57BL/10 (bbbbb)	b	b	b	b	25-35%	b	25-35%
B10.D2 (ddddd)	d	d	d	d	15-25	d	15-25
B10.BR (kkkkkk)	k	k	k	k	25-35	k	0-10
B10.A (kkkddd)	k	k	d	k	25-35	d	0-10
B10.A(2R) (kkkddb)	k	k	b	k	25-35	b	0-10
B10.A(4R) (kkbbbb)	k	b	b	k	25-50	b	0-30

149

Since: (a) The B10.A(4R) expresses b alleles in I-B and I-C
and is one of the strains with weaker reactivity against modified D-end products, and (b) other strains expressing b
alleles throughout the I region respond equally well to TNP-
modified products of both ends, the results suggest that the
Ir gene(s) controlling responsiveness to TNP-modified H-2D^b
(and possibly to modified H-2D^d) products map to the left of
I-B. It remains to be established whether the gene(s) maps
in or to the left of I-A.

CONCLUSIONS AND SPECULATIONS

The in vitro chemically modified autologous CML model
is unique in that it provides one of the first examples of
histocompatibility linked regulation of cell-mediated immunity at two distinct functional levels. One level is the
formation of new self-antigens by modification of cell surface products of genes mapping in or near the serologically
defined regions. The other level of function is expressed in
responding lymphocytes, is defined by immune response potential to the modified autologous specificities, and is controlled by Ir genes mapping in or near the I-A subregion. In
order for a cell-mediated immune response of this type to
occur within a given individual, a new antigenic specificity
must be formed and the proper immune response genes must be
expressed. Comparison of responsiveness in various C57BL/10
congenic and B10.A recombinant mouse strains suggests a pattern of response potential such that lymphocytes from animals
expressing k alleles in the K, I-A, and I-B regions respond
poorly to TNP- and N-modified products of the k, d, and b
haplotypes of H-2D. In contrast, mice expressing b or d
alleles at K, I-A and I-B responded equally well to TNP-modified products of both serological regions. For a given modifying agent there may be patterns of immune responsiveness
which might suggest control by a single Ir gene (or at most
an Ir gene set), despite the fact that the cytotoxic specificities are different (i.e., TNP-modified k, d, and b haplotypes of H-2D). Since synergy has been demonstrated between
subpopulations of cells generating CML to TNP-modified autologous components (24), such a lack of responsiveness to different haplotypes of TNP-modified H-2D products might be
accounted for not by the absence of multiple specific clones
of cytotoxic precursors, but by an Ir gene defect in the interaction with a collaborating cell. The specificity of this
latter cell might be directed against a common antigen expressed by these different TNP-modified H-2D products. The
lack of immune response potential to a specific immunogen

could be either a defect in a collaborating cell or a defect in the specific clone of CML precursors. An analogous system to this may be the example of $\underline{Ir}$ gene control of antibody production to the Ala--Lys (A--L) series of multichain synthetic polypeptides. It was found that $\underline{H-2^k}$ mice are low responders to (T,G)-A--L but high responders to (H,G)-A--L and (Phe,G)-A--L, whereas $\underline{H-2^s}$ mice are non-responders to all three of these immunogens (25). In $\underline{H-2^k}$ mice the $\underline{Ir}$ gene defect has been shown to be expressed in the B-cell population (25). More recently, it has been found that the B cells of these mice lack the acceptor site for antigen-specific T-cell mediators, which are produced in that strain (26). In contrast, the defect associated with $\underline{H-2^s}$ was expressed both in the B-cell population and in the production of antigen-specific T-cell helper product (27,26). These two types of defects have been shown to be controlled by independent genes located in the MHC as demonstrated by complementation in F_1 hybrid mice between $\underline{H-2^k}$ mice, which express only the B-cell defect, and $\underline{H-2^f}$ mice which have functional B-cells, but are deficient in the production of antigen-specific T-cell factor (26).

The TNP- and N-modifying agents have been demonstrated not to be crossreactive at the sensitization and lytic phases (4, and Table V). Furthermore, in certain examples the patterns of responsiveness suggest them to be independently controlled at the $\underline{Ir}$ level. For example, in the N-modification model, C57BL/10 lymphocytes respond preferentially to modified K-end products, whereas in the TNP-modification system, lymphocytes from the same mice respond equally well to modified K-end and D-end products (4). From this it would appear that patterns of responsiveness toward modified self components are dependent upon the modifying agent. Further evidence supporting this comes from comparisons of the viral-induced modifications resulting from lymphocytic choriomeningitis and ectromelia infection, in which mice expressing $(\underline{K}, \underline{I-A}, \underline{I-B})^k$ respond well to $\underline{H-2D}$ region modified products (6,7).

A function for products of the serologically defined (and possibly lymphocyte defined) MHC regions could be to serve as efficient sites for modification by infectious agents (14). Depending on: (a) the modifying agent; (b) the serologically defined MHC haplotype; and (c) the $\underline{Ir}$ genes, an immune reaction will or will not be elicited against the modified autologous cell in an individual. Such a reaction can be detrimental to the organisms (e.g., lymphocytic choriomeningitis, ref. 2), whereas it may be beneficial in eliminating viral-infected cells and neoplastic cells expressing tumor-associated antigens, possibly related to serologically defined alloantigens (28,12). MHC polymorphism may have evolved to provide a large number of permutations and combinations of antigenic modifying sites and immune response genes within a population in order to insure that some individuals will possess the immunological machinery necessary to cope with the appearance of new types of infectious agents.

ACKNOWLEDGMENTS

The authors are grateful to Carol Garbarino for technical assistance and to Marilyn Schoenfelder for preparation of the manuscript.

REFERENCES

(1) G.M. Shearer. Eur. J. Immunol. 4 (1974) 527.

(2) G.M. Shearer, T.G. Rehn and C.A. Garbarino. J. Exp. Med. 141 (1975) 1348.

(3) J. Forman. J. Exp. Med. 142 (1975) 403.

(4) T.G. Rehn, G.M. Shearer, H.S. Koren and J.K. Inman. J. Exp. Med. In press.

(5) R.M. Zinkernagel and P.C. Doherty. Nature (Lond.) 248 (1974) 701.

(6) R.M. Zinkernagel and P.C. Doherty. J. Exp. Med. 141 (1975) 1427.

(7) I.D. Gardner, N.A. Bowern and R.V. Blanden. Eur. J. Immunol. 5 (1975) 122.

(8) U. Koszinowski and R. Thomssen. Eur. J. Immunol. 5 (1975) 245.

(9) R.D. Gordon, E. Simpson and L.E. Samuelson. J. Exp. Med. 142 (1975) In press.

(10) R.D. Gordon and E. Simpson, in: Proceedings of the
      Tenth Leukocyte Culture Conference. eds. V.P.
      Eijsvoogel, Dr. Roos and W.P. Zeylemaker (Academic
      Press, New York, in press).

(11) M.J. Bevan. Nature (Lond.) 256 (1975) 419.

(12) R.N. Germain, M.E. Dorf and B. Benacerraf. J. Exp.
      Med. 142 (1975) 1023.

(13) A. Schmitt-Verhulst and G.M. Shearer. J. Exp. Med.
      142 (1975) 914.

(14) G.M. Shearer, in: Immune Recognition. ed. A.
      Rosenthal (Academic Press, New York, 1975) p. 21.

(15) H.S. Koren, J.R. Wunderlich and J.K. Inman. Transpl.
      Proc. VII, Sup 1 (1975) 169.

(16) H.S. Koren, J.R. Wunderlich and J.K. Inman. J.
      Immunol. In press.

(17) R.M. Zinkernagel and P.C. Doherty. Nature (Lond.)
      251 (1974) 547.

(18) B. Benacerraf and D.H. Katz. Adv. Cancer Res. 21
      (1975) 121.

(19) A.M. Schmitt-Verhulst, D.H. Sachs and G.M. Shearer.
      J. Exp. Med. In press.

(20) M. Nabholz, J. Vives, H.M. Young, T. Meo, V. Miggiano,
      A. Rijnbeek and D.C. Shreffler. Eur. J. Immunol. 4
      (1974) 378.

(21) D.H. Sachs and J.L. Cone. J. Exp. Med. 139 (1973)
      1289.

(22) S.E. Cullen, B.D. Schwartz, S.G. Nathenson and M.
      Cherry. Proc. Natl. Acad. Sci. 69 (1972) 1399.

(23) C. Neauport-Sautes, F. Lilly, D. Silvestre and F.
      Kourilsky. J. Exp. Med. 139 (1973) 511.

(24) R.J. Hodes, K.S. Hathcock and G.M. Shearer. J.
      Immunol. 115 (1975) 1122.

(25)   E. Mozes and G.M. Shearer, in: Current Topics in
       Microbiology and Immunology 59 (1972) 167.

(26)   A.J. Munro and M.J. Taussig. Nature (Lond.) 256
       (1975) 103.

(27)   L. Lichtenberg, E. Mozes, G.M. Shearer and M. Sela.
       Eur. J. Immunol. 4 (1974) 430

(28)   G. Invernizzi and G. Parmiani. Nature (Lond.) 254
       (1975) 713.

DISCUSSION FOLLOWING GENE SHEARER

McDEVITT: Can you keep the I region constant (for example, the I^k region) and vary the K and D regions and show a difference in response to different K-TNP and D-TNP products?

SHEARER: If we keep the I-A region constant (K allele) and vary the D region (i.e. D^d, D^b, D^b), the responding lymphocytes still express the defect(s).

McDEVITT: Do you know whether Ia antigens are substituted with TNP by your method?

SHEARER: We suspect that they may be and are currently working on this problem.

BENACERRAF: We have used Shearer systems in our laboratory with identical results particularly with respect to the inhibitory activity of allo-antisera directed against the SD specificities of the conjugated targets. These experiments have been carried out by Steve Burakoff and Ronald Germain. They have also demonstrated the blocking activity of anti-hapten antibodies on both congenic and allogeneic conjugated targets. Our only additional observation is our demonstration that the smaller reactivity observed on allogeneic TNP targets can be nevertheless inhibited also by alloantibodies directed against H-2 specificities. We conclude, therefore, that in all cases the cytotoxic T cells generated by syngeneic TNP cells are directed to modified products of the H-2 complex; the cross-reactivity observed on allogeneic TNP cells depends upon the cross-reactivity between the related syngeneic and allogeneic H-2.

SHEARER: I think our results are in agreement.

HÄMMERLING: Does one obtain a proliferative MLC response using lymphocytes and TNP-modified syngeneic stimulators?

SHEARER: The MLC response to TNP-modified autologous spleen cells is very weak (two-to-four-fold stimulation, only), despite the fact that the cytotoxic activity is appreciable.

HÄMMERLING: Recently, Koszinowsky and Ertl (Nature, 257: 596, 1975) demonstrated that vaccinia-infected cells bind less anti-*H-2* antibody than normal cells which was interpreted in a way that viruses had modified *H-2* antigens. I don't consider this conclusion evidence for chemical modification and I wonder if there are solid biochemical data on this point, such as chemical extraction, co-capping experiments with anti-TNP and anti-*H-2*, etc?

SHEARER: Not from our laboratory.

[*EDITOR'S NOTE*: Evidence was presented later in the conference by Bruce Cunningham that recent data of J. Schrader and G. Edelman indicated co-capping of *H-2* and virus in tumor cells with anti-*H-2* sera. However, this cannot be considered conclusive until studies are performed to rule out the possible existence of anti-viral antibodies in the anti-*H-2* sera employed in such studies - DHK.]

ZINKERNAGEL: LCM-infected target cells do not show obvious diminution of susceptibility to killing by anti-allo-antigen-reactive T cells. LCM virus does not have a cytopathic effect and does not alter greatly host protein synthesis. The findings in the pox virus system first reported by Gardner *et al* (Eur. J. Immunol. 5: 122, 1975) are most probably due to the fact that pox viruses shut off host cell protein synthesis; therefore *H-2D* and *D* structures having a short half-life will increase on infected targets.

PAUL: Gene, could you expand on the specificity problems implicit in the priming with TNP-allogeneic cells to which you referred in the course of your lecture.

SHEARER: Effector cells generated by allogeneic sensitization will lyse any target cell if it is TNP-modified. This occurs even when the allogeneic stimulating cells are not modified by TNBS. This is not the case, however, when responding lymphocytes are stimulated with TNP-modified autologous sensitizing cells assayed on TNP-modified spleen target cells.

WILSON: The chairman, Morten Simonsen, knows his history better than I do, but is it possible that Shearer's and the Zinkernagel/Doherty experiments provide an explanation for the phenomenon described sometime ago by Brondz? He showed that targets were killable only if they shared a very large portion of the "immunizing" complex of surface determinants.

SIMONSEN: I believe the Brondz data were eventually accounted for by shared private specificities between stimulator and target cells.

VITETTA: I would like to mention several experiments that Drs. James Forman, Jan Klein and I have done in the attempt to determine whether $H-2$ antigens are haptenated on TNP-modified cells. In these experiments we radio-iodinated splenocytes, haptenated them and lysed the treated cells with $NP40$. When lysates were treated with anti-TNP antibody, we found that the majority of the surface proteins could be precipitated. Subsequent precipitation of the supernatant with anti-$H-2$ antibody failed to demonstrate any remaining $H-2$ molecules, indicating that they had been precipitated by the anti-TNP antibody.

NOSSAL: Conceptually, there is a big difference between the haptenation experiments and the virus-modification experiments. In the former case, a highly reactive hapten actually couples to a protein, clearly creating a new, compound antigenic structure. In the latter case, one is dealing with two separate complex antigenic mosaics; the viral antigens and the SD antigens, with no evidence having been presented for an actual physical association between the two. In other words, the altered self hypothesis is much easier to grasp in the hapten case than in the viral case.

THE ROLE OF Ia ANTIGENS IN MLC STIMULATION

DAVID H. SACHS, RONALD H. SCHWARTZ
AND C. GARRISON FATHMAN

Transplantation Biology Section
Immunology Branch
National Cancer Institute
and
Laboratory of Immunology
National Institute of Allergy and Infectious Diseases

Abstract: A (B10.AxA)F_1 anti-B10 antiserum with a demonstrably high cytotoxic titer of anti-Ia.8 antibody (tested on B10.D2 lymphoid cells) has been found to specifically inhibit stimulation of B10.A responder cells by B10.D2 stimulators. The suppressed level of stimulation was comparable to that of (B10xB10.A)F_1 responders to B10.D2, in which case there is a genetic block of the Ia antigen shared between B10 and B10.D2. This same antiserum had no effect on B10.D2 responder cells in the reverse MLC reaction. In addition, it blocked (B10.AxB10.D2)F_1 stimulator cells from stimulating B10.A responders, but not B10.D2 responders, indicating that binding of antibodies to the nonrelevant parental antigens on the F_1 cells did not interfere with stimulation by antigens of the other parental strain. These results are all consistent with the hypothesis that Ia alloantigens are responsible for stimulation of Ir region associated MLC reactions.

INTRODUCTION

Previous studies from this laboratory have suggested, on a genetic basis, that Ia antigens may play a major role in stimulation of the MLC reaction (1,2). An Ia antigen could be detected on B10.A(2R) lymphoid cells, but no corresponding Ia antigen could be demonstrated on B10.A(4R) cells (1). This result was precisely parallel to the "one-way" MLC reactions previously reported between these two recombinant

strains (3, 4). In addition, B10.A cells were shown to respond significantly better to B10.D2 stimulator cells than
did (B10xB10.A)F$_1$ responder cells, and this difference was
attributed to a genetic block of the Ia antigens shared between B10 and B10.D2 (2).

Both of these genetic arguments leave open the possibility that the Ia antigens and the cell surface antigens stimulating the MLC reaction are encoded by closely linked but not
identical genes. If, however, it could be shown that antibodies to the Ia antigens could specifically block stimulation of an MLC reaction, such results would indicate that
both products must be closely associated at the cell surface
as well as at the genetic level, making identity of the determinants more likely. We report here the results of such
blocking studies for the same Ia antigen(s) as we have previously studied genetically. A comprehensive description of
these studies will be published elsewhere (5).

MATERIALS AND METHODS

Animals were either purchased from Jackson Laboratory,
Bar Harbor, Maine, or were produced in our own colony using
parental stock obtained from Jackson. Male mice, 2-5 months
of age, were used for all experiments. MLC reactions were
performed in modified EHAA medium (6,7) with the addition of
fresh mouse serum or mouse serum stored at -80° in the presence of 2-mercaptoethanol. One-way MLC reactions employed
stimulator cells treated with 2000R using a ^{137}Cs source.
Cultures were carried out for 4 or 5 days before harvesting.

Antisera were produced by immunization as previously
described (8) and the sera of individual animals were titered
1 week after each boost. Only sera with a high anti-Ia.8
titer were pooled.

Details of these methods will be published elsewhere
(5).

RESULTS

Initial attempts to perform MLC blocking studies with
available anti-Ia antisera met with limited success, giving
erratic results. Three major problems had to be overcome in
order to obtain consistent results.

First, the levels of stimulation by strain combinations in which I-region MLCs could be examined were very low by conventional techniques (2,3). In order to quantitate levels of inhibition of the MLC reaction, much larger levels of stimulation were desirable. In addition, the need for a medium which could accommodate mouse serum made the EHAA medium (6,7) an attractive choice. Table I shows a comparison of the stimulations obtained in the genetic block experiment (2) using RPMI plus fetal calf serum as the medium and using the new EHAA medium supplemented with fresh normal mouse serum.

TABLE I

IMPROVEMENT OF MLC RESPONSES BY CHANGE OF
CULTURE CONDITIONS

Responder	Stimulator*	CPM ± S.E. RPMI + FCS	CPM ± S.E. EHAA + NMS
B10.A	B10.A$_x$	820 ± 70	920 ± 200
B10.A	B10.D2$_x$	2500 ± 300	19400 ± 2000
(B10xB10.A)F$_1$	(B10xB10.A)F$_{1x}$	1400 ± 200	520 ± 50
(B10xB10.A)F$_1$	B10.D2$_x$	2100 ± 350	7800 ± 1800

*Stimulator cells irradiated with 2000R

As can be seen from this table, the background levels of thymidine incorporation are not very different in the two media. However, the levels of stimulation in the two allogeneic mixtures are 5- to 10-fold higher with the EHAA medium. The decrease in stimulation seen for the (B10xB10.A)F$_1$ responder relative to the B10.A responder is readily apparent in both culture conditions.

The second problem was the low titer of anti-Ia.8 antibodies in the original B10.A anti-B10 antisera (8), which had anti-Ia titers of only 1:8 to 1:16. The concentrations of these sera required to obtain blocking were so high that often the normal serum controls also produced significant blocking. To overcome this problem, we produced anti-Ia.8 antisera in a variety of hybrid hosts with B10.A as one of the parentals and with a noncongenic strain not bearing Ia.8 as the other parental. This approach makes use of the additional immune response capabilities of the noncongenic strain in the production of anti-Ia antibodies. The (B10.AxA/J)F$_1$ hybrid proved to be an excellent antibody producer for this purpose. The anti-Ia.8 titers in (B10.AxA/J)F$_1$ anti-B10 antisera ranged between 1:64 and 1:512. Like the B10.A anti-B10 antisera, these hybrid antisera did not show any detectable cytotoxic reactivity with the K or D region antigens of B10.D2.

The third problem was the requirement for a control which could indicate nonspecific toxicity of the mouse serum added to MLC cultures. Since sera produced in (B10.AxA/J)F_1 hybrids do not react with either the B10.A or the A/J parental strains, an M-locus response between these two strains was used to assess toxicity of all sera used in these studies. Only paired immune and normal F_1 sera showing no difference in effect on this M-locus MLC were used in these experiments.

Serologic assays of the (B10.AxA/J)F_1 anti-B10 antisera used in this study showed that they contained multiple anti-Ia specificities as well as anti-$H-2K$ and anti-$H-2D$ region specificities when tested on B10. However, when tested on B10.D2 only anti-Ia.8 reactivity was detected. This is consistent with present knowledge of the public H-2 specificities (9), and indicates that if $H-2K$ region antigens are shared between $H-2^b$ and $H-2^d$, they are not detectable by sera raised in either the B10.A or the (B10.AxA/J)F_1 strains.

Under a variety of conditions including a range of antiserum concentrations and ratios of numbers of responder and stimulator cells, the (B10.AxA)F_1 anti-B10 antiserum inhibited the response of B10.A responders to both B10 and B10.D2 stimulator cells. Table II shows representative data from these blocking experiments.

TABLE II

ASSESSMENT OF THE CELLS AFFECTED BY AN ANTI-Ia ANTISERUM
IN MLC REACTIONS

| | | MLC (CPM ± S.E.) in Presence of | |
| | | 1% Normal (B10.AxA) | 1% (B10.AxA) Anti-B10 Anti- |
Responder (4×10^5)	Stimulator (2×10^5)	Serum	serum
B10.A	B10.A$_x$	260 ± 10	930 ± 60
B10.A	B10.D2$_x$	23400 ± 3500	7400 ± 1200
B10.A	B10$_x$	48300 ± 6600	6100 ± 1300
B10.D2	B10.D2$_x$	600 ± 90	600 ± 30
B10.D2	B10.A$_x$	34800 ± 8700	34200 ± 5200
B10.D2	B10$_x$	130600 ± 15100	15400 ± 1800

Also shown in Table II is an MLC using this same F_1 antiserum to assess the effect of anti-Ia.8 antibodies on the responder cell. As seen in the 4th line of Table II, the antiserum had no significant effect on the response of B10.D2 to B10.A stimulators. In the same experiment (line 5) the antiserum had a marked effect on the response of B10.D2 responders if the stimulator cell was $B10_x$ instead of $B10.A_x$, again indicating an effect on the stimulator and not the responder cell.

However, while all of the high titered anti-Ia.8 antisera which we have assessed were found to inhibit stimulator function, there were a few (unlike that shown in Table II) which also produced inhibition of the responder cell. This inhibition was only partial and was erratic, and we have not yet determined whether it can be attributed to the same or to different antibodies in these sera.

Finally, when inhibition was assessed using this same antiserum on a (B10.AxB10.D2)F_1 stimulator in which the serum could react with the Ia antigens of only one parental strain, a significant inhibition was obtained for B10.A responders, but not for B10.D2 responders.

DISCUSSION

These results indicate that anti-Ia antibodies directed toward an Ia antigen shared between B10 and B10.D2 are sufficient to cause significant inhibition of stimulation of the MLC reaction. The block obtained was not complete, but the extent of inhibition was comparable to the decrease obtained by genetic removal of this shared Ia specificity in the (B10xB10.A)F_1 responder. The comparability of genetic and antibody-mediated inhibition is illustrated in Fig. 1.

The inhibition of stimulator cells but not of responder cells by anti-Ia antibodies is in agreement with the results of Meo, et al. (10), who used A.TH anti-A.TL antibodies to inhibit a variety of MLC responses. However, these authors reported that blocking was only effective if the sera were directed against the entire I region, rather than against individual subregions or shared Ia antigens. It is not clear from their report, however, whether the antisera they were using had comparable titers against each of the component Ia specificities. Since we have found a high anti-Ia titer to be of crucial importance in obtaining significant inhibition,

this difference may explain their failure to block with antisera to shared Ia determinants.

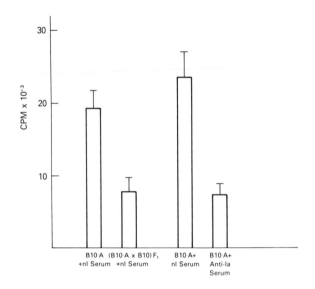

Figure 1. Comparison of Genetic and
Antibody-Mediated MLC Inhibition: Responses
were of B10.A or (B10.AxB10)F₁ responders to
B10.D2 stimulators under incubation conditions
indicated below each bar.

In summary, these studies indicate that the serologically detected Ia antigens and the cell surface antigens
which stimulate an *I*-region associated MLC reaction are
either identical or are both closely associated on the cell
surface and are determined by closely linked genes.

REFERENCES

(1) E.C. Lozner, D.H. Sachs, G.M. Shearer and W.D. Terry.
Science 183 (1974) 757.

(2) C.G. Fathman, B.S. Handwerger and D.H. Sachs. J. Exp.
Med. 140 (1974) 853.

(3) M.L. Bach, M.B. Widmer, F.H. Bach and J. Klein.
Transplant. Proc. 5 (1973) 369.

(4) T. Meo, J. Vives, V. Miggiano and D. Shreffler. Transplant. Proc. 5 (1973) 377.

(5) R.H. Schwartz, C.G. Fathman and D.H. Sachs. Submitted for publication.

(6) E. Heber-Katz, A.B. Peck and R.E. Click. Eur. J. Immunol. 3 (1973) 379.

(7) A.B. Peck and F.H. Bach. J. Immunol. Methods 3 (1973) 147.

(8) D.H. Sachs and J.L. Cone. J. Exp. Med. 138 (1973) 1289.

(9) D.C. Shreffler and C.S. David. Adv. Immunol. 20 (1975) 125.

(10) T. Meo, C.S. David, A.M. Rijnbeek, M. Nabholz, V.C. Miggiano and D.C. Shreffler. Transplant. Proc. 7 (1975) 127.

H-2 ASSOCIATED MLR DETERMINANTS:
IMMUNOGENETICS OF THE LOCI AND THEIR PRODUCTS

TOMMASO MEO, CHELLA S. DAVID AND DONALD C. SHREFFLER

Department of Genetics
Washington University School of Medicine

MAPPING OF MLR GENES

An extensive analysis of the available intra-H-2 recombinants led us to hypothesize that the loci controlling
stimulation in the mixed leucocyte culture reaction (MLR)
are discretely distributed within the H-2 complex. The
observation that incompatibility for the I-B, the I-C, the
S or the G regions caused stimulation only in some combinations, supported the tentative generalization that the
relevant loci are organized in a bipartite fashion respectively to the left of the I-B and to the right of the S
regions (1). New combinations tested include the recombinant haplotypes t4, ap2, ap3, ap4, ap5 and an1. The most
relevant results were obtained with the strain A.TFR5 (ap5),
which consistently gave moderate stimulation with responder
strains A.TFR2, A.TFR3, and A.TFR4, carrying the haplotypes
ap2, ap3 and ap4. The latter three strains arose from independent crossover events (2), but are indistinguishable
from one another, serologically as well as in MLR. The
incompatibility of strain A.TFR5 with these strains is
restricted to the S and G regions. The products of these
loci have not yet been unequivocally demonstrated on lymphocytes, and do not determine MLR stimulation in other combinations (for instance A with A.AL or B10.HTT with B10.S(9R)).
To account for this MLR incompatibility, one is led to
postulate a new locus between the I-C and S regions or to
assume an allelic difference at the locus already postulated
to the right of the S region (1,3). The above postulation
implies that different allelic combinations are functionally equivalent in MLR competence.

MLR ASSAY IN RECOMBINANT SCREENING

Recently we have set up an integrated screening system for the detection of H-2 recombinants or mutants, typing the progeny of a number of backcross matings simultaneously by serology, MLR and skin grafting. This screening system should detect in an unbiased manner any new genotype arising in a selected small group of H-2 haplotypes. A partial summary of these results is given in Table 1. Only five animals out of 823 segregants displayed incompatibility with both haplotypes of the heterozygous parent in bidirectional splenocyte MLR. Three of these animals were simultaneously serotyped as intra-H-2 crossovers, while serotyping for the other two was inconclusive, but indicated that the animals were variants of some type. It is noteworthy that MLR stimulation was observed in every instance in which a cross-over was detected by serotyping that should have resulted in a K end MLR incompatibility. Conversely, three serologically detected crossovers involving the D end went undetected in MLR, probably due to the known weaker stimulus of the D end gene products in MLR. Progeny tests and more complete analyses of these new recombinants is underway.

Table 1. Preliminary summary of a study to detect H-2 recombinants or mutants by simultaneous MLR and serotyping.

Type of Backcross	Number of Progeny Typed in MLR	Animals MLR Incompatible with both Parental Haplotypes	Intra-H-2 Recombinants Detected by Simultaneous Serotyping	MLR/Serotyping Disagreement	
				K-end	D-end
(B10.K x B10.D2)F$_1$ x B10	116	0	1	0	1
(B10 x B10.A)F$_1$ x B10.S	217	0	0	0	0
(B10.A x B10.S)F$_1$ x B10	366	3	5	0	2
(B10.T x B10.A)F$_1$ x B10.S	124	2	2[*]	[*]Serotyping incomplete	

The average length of heterozygous chromosome segment expected to segregate in each of the above backcrosses is 9 cM on each side of H-2.

The fact that we did not find MLR incompatibility among progeny that were not also typed serologically as variants in this study, strongly supports the current notion that the genetic organization of the H-2 complex differs from that of other species, notably man. The animals tested in this screening program were all progeny of crosses involving H-2-congenic strains. The average length of heterozygous chromosome segment expected to segregate in these matings is approximately 9 cM on each side of H-2, as estimated according to Bartlett and Haldane's formula (4). This estimate is based on the number of backcrosses performed to produce the congenic strains used as parents in this study (ISM No. 7, Companion Issue to Mouse News Letter No. 45). It is particularly interesting that in the mating (B10.T x B10.A)F₁ x B10.S the parental strains of the F₁ hybrid parent are congenic for different loci, the T complex for B10.T, the H-2 complex for B10.A. The estimated average length of the heterozygous chromosome segments on each side of the two loci involved are 4 and 9 cM, respectively. Therefore the expected length of heterozygous chromosome approaches the estimated distance between the T and H-2 complexes and extends on either side, covering about 35 cM of the centromeric half of the 17th chromosome. Eleven crossovers between the T and H-2 complexes were recovered from this mating. All displayed MLR stimulation only with the parental haplotype incompatible at the H-2 complex, indicating that there are no genetic differences at the T complex or elsewhere in the heterozygote chromosome segment that cause a significant MLR (Table 2).

MLR with 11 T/H-2 Recombinants in the Backcross $\frac{T\ H\text{-}2^b}{+\ H\text{-}2^a} \times \frac{+\ H\text{-}2^s}{+\ H\text{-}2^s}$

Typing Cells	Recombinant Type T/H-2ᵃ				Recombinant Type +/H-2ᵇ						
T H-2ᵇ	4.0	2.5									
+ H-2ᵃ	0.7	0.7	1.1	1.1	3.3	2.5	3.9	3.8	2.7	5.2	2.4
+ H-2ᵇ			2.7	2.6	1.0	1.0	0.8	1.1	1.1	1.0	0.9

Table 2. Typing animals were heterozygous with + H-2ˢ haplotype. Figures represent stimulation indices (S.I.) of bidirectional cultures with splenocytes of each recombinant with typing cells of both parental types. Control cultures contained 0.5 x 10⁶ cells and experimental cultures 0.25 x 10⁶ cells of each partner. All cultures were done in triplicates.

S.I. = average c.p.m. in experimental divided by half
the sum of average c.p.m. in the controls.

Thus, we believe that this study strengthens the contention that no MLR locus maps outside the H-2 complex.
The possibility cannot be ruled out that either such a locus
does exist with a considerably lower degree of polymorphism,
or that it is outside but causes very little stimulation and
is tightly linked to the H-2 complex. The maximum estimated
recombination frequency between such a locus and H-2K or
H-2D would be $\lesssim 3.6 \times 10^{-3}$; $p = 0.05$. These results are in
contrast to data on the human MHC, where the strongest MLR
determinants are located on the external centromeric side of
the LA-Four segment, at a map distance of approximately 1 cM.

THE INHIBITION OF MLR WITH ANTI-Ia SERA

The nature of the MLR gene products has been as enig-
matic as the map positions of the controlling loci. The
discovery that genes of the H-2I region code for immunogenic
membrane components, the Ia antigens (5,6,7,8,9), dictated a
series of experiments in which anti-Ia sera were tested for
their capacity to inhibit the MLR reaction. Alloantisera
used in this study are described in Table 3. The experiment

Table 3. Description of Antisera Used

| Antiserum | Specificities | | | Titer (^{51}Cr) |
	H-2	Ia	Tla	
A.TH anti-A.TL	-	1,2,3,7,15	-	2560
A.TL anti-A.TH	-	4,5	+	2560
(A.TH x B10.D2)anti-A.TL	-	1,2,3	-	1280
(B10.D2 x A)anti-HTI	33	9,W20	-	1280

reported in Table 4 shows that anti-Ia sera used in unidirectional MLR cultures, specifically inhibit stimulator
lymphocytes, but fail to inhibit the same lymphocytes when
they are used as responders. Even when used at the highest
concentrations, where nonspecific inhibition is seen with
syngeneic lymphocytes, these antisera fail to completely
suppress the response. The same results were seen with all
reagents tested that contain cytotoxic anti-Ia activity.

Table 4. Inhibition of Unidirectional Lymph Node
MLR with Anti-Ia Sera.

Serum	Dilution	A.TH A.TH[a]	A.TH A.TL	A.TL A.TL	A.TL A.TH
	1[b]	1,572[c]	56,490	417	442
	1:2	3,544	240,052	3,214	3,434
	1:4	17,554	284,046	5,418	11,438
A.TL α A.TH	1:8	11,562	310,693	12,087	27,401
	1:16	15,057	364,149	8,795	50,843
	1:32	19,715	319,149	10,054	75,676
	1:64	18,291	366,114	9,294	105,317
	1	1,585	1,011	458	1,947
	1:2	10,432	8,119	1,528	63,626
	1:4	15,722	14,494	3,161	114,541
A.TH α A.TL	1:8	14,126	14,913	4,056	119,899
	1:16	14,360	43,938	5,416	125,142
	1:32	16,218	163,392	6,811	134,752

[a]Stimulators are underlined.
[b]Final concentration of undiluted serum 9%.
 Final volume of microcultures 110 µl containing 0.5 x 10^6 responders and 10^6 stimulators, irradiated with 3300 Rads.
[c]Mean c.p.m. of triplicate determinations.

A sucrose gradient fractionation of an anti-Ia serum [(A.TH x B10.D2) anti-A.TL] was performed in an attempt to remove the nonspecific inhibitory activity of the serum from the fraction containing the antibodies. The results, shown in Table 5, demonstrate that the specific inhibition cosediments with the 7S Ig peak containing the cytotoxic antibodies, whereas the nonspecific inhibition is found in the less dense fractions.

Experiments were performed to check whether the inhibitory effect of anti-Ia on the stimulating but not on the responder lymphocytes was due to the fact that the stimulatory cells are irradiated in the unidirectional MLR test. The experiment compared stimulating populations of irradiated and nonirradiated cells from heterozygous (A.TH x A.TL)F_1 animals, in combination with one or the other parental cell population. The results shown in Table 6 demonstrate that whether the F_1-stimulating cells are irradiated or not, the effect of the antiserum remains the same. Moreover, the results illustrate the fine specificity of the suppression in that either antiserum inhibits only when it is directed against the haplotype that is allogeneic in the parental-F_1 combinations. This finding is critical to the interpretation of MLR inhibition by anti-Ia antisera, which will be further discussed below. However, these data prove that the inhibition is not mediated by the release or production of nonspecific soluble factors, nor by the abolition

171

Table 5. Sucrose gradient fractionation of serum (A.TH × B10.D2)F$_1$ anti A.TL

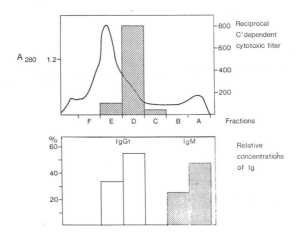

| Fraction | | Responder A.TH | | |
Pools	Stimul.	500[a]	100	20
A	A.TH	1740[b]	1578	1581
	A.TL	29.011	18.699	15.851
B	A.TH	1686	1914	1765
	A.TL	24.667	16.060	16.996
C	A.TH	2.410	1701	1875
	A.TL	20.520	17.982	13.544
D	A.TH	1.444	2085	2107
	A.TL	2.727	5.827	7.444
E	A.TH	487	1485	1.480
	A.TL	1.733	9.606	15.505
F	A.TH	499	1394	1316
	A.TL	2.923	15.136	14.090

[a]µg of added proteins per ml.

[b]Mean c.p.m. of triplicates. Mean c.p.m. in cultures without serum were respectively 1.377 and 14.578.

Inhibition of Heterozygous Stimulating Lymphocytes only by anti-Ia Sera Reacting with the Haplotype Allogeneic in the Parental-F_1 Combinations.

Bidirectional Cultures

Serum	A.TH	A.TH + (A.TH x A.TL)F_1	(A.TH x A.TL)F_1
—	1.206	65.108	2.803
A.TH α A.TL	1.406	1.104	1.913
A.TL α A.TH	994	58.898	2.624

Unidirectional Cultures

	A.TH A.TH	A.TH (A.TH x A.TL)F_1	A.TL A.TL	A.TL (A.TH x A.TL)F_1
—	1.196	168.819	3.630	75.612
A.TH α A.TL	1.047	1.205	4.140	69.314
A.TL α A.TH	982	159.716	2.914	3.115

Table 6. Figures represent average c.p.m. of triplicate determinations. X-irradiated cells are underlined. Bidirectional lymph node cultures contain 0.5×10^6 cells in the controls and 0.25×10^6 cells of each partner in the experimental cultures. Unidirectional lymph node MLR contain 0.5×10^6 responders and 10^6 stimulators. Final concentration of both antisera is 2.25%.

---

of the cooperative macrophagic activity needed for MLR.

To test whether presence of antiserum during the entire culture period is a prerequisite for the inhibition, cells to be used as stimulators were precoated with antisera. Twenty million viable lymph node cells of each stimulator strain were resuspended, before irradiation, in 500 µl of undiluted sera and incubated 1 hr at 37°C and 1/2 hr in ice bath. After two washes, the cells were counted, irradiated and distributed at 10^6/culture with 0.5×10^6 responder cells. The data (Table 7) show that precoating of the stimulators is sufficient to prevent triggering of responding cells and presence of excess antibody in the culture medium is not required for effective inhibition. The possibility that the impaired cells can reacquire the capacity to stimulate was not investigated. In the same experiment, an anti-H-2K serum did not inhibit the stimulator lymphocytes. However, it should be noted that the combinations tested in this experiment share the same H-2K allele. Thus, the results simply show that perturbation of H-2^K molecules that

173

Precoating of Different Cell Populations
used as Stimulators of strain A.TH.

Stimulating Cells	Preincubated with			
	Normal Mouse Serum	A.TH α A.TL	A.TL α A.TH	A.AL α A.TL
A.TH	4.810	4.190	3.165	4.631
A.TL	30.814	3.684	32.118	31.025
(A.TH x A.TL)F₁	32.384	4.612	33.024	29.012

Table 7. Figures represent mean c.p.m. of
triplicate determinations. Titer of A.TL α A.AL:
1/2560 by Cr^{51} release.

are irrelevant for MLR stimulation in this combination, does
not interfere with the MLR stimulatory determinants on the
cell surface. This evidence is in agreement with the notion
of independent representation of the H-2K and Ia determinants stemming from cytodynamic and cross-immunoprecipitation
studies (10,11) of lymphocyte membranes.

Antiserum A.TH α A.TL containing antibodies to Ia
specificities 1, 2, 3, 7 and 15 and capable of strongly
suppressing stimulation of A.TH by A.TL lymphocytes, was
tested for its ability to inhibit strains bearing cross-
reacting Ia determinants (Ia 1, 3, 7). A very modest effect
(9% inhibition) was observed with strain A.TFR3 lymphocytes
(bearing the specificity Ia.1) in cultures with A.TH responding cells. The effect on cultures of B10.S(9R) cells responding to B10.A(5R) lymphocytes, differing in specificities Ia.3 and 15, was even more marginal (< 1%). This
observation indicated that the bulk of inhibition on the
immunizing haplotype of strain A.TL (99%) is probably due
to the potency of the antibodies reacting with the molecules
carrying specificity Ia.2, which is determined only by the
H-2^k haplotype and its derivative recombinant genotypes.
This correlation is not surprising in view of the differential titers of the antiserum for the various specificities
that it recognizes (12).

The experiments with the pure anti-H-2 serum and the
behavior of the F_1 stimulating cells show that the antibodies reacting with H-2 or Ia antigens do not induce a
propagated, cooperative membrane perturbation, or a steric
hindrance affecting the function of MLR determinants on
neighboring molecules. (This interpretation of the F_1

results assumes no allelic exclusion in Ia expression, an
assumption supported by the observation that mixtures of
anti-Ia sera against products of different haplotypes kill
no more heterozygous target cells than the individual antisera alone (13)). Therefore it was of interest to explore
the discriminating power of the inhibiting antibodies testing them on a mutant of the haplotype used for the immunization. The results are illustrated in Table 8. The antiserum (B10.D2 x A) α HTl contains cytotoxic antibodies
reacting with H-2K^b specificity 33, as well as anti-Ia
specificities 9, 20. The relevant combinations in this
experiment are the ones involving the mutant strain B6.HZl,
which is coisogeneic with the strain B6 for a mutation
mapping in the K or I region and detectable only by MLR or
skin grafting (14,15). The antiserum strongly inhibits

Steric Hindrance or Conformational Changes
Induced by MLR Inhibiting Antibodies.

Responders	Stimulators	Control	Antiserum (B10.D2 x A)αHTl	Inhibition
B10.D2	B10.D2	1.656	989	
	B10.A(5R)	32.899	3.134	.93
	B10.A	17.939	16.225	.06
B10.A(4R)	B10.A(4R)	1.807	1.012	
	B6.HZl	47.474	13.613	.72
	B6	23.964	3.837	.87
B6.HZl	B6.HZl	1.226	1.039	
	B10.A(4R)	41.198	38.891	.05
	B6	9.006	1.226	.98
B6	B6	1.236	991	
	B10.A(4R)	54.623	51.610	.07
	B6.HZl	30.895	16.415	.48

Table 8. Unidirectional lymph node cultures of
110 µl total volume. Final concentration of antiserum
1.5%. Figures represent mean c.p.m. of triplicate
determinations. Percent inhibition = 1 - (increment
c.p.m. in presence of antiserum/increment c.p.m. in
absence) x 100.

the capacity of both strain B6 and strain HZl to stimulate strain B10.A(4R), to which both are incompatible for the K and I regions. On the other hand, the marked inhibition by the antiserum of strain HZl in stimulating B6 must be ascribed to steric hindrance or to conformational changes induced by antibodies not specific for the HZl MLR sites stimulating B6. Lack of information on the size (and even the nature) of the structure recognizing an MLR determinant makes it impossible to anticipate whether use of monomeric Fab fragments will discern the mechanisms. This observation indicates that anti-Ia serum inhibition can be usefully employed for recognizing molecules that are responsible for MLR stimulation, but that it may give equivocal answers on the relationship of serologically detected antigenic determinants to MLR-stimulating sites.

Whatever the molecular basis, specific MLR inhibitory activity has been conclusively demonstrated in a number of anti-Ia reagents in our studies. Since our initial report (16), confirmatory evidence has been obtained by Kano and Bloom (personal communication), Lonai and McDevitt (17), Schwartz and Sachs (17) and Staines (18). All these studies support the conclusion that the Ia determinants are not the MLR recognizing structures, whose nature remains unclear. On the other hand, some peculiarities of the MLR stimulatory determinants (for instance, the requirement for intact, viable and metabolically active cells, and the failure in vivo to induce positive memory) mark them as a rather unusual type of immunogen. The present data are compatible with the hypothesis that an incongruity in some specialized membrane structures coded by the MHC (Ia) may be the primary prerequisite for some cellular interactions that might subsequently mediate triggering through a secondary mechanism controlled by genes that are not necessarily polymorphic. At present it is generally accepted that the MLR-stimulating determinants are immunogenic membrane components. If this is the case, the Ia molecules are certainly the primary candidates, as implied by the previous studies (1,3) on the genetic requirements of the reaction. Barring allelic exclusion as an explanation for the haplotype-specific inhibition of F_1 stimulator cells, three possible explanations can be offered for these observations:

a) The anti-Ia sera contain additional, noncytotoxic, anti-MLR-specific antibodies, and the association of the two types of determinants is merely at level of gene linkage. The lack of molecular heterogeneity in the labeled membrane components precipitated by anti-Ia reagents (11) weighs against this.

b) The antisera contain only anti-Ia antibody. The MLR determinants are distinct molecules that are expressed in a heterozygous individual in a cis-coordinate association with the Ia molecule. This is a formally acceptable, but highly unorthodox and unlikely possibility.

c) The MLR determinants are immunogenic sites on the Ia molecules. On the whole, the current data most strongly favor this possibility.

ACKNOWLEDGMENTS

This work was supported by U.S.P.H.S. Grants GM15419 and AI11962 and Contract NCI-CB-43936-31 and by American Cancer Society Research Grant IM-74. We are grateful to Mrs. Carol Jones for her skillful assistance in preparation of the manuscript.

REFERENCES

(1) T. Meo, J. Vives, A.M. Rijnbeek, V.C. Miggiano, M. Nabholz and D.C. Shreffler. Transplant. Proceed. Vol. V, No. 4 (1973) 1399.

(2) C.S. David et al., in preparation.

(3) M.B. Widmer, A.B. Peck and F.H. Bach. Transplant. Proceed. Vol. V, No. 4 (1973) 1501.

(4) M.S. Bartlett and J.B.S. Haldane. J. Genet. 31 (1935) 327.

(5) C.S. David, D.C. Shreffler and J.A. Frelinger. Proc. Nat. Acad. Sci. U.S. 70 (1973) 2509.

(6) V. Hauptfeld, D. Klein and J. Klein. Science 181 (1973) 167.

(7) D. Gotze, R.A. Reisfeld and J. Klein. J. Exp. Med. 138 (1973) 1003.

(8) D.H. Sachs and J.L. Cone. J. Exp. Med. 138 (1973) 1289.

(9)   G.S. Hammerling, B.D. Deak, G. Mauve, U. Hammerling and H.O. McDevitt. Immunogenetics 1 (1974) 68.

(10) E.R. Unanue, M. Dorf, C.S. David and B. Benacerraf. Proc. Nat. Acad. Sci. U.S. 71 (1974) 5014.

(11) S.E. Cullen, C.S. David, D.C. Shreffler and S.G. Nathenson. Proc. Nat. Acad. Sci. U.S. 71 (1974) 811.

(12) D.C. Shreffler and C.S. David. Adv. Immunol. 20 (1975) 125.

(13) J.A. Frelinger, J.E. Niederhuber, C.S. David and D.C. Shreffler. J. Exp. Med. 140 (1974) 1273.

(14) D.W. Bailey, G.D. Snell, M. Cherry: Proc. Symp. Immunogenetics of the H-2 System, Liblice, Prague 1970, 155.

(15) M.B. Widmer, B.J. Alter, F.H. Bach and M.L. Bach. Nature (New Biol.) 242 (1973) 239.

(16) T. Meo, C.S. David, M. Nabholz, V. Miggiano and D.C. Shreffler. Transplant. Proc. 5 (1973) 1507.

(17) Meeting Report of a Workshop on Ia Antigens. National Institutes of Health. Nov. 1974. Immunogenetics 2 (1975) 301-312.

(18) N.A. Staines. Behring Inst. Mitt. 57 (1975) 122.

RESPONSES OF ALLOANTIGEN REACTIVE LYMPHOCYTES TO CONVENTIONAL ANTIGENS

D.B. Wilson, E. Heber-Katz, R.T. Woodland, and J.C. Howard

Immunobiology Research Unit, Department of Pathology, University of Pennsylvania School of Medicine, Philadelphia, Pa.

Numerous studies over the past several years have been interpreted to indicate an unusually high frequency of T cells in the recirculating lymphocyte pool responsive to strong alloantigens of the major histocompatibility complex (MHC) (1, 2, 3). Such a high frequency provides a possible basis for the disproportionate intensity of alloaggressive reactions directed at major alloantigens in the species in comparison to the much weaker responses to minor transplantation antigens, a comparison easily ween with mixed lymphocyte interactions (MLI) and with graft-versus-host (GVH) reactions. These frequency estimates of MHC reactive cells have recently received a direct and gratifying confirmation from the recent elegant studies of Binz and Wigzell (4) demonstrating the presence among rat peripheral lymphocyte populations of large numbers of T cells bearing receptors similar in idiotype to immunoglobulins of the same specificity directed to a chosen MHC haplotype. In addition, antisera prepared in F_1 animals against these parental strain receptors could be used for the selective depletion or enrichment of functional T cell responses to specified MHC alloantigens on affinity columns (5).

Anti-idiotypic antisera showing specificity for antigen reactive T cells will undoubtedly provide an important means for probing several fundamental and obvious questions of current immunology: (i) isolation and characterization of the T cell receptor, and (ii) the possibility of selectively modulating immune responsiveness for specific antigens without the use of antigen itself. However, an additional and equally fundamental problem raised by the high frequency of allo-antigen reactive cells also remains.

Considering the number of different MHC haplotypes that has already been identified in mice and rats, given the large proportion of T cells reactive to each of these various haplo-types, and in view of the evidence from positive and negative selection experiments for clonal distribution of T cell responses to different haplotypes (5, 6, 7, 8), it would appear that all or nearly all of the T cells comprising the recirculating lymphocyte pool possess specificity for one or another of the strong alloantigens of the species. This raises questions of the identity of the cell and the nature of the

receptor responsible for T lymphocyte mediated immune responses
to the universe of non-H antigens.

If T cells can be shown to possess specificity for alloantigens as well as for conformationally dissimilar determinants of conventional antigens, then if follows that these two
reactivities must involve either the same or different domains
of the same receptor or else two distinct receptor molecules.

Our attempts at arriving at an understanding of this
problem have led us to the development of a model for positive
selection of specific MHC alloantigen reactive T cell populations based on their selective survival following stimulation
in bulk MLI cultures (6, 7). After "parking" these cells in
syngeneic T cell deprived (B) rats and subsequent recovery
from these recipients, reactivity both in analytical MLI and
GVH reactions to the selecting haplotype can be shown to be
specifically enriched 10 fold or more. Also, the level of
killer activity that can be generated from cytotoxic T lymphocyte precursors (CTLP) is substantially increased (9). It
then becomes pertinent to determine the immune potential of
T cells in such alloantigen selected lymphocyte populations
for immune reactivity to conventional antigens.

In our first approach to this question, we used a
qualitative assay for T cell help in the stimulation of SRBC
specific PFC microcultures system. In this assay, titration
of varying numbers of T cells into cultures having constant
numbers of B cells stimulated for 5 days with SRBC gives a
linear dose response curve of PFC on log-log plots. Direct
comparison of T cells from positively selected TDL populations, having 10 fold enriched GVH and MLI reactivity to a
chosen MHC haplotype, with normal unselected T cells, showed
quantitatively similar helper effects for SRBC PFC responses
by these two populations (10).

It can be concluded from this finding that T helper cells
for SRBC responses are included in the T cell population
reactive to strong histocompatibility alloantigens, and that
they do not belong to different T cell subsets. Such a
conclusion follows from our interpretation of the cellular
basis of positive selection of specific alloantigen reactive
cells in MLI cultures; namely, that enriched reactivity to a
chosen MHC haplotype depends on both the antigen stimulated
survival of the relevant lymphocyte subpopulation and the
concomitant disappearance of cells lacking specificity for
the selecting antigens (6). Thus, if SRBC reactive T cells
belonged to a different subset, they would not be favored
for survival during the selection of specific alloantigen-
reactive T cells and they would be depleted from the cultures.

In this particular experiment, we have little knowledge

of the possibility of extensive cross reactivity of alloantigen reactive cells with an unknown and probably large
number of different surface determinants of SRBC. Because of
this concern, we have initiated a modified version of this
experiment employing T cell proliferative responses to known
sequence amino acid polymers. Immune reactivity to these
antigens is known to be under genetic control, and consequently, the T cell response to them may be more restricted.

One possible objection to interpretation of these studies
is concerned with the "purity" achieved in the positively
selected alloantigen reactive T cell populations in terms of
the extent of contamination by irrelevant bystanders.
Several lines of evidence have been described elsewhere (6, 7,
9, 10), indicating that the extent of positive selection
achieved with this model makes it unlikely that third party
effects and the presence of responses to conventional antigens can be accounted for by bystanders. This evidence is
indirect, however, and at present we cannot formally refute
the possibility of contaminating bystanders.

Nevertheless, if bystanders are provisionally discounted,
then the results described rule out the possibility that a
minority subpopulation of T cells unreactive to alloantigens
is responsible for responses to conventional antigens. The
most direct explanation then is that T cells have more than
a single specific reactivity. Thus, a given T cell reactive
to one or another of the strong alloantigenic determinants
apparently also is capable of recognizing other determinants
of the antigenic universe due to (a) conformational
similarities with specificity for a single combining site,
(b) the association of multiple combining sites with different specificities on the receptor molecule, or (c) the
presence of different receptor molecules with different
specificities on the same T cell. This last suggestion has
been made elsewhere (11): it postulates the existence of 2
different receptor molecules, each randomly and independently
distributed in a clonal manner among T cell populations. It
can be directly predicted from such a model that T cell
responses to non-H antigens should be quantitatively normal
among T cell subpopulations positively selected to a specific
MHC haplotype, and that positive selection of T cells for a
conventional antigenic determinant, with diminished responses
to other non-H antigens, should nevertheless show normal
reactivity to strong alloantigens.

REFERENCES

1. Wilson, D.B., J. L. Blyth, and P.C. Nowell. 1968. J. Exp. Med. 129:1157.

2. Nisbet, N. W., M. Simonsen, and M. Zaleski. 1969. J. Exp. Med. 129:459.

3. Ford, W.L., S.J. Simmonds, and R.C. Atkins. 1975. J. Exp. Med. 141:681.

4. Binz, H., and H. Wigzell. 1975. J. Exp. Med. 142:1218.

5. Binz, H., and H. Wigzell. 1975. J. Exp. Med. 142:1241.

6. Howard, J. C., and D.B. Wilson. 1974. J. Exp. Med. 140:660.

7. Wilson, D.B., A. Marshak, and J.C. Howard. 1976. Immunol. In press.

8. Wilson, D.B., and P.C. Nowell. 1970. J. Exp. Med. 131:391.

9. Wilson, D.B., A. Marshak, G. Pierson, and J.C. Howard. 1976. Submitted.

10. Heber-Katz, E., and D.B. Wilson. 1976. J. Exp. Med. In press.

EVIDENCE FOR SEVERAL CLOSELY LINKED GENES INVOLVED IN GENERATION OF PROLIFERATION IN MLC.

BO DUPONT, JOHN A. HANSEN AND CAROLYN WHITSETT

Tissue Typing Laboratory

Sloan-Kettering Institute for Cancer Research

Abstract: Eight provisional groups of HLA-D specificities (MLR stimulating determinants) have been defined during the VI International Histocompatibility Workshop 1975. Each D-specificity group was defined by two or more D-locus homozygous typing cells. Population studies with the typing cells and mutual MLR between cells belonging to the same group demonstrate some differences within each D-specificity group.

In this study we present data obtained with two HLA-D homozygous typing cells representing the DW4 specificity group. Both cells were included in the workshop and were shown in population studies to belong to the DW4 group. Mutual MLR between the two cells, however, is positive. The differences in the determinants expressed by these two cells are confirmed in family-studies including parents and other family members of each typing cell donor and of families unrelated to both cell donors.

The typing cells homozygous for B12,DW4 shows very low typing responses when tested against some responders heterozygous for B12 while the BW15,DW4 homozygous typing cells shows the lowest typing responses to some BW15 heterozygous responders.

One family is presented where both parents express a DW4 determinant. The parents show different response pattern to the two typing cells. Independent segregation of the two different DW4 is observed in the family.

This data suggests that the HLA-D region may be composed of genetic subloci. The two different DW4 specificities described in this paper may express determinants on more than one locus. These determinants could, however, occur in the population in strong positive genetic linkage disequilibrium.

INTRODUCTION

Identification of the genetic determinants responsible for human lymphocytes interaction in the Mixed Lymphocyte Culture Reaction (MLR) was originally made indirectly by evaluating the results of MLR in families with recombination within the Major Histocompatibility Complex (MHC). During the last three years the direct identification of the gene products of the MLR stimulating locus (HLA-D)* has been possible by the use of HLA-D locus homozygous typing cells (1,2,3,4). Collaborative studies between 15 laboratories in the VI International Histocompatibility Workshop 1975 using 62 typing cells demonstrated that six well defined non-cross-reacting HLA-D specificity groups could be identified (DW1-DW6). In addition, two less well defined specificity groups were identified (LD107 and LD108). The combined gene frequencies for these D-specificity groups accounts for approximatly 50-70 percent of the D-specificities in the Caucasian population.

The present study was performed with two of the Workshop typing cells which belong to the DW4 specificity group. We present the results of simultaneous HLA-D typing of the parents of the two unrelated typing cell donors and the segregation of the HLA-DW4 specificities in additional unrelated families. It is the purpose of this presentation to demonstrate that two homozygous typing cells from the same DW specificity group express different but crossreacting D-specificities. These data indicate that the HLA-D locus probably is a genetic region composed of subloci.

EVIDENCE THAT TWO D-LOCUS HOMOZYGOUS TYPING CELLS BELONG TO THE SAME DW SPECIFICITY GROUP.

The two HLA-D homozygous typing cells included in this study were obtained from unrelated blood donors (Workshop Cell #3-0003,ER, HLA-A2,B12,CW3,DW4 homozygous and Workshop Cell #3-0004,JH, HLA-A2,BW15,CW3,DW4 homozygous) (5,6).

Population studies in our laboratory as well as the

---

* The terminology for HLA determinants is the one agreed on by the Nomenclature Committee 1975, "Histocompatibility Testing 1975". The A locus=LA or first locus, B=FOUR or second locus, C =AJ or third locus and D=MLR-S locus, MLC-locus or LD-1 locus

Workshop study demonstrated that these two cells had similar typing response patterns. They were defined as belonging to the DW4 specificity group. The DW4 specificity is in positive genetic linkage disequilibrium with HLA-BW15 and also with HLA-CW3(UPS).

MLC typing in family Mat (Figure 1) demonstrates a correlation in the typing responses elicited by the two DW4 homozygous typing cells. The maternal HLA haplotype A1,BW15, CW3 was inherited by four HLA identical children. Typing responses were obtained with the BW15,DW4 homozygous typing cell in all individuals possessing the A1,BW15,CW3 haplotype. The responses to the B12,DW4 homozygous typing cell,however, were consistently higher than the responses to the BW15,DW4 typing cell.

Other families and single individuals studied with these two typing cells have demonstrated that the MLR response level of individuals with B12 normally is lowest to the B12,DW4 homozygous typing cell, while the response level of BW15 heterozygous individuals is lowest to the BW15,DW4 homozygous typing cell.

EVIDENCE FOR DIFFERENCES IN D-LOCUS SPECIFICITY BETWEEN TWO TYPING CELLS OF THE DW4 SPECIFICITY GROUP.

The MLR between the two DW4 homozygous typing cells B12,DW4 and BW15,DW4 have been shown in repeated experiments to be positive with relative responses (RR) between 35 to 80 percent (5). This is shown in a time course experiment in figure 2. Typing responses in our laboratory are defined by $RR \underset{<}{=} 35\%$.

Figure 3 and Figure 4 demonstrate the RR obtained in HLA-D typing experiments in which the parents of cell donor B12,DW4 (Fig. 3) and the parents of cell donor BW15,DW4 (Fig. 4) are tested against both DW4 typing cells. In both situations, the unrelated DW4 typing cell shows a higher level of stimulation than the homozygous offspring. When the stimulating lymphocytes were from the homozygous child, the parental MLR responses were regularly very low (usually less than 10 percent). It was confirmed by including other family members in the study that the typing cell within its own family showed clear typing responses when the responder carried the appropriate HLA haplotype while the unrelated typing cell produced a stronger stimulation of these individuals.

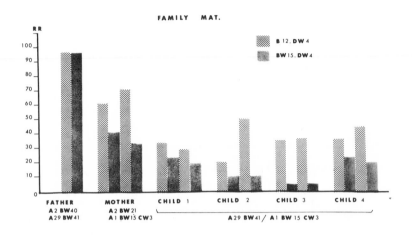

Figure 1. MLC typing of family members of
Family Mat. with the two DW4 homozygous typing
cells #3-0003, A2,B12,CW3,DW4,ER and #3-0004, A2,
BW15,CW3,DW4,JH. The father shows a normal response to both typing cells. The mother and the
four HLA identical children all demonstrate typing responses to cell 3-0004(BW15,DW4). The response levels to the other typing cell (B12,DW4)
is intermediate between normal response and typing response.

In order to demonstrate the independent segregation of
the two different DW4 specificities expressed by these two
typing cells, we searched for families where the parents both
carried an HLA haplotype with the DW4 specificity. An example of such a family (Pen.) is given in Figure 5. The HLA-
D typing experiment in this family included typing cells representing the different DW1-DW6 specificity groups and additional typing cells different from the presently defined
D-specificities.

Family Pen. consisted of the paternal grandfather
(I-1), his two HLA-identical sons (II-1 and II-2) and the
wife of II-2 (II-3). The four children of II-2 and II-3 were

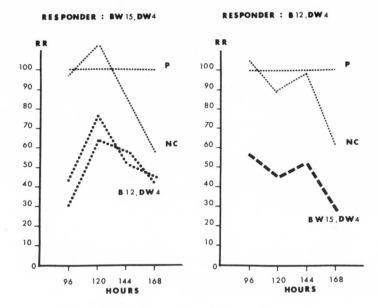

Figure 2. Mutual MLC testing between the two DW4 homozygous typing cells. The relative response (RR) is calculated as the percentage of the net cpm in stimulated cultures relative to the net reference response (=100%). The reference response is indicated in this figure by P. "P" is defined as the response in cpm by the responder cell to the stimulation of a pool of irradiated, stimulating cells of four unrelated cells. This response is defined as 100% response. NC demonstrates the response of the responder cell to a single stimulating, unrelated 2-haplotype different cell. The data are given as time-course experiments with pulse labeling (C-14-Tdr) for 24 hours between 96 hours to 168 hours of culture. The figure on the left demonstrate the responses of cell 3-0004(BW15,DW4) to stimulation from typing cell 3-0003(B12,DW4). The figure on the right demonstrate the response of cell 3-0003 (B12,DW4) to the stimulation from typing cell 3-0004(BW15,DW5). The two DW4 homozygous typing cells shows mutual positive MLR.

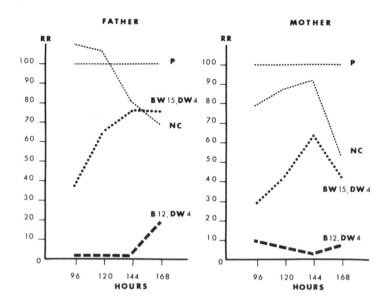

Figure 3. MLC Typing experiments of the parents of typing cell donor 3-0003(B12,DW4) with the two DW4 homozygous typing cells. The response level to the DW4 cells of the offspring is lower than the response level to the unrelated DW4 typing cell (BW15,DW4). The data are expressed as in figure 2.

also included (III-1,2,3,4).

    The HLA-D typing in this family demonstrates that the mother (II-3) gives a clear typing response (RR 2%) to the B12,DW4 cell but a high response to the BW15,DW4 cell (RR 42%). Two of the children(II-1 and 2) are HLA-identical and inherited the HLA-haplotype AW24,B12,CW5 from the mother. They both show very low typing responses to the B12,DW4 typing cell but a positive response to the BW15,DW4 typing cell. Child III-3 inherited the A2,B12,CW5 haplotype from the mother and demonstrates the same typing response pattern. The father (II-2) and his HLA-identical brother showed typing responses to both DW4 homozygous typing cells. They both carry the HLA haplotype AW24,BW15,CW3. Child III-4 inherited this haplotype from the father and the A2,B12,CW5 haplotype from the mother. This child shows typing responses to both

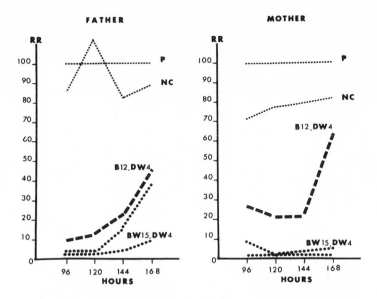

Figure 4. MLC typing of parents of typing cell 3-0004(BW15,DW4) with the two DW4 homozygous typing cells. The response level for typing responses to the DW4 typing cells of the offspring are generally at a lower level than the typing responses to the unrelated DW4 typing cell.

DW4 homozygous typing cells.

The paternal HLA-haplotype AW24,BW15,CW3 in this family is therefore assumed to carry the DW4 specificity defined by the two DW4 homozygous typing cells, while the two maternal HLA haplotypes AW24,B12,CW5 and A2,B12,CW5 each carry the DW4 specificity defined only by the B12,DW4 homozygous typing cell.

The mother in the Pen family (II-3), according to the MLC-typing experiments, is homozygous for the DW4 specificity defined by the B12,DW4 typing cell. She must, however, carry a different DW4 specificity than the one defined by the BW15, DW4 homozygous typing cell. The family MLC study confirms that the mother is homozygous for DW4: (1) the three siblings (III-1,2,3) who all have inherited the A1,BW37 haplotype from the father and a B12,DW4 determinant from the

Family Pen.

	HLA Genotypes						DW4 Typing Cells				Reference Value	
	1. Haplotype			2. Haplotype			BW15,DW4		B12,DW4			
	A	B	C	A	B	C	cpm	RR%	cpm	RR%	cpm	RR%
I-1	1	W37		11	5		11299	92	7926	68	12228	100
II-1	1	W37		W24	W15	W3	560	3	1878	12	15163	100
II-2	1	W37		W24	W15	W3	2396	16	2778	18	14715	100
II-3	W24	12	W5	2	12	W5	5043	42	259	2	11898	100
III-1	1	W37		W24	12	W5	7189	96	1354	18	7480	100
III-2	1	W37		W24	12	W5	11696	89	1059	8	13131	100
III-3	1	W37		2	12	W5	7128	56	418	3	12683	100
III-4	W24	W15	W3	2	12	W5	1557	8	493	0	11734	100

Figure 5. MLC typing in family Pen. with
the two different DW4 homozygous typing cells.
The two HLA identical brothers II-1 and 2 and
child III-4 show typing responses to both DW4 typing cells, and they all three carry the AW24,BW15,
CW3 haplotype. The mother II-3 is HLA-B12
homozygous. Typing responses to the B12,DW4 are
obtained while the responses to the BW15,DW4 homozygous cell are positive. The three children
III-1,2 and 3 all demonstrate a similar pattern
of reactions to the two typing cells.

---

mother react with only very weak responses to the paternal
lymphocytes. (2) the mutual MLR between the two HLA identical children(II-1 and 2)and child III-3 who inherited the
A2,B12,CW5,DW4 HLA-haplotype from the mother is also showing
only weak responses (RR at the 10 percent level).

Even though the mother (II-3) is homozygous for the DW4
specificity as defined by the B12,DW4 typing cell she is not
HLA-D homozygous. Her cells stimulate the cells of all four
children and the cells of her husband (II-2) and his HLA
identical brother (II-1). The stimulation level is 50 percent in RR and this is consistant with a one haplotype response.

The four HLA haplotypes segregating in the Pen. family

190

(II-2 x II-3) appear to express at least three different DW4 specificities. The differences between the DW4 specificities are clearly shown in typing experiments. When such differences, however, are tested between haploidentical responders and stimulators who differ only by these DW4 specificities, the stimulation is not significant.

CONCLUSIONS

The presently identified eight provisional HLA-D specificity groups DW1-6, LD107 and LD108 are each defined by two or more HLA-D homozygous typing cells. Each group of D-specificities, however, defines a cluster of closely related D-locus determinants. We have used two typing cells from the DW4 specificity group to analyse some shared characteristics and differences between two closely related HLA-D determinants. There are at least three possibilities to explain the differences seen within each HLA-D specificity group: (1) each provisional group of D-locus specificity represents broadly crossreacting clusters of alleles of the same locus; (2) the crossreacting D-specificities represent determinants of closely linked genes or subloci within the same genetic system and the expression of these subloci represents determinants in strong positive linkage disequilibrium in the population; or (3) the clusters represent typing cells with different HLA-D specificities for which the responder cells cannot generate a proliferative response because of restriction in immune response capacity. This last hypothesis is supported by the study of a recombinant family with recombination between the HLA-B and HLA-D locus (7).

None of these three hypothesis can at present be rejected and most likely all three mechanisms are operating. In this presentation we have studied the responses in families to two typing cells which belong to the same DW specificity group. These two homozygous cells are mutually responsive in MLR. This unusual situation has generated support for the hypothesis that at least two different loci within the HLA-D region are responsible for MLC stimulation. The mutual positive MLR between the two typing cells demonstrates that they are HLA-D different, while the population studies demonstrate that they belong to the same D-specificity group. The family studies presented demonstrate that the D-specificity defined by the two different cells can segregate with the same HLA haplotype, while in other situations they can segregate independently.

ACKNOWLEDGEMENTS

This work was supported by grants from American Cancer Society, US Public Health NCI-CA17404-01 and a grant from the Special Fund for the Advanced Study of Cancer. Ms. S. Jaramillo, Ms. S. Feuerstein and Ms. P. Onassis are gratefully acknowledged for their excellent performance of the experiments. A special thanks is extended to the J. Penniman family, the E. Kelly family and our blood donors.

REFERENCES

(1) Mempel, W., Grosse-Wilde, H., Baumann, P., Netzel, B., Steinbauer-Rosenthal, I., Scholz, S., Bertrams, J. and Albert, E.D. Transplant. Proc. 5 (1973) 1529.

(2) Dupont, B., Jersild, C., Hansen, G.S., Nielsen, L.S., Thomsen, M. and Svejgaard, A. Transplant Proc. 5 (1973) 1543.

(3) Tweel, J.G. van den, Blusse, van Oud Alblas, A., Keuning, J.J., Goulmy, E., Termijtelen, A., Bach, M.L. and Rood, J.J. van. Transplant. Proc. 5 (1973) 1535.

(4) Jörgensen, F., Lamm, L.U. and Kissmeyer-Nielsen, F. Tissue Antigens 3 (1973) 323.

(5) Hansen, J.A., Dupont, B., Rubinstein, P., Suciu-Foca, N., Fu, S.M., Mickelson, E., Whitsett, C., Jersild, C., Kunkel, H.G., Day, N.K., Good, R.A., Thomas, E.D., Rempsma, K., Allen, F.H. Jr., and Fotino, M. (in press) in "Histocompatibility Testing 1975", Munksgaard, Copenhagen.

(6) Joint Report on LD-Typing. eds. E. Thorsby and A. Piazza. In "Histocompatibility Testing 1975", Munksgaard, Copenhagen. (in press).

(7) Dupont, B., Yunis, E.J., Hansen, J.A., Reinsmoen, N., Suciu-Foca, N., Mickelson, E. and Amos, D.B. (in press) in "Histocompatibility Testing 1975". Munksgaard, Copenhagen.

SUPPRESSIVE INTERACTIONS BETWEEN DIFFERENT MLR LOCI

RICHARD K. GERSHON

Department of Pathology
Yale Medical School

Abstract: The DNA synthetic response of lymph node T cells
to foreign M loci is inhibited by the presence of
foreign H-2 loci on stimulator cells. The inhibition
can be overcome by pulsing the responding cells with
either cortisone or cycloheximide. Splenic T cells
are not inhibited. In light of present knowledge of
the H-2 locus and T cell subsets these data are interpreted as follows: $Ly-2^+, 3^+$ cells, activated by H-2D
or H-2K determinants act as the suppressors and that
the $Ly-1^+, 2^+, 3^+$ splenic T cells either prevent the
suppressive interaction or obscure it by making a strong
positive response of their own.

INTRODUCTION

The major histocompatibility complex (MHC) of mice and
men can be subdivided into several regions. The MHC of the
mouse, the H-2 system, contains at least two functionally and
structurally distinct regions (see 1). One of these has been
defined by serological means and thus is sometimes referred
to as "SD" for serologically determined. It is probably controlled by 2 single genes, H-2K and H-2D, whose products are
cell membrane proteins and are the classic H-2 antigens. The
other region called the I region contains at least three
distinct genes and subregions and possibly more. It was initially discovered because it stimulated a mixed lymphocyte
reaction (MLR) and thus has been referred to as "LD" for
lymphocyte defined. While it is now clear that antibodies
can be raised against LD regions and that SD regions can stimulate MLR's, the SK LD terminology is still useful and has
lingered in the literature because it defines a predominant,
though clearly not absolute, functional distinction.

Another system outside of the H-2 system, controlled by the M locus (2), shares many of the features of the LD or I region. Thus the M locus is capable of generating a vigorous MLR and is hard to define with antibody. Not all M loci generate vigorous MLR's; some are quite weak and some only work in one direction. Another attribute shared by the I region and the M locus is that neither locus generates much killer cell activity directed against itself under ordinary circumstances, while both loci seem to activate a helper mechanism (3) which improves the generation of killer cells directed against the K and D regions of the H-2 locus.

The basis for these phenomena has become more clear with the recent defining of T cell subsets by use of antisera against T cell differentiation antigens. Using the Ly system (4), which comprises a number of genetic loci each with two alternative alleles, with each allele specifying an alternative alloantigen, Cantor and Boyse (5,6) have defined three T cell subsets; one which expresses the Ly-1 alloantigen comprises approximately 30% of the adult T cell population. Another expresses both the Ly-2 and the Ly-3 alloantigens comprises about 8% of the population. A third expresses all three Ly alloantigens and makes up approximately 50% of the T cell population in adult mice. The Ly-1$^+$ cell acts as a helper cell in antibody production and also for the production of killer cells. It is not itself a killer cell; that function is mediated by Ly-2$^+$, 3$^+$ cells. The Ly-1$^+$ cell is the cell which is stimulated by I region (LD) antigen. The Ly-2$^+$, 3$^+$ cells react mainly with K and D region antigen. The role of the Ly-1$^+$, 2$^+$, 3$^+$ cells has not yet been clearly defined.

EXPERIMENTAL DETAILS

The work presented herein, is an examination of how different responder T cells react when presented with foreign cells which differ either at the M locus, the H-2 locus, or the two loci together. The technique used to measure the DNA synthesis engendered in this reaction is a little different from the one standardly used. It is a mixture of an MLR and a graft versus host (GVH) reaction and actually can be thought of as an in vivo MLR. The technique consists of lethally irradiating (850R) recipient mice whose cells act as stimulator cells. The irradiated mice are inoculated with responder cells and the DNA synthetic response the inoculated cells undergo is measured in vivo, by pulsing the recipient animals with ^{125}iodine labelled 5-iodo-2-deoxyuridine (IUdR) which is incorporated into the DNA of the responding cell. Within

12-24 hrs after the injection of IUdR, all product not associated with DNA has been cleared from the body of the recipient
mice. One can then harvest the lymph nodes and the spleens
of the recipients, place them in a gamma counter and the
number of counts emmited, over background, is a reflection of
the amount of DNA which was synthesized by the inoculated
cells in the harvested organs. Detailed studies of reactions
to MHC antigens, using this technique, have been published
(7). The technique offers the advantage over the in vitro
MLR in that the inoculated cells segregate themselves into
spleen and lymph node seeking populations and differences
between these populations can be seen. In addition interactions between the two populations have been documented (8).

In the studies reported below Balb/C mice ($H-2^d$; M^2)
have been chosen as the responding strain. Balb/C cells have
been inoculated into irradiated DBA/2 mice which are $H-2^d$,
like the responder strain, but are M^1. M^1 is a very stimulatory M locus. The strain used for H-2 stimulation is C57BL/6
which is $H-2^b$ and has the same M locus (M^2) as the Balb/C
responders. The strain used to stimulate with M plus H-2
was the F_1 cross between the C57BL/6 and DBA/2; hereafter
referred to as BDF_1. The DNA synthetic response in the
lethally irradiated recipients was measured on days 3,4, and
5 after inoculation (4 mice/group/day). The results are
presented as the mean total amount of DNA synthesized over
the course of the three days and thus each bar in the graph
represents the results from 12 test mice.

RESULTS

a) In Untreated Recipients

Inspection of Figure 1 (next page) shows that Balb/C
cells respond much better in DBA/2 mice than they do in BDF_1
hybrids, both in the spleen and the lymph nodes. This is a
surprising result because the BDF_1 mice should present the
same M locus difference to the responding cells as the DBA/2
mice but should present in addition an H-2 difference. It is
possible that the presence of the foreign H-2 locus suppressed the response to the M locus in the BDF_1 mice.

b) In Cortisone Treated Recipients

To test the possibility that the H-2 antigens were
generating suppression, some of the recipient mice were
pulsed with cortisone 3 hrs after the cells had been inocu-

195

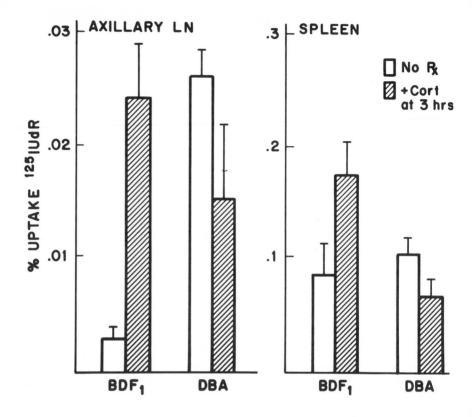

Figure 1. The DNA synthetic response of
Balb/C lymph node cells in the axillary lymph nodes
and spleens of lethally irradiated (850R) BDF_1 or
DBA/2 mice. Some of the recipient mice were
pulsed with cortisone 3 hours after the Balb/C
cells were inoculated.

lated. Previous work had shown that this treatment could
alleviate suppressive influences under a number of circumstances. The basis for the action of the cortisone has been
considered in detail in other papers (9,10) and will not be
discussed any further. I would just like to mention that,
in lieu of cortisone, one can also use cycloheximide and get
similar results, indicating that suppression of protein synthesis is involved in this alleviation of suppression. The
timing of the injection of the drug(s) is very important because by 24-48 hours after the start of the reaction the
main protein synthesis occurring is that which helps the
response. Again I should mention that the very early genera-

tion of suppressor cells, prior to the generation of helper cells, has been noted by a number of workers in diverse situations, even though there often is a significant latent period before the suppression can be seen (see 11).

In any case, using this technique one can see (Figure 1) that the response of the Balb/C lymph node cells in BDF_1 mice was markedly augmented by the treatment which relieved suppression, while the same treatment in the DBA/2 mice not only did not augment the response, but it actually reduced it. These results are thus consistent with the interpretation offered above; that there is something in the MHC which activated suppressor cells and thus knocked out the response to the M locus. In addition, it would seem that the M locus itself failed to activate these suppressor cells.

c) Gene Dosage Studies

One other reason the results are so different in the DBA/2 and the BDF_1 mice could be due somehow to a gene dosage effect in that the DBA/2 mice have two chromosones coding for an M^I locus where there is only one in the BDF_1 mice. To test this possibility, we made F_1 hybrids between Balb/C mice and either C57BL/6 mice (Balb X C57) or DBA/2 mice (Balb X DBA). The results (Figure 2) (next page) show that the response of Balb/C lymph node cells in these F_1 hybrids was no different than it was in the previous experiment (Fig. 1); that is to say, there was a poor response against the H-2 antigens, which was markedly augmented by the treatment with cortisone while the response against the M^I locus (this time being carried by only one of the two recipient chromosones) was just the same as in the mice homozygous at this locus.

d) Use of Splenic Responder Cells

The results reported above all concern inoculation of Balb/C lymph node cells into recipients. When spleen cells or splenic T cells were used as responder cells the results were markedly different. In this case (results not presented, but to be presented in full detail in the near future) the response was much greater when there was an H-2 difference or an H-2 and M difference than was the response when there was an M difference only (ie: there was no evidence for H-2 generated suppression). It should also be mentioned (and again this will be reported in more detail later) that the type of interaction between M and H loci reported above is not confined to the strains reported on in this paper.

197

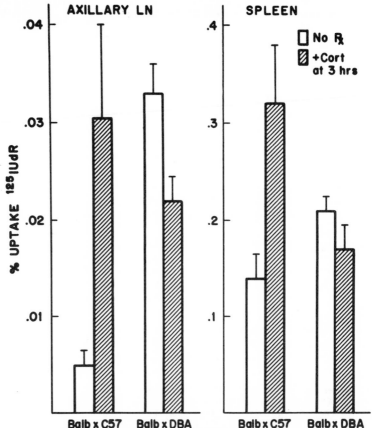

Figure 2. The DNA synthetic response of
Balb/C lymph node cells in the axillary lymph nodes
and spleens of lethally irradiated (850R) Balb/C X
C57BL/6 or Balb/C X DBA/2 mice. Some of the recipient mice were pulsed with cortisone 3 hours after
the Balb/C cells were inoculated.

DISCUSSION

I would like to offer the following interpretation for
the above results: At the present time, two types of suppressor T cells have been found. Most workers find that the
Ly-2$^+$, 3$^+$ T cell can act as a suppressor cell. Although
none of this work has yet been published, it has been found
in the allotype suppression story by Cantor and Herzenberg;
in the Con A suppression story by Pierce, Jandinski and
Cantor; in an antigen specific suppressor situation by both
Cantor and Boyse as well as Marc Feldmann and in delayed

type hypersensitivity situations by Huber, Cantor, Devinsky and myself.

There is much less data concerning the suppressive role of the $Ly-1^+$, 2^+, 3^+ cell. However, in several experiments Askenase, Cone, Eardley, Cantor and myself have shown a suppressive role for this 1^+, 2^+, 3^+ cell. In addition, the suppressive potential of the 1^+, 2^+, 3^+ cell can be inferred from the fact that the T cells from newborn animals are highly suppressive in a number of situations (12). Cantor and Boyse have shown that all the $Thy-1^+$ cells of the newborn are also $Ly-1^+$, 2^+, 3^+.

In addition, those workers who have tried to see whether spleen seeking or lymph node seeking cells contain suppressor cells have almost uniformly found that it is the spleen seeking cell which contains the suppressor cell (8, 13-15). There is an interesting and not readily apparent dichotomy in this. That is, that immature cells are almost certainly the 1^+, 2^+, 3^+ cells and have a predilection for localizing in the spleen. The $Ly-2^+$, 3^+ cell, which is also the killer cell, is a mature recirculating cell and therefore should not localize preferentially in the spleen. One might hypothesize that when an $Ly-2^+$, 3^+ cell localizes in the spleen the microenvironment there might induce it to be a suppressor. However, I have previously presented evidence that this is not the case, in that when lymph node cells are injected into histoincompatible mice and the spleen localizing population removed, there is no augmentation of the response in the lymph nodes (14). The same procedure done with splenic cells produces a marked augmentation in the lymph nodes (14). This confirms the notion that the spleen contains the spleen seeking cell which suppress the response of other cells and it is not necessarily the micro-environment at the time of the reaction to antigen that induces the suppressor effect. Wu and Lance have similar results (15).

Now, how to put all this information together into a possible hypothesis. I think that the $Ly-2^+$, 3^+ cell is preferentially stimulated by a part of the MHC region. The best guess at this stage would be that it would be SD antigens because it is the $Ly-2^+$, 3^+ cell which becomes the killer and killing is predominantly directed against these antigens.

The $Ly-2^+$, 3^+ cell is a mature cell and therefore most likely represented in the recirculating pool. In fact in the studies that have been done of the interactions between T-1 and T-2 type cells (16) in congenic Thy-1 chimeras, it has been shown that the recirculating T-2 cell is the cell that becomes the killer and the T-1 cell is the immature non-recirculating cell which tends to localize in the spleen and regulate the killer (17,18).

We then come to the question of why splenic T cells behave so differently and are not activated by SD antigens to produce this suppressive effect. Surely Ly-2$^+$, 3$^+$ cells are present in the spleen. The reason for this may be that the T-1 cell, which is most likely Ly-1$^+$, 2$^+$, 3$^+$ has a special predilection for responding in a positive fashion to the antigens of the MHC locus. Which of these antigens are involved has not yet been clearly defined. However because of this special predilection, they do not produce the suppressive effect seen when lymph node cells are inoculated.

There is some precedent for this type of interpretation; a number of workers have found that pretreatment of mice with cyclophosphamide markedly augments the delayed type hypersensitivity response (DTH) to sheep red blood cells (see 19). In addition, we (A. Schwartz and K. Kondo) have found that similar pretreatment augments the DNA synthetic response of splenic T cells to sheep red blood cell antigens and also augments the generation of helper cells against this antigen. We have also found that the exact same pretreatment reduces the DTH response against antigens of the major histocompatibility locus. Thus, we suggest that cells in the T-1 class, probably Ly-1$^+$, 2$^+$, 3$^+$ react differently to antigens in the MHC locus than they do to standard antigens and because of this differential reaction to the 2 types of antigens, we get the 2 types of responses we have reported. At the present time, we are accumulating the appropriate recombinant mice to be able to test some of these hypotheses and find out which of the antigens in the MHC locus are responsible for the suppressive effects we have seen. We are also using the appropriate Ly differentiation antisera to determine which of the responding cells are responsible for the reactions.

One other significant point emerges from these findings; that is herein lies a possible basis for the phenomenon known as immunodominance. It is well known that in a number of situations when a strong antigen is present, responses to weaker antigens are suppressed. This phenomenon may be related to the phenomenon of antigenic competition which has clearly been shown to be mediated by a suppressor T cell (20). Thus, strong antigens in general may have a predilection for activating suppressor T cells, but they themselves may escape the action of the suppressor T cell because of the above mentioned latent period before suppressor T cell action is effected, after it has been generated. Weaker antigens having longer latent periods may therefore be more susceptible to the actions of suppression. Therefore, as it has been empirically known for a long time, in order to get a response to a weak antigen one can make the responder animal tolerant to the stronger antigen and then find a good response to the weaker antigen. It is clear from the work presented above that the interacting antigens can be on the same cell. In some cases they may even be interacting determinants on the same molecule.

In summary I have shown that some types of cellular antigens present on the same cell can interact in a way so that one produces a suppressor effect against the other. The working hypothesis is that any antigen which will preferentially activate an $Ly-2^+$, 3^+ cell will generate considerable suppression and may prevent the response to other antigens. We hope, with the appropriate use of the recombinant mice which are now available, to be able to study this phenomenon in more detail and perhaps have the answers to some of the questions and theoretical notions raised by the results presented.

ACKNOWLEDGMENTS

K. Kondo and E. Searle rendered the technical assistance (did the experiments); grants CA 08593, AI 10497 from the NIH rendered the needed financial assistance and A. Swanson rendered the secretarial help.

REFERENCES

(1) D.C. Shreffler and C.S. David. Adv. Immunol. 20 (1975) 125.

(2) H. Festenstein and P. Demant. Transpl. Proc. 5 (1973) 1321.

(3) D. Schendel, E. Simpson and H. Wagner, personal communication.

(4) E.A. Boyse, M. Miyazawa, T. Aoki and L.J. Old. Proc. Roy. Soc. (B) 170 (1968) 175.

(5) H. Cantor and E.A. Boyse. J. Exp. Med. 141 (1975) 1376.

(6)   H. Cantor and E.A. Boyse. J. Exp. Med. 141 (1975) 1390.

(7)   R.K. Gershon and S.A. Liebhaber. J. Exp. Med. 136 (1972) 112.

(8)   R.K. Gershon, E.M. Lance and K. Kondo. J. Immunol. 112 (1974) 546.

(9)   P. Cohen and R.K. Gershon. Ann. N.Y. Acad. Sci. 249 (1975) 451.

(10) R.K. Gershon, K. Kondo and S. Orbach-Arbouys. In preparation.

(11) R.K. Gershon. Transpl. Rev. 26 (1975) 170.

(12) D.E. Mosier and B.M. Johnson. J. Exp. Med. 141 (1975) 216.

(13) R.K. Gershon. Contemp. Top. Immunobiol. 3 (1974) 1.

(14) R.K. Gershon. In: The Immune System: Genes, Receptors, Signals (E. Sercarz, A. Williamson and C.F. Fox eds.) Academic Press, N.Y. (1974) p.471.

(15) C.W. Wu and E.M. Lance. Cell. Immunol. 13 (1974) 1.

(16) M.C. Raff and H. Cantor. Prog. Immunol. 1 (1971) 83.

(17) H. Wagner. J. Exp. Med. 138 (1973) 1379.

(18) H. Cantor and E. Simpson. Eur. J. Immunol. 5 (1975) 330.

(19) P.W. Askenase, B.J. Hayden and R.K. Gershon. J. Exp. Med. 141 (1975) 697.

(20) R.K. Gershon and K. Kondo. J. Immunol. 106 (1971) 1524.

DOES THE APPARENT H-2 COMPATIBILITY REQUIREMENT FOR VIRUS-SPECIFIC T CELL-MEDIATED CYTOLYSIS REFLECT T CELL SPECIFICITY FOR "ALTERED SELF" OR PHYSIOLOGICAL INTERACTION MECHANISMS?

ROLF M. ZINKERNAGEL* AND P.C. DOHERTY †

*Department of Immunopathology
Scripps Clinic and Research Foundation

†The Wistar Institute

Abstract: Virus-specific cytotoxic T cells lyse infected targets only when they are compatible at the $\underline{K}$ or $\underline{D}$ region of H-2. $\underline{I}$ region compatibility is neither sufficient nor obviously required. Experiments with H-2$\underline{K}$ mutant Hz1 and Hz170 mice indicate that the cistron coding for the structure in the $\underline{K}$ region, which is central to the apparent restriction, is defined by the two mutants. The findings and previous results are discussed with respect to whether the "altered self" model, which proposes that T cells are specific for virus altered self markers coded in the $\underline{K}$ or $\underline{D}$ region of H-2, or the physiological interaction model best explain the experimental data including reactivity against alloantigens. The altered self concept appears to accommodate the results most easily. However, as long as direct evidence such as biochemical characterization of altered self or, alternatively, interaction structures is lacking, any arguments are based on circumstantial evidence and the issue remains open.

The association of an ever increasing number of T cell effector functions (1-10) with the H-2 gene complex makes it difficult to believe that this phenomenon is merely an experimental artefact. This is particularly unlikely when specific cytotoxic T cells are generated during virus infections in mice, because experimental manipulation is minimal. Furthermore, results produced in such models in vitro (3-6) are essentially substantiated in vivo during functional experiments like adoptive induction of inflammatory processes (11), transfer of protection against virus infection (12), or adoptive induction of delayed type hypersensitivity (R.M. Zinkernagel and P.C. Doherty, submitted). Therefore, the apparent restriction in vitro and in vivo of effector T cell's activity probably reflects fundamental biological mechanisms relevant to general and/or immunological homeostasis.

Whether the phenomenon is the expression of physiological cell-cell interactions, apparently centered around structures coded in the K or D regions of H-2, or is an immunological event [which possibly evolved from more ancient cell-cell interactions (13)] is unclear (14). Why should cytolytic T cell functions be intimately associated with structures coded in H-2K or D? A variety of hypotheses have been proposed in attempts to relate H-2 gene complex, H-2 polymorphism, immunosurveillance and structural similarities between H-2 structures and immunoglobulins (5, 9,11,14-16; A.J. Hapel, D. Jackson, R.E. Langman, personal communications).

Two possible explanations fit the mechanics of this lytic process. First, cell damage resulting in ^{51}Cr release occurs most efficiently when structures coded in K or D of H-2 are attacked by immunologically specific recognition entities and/or by physiological interaction with these structures in addition to immunological recognition of a specific (e.g. viral or TNP) antigen on the cell surface. Second, cytotoxic activities associated with K or D structures are most readily detected by ^{51}Cr release assays because these structures have some special relationship to other structures present on lymphoid cells and   capable of stimulating generation of great numbers of effector cells (17, and personal communication, P.A. Bretscher).

Two alternative models have been proposed to explain the apparent requirement for H-2K or H-2D region compatibility between cytotoxic T cells and infected targets for virus-specific lysis to occur (3-5,7,11,14). According to the "altered self" concept, cytotoxic T cells are specific for altered self (a complex of a self marker coded in K or D and viral antigen or a biochemical alteration of the self marker); the apparent restriction would thus reflect T cell

specificity. Alternatively, the physiological interaction
model proposes that virus-specific cytotoxic T cells are
sensitized to viral cell surface antigens alone, but for
lysis to occur an additional second interaction of like
H-2 is necessary.

The idea that cytotoxic T cells may be quite generally
specific for altered self apparently accommodates experimental evidence obtained with T cells cytotoxic for virus
infected or TNP modified cells and also activity against
allogeneic targets (which obviously does not need physiological interaction structures) more readily than the physiological interaction model (or at least requires less assump-
tions and less exceptions). The former concept also explains
recent findings derived from measuring virus-specific cytotoxic activity generated in H-2 mutant mice.

Strong experimental evidence indicates that in homozygous mice two distinct sets of cytotoxic T cell
specificities are generated, each associated with the $\underline{K}$ or
$\underline{D}$ region of H-2 (5). The gene of the $\underline{K}$ region coding for
the structure which is central to the apparent restriction
can be defined by using H-2$\underline{K}$ mutant mice (11,18, Tables I
and II).

H-2 mutants, like B.6.Hz1 (H-2^{ba}) and B.6.Hz170
(H-2^{bf}), are derived from C57B1.6 mice, and define a locus
in the $\underline{K}$ region that is responsible for reciprocal skin
graft rejection, positive mixed lymphocyte reactions (MLR)
and generation of cytotoxic T cells $\underline{in\ vitro}$. In many cases
the mutants are no different serologically from wild type
mice (Dr. D.W. Bailey, personal communication, 19-22). Hz1
and Hz170 mice probably carry a point mutation affecting the
same cistron in the $\underline{K}$ region. Virus specific cytotoxic
activities associated with the $\underline{K}$ region generated in these
mutant and wild type C57B1.6 mice are not cross-reactive
(Table I and II, 11, 18). These results emphasize again
that $\underline{I}$ region compatibility is not sufficient for virus
specific cytolysis (6). Cold target competition experiments
(5) demonstrate that the inability of H-2 mutant mice to
generate T cells cytotoxic against infected wild type targets does not result from a deletion but rather from a
positive mutation of the structure involved (Table II).
Again, these results are most compatible with the altered
self concept. Accordingly, H-2 mutant mice define the cistron in the $\underline{K}$ region which codes for the modifiable self
marker.

TABLE I

Lymphocytic Choriomeningitis (LCM) Virus Specific Activity
of Wild Type and H-2K Mutant H-2^b Mice

Immune spleen cells[b] from mouse strain (H-2 haplotype)	% Specific ^{51}Cr release from infected macrophage targets[a]	
	C57B1.10 b bbb b b	B10.A(5r) b bbd d d
B6.Hz1 ba bbb b b	37[c],[d]	0
B6.Hz170 bf bbb b b	61	0
C57B1.10 b bbb b b	59	27

[a]Targets were prepared as described (3,17).

[b]Mice were immunized 7 d previous to assay with
2 x 10^5 intracerebral LD$_{50}$ of the WE strain of
LCM virus, kindly donated by Drs. M.B.A. Oldstone
and R. Welsh.

[c]Spontaneous release and release by normal spleen
cells was between 30 and 35%; specific ^{51}Cr
release is calculated by the formula:

$$\frac{\text{immune cell release} \quad - \quad \text{medium release}}{\text{water release} \quad - \quad \text{medium release}} \times 100$$

[d]Release by immune cells on uninfected targets was
not significantly different from that by normal
spleen cells on infected targets or by medium.

Nevertheless, these and previously reported results
(3-6,11,18) could be interpreted differently in terms of a
physiological interaction mechanism. As discussed in more
detail elsewhere (5,11,14,18) any physiological interaction
structure for like H-2 would have to be controlled by a
complex genetic regulatory mechanism. Phenotypic expression
is simultaneously subject to allelic exclusion and to reciprocal exclusion of the interaction structure coded in the
K region for like K and in the D region for like D. The
evidence for this postulate derives from cold target
competition experiments with virus immune T cells from F$_1$
and H-2 recombinant mice. Activities of both can be blocked
only by cold targets which are compatible with both immune
T cells and infected targets (5). Furthermore, their interaction structures would have to be clonally expressed, as
shown by selective proliferation experiments in vivo.
Immune T cells from F$_1$ or H-2 recombinants proliferate in

TABLE II

Vaccinia-Virus Specific Cytotoxic Activity of Wild Type
And H-2K Mutant H-2^b Mice

Mouse strain H-2 haplotype K $\dfrac{1}{ABC}$ S D	Spleen cells	Cold[a] competitor B10	Specific ^{51}Cr release from macrophage targets[b]			
			B10.A(5r)	B6. H-2^{ba}	B6. H-2^{bf}	B10
B6.H-2^{ba}	I[c]	--	7.1[d]	50.2	29.8	27.5
ba bbb b b	I	Inf.	--	34.7	--	4.8
	I	Nor.	--	36.1[e]	--	26.9
	N	--	4.7	1.3	1.6	2.7
B6.H-2^{bf}	I	--	9.3	59.5	32.2	40.5
bf bbb b b	I	Inf.	--	--	23.8	21.3
	I	Nor.	--	--	26.3[e]	39.4[f]
	N	--	6.4	2.4	--	2.0
B10.A(5r)	I	--	54.5	4.1	3.7	47.7
b bbd d d						
B10	I	--	63.9	37.7	55.9	84.6
b bbb b b	N	--	0.9	5.1	0.5	5.3

[a]Unlabeled infected (Inf.) or uninfected (Nor.)
macrophage targets were added 8 times in excess of
the ^{51}Cr labeled targets.

[b]Macrophage targets were obtained and infected as
described (3,18) and results calculated as in Table I.

[c]Mice were immunized (I) with 2 x 10^7 PFU of the WR
strain of vaccinia virus kindly donated by Dr. W.K.
Joklik. Normal spleen cells (N).

[d]Means of triplicate. Underlined values are statistically different from either immune spleen cells on
uninfected targets or normal spleen cells on infec-
tected or uninfected targets (p< 0.05).

[e]Blocking by infected cold targets is not significantly greater than by uninfected competitors.

[f]Specific blocking by infected cold competitors
(p< 0.05).

virus infected, irradiated recipients only to increase cytotoxicity against infected targets compatible with both
immune cell donors and recipient mice (5).

Since the mutation probably affects a single cistron,
the results obtained with the H-2 mutant mice could indicate
that self marker and interaction units are part of the same
structure (11,18). This is possible, although unlikely. If
such a genetic regulatory mechanism existed, it follows
that the interaction unit would have to be suppressed while
the self marker part is expressed. There is no evidence
that alloantigens participating in skin graft rejection,
MLR and cytotoxicity by T cells are not co-dominantly
expressed (11,17). Including this complication in a
rational explanation of the apparent H-2K or D restriction
of cytotoxic T cells could be avoided by postulating a
mechanism like somatic translocation for the interaction
unit, such as Gally and Edelman proposed for regulation of
immunoglobulin synthesis (11,23).

Alternatively, one could propose that physiological
interaction structures are coded by evolutionarily ancient
genes, which are common to all mice. Therefore, these genes
could be located anywhere in the genome and not necessarily
in the K or D regions of H-2 (11,17). Parallel mutations of
a self marker and an interaction structure (13) would be
unnecessary if any newly evolving self marker is permissive
only when a corresponding interaction structure is coded by
one of many genes covering a wide variety of possible self
markers or else by few genes having a high rate of somatic
mutation (11,17,24).

Obviously any of these alternative models is much
more complicated than the altered self hypothesis. However,
all the models are theoretically possible and the altered
self concept attracts mainly by its simplicity and
apparent general applicability.

Since neither the hypothetical interaction structure
for like self nor the antigenic entity of "altered self"
has been defined biochemically, all arguments are based on
circumstantial evidence derived from biological experiments
and are subject to the inherent criticisms thereof. It thus
seems unwise and premature to exclude either of the possible
mechanisms as an explanation for this strong and probably
biologically important phenomenon.

ACKNOWLEDGMENTS

We thank Drs. R.V. Blanden, A.J. Cunningham, L. Pilarski, A.J. Hapel, K. Lafferty and G. Ada of the Department of Microbiology, John Curtin School of Medical Research, Canberra, Australia, for stimulating discussions. This is publication number 1061 from the Department of Immunopathology, Scripps Clinic and Research Foundation, 476 Prospect Street, La Jolla, California 92037. These studies were supported in part by United States Public Health Service Grant AI-07007 and Contract No. NO1 CP 43375 within the Virus Cancer Program of the National Cancer Institute.

REFERENCES

(1)   B. Kindred and D.C. Shreffler, J. Immunol. 109 (1972) 940.

(2)   D.H. Katz, T. Hamaoka, M.E. Dorf and B. Benacerraf. Proc. Nat. Acad. Sci. 70 (1973) 2624.

(3)   R.M. Zinkernagel and P.C. Doherty. Nature (London) 248 (1974) 701.

(4)   P.C. Doherty and R.M. Zinkernagel, J. Exp. Med. 141 (1975) 502.

(5)   R.M. Zinkernagel, and P.C. Doherty. J. Exp. Med. 141 (1975) 1427.

(6)   R.V. Blanden, P.C. Doherty, M.B.C. Dunlop, I.D. Gardner, R.M. Zinkernagel and C.S. David. Nature (London) 254 (1975) 269.

(7)   G.M. Shearer. Eur. J. Immunol. 4 (1974) 527.

(8)   J. Forman. J. Exp. Med. 142 (1975) 403.

(9)   M.J. Bevan. Nature (London) 256 (1975) 419.

(10) R.D. Gordon, E. Simpson and L.E. Samelson. J. Exp. Med. (1975) In press.

(11) P.C. Doherty, R.V. Blanden and R.M. Zinkernagel. Transplant. Rev. (1976) In press.

(12) R.V. Blanden, N.A. Bowern, T.E. Pang, I.D. Gardner, and C.R. Parish. Austr. J. Exptl. Biol. Med. Sci. 53 (1975) 187.

(13) W.F. Bodmer. Nature (London) 237 (1972) 139.

(14) P.C. Doherty and R.M. Zinkernagel. Lancet i (1975) 1406.

(15) G.M. Shearer, T.G. Rehn and C.A. Garbarino. J. Exp. Med. 141 (1975) 1348.

(16) D.H. Katz and B. Benacerraf. Transplant. Rev. 22 (1975) 175.

(17)   P.A. Bretscher. Cell. Immunol. 13 (1974) 171.

(18)   R.M. Zinkernagel. J. Exp. Med. Submitted.

(19)   D.W. Bailey, D.G. Snell and M. Cherry. Proc. Symp.
        Immunogenetics of the H-2 System. Karger, Basel
        (1971) 55.

(20)   M.B. Widmer, B.J. Alter, F.H. Bach, M.L. Bach and
        D.W. Bailey. Nature (London) New Biol. 242 (1973) 239.

(21)   D.C. Shreffler and C.S. David. Adv. Immunol. 21
        (1974) 125.

(22)   J. Klein. Current Topics in Immunobiol. 5 (1975)
        In press.

(23)   J.A. Gally and G.J. Edelman. Nature (London) 227
        (1970) 341.

(24)   N.K. Jerne. Eur. J. Immunol. 1 (1971) 1.

THE BIOLOGY OF MIXED LYMPHOCYTE INTERACTIONS AND CELL-MEDIATED CYTOTOXICITY REACTIONS

Morten Simonsen, Chairman

van ROOD: I would like to make a comment regarding Bo DuPont's presentation. I agree with you that bimodality of the results of the 4 typing cells you showed is utterly unconvincing. However some typing cells give a very clear bimodality between negative or weakly reactive reactions (typing responses) and positive reactions. Could it not be that there are "good" and "bad" typing cells just as there are good and bad typing sera?

J. KLEIN: I would like to make two comments concerning Rolf Zinkernagel's presentation. First, Jim Forman tested the *H-2* mutants for cross-reactivity using the TNP-system and obtained just the opposite results. Namely, he observed a clear-cut cross-reactivity between the original and the mutant *H-2* haplotype. His observation is thus the first documented case of dichotomy between the viral and the TNP systems.

My second comment concerns the dual recognition model. I suggest the following hypothesis. The receptor on an effector cell can react with the antigen on the target cell only if the two share *H-2K* or *H-2D* molecules. The reaction establishes a permanent association in the membrane of the *effector* cell between the receptor and an *H-2* molecule. This molecular complex (receptor-*H-2*) is then capable of recognizing the antigens on the target cell only if the latter carries the same *H-2* molecule present in the complex. This hypothesis explains the F_1 hybrid data without requiring allelic exclusion of *H-2* or any other complicated or unlikely events. It differs from the models of dual recognition that have been proposed in that it postulates interaction on the effector cell rather than on the target cell and in that the interaction occurs between the receptor and *H-2* rather than between an antigen and *H-2*. It thus also eliminates the problem of how the *H-2* molecule "recognizes" such a variety of antigenic molecules (haptens, viral antigens, various histocompatibility antigens, etc.) shown to be operative in this system.

BENACERRAF: I would like to ask Jan Klein whether the TNP-mutant experiments to which you referred demonstrate identical killing on the TNP-mutant target as to the TNP-target used for sensitization. This is particularly important in the TNP-modified *H-2* system since such cross-reaction can be demonstrated between syngeneic and allogeneic haptenated cells in this system.

J. KLEIN: As far as I remember the degree of killing of the cross-reactive cell is about the same as that of the homologous cell.

von BOEHMER: I have a suggestion for Dr. Klein who observes cross-reactivity in response to different TNP-modified mutants. It is possible that anti-TNP antibody is produced in the cultures and that Dr. Klein is looking at antibody-mediated killing rather than killing by cytotoxic lymphocytes. Therefore, it should be checked whether anti-TNP antibody is produced, and whether the same cross-reactivity is observed when a pure T cell population is used as the responder cell population. The extent of antibody production may vary in different culture systems and therefore differing results may be obtained in different laboratories.

J. KLEIN: This possibility, I believe, has not been ruled out. However, since the TNP system used in the mutant studies is the same as that used in the strictly syngeneic system, I think it is unlikely that the two operate by two different mechanisms.

E. MÖLLER: The differences in specificity found in different systems could be related to the degree of haptenation of target cells. Thus, we heard from Ellen Vitetta that they have TNP-labelled most cell surface structures, whereas in Gene Shearer's experiments epitope dinsity might be less.

Secondly, I would like to ask Gene Shearer whether the effector stage could be inhibited by free TNP?

SHEARER: We have not succeeded in blocking the lytic phase of an autologous TNP-modified cell-mediated lympholysis (CML) either with TNP-modified non-*H-2K* or non-*H-2D* matched, unlabelled targets.

The demonstration that *Ir* genes are involved in the

214

TNP-autologous CML model makes the cell-interaction model more complicated than an altered-self hypothesis. The preferential reactivity of B10.A responding lymphocytes against K-end TNP-modified stimulating cells indicates that the *Ir* gene is not controlling the TNP exclusively, but that the *Ir* gene must involve either reactivity against altered-self or against TNP plus unaltered self (presumably required for the cell interactions).

E. MÖLLER: It is difficult to inhibit binding of hapten-reactive T cells to haptenated target cells with free hapten; you need the homologous conjugate for *efficient* inhibition. However, the N-system, with NIP associated with a tripeptide might be more informative since this molecule in itself would create a greater part of the size of a single determinant.

KATZ: I would like to ask Gene Shearer if he has given any thought to the possibility that the *Ir* gene regulation of responses to TNP-modified *H-2* antigens may represent a system of two complementing *Ir* genes similar to the *Ir-GLT* gene system of Dorf, et al. (*J. Exp. Med.* 141: 1459, 1975). If this were the case, then I would suggest that the differences in the magnitude of responses to various TNP-modified *H-2* products may reflect a *cis-trans* effect similar to that which has been described in our laboratories.

SHEARER: Such a two gene model is a viable possibility, although we have not considered it in detail before you mentioned it.

GREEN: Dr. Zinkernagel, what is the relationship between auto-killing described by Irun Cohen and the killing of viral-infected or hapten-treated cells?

ZINKERNAGEL: Cohen's auto-sensitization appears to behave similarly to the virus models, at least as shown for the *K* end in Eva Klein's lab.[*] One of probably many possible explanations could be that endogenous virus plays a role.

*[*EDITOR'S NOTE:* For references to these points see:
1. Cohen, I.R. and Livnat, S. *Transplantation Rev.* vol. 29, 1975, in press.
2. Ilfeld, D., Carnaud, C. and Klein, E. *Immunogenetics*

215

2: 231, 1975 - DHK.]

CUNNINGHAM: I will present the data on Thursday, but I
     would like to make one comment relevant to the distinc-
     tion between the dual recognition model and the concept
     of altered self. John Schrader, Gerry Edelman and I
     have attempted to gain some clues on the role of *H-2*
     antigens by a variety of procedures. One of these ap-
     proaches was to look for the co-capping of *H-2* and viral
     antigens. The experiments do indicate that these an-
     tigens co-cap supporting the altered self concept.

     [*EDITOR'S NOTE:* See Cunningham, et al, this volume -
     DHK.]

PAUL: Dr. Zinkernagel, the cold target inhibition of cyto-
     toxicity has been a powerful analytic tool. However, I
     would raise the question as to whether this probes
     simply the specificity of the antigen-binding receptor
     or whether it may reflect the capacity of the cold tar-
     get to be killed. It is quite possible that in the
     former instance, there may be a higher degree of re-
     versibility of the interaction than in the latter and
     that receptor specificity is not being determined by
     this method. It might be quite informative to deter-
     mine whether isolated membranes or dead cells can block
     T cell-mediated killing in these systems.

ZINKERNAGEL: Our interpretation of cold target blocking
     experiments is based on the argument that if cytotoxic
     T cells are specific for altered self it is expected
     that cytotoxicity by F_1 or *H-2*-recombinant can be
     blocked by cold target expressing the same altered self
     marker as the target and the donor of immune cells. If
     the specificity of cytotoxic T cell is against viral
     antigen alone and has to be complemented by a second
     physiological interaction a target cell not *H-2*-compat-
     ible with the target but with the immune cell donor
     should be able to block.

UHR: The problem of the energetics of binding of ligands
     to cells is pertinent to interpreting the studies of
     Zinkernagel and Shearer, in particular, the blocking
     studies. It is noteworthy that free DNP is quite inef-
     fective in blocking the binding of DNP-conjugates to
     MOPC 315 plasma cells (which have a surface Ig which
     reacts with DNP). There is an enormous energetic

216

advantage of the polyvalent over the univalent antigen.
These considerations bear on the Zinkernagel studies by
indicating the great advantage of multipoint binding
and the ease of not detecting binding of lower valency.

GERSHON: I still don't understand the reason Dennert can
block killing with TNP on chicken red blood cells
(CRBC)*. Whatever the mechanism is for generating killers,if cold TNP-CRBC blocks it suggests the killers
see TNP as well as TNP-modified K and D.

*[EDITOR'S NOTE: See Dennert, G. Nature 255: 712, 1975-
DHK.]

SHEARER: The in vitro CML reactions observed in Dennert's
experiments were generated by a C57BL/6 anti-P-815-TNP
CML assayed on EL-4-TNP targets. We have seen that effector cells generated in an allogeneic CML not involving TNP in the sensitization will kill any TNP-modified target cell. Therefore, I think those CML blocking experiments using TNP-chicken erythrocytes to inhibit effector cells generated in an allogeneic CML are
difficult to interpret, since this phenomenon may have
nothing to do with TNP-modified sensitization.

SIMONSEN: I will turn the floor over to David Sachs, whose
time I inadvertently cut short during his presentation.

SACHS: The studies by Drs. Fathman, Schwartz and myself,
which I presented earlier in this session indicated an
association, both at the genetic level and at the cell
surface level, between Ia antigens and the cell surface
structures which stimulate an I-region associated MLC
reaction. In view of the interest expressed in the previous session in the possible existence of B cell alloantigens not linked to the MHC, I would like to mention
one other B cell alloantigenic system which Dr. Dickler
and I have been studying.

You will recall that we have described a close phyical
relationship between Ia antigens and the Fc receptor on
the B cell surface. Antibodies to any of a large number of Ia antigens, but not to $H-2K$ or $H-2D$ region antigens, were found to specifically inhibit the binding
of aggregated immunoglobulin to the B cell Fc receptor.
Subsequent to those studies, we noted that an A/J anti-
B10 antiserum could also block the Fc receptor of

217

B10.A B cells, i.e. blocking due to non-*H-2* antibodies. The assay was then applied to an available (B6A)F$_1$xA backcross population. Of the 10 backcross animals examined, 4 were uninformative since they had inherited the *H-2^b* haplotype and therefore were blocked by anti-*I^b* antibodies in this serum. The results with the remaining six animals indicated that the relevant antibodies were probably directed toward the products of one non-*H-2* linked locus (Dickler, H.B. et al., *J. Exp. Med.* 142: 796, 1975).

We have subsequently extended this blocking study to a larger (B10.AxA)F$_1$ x A backcross population, all of which animals are informative, since they all bear the *H-2$^{a/a}$* genotype. The results of Fc receptor blocking studies with the A/J anti-B10 antiserum on these backcross animals is shown in Table I below. These data

TABLE I
ANALYSIS OF (B10.AxA)xA BACKCROSS

Category Coat Color	Sex	Allotype	Number of Animals	Fraction Fc Receptor Blocked
White	Male	aa	5	1/5
		ab	0	
	Female	aa	3	1/3
		ab	3	1/3
Black	Male	aa	5	3/5
		ab	2	1/2
	Female	aa	1	1/1
		ab	3	3/3
Brown	Male	aa	2	0/2
		ab	2	2/2
	Female	aa	1	0/1
		ab	2	1/2
Total			29	14/29

likewise indicate that there is one non-*H-2* linked locus, the products of which, like Ia antigens, are closely associated with the Fc receptor on the B cell surface. The data indicate further that this locus does not appear to be sex-linked, nor linked to the heavy chain allotype locus, nor to coat color genes.

Unfortunately, we could not type these backcross animals for the M locus since the M2 allele possessed by the B10 background is non-stimulatory (Festenstein, H., *Transplant. Rev.* <u>15</u>: 62, 1973). We are presently attempting this study in the reverse direction in order to assess this possibility. If such a relationship were to be found, we would have two B cell alloantigenic systems, both potent stimulators of the MLC reaction, and both of which are closely associated with the B cell Fc receptor.

In this regard, Dr. Henry Winn has kindly given me permission to mention a cytotoxic antiserum produced in the C3H anti-CBA system in his laboratory (Tonkonogy, S. and Winn, H., *J. Immunol.*, in press) which appears to detect a product of the M locus or a locus closely linked to the M locus. We have recently prepared an antiserum in the same strain combination and have found that it too blocks the B cell Fc receptor. However, since we have not independently tested a backcross population for both properties and since such antisera could theoretically contain more than one antibody specificity, I consider these results to be suggestive but still preliminary.

MEO: I would like to direct a question to David Sachs' presentation. Does the B10.A anti-A serum block the capacity of A cells to stimulate B10.A cells in a one-way MLR?

SACHS: We haven't tried this as yet.

GERSHON: Does yours or Tonkonogy and Winn's antiserum block an M-locus response?

SACHS: We tried this with irradiated parental cell but, unfortunately, such cells failed to stimulate well, so we are waiting for the appropriate F_1's to be bred to use as the stimulator cells in the MLC across an M-locus.

BACH: What evidence does Winn have regarding the association of his serum and the M-locus?

SACHS: The association is that in backcross animals the antiserum reacts with the same animals which stimulate the M-locus MLC.

BENACERRAF: Do you have any information concerning the Fc receptor on macrophages and Ia? Is it the same as on B cells?

SACHS: Dr. Dickler and I have looked very hard at the possible relationship between Ia antigens and the macrophage Fc receptor. We have had great difficulty detecting Ia antigens on macrophages by a variety of techniques and presently feel that while the Ia antigens are present on macrophages they must be present in very small amounts relative to the amounts on B cells. On the other hand, Fc receptors are readily detectable on these macrophages and none of our anti-Ia reagents cause inhibition of these Fc receptors. We therefore feel that the Fc receptors of B cells and of macrophages may be different entities.

STROMINGER: The following observation is not in total agreement with that reported by David Sachs. Antiserum prepared in rabbits against a highly purified human Ia antigen (defined as Ia by its content of polypeptides of 30,000 and 23,000 daltons) does not block the MLC.

van ROOD: Jack, how did you determine that the rabbit anti-human Ia antiserum does, in fact, recognize the Ia determinant?

McDEVITT: Yes, Jack, how do you know your serum is directed against human "Ia"?

STROMINGER: It reacts with all human B cells, and precipitates a molecule with two polypeptides of the right molecular weight.

McDEVITT: Then it may be directed against species-specific determinants, which are not recognized in the MLR, which is due to individual specific, allelic differences. To prove you have a "rabbit anti-human Ia" you should prove that a known anti-HLA-D-specific serum clears a labelled membrane extract for reactivity with your rabbit "anti-human Ia" (i.e., your rabbit anti-HLA-D).

220

J. KLEIN: I want to return to Tommy Meo's experiment designed to test the presence of an MLR locus outside of *H-2*. The main problem with this approach is that one is starting with mouse lines that might have already lost the right alleles at this hypothetical locus by recombination. A more informative way to do this experiment would be to take two totally unrelated mice (for instance, a wild mouse and an inbred mouse), suppress recombination in the chromosome 17 in one of these (by introducing a t factor), produce a congenic line differing in a large segment of chromosome 17 and only then remove the crossover suppressor and start dissecting the chromosome by recombination. In the available congenic lines one does not know how long the "foreign" segment on both sides of *H-2* may be; in the approach I am proposing one would assure that a considerable length of the chromosome remains foreign until the actual search for recombinants. The approach would increase the probability of detecting polymorphism at the hypothetical locus even if this polymorphism is rather low.

MEO: I made clear that the length of heterozygous segments are virtual, average measures, or as Dr. Klein says, hard on statistics. But I also believe that statistics relies on the representability of samples. To the number of combinations I have shown, I might add other cases in which a non-*H-2*-incompatibility can be expected and yet there is no detectable MLR. These are B10.K↔B10.BR, A↔A.A1 and BALB/c↔B10.D2. As an example of the extent of contamination brought in by backcrossing and selection for *H-2* as a differential marker, I should like to mention that most of the *H-2* congenic strains have also been found congenic for the *Tl* locus.

SACHS: I would like to ask Fritz Bach if he would give us his views on the relationship between Ia and the MLC stimulators.

BACH: No, I have nothing really to add to Meo's summary. It seems to me that an important point to be made is that if the LD determinants can be detected serologically, this does not tell us anything about the differential role of LD and SD antigens in activating different subpopulation of T lymphocyte.

Immune Response *(Ir)* Gene Systems

MICHAEL SELA, CHAIRMAN

THE NATURE AND FUNCTION OF SPECIFIC H-LINKED
IMMUNE RESPONSE GENES AND IMMUNE SUPPRESSION GENES

BARUJ BENACERRAF AND MARTIN DORF

Department of Pathology
Harvard Medical School

THE ACTIVITIES OF COMPLEMENTING HISTOCOMPATIBILITY-LINKED
Ir GENES IN THE CONTROL OF IMMUNE RESPONSES TO SYNTHETIC
ANTIGENS

The recognition of most antigens as immunogens by
individual animals and inbred strains is governed by the
products of dominant immune response (*Ir*) genes located in
the genome linked to the major histocompatibility complex
(1-3). This has now been verified in rodents (4-6), birds
(7) and primates (8, 9). These genes have been termed
histocompatibility or H-linked *Ir* genes. The presence of
the relevant genes permit immune responses to be formed,
characterized by cellular immunity and antibody synthesis
against the determinants on the antigens concerned. Three
types of antigens have been most useful in the identification of H-linked *Ir* genes: 1) synthetic polypeptides with
limited structural heterogeneity; 2) alloantigens which
differ slightly from their autologous counterparts; and 3)
complex multi-determinant antigens administered in limiting
immunizing doses in conditions where presumably only the
most immunogenic determinants are recognized. All of these
antigens share also an important characteristic: they are
thymus-dependent antigens. To date, no H-linked *Ir* gene
control has been observed of a thymus-independent response,
which may have considerable significance when an analysis
is made of the processes controlled by H-linked *Ir* genes.
Such simple genetic control of specific immune responses has
been totally unexpected for immunologists, considering the
complexity of immune phenomena and the enormous range of
specificities against which antibodies can be formed.

225

These observations provide, therefore, both a challenge to the classical theory of the recognition of immunological specificity solely by pre-existing immunoglobulin receptors on immunocompetent cells, as well as powerful tools to analyze the complex interactions between antigens and the various cell types (macrophages, B and T cells) concerned collectively with the development of specific immunity.

The activities of histocompatibility (H)-linked *Ir* genes have become a problem of increasing interest for immunologists, particularly since the mapping of these genes has been localized to a chromosomal region, the *I* region, which also controls other important traits such as cell interaction in the regulation of immune responses (10-12), mixed lymphocyte and graft-versus-host responses (13-15), and expression of a new class of alloantigens, Ia antigens, on the surface of B cells, T cells and macrophages (16-18). The increasing awareness of the role of these genes in the control of responsiveness to thymus-dependent antigens and the demonstration from several laboratories of the production of factors from activated T cells possessing determinants coded for in the same *I* region (19,20) have further emphasized the importance of understanding the function of *Ir* genes and their products.

It has generally been assumed that a single histocompatibility-linked Ir gene was required for responsiveness to a specific antigen. There were, however, indications that in some systems two H-linked Ir genes were needed for responsiveness. In 1972, Stimpfling and Durham (21) first postulated that the immune response of mice to the alloantigen H-2.2 might be controlled by two interacting genes localized within the *H-2* complex. In addition, rare instances have been reported where F_1 hybrids between two low responder strains gave responses higher than either parental strain (22-24).

The first documented example of dual H-linked Ir gene control of the response to a single antigen was demonstrated in our laboratory using the terpolymer of L-glutamic acid, L-lysine and L-phenylalanine (GLφ) (25). The immune response to this synthetic polypeptide was previously characterized by Merryman *et al* (26). These investigators demonstrated that the immune response to GLφ is inherited as a Mendelian dominant character and the gene controlling GLφ responsiveness is linked to the *H-2* complex. In preliminary reports, using *H-2* recombinant mice, Merryman *et al* (27) and Dorf *et al* (28) tentatively mapped the *Ir-GLϕ* gene within the *I* region of the *H-2* complex. Following a more extensive analysis undertaken in our laboratory, we suggested the requirement for at least two complementing *H-2*-linked *Ir-GLϕ* genes for GLϕ responsiveness (25,29). We proposed these genetic requirements based on the findings that the mating of two non-responder strains produced responder F_1 hybrids, which provided evidence for complementation of the non-responder *H-2* alleles. This observation, coupled with the fact that selected recombinant strains (derived by recombination between two non-responder *H-2* haplotypes) are GLϕ responders, indicates that at least two distinct *Ir* loci are concerned with responsiveness to GLϕ.

We tentatively localized one of the *Ir-GLϕ* genes in a new region of *I*, termed *I-F* which is a subdivision of the *I-C* region, based on the responses of the 9R, B10.HTT, BSVS and QSR-1 recombinant strains (see Table II). For convenience, we have designated this *Ir-GLϕ* gene α and its alleles $\alpha(+)$ and $\alpha(-)$. The *H-2^a* and *H-2^k* non-responder haplotypes carry the $\alpha(+)$ allele. This represented the first documented data localizing an *Ir* gene in the *I-C* portion of the *H-2* chromosome. The other *Ir-GLϕ* gene termed β must lie to the left of the 3R, 5R, 9R and B10.HTT cross-over positions and, based on the response patterns of the (A x 4R)F_1 and (B10.A x D2.GD)F_1 hybrids, presumably lies in the *I-A* region of the *H-2* complex (Table III). The data supporting these conclusions are shown in Tables I, II and III. In Table I we present the strain distribution of responsiveness to GLϕ among 17 inbred congenic strains. All mice were immunized and boosted 3 weeks later with 100 µg of GLϕ in complete Freund's adjuvant administered intraperitoneally. The secondary sera were obtained 8 days following challenge.

TABLE I

ANTIBODY RESPONSES TO GLϕ BY INBRED AND CONGENIC STRAINS

Strain	H-2	N	GLϕ Response* (% binding + SE)
A/J	*a*	11	1.9 $\pm$ 1.6
B10.A	*a*	7	3.9 $\pm$ 2.1
A.BY	*b*	4	-0.2 $\pm$ 0.5
C57BL/10	*b*	13	0.5 $\pm$ 2.5
B10.D2	*d*	9	60.9 $\pm$ 4.7

TABLE I   (continued)

ANTIBODY RESPONSES TO GLϕ BY INBRED AND CONGENIC STRAINS

Strain	H-2	N	GLϕ Response* (% binding + SE)
A.CA	f	3	-0.6 ± 0.6
B10.M	f	5	1.0 ± 1.3
B10.WB	ja	3	79.3 ± 7.2
B10.BR	k	12	5.1 ± 3.0
B10.P	p	3	79.5 ± 1.5
B10.Y	pa	4	81.3 ± 0.6
B10.G	q	3	64.3 ± 6.3
B10.RIII	r	5	68.6 ± 4.2
A.SW	s	5	1.6 ± 3.1
B10.S	s	7	-1.4 ± 1.3
B10.PL	u	3	62.7 ± 6.1
B10.SM	v	3	8.9 ± 5.5

* Mean percentage of radio-labelled GLT ligand bound by 1:5
dilutions of serum $\pm$ standard error.

Following secondary immunization , mice carrying the $H-2^d$,
$H-2^j$, $H-2^p$, $H-2^q$, $H-2^r$, and $H-2^u$ haplotypes made high levels
of anti-GLϕ antibody. In contrast, mice homozygous for $H-2^a$,
$H-2^b$, $H-2^f$, $H-2^s$, and $H-2^v$ haplotypes made no detectable
antibody responses after secondary challenge.

The anti-GLϕ antibody response of 12 selected recombinant strains are shown in Table II. Several recombinant
strains which were independently derived from crossovers
between two non-responder haplotypes are GLϕ responders.
These include the 3R and 5R strains which were derived by
recombination of the $H-2^a$ and $H-2^b$ haplotypes and the 9R,
B10.HTT and BSVS strains in which crossing over occurred between the $H-2^s$ and $H-2^a$ or $H-2^{al}$ haplotypes (30). It is
important to note that the latter strains all represent examples of recombination within the I region, either between
the $I-B$ and $I-C$ subregions or, in the case of the "natural
recombinant" BSVS, between $I-C$ and $I-F$.

TABLE II

HUMORAL RESPONSES TO GLϕ BY H-2 RECOMBINANT STRAINS[a]

Recombinant Strains	H-2 Haplotypes	n	K	A	B	C	F	S	D	GLϕ Response (% binding $\pm$ SE)
D2.GD	g4	5	d	d	b	b	b	b	b	-3.6 $\pm$ 5.0
4R	h4	4	k	k	b	b	b	b	b	1.0 $\pm$ 3.6
3R	i3	5	b	b	b	d	d	d	d	58.5 $\pm$ 7.0
5R	i5	10	b	b	b	d	d	d	d	73.3 $\pm$ 5.0
18R	i18	5	b	b	b	b	b	b	d	4.7 $\pm$ 2.4
A.TL	t1	3	s	k	k	k	k	k	d	3.6 $\pm$ 2.9
A.TH	t2	3	s	s	s	s	s	s	d	8.7 $\pm$ 3.1
B10.HTT	t3	5	s	s	s	k	k	k	d	76.5 $\pm$ 6.9
9R	t4	4	s	s	s	d	d	d	d	70.6 $\pm$ 9.5
BSVS	t5	8	s	s	s	s	d	d	d	43.8 $\pm$ 10.8
QSR-1		2	s	s	s	s	s	q	q	4.8 $\pm$ 3.2
8R		4	k	k	k	s	s	s	s	7.3 $\pm$ 2.1

[a] See legend for Table I.

[b] Letters indicate parental origin of the genes in each *H-2* region. Vertical bars indicate position of crossing over.

TABLE III

ANTIBODY RESPONSES OF F_1 HYBRIDS FOLLOWING IMMUNIZATION WITH GLϕ[a]

F_1 Hybrid	H-2	n	GLϕ Response (% Binding $\pm$ SE)
B10.HTT x A.CA	t3 x f	3	57.8 $\pm$ 8.3
DBA/2 x 4R	d x h4	4	58.7 $\pm$ 5.2
A x B10.A	a	5	7.5 $\pm$ 2.3
A x B10.BR	a x k	5	0.3 $\pm$ 3.7
A x B10	a x b	5	62.8 $\pm$ 5.8

TABLE III   (continued)

ANTIBODY RESPONSES OF F_1 HYBRIDS FOLLOWING IMMUNIZATION
WITH GLϕ[a]

F_1 Hybrid	H-2	n	GLϕ Response (% Binding $\pm$ SE)
A x 18R	a x i18	10	64.1 $\pm$ 5.7
A x 4R	a x h4	5	1.4 $\pm$ 3.2
C3H x A	k x a	5	4.4 $\pm$ 2.5
C3H x B10	k x b	5	80.0 $\pm$ 1.7
B10 x B10.BR	b x k	3	68.3 $\pm$15.7
SJL x C3H	s x k	6	48.8 $\pm$13.8
B10.BR x B10.S	k x s	5	28.2 $\pm$ 7.8
B10.A x D2.GD	a x g4	5	46.4 $\pm$ 9.2
D2.GD x AKR	g4 x k	5	38.9 $\pm$ 5.2
A x A.Ca	a x f	3	3.5 $\pm$ 2.6
A.Ca x B10	f x b	4	-0.5 $\pm$ 3.2

[a]Refer to legend Table I.

Table III illustrates the GLϕ responses of 16 F_1 hybrids following immunization with 100 μg GLϕ. All F_1 hybrids between responder and non-responder strains were responders. Two examples of the latter type of hybrid, the (B10.HTT x A.CA)F_1 and (DBA/2 x 4R)F_1, are presented. Several hybrids which were the product of two non-responder parental strains also responded to the GLϕ terpolymer. Thus, all F_1 hybrids which carried at least one β gene derived from the I-A subregion of the H-2^b, H-2^d haplotypes, or from I-A or I-B subregions of the H-2^s haplotype plus one α gene derived from the I-C chromosomal segments of the H-2^a, H-2^d or H-2^k haplotype could respond to the GLϕ terpolymer.

The H-2^f or H-2^{h4} haplotypes appear to lack both the α and β genes. Thus, attempts to complement the A.CA or 4R strains by producing F_1 hybrids with either the A or B10 strains were uniformly unsuccessful. Localization of the β gene in the H-2^b haplotype to the K or I-A subregions was shown by the inability of the (A x 4R)F_1 hybrid to complement, thus mapping the β gene of the H-2^b haplotype to the left of the I-B region. In addition, the ability of the (B10.A x D2.GD)F_1 and the (D2.GD x AKR)F_1 hybrids to make anti-GLφ antibody suggests that the β gene derived from the H-2^d haplotype also lies in the K or I-A regions. Localization of the β gene of H-2^s in the I-A or I-B subregions resulted from comparisons of the anti-GLφ responses of the A.TL and B10.HTT recombinant strains (Table II).

The summary of α and β genotypes for 11 H-2 haplotypes and 9 recombinant H-2 haplotypes is presented in Table IV.

TABLE IV

SUMMARY OF α AND β GENOTYPES

H-2 Haplotype	GLφ Phenotype	Ir-GLφ Genotype	
		α	β
a	−	+	−
b	−	−	+
d	+	+	+
f	−	−	−
j	+	+	+
k	−	+	−
p	+	+	+
q	+	+	+
r	+	+	+
s	−	−	+
u	+	+	+
Recombinant H-2 haplotypes			
$h2$	−	+	−
$h4$	−	−	−
$i5$	+	+	+
$i18$	−	−	+
$g4$	−	+	−
$t1$	−	−	+

TABLE IV (continued)

SUMMARY OF α AND β GENOTYPES

Recombinant _H-2_ Haplotypes	GLϕ Phenotype	_Ir_-GLϕ Genotype α	β
_t_2	−	+	−
_t_3	+	+	+
_t_4	+	+	+

No differences can be detected in the α genes of the H-2^a, H-2^k or H-2^d haplotypes. There is clear evidence, however, that the β genes derived from the H-2^b and H-2^s haplotypes are not identical. As shown in Table III, complementation in F_1 hybrids between the same α gene and β genes derived from the H-2^s haplotypes resulted in significantly lower antibody responses than in F_1 hybrids in which the β gene was derived from the H-2^b haplotype.

The gene complementation observed for the response to GLϕ raises the issue whether gene complementation is always required in immune responses under H-linked Ir gene control. It would appear that this phenomenon can probably be generalized to other systems under H-linked Ir gene control. The observations of Zaleski _et al_ (24) and of Rude and Günther (22) who demonstrated that the mating of selected low responder animals produced intermediate or high responder offspring for the Θ antigens of mice and the synthetic branched polymer (T,G)-A--L in rats, respectively, are compatible both with the conclusion that we are dealing with a general phenomenon. This view is supported further by the finding by Munro and Taussig (31) of complementing Ir genes in the (T,G)-A--L system controlling antibody responses to this antigen in F_1 hybrid mice of two non-responder strains.

We have ourselves additional examples of H-2-linked Ir gene complementation in the immune responses to two other antigens; the terpolymers of L-glutamic acid, L-lysine and L-tyrosine (GLT) and of L-glutamic acid, L-lysine and L-leucine (GLleu). The data documenting the control of responsiveness to GLleu by two complementing Ir genes are found in Table V.

TABLE V

CONTROL OF GLleu RESPONSIVENESS BY TWO COMPLEMENTING *Ir* GENES[a]

Strain	*H-2* Haplotype	*H-2* Region Formulae						GLleu Response (% Ag Binding ± SE)
		K	*I-A*	*I-B*	*I-C*	S	D	
B10.BR	*k*	*k*	*k*	*k*	*k*	*k*	*k*	-0.7 ± 1.7
C3H	*k*	*k*	*k*	*k*	*k*	*k*	*k*	3.5 ± 6.4
AKR	*k*	*k*	*k*	*k*	*k*	*k*	*k*	-1.6 ± 1.8
B10.S	*s*	*s*	*s*	*s*	*s*	*s*	*s*	1.8 ± 6.1
SJL	*s*	*s*	*s*	*s*	*s*	*s*	*s*	-5.8 ± 1.6
A.SW	*s*	*s*	*s*	*s*	*s*	*s*	*s*	-1.7 ± 1.6
A/J	*a*	*k*	*k*	*k*	*d*	*d*	*d*	2.8 ± 3.8
B10.HTT	*t3*	*s*	*s*	*s*	*k*	*k*	*d*	59.5 ± 11.6
9R	*t4*	*s*	*s*	*s*	*d*	*d*	*d*	79.6 ± 6.2
(B10.BR x A.SW)F₁	*k* x *s*	*k/s*	*k/s*	*k/s*	*k/s*	*k/s*	*k/s*	95.9 ± 0.8
(B10.BR x B10.S)F₁	*k* x *s*	*k/s*	*k/s*	*k/s*	*k/s*	*k/s*	*k/s*	74.0 ± 11.0

[a]See legend for Table I.

233

At least one of the genes responsible for the GLleu responses is distinct from the gene controlling GLϕ responses since the distribution of H-2 responder haplotypes for GLϕ and GLleu are different as seen in Table VI when the Ir gene control of antibody responses to the terpolymers of L-glutamic acid, L-lysine and a third amino acid are compared in different H-2 haplotypes.

In contrast, complementing Ir genes controlling the responses to GLT and GLϕ are probably the same in strains which respond to both antigens. We base this conclusion on the finding that the responder H-2 haplotypes for GLT are all responders to GLϕ which elicit always a stronger response than GLT in the same strains. Some H-2 haplotypes, however, confer responsiveness to GLϕ but not to GLT. Thus, a heirarchy of immunogenicity can be observed for the terpolymers GLT^5, GLT^{15} and GLϕ in both the quantitative and qualitative responses of related inbred strains to these antigens. We propose to consider this type of reactivity an inclusion group system under the same Ir gene control in animals bearing responder haplotypes for the three related polymers (32). In contrast, the patterns of responsiveness to GL alanine, GL serine, GL proline and GL leucine differ from each other and from that to GLϕ (Table VI).

We would like to conclude that all responses under H-linked Ir gene control are probably the result of gene complementation. However, since as will be discussed below, Ir gene complementation, in many instances, is more effective in the *cis* than in the *trans* position, the induction of immune responsiveness by gene complementation in F_1 hybrids derived from mice bearing non-responder haplotypes may be difficult to observe although the same genes could complement efficiently in the *cis* position.

This may explain why: 1) Ir gene complementation has not been detected until recently and why 2) it was more easily demonstrated in the GLϕ system. In this system, the α gene which maps within the I-C region of H-2 is the only H-linked Ir gene identified to date in this region. The fact that the responses of mice bearing the *H-2^a* or *H-2^k* haplotypes, which are identical at I-A and I-B but not in I-C are the same for 23 antigens besides GLϕ (3) suggest that if complementing genes are required for many of these responses, they both map in I-A or I-B, rather than I-C. An alternative explanation is that the H-2^a and H-2^k haplotypes share the same α (+) allele in the I-C region for responses to all these antigens; however, the responses to some of these antigens by α (-) strains is not compatible with this explanation. Complementation between I-A and/or I-B Ir genes should be more difficult to detect than in the GLφ, GLT system because of the limited number of recombinants in I-A/I-B regions and the decreased effectiveness of complementation in the trans position.

Gene complementation was also reported by Munro and Taussig (31) in the (T,G)-A--L system. These investigators proposed that in their system one of the complementing gene controls the formation of specific helper factors by T cells and the other, the interaction of the factor with a B cell receptor. We have investigated the requirements for the α and β genes in T and B lymphocytes for responses to GLφ. In collaboration with Drs. Schwartz and Paul, we have studied the response to GLφ of specific T cells capable of being stimulated by GLφ in culture to show increased incorporation of ^{3}H-thymidine. Both α and β genes were demonstrated to be clearly required for the stimulation of T cell immunity by GLφ. Thus, after GLφ immunization mice bearing the $H-2^\alpha$ or $H-2^b$ haplotypes did not display increased ^{3}H-thymidine incorporation, whereas the T cells from the recombinant strain and $(H-2^\alpha$ x $H-2^b)F_1$ mice showed specific responses to GLφ in culture comparable to their PPD responses. These experiments demonstrated that both α and β genes are required for T cell activation by GLφ.

Other experiments were carried out in collaboration with Katz to investigate the requirements for α and/or β genes for the secondary anti-hapten response to DNP-GLφ. These experiments are described in detail in another paper in this volume. The genetic requirements for the cooperative interactions between GLφ splenic T cells and DNP-specific B cells were explored. The results demonstrated the need for both α(+) and β(+) alleles for 1) the generation of GLφ helper T cells and 2), in the B cells, for effective stimulation of DNP-specific B cells by DNP-GLφ with the help of GLφ primed 5R responder T cells. The conclusion can be reached, therefore, that in the GLφ system there is no indication that one of the complementing α or β genes is expressed exclusively in one of the cell types of the immune system in contrast with the situation in the (T,G)-A--L system investigated by Munro and Taussig (31).

TABLE VI

Ir GENE-CONTROLLED RESPONSES TO SYNTHETIC POLYPEPTIDES IN MICE[a]

Random Sequence Linear Polypeptide Antigens

H-2 Haplotype	GLA^{10}	GLA^{30}	GLser	GLpro	GLleu	GLT^5	GLT^{15}	GLΦ	GL
a	+	+	+	−		−	−	−	−
b	+	+	−	−		−	−	−	−
d	+	+	−	−	−	+	+	+	−
f	+	+	+	−		−	−	−	−
j	+	+	−	−	+	+	+	+	−
k	−	−	+	−	−	−	−	−	−
p	−	−	−	−	−	−	−	+	−
q	−	+	−	−	+	+	+	+	−
r	+	+	−	−	−	−	+	+	−
s	+	+	−	+	+	−	−	−	−
u	+	+	−	−	+	+	+	+	−
v	+	+	−	−	+	−	−	−	−

[a]Humoral responses following secondary immunization with 100 μg of the respective polymers in CFA as determined by antigen binding assays. A positive (+) indicates all animals bearing the respective *H-2* haplotypes were phenotypic responders. The *H-2* haplotypes of the strains bearing the non-responder *Ir* alleles are indicated by a minus (−) sign.

CIS-TRANS EFFECTS IN THE COMPLEMENTING OF α AND β GENES

The Ir genes required for GLϕ responses are able to complement in both the cis and trans position. However, a comparison of the effectiveness of gene interactions in the cis and trans position for GLϕ responses revealed that the $\beta(+)$ allele derived from the H-2^s haplotype complements better with a(+) alleles in the cis (i.e. recombinant strains 9R, B10.HTT) than in the trans position (i.e. (B10.BR x B10.S)F$_1$ hybrids (Table VII). The lower responses of the (B10.A x D2.GD)F$_1$ and (D2.GD x AKR)F$_1$ hybrids compared to the (DBA/2 x 4R)F$_1$ are consistent with this interpretation (Table III). However, this was not apparent for the GLϕ response in the case of the $\beta(+)$ allele from the H-2^b haplotype (Table VII). However, when the response to GLT is investigated, gene complementation between α genes from the H-2^a and β gene from the H-2^b haplotypes is only observed in the recombinant 5R strain but not in the (C57BL/6J x A/J)F$_1$ nor in the (C3H/HeJ x C57BL/10J)F$_1$ hybrids. Cis versus trans preference for effective complementation can also be observed, therefore, with the β gene from the H-2^b haplotype if the antigen is weaker such as GLT compared to GLϕ. It is important to note that the α (+) and $\beta(+)$ alleles which control GLϕ responsiveness are fully dominant as evidenced by the responses of F$_1$ hybrids between the B10.HTT responder strains with the $\alpha(-)$ and $\beta(-)$ non-responder A.CA strain (Table VII), or the (DBA/2 x 4R)F$_1$,(Table III).

What is the significance of gene interactions between distinct Ir genes for the control of specific immune responses to antigens such as GLϕ or GLleu? The cis-trans effects described in this report are similar in many respects to the gene interactions noted between C$_H$ and V$_H$ immunoglobulin genes. Thus, in F$_1$ hybrid animals, heterozygous for the heavy chain allotypes, the V$_H$ allotype and idiotype markers are generally associated with the constant region heavy chain allotype markers of the respective C$_H$ alleles found in the cis configuration (33,34). These restrictions in the expression of the immunoglobulin C and V genes are related to the allelic exclusion phenomenon and also have been interpreted to indicate gene interaction at the level of the DNA. It is tempting to conclude similarly that the cis-trans effect observed with complementing Ir genes imply also interactions at the DNA or at least the RNA level before expression of the Ir gene product.

237

TABLE VII

CIS—TRANS EFFECTS FOR GLφ AND GLT RESPONSES

Strains	H-2 Haplotype	Genotype $\alpha,\beta / \alpha,\beta$	Response GLφ % Binding	GLT	Chromosomal Relationship
B10.A; B10.BR	$a;k$	+,-/+,-	-	-	
C57BL/10; B10.S	$b;s$	-,+/-,+	-	-	
A.CA	f	-,-/-,-	-	-	
5R	$i5$	+,+/+,+	73	28	cis (2x)
(C57BL/6 x A/J)F$_1$	b x a	-,+/+,-	85	-	trans (1x)
(C57BL/10 x C3H/He)F$_1$	b x k	-,+/+,-	80	-	trans (1x)
B10.HTT	$t3$	+,+/+,+	65	-	cis (2x)
9R	$t4$	+,+/+,+	70	-	cis (2x)
(B10.HTT x A.CA)F$_1$	$t3$ x f	+,+/-,-	58		cis (1x)
(A.SW x B10.A)F$_1$	s x a	-,+/+,-	17		trans (1x)
(B10.S x B10.BR)F$_1$	s x k	-,+/+,-	28		trans (1x)

This interpretation would imply that Ir gene products can display considerable heterogeneity and may have a role in the recognition of antigens, either directly or indirectly as postulated earlier (3). The demonstration that both complementing genes are required in both T cells and B cells leads to the conclusion that these recognition systems are expressed in both cells and regulate their specific interactions in the responses to thymus dependent antigens. The recent discovery of specific active factors from activated T cells with helper (20,35) or suppressor properties (36,37,38) and determinants coded for by the I region should permit when their structure are understood the definitive clarification of these issues.

The cis-trans effects may also explain the selective forces which maintained the close linkage among individual Ir genes during mammalian evolution. Since the most efficient mechanism for Ir gene interaction appears to require that complementing genes reside on the same haplotype, strong selective pressures would favor the maintenance of a cluster of Ir genes within the genome.

GENETIC CONTROL OF SPECIFIC IMMUNE SUPPRESSION

In earlier studies from our laboratory, mice which are non-responders ($H-2^P$, $H-2^q$, $H-2^S$) to the terpolymer of L-glutamic acid^{60}-L-alanine^{30}-L-tyrosine^{10} (GAT) were shown to develop suppressor T cells capable of inhibiting GAT-specific responses to GAT complexed with methylated bovine serum albumin (GAT-MBSA) (39). This finding raised several important points: 1) Could suppressor T cells be demonstrated in non-responder mice immunized with antigens other than GAT? 2) Do all non-responder strains unable to form an antibody response to an antigen under H-2-linked Ir genes control develop suppressor cells? 3) If the ability to generate suppressor cells in response to an antigen is observed in some mouse strains but not in others, are these phenotypic differences under genetic control? 4) If such genetic control is observed, are the responsible genes linked to the major histocompatibility complex of the mouse in a manner similar to what has been demonstrated for the control of antibody responses by H-2-linked Ir genes (1-3)? We have selected the copolymer of L-glutamic acid^{50} and L-tyrosine^{50} (GT) to investigate this point. This copolymer which is immunogenic in strain 13 guinea pigs, stimulates antibody responses by some random-bred Swiss mice but not in inbred strains of mice bearing different H-2 haplotypes (40).

TABLE VIII

IMMUNE RESPONSE TO THE GT COPOLYMER MEASURED BY
ANTIGEN-BINDING ASSAY

Strain	H-2 Haplotype	No. Tested	Antigen Binding ($\pm$ SE)
B10.A	a	5	0.7 ± 1.4
A/J	a	4	1.9 ± 3.9
C57BL/10J	b	4	-3.4 ± 2.4
B10.D2n	d	5	6.4 ± 4.0
BALB/c	d	3	-7.7 ± 3.7
B10.M	f	5	6.3 ± 4.0
B10.BR	k	5	-3.5 ± 3.2
DBA/1J	q	8	8.6 ± 4.1
T138	q	3	-0.2 ± 2.5
SWR/J	q	2	-6.1 ± 5.7
SJL/J	s	5	-3.3 ± 1.7
Swiss	Random bred	3	44.8 ± 9.5
Swiss	Random bred	12	6.8 ± 1.6

It would appear, therefore, that in mice Ir genes controlling antibody responses to GT are not widely represented.
Non-responder mice can, however, produce anti-GT antibodies
following immunization with GT complexed with an immunogenic
carrier, MBSA, as observed in other systems. The restricted
immunogenicity of GT for mice renders this antigen well
suited for studies on the stimulation of specific immune
suppression using the types of protocols which permitted
the identification of GAT-specific suppressor T cells in
mice bearing the H-2^{p,q,s} haplotypes and unable to respond
to GAT (39). Experiments were designed to establish first
the conditions for the demonstration of the suppressive
properties of GT in a model mouse strain (40).

BALB/c mice were injected intraperitoneally with 10 µg
of GT in Maalox or Maalox alone three to seven days before
immunization with GT-MBSA. All mice were sacrificed seven

days later and their spleens examined for GT-specific IgG plaque forming cells (PFC). Immunization with either 10 or 100 μg of GT three, five, or seven days before GT-MBSA challenge caused a significant decrease in the antibody response of BALB/c mice to GT-MBSA. The tolerance induced by GT pre-immunization was specific, since the administration of 100 μg of GT in Maalox failed to suppress the primary anti-DNP PFC response to an unrelated antigen DNP-KLH. A more detailed study of the kinetics of the stimulation and duration of the GT-specific suppressor effect was then performed. One hundred μg GT in Maalox was injected into six groups of BALB/c mice at times ranging from 28 days before to one day after GT-MBSA immunization. The seven-day PFC responses are shown in Figure 1.

FIGURE 1

Kinetics of the Suppression of the GT-MBSA Response.

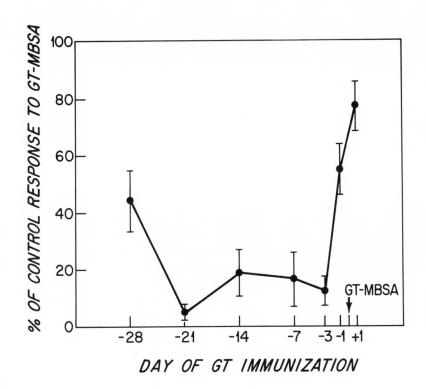

The earliest that GT preimmunization causes a marked decrease
in the response to GT-MBSA is three days before immunization
with GT-MBSA. At that time, the suppressive effect is
already maximal and is maintained unchanged, as determined
by *in vivo* experiments, up to 21 days following GT priming.
The intensity of the suppression decreases by day 28.

An experiment was then performed to determine whether
the inhibition of the antibody response to GT-MBSA in BALB/c
mice caused by GT preimmunization was an active process resulting from the stimulation of specific suppressor cells.
The ability of BALB/c mice rendered tolerant to GT to transfer specific unresponsiveness to GT-MBSA to syngeneic
recipients was investigated. BALB/c mice were injected with
either 100 µg of GT in Maalox or Maalox alone. Three days
later, 20×10^6 spleen cells or thymocytes obtained from
these two groups of animals were transferred intravenously
into normal syngeneic recipients, and all recipient mice
were immunized with GT-MBSA in CFA. Their antibody response
was assayed seven days later.

TABLE IX

TRANSFER OF GT-SPECIFIC SUPPRESSION TO
NORMAL SYNGENEIC RECIPIENTS

(BALB/c Mice)

Cells Transferred*	Specific IgG PFC/Spleen (Ar. Mean and SE)	Inhibition P < .03
Control Spleen	$19,468 \pm 3,184$	
		87%
GT-Primed Spleen	$2,678 \pm 1,032$	
Control Thymus	$22,781 \pm 6,861$	
		85%
GT-Primed Thymus	$3,587 \pm 1,406$	

* Twenty $\times 10^6$ cells from donors immunized three days before
with Maalox or 100 µg of GT in Maalox were injected i.v.
into normal syngeneic recipients. On the same day, these
animals were immunized with 10 µg GT complexed with MBSA
in CFA i.p. Seven days later, the number of GT-induced
IgG PFC per spleen were enumerated using GAT-SRBC.

As can be seen in Table IX, the mice which received spleen cells or thymocytes from mice preimmunized with GT showed decreased PFC responses when compared to mice which received the same numbers of control spleen cells or thymocytes. The conclusion can, therefore, be made that GT induces suppressor cells in the spleen and thymus of BALB/c mice.

STRAIN DIFFERENCES IN THE SUPPRESSION BY GT OF THE PRIMARY RESPONSE TO GT-MBSA

We compared the ability of preimmunization with GT to specifically inhibit the immune response to GT-MBSA in several inbred strains of mice. 100 µg GT in Maalox, or Maalox alone as control, were injected intraperitoneally 3 days before immunization with GT-MBSA. Seven days later the specific IgG PFC per spleen were enumerated (no IgM PFC were detected following immunization with GT or GT-MBSA as was observed in the response to GAT or GAT-MBSA). A three-day interval was selected between the administration of GT and GT-MBSA in all experiments as this was the earliest time when maximal suppression of the primary response was observed in the well-studied BALB/c mouse model (41). The results of these experiments are shown in Table X.

Some but not all inbred non-responder strains were found to develop GT induced suppression of GT-MBSA responses. We may, therefore, conclude: a) that immune suppression cannot account for non-responder status in all cases, b) that GT immunization permits us to identify two distinct phenotypes among inbred strains of mice that differ in their suscept-ibility to GT induced suppression. We shall refer to these as "suppressor" and "nonsuppressor" phenotypes. The genetic analysis of the specific suppressor responses could only be carried out by using an antigen that does not stimulate anti-body responses in a large number of mouse strains. The capacity to develop GT induced suppression of GT-MBSA responses was shown to be inherited as a dominant trait in F_1 hybrids resulting from the mating of "suppressors" with "nonsuppressor" strains. This trait is, therefore, under the control of a gene or genes which we have designated as specific immune suppression gene(s)(*Is* genes) to distinguish them from *Ir* genes. In contrast, the F_1 crosses between GAT responders and nonresponders behaved as responders to GAT, in keeping with the dominant character of *H-2* linked-*Ir* genes, indicating that responder phenotypes are generally dominant over suppressor phenotype (42,43).

243

TABLE X

STRAIN DIFFERENCES IN SUPPRESSION BY GT OF PFC RESPONSES TO GT-MBSA[1]

Strain	H-2	Maalox + GT-MBSA PFC/Spleen (Ar. Mean ± SE)	GT + GT-MBSA PFC/Spleen (Ar. Mean ± SE)	% Suppression	P Value
A/J	a	10,436 ± 1,952	12,593 ± 1,714	0	.4
B10.A*	a	12,118 ± 1,746	15,631 ± 3,398	0	.3
A.By	b	11,075 ± 2,174	14,286 ± 2,179	0	.3
C57BL/10	b	17,325 ± 3,445	15,843 ± 3,549	0	.7
BALB/c	d	12,658 ± 750	2,566 ± 492	80	.000001
B10.D2	d	9,187 ± 977	3,325 ± 1,920	64	.03
D1.C	d	15,503 ± 3,001	3,753 ± 1,271	76	.002
A.CA	f	10,775 ± 2,049	<200	100	.00009
DBA/1	q	7,374 ± 1,028	9,562 ± 843	0	.1
SJL	s	10,401 ± 887	3,012 ± 652	72	.000001
A.SW	s	8,500 ± 1,300	2,800 ± 800	68	.001
(BALB/c x A/J)F₁	a/d	10,437 ± 1,443	2,809 ± 1,075	74	.0001
(DBA/1 x SJL)F₁	q/s	13,555 ± 2,019	1,360 ± 838	90	.0005

[1] One hundred μg of GT in Maalox or Maalox alone was administered i.p., followed 3 days later by 10 μg of GT complexed with MBSA. Seven days later, the number of IgG-specific PFC per spleen were counted using sheep red blood cells coated with GAT.

*B10.A mice were immunized with GT-MBSA with Maalox and *B. Pertussis* as adjuvant.

The other major conclusion from the strain distribution of GT-induced suppression of GT-MBSA responses is that the Is gene(s) controlling these responses are coded for in the $H-2$ complex. Mice bearing $H-2^a$, $H-2^f$, or $H-2^s$ haplotypes exhibit the GT specific "suppressor" phenotype while mice possessing the $H-2^a$, $H-2^b$, or $H-2^q$ haplotypes are GT "nonsuppressors" irrespective of non-$H-2$ background genotypes. The $H-2$-linked Is gene(s) controlling GT-induced immune suppression identified in this study are "specific" for this antigen. They are not concerned with the general capacity to develop suppression, since DBA/1 ($H-2^q$) mice which develop suppressor T cells following GAT immunization are not specifically suppressed by GT and, therefore, lack the GT Is gene. Genetic similarities between H-linked Is and Ir genes are illustrated by the following observations: 1) Ir genes have been shown to be concerned with the expression of helper function in T cell-dependent responses (1-3); 2) helper and suppressor activity of T cells appear to be two related aspects of the regulatory activity of these cells on specific immune responses; 3) the ability to mount antibody responses in systems under Ir gene control has been shown to be associated with the production of antigen-specific factors produced by responder T cells and endowed with helper activity for B cells (20,35); 4) similar antigen-specific factors with specific suppressor activity have been obtained from suppressor T cells (36, 37, 38); and 5) both helper and suppressor factors have similar molecular size and possess antigenic determinants coded for in the I region of the $H-2$ complex (36-38).

Compared to the extensive information concerning mouse $H-2$-linked Ir genes and their precise mapping in subregions of I, our understanding of Is genes is as yet very limited.

The detailed analysis which is in progress of the structural and biological relationships of antigen-specific helper and suppressor factors from T cells should permit a better understanding of the function of $H-2$-linked Is and Ir genes and their products.

REFERENCES

1. B. Benacerraf and H.O. McDevitt. Science 109 (1972) 273.

2. B. Benacerraf and M.E. Dorf. Progress in Immunol. II 2 (1974) 181.

REFERENCES (continued)

3. B. Benacerraf and D.H. Katz. Adv. Cancer Research 21 (1975) 121.

4. H.O. McDevitt and A. Chinitz. Science 163 (1969) 1207.

5. L. Ellman, I. Green, W.J. Martin and B. Benacerraf. Proc. Nat. Acad. Sci. U.S.A. 66 (1970) 322.

6. E. Rüde and E. Günther. Progress in Immunol. II. 2 (1974) 223.

7. E. Günther, J. Balcarova, K. Hala, E. Rude and T. Hraba. Eur. J. Immunol. 4 (1974) 548.

8. M.E. Dorf, H. Balner, M.L. de Groot and B. Benacerraf. Transplant. Proc. 6 (1974) 119.

9. M.E. Dorf, H. Balner and B. Benacerraf. J. Exp. Med. 142 (1975) 673.

10. D.H. Katz, M. Graves, M.E. Dorf, H. DiMuzio and B. Benacerraf. J. Exp. Med. 141 (1975) 263.

11. M.E. Dorf, D.H. Katz, M. Graves, H. DiMuzio and B. Benacerraf. J. Immunol. 114 (1975) 1717.

12. B. Benacerraf and D.H. Katz. in: Immunogenetics and Immunodeficiency. ed. B. Benacerraf. (Tech. Pub., London, 1975). In Press.

13. F. H. Bach, M. L. Bach, P. M. Sondel and G. Sundharadas. Transplant. Rev. 12 (1972) 30.

14. T. Meo, J. Vives, V. Miggiano and D.C. Shreffler. Transplant. Proc. 5 (1973) 377.

15. J. Klein and J.M. Park. J. Exp. Med. 137 (1973) 1213.

16. D.C. Shreffler and C.S. David. Adv. Immunol. 20 (1975) 125.

17. V. Hauptfeld, D. Klein and J. Klein. Science (Wash. D.C.) 181 (1973) 167.

REFERENCES   (continued)

18. E.R. Unanue, M.E. Dorf, C.S. David and B. Benacerraf. Proc. Nat. Acad. Sci. U.S.A. 71 (1974) 5014.

19. D.H. Katz, M.E. Dorf, D. Armerding and B. Benacerraf. in: Molecular Approaches to Immunology. Miami Winter Symposia, Vol. 9. eds. E.E. Smith and D.W. Ribbons. (Academic Press, New York). p. 211.

20. M.J. Taussig. Nature. 248 (1974) 234.

21. J.H. Stimpfling and T. Durham. J. Immunol. 108 (1972) 947.

22. E. Rüde and E. Günther. Prog. Immunol. II. 2 (1974) 223.

23. E. Günther, J. Balcarova, K. Hala, E. Rüde and T. Hraba. Eur. J. Immunol. 4 (1974) 548.

24. M. Zaleski, H. Fuji and F. Milgrom. Transplant. Proc. 5 (1973) 201.

25. M.E. Dorf, J.H. Stimpfling and B. Benacerraf. J. Exp. Med. 141 (1975) 1459.

26. C. Merryman, P.H. Maurer and D.W. Bailey. J. Immunol. 108 (1972) 937.

27. C. Merryman, P.H. Maurer and J.H. Stimpfling. Immuno- genetics 2 (1975) 441.

28. M.E. Dorf, F. Lilly and B. Benacerraf. J. Exp. Med. 140 (1974) 859.

29. M.E. Dorf and B. Benacerraf. Proc. Nat. Acad. Sci. (1975) 3671.

30. D.C. Shreffler and C.S. David. Adv. Immunol. 20 (1975) 125.

31. A.J. Munro and M.J. Taussig. Nature 256 (1975) 104.

32. M.E. Dorf, P.H. Maurer, C. Merryman and B. Benacerraf. Manuscript in preparation.

REFERENCES   (continued)

33.   S.L. Tosi, R.G. Mage and S. Dubiski.   J. Immunol. 104
      (1970) 641.

34.   K. Eichmann.   J. Exp. Med. 137 (1973) 603.

35.   E. Mozes, R. Isac and M.J. Taussig. J. Exp. Med.   141
      (1975) 703.

36.   T. Tada, M. Taniguchi and T. Takemori.   Transplant.
      Rev. 26 (1975) In Press.

37.   M. Zembala, G.L. Asherson, B. Mayhem and J. Krijci.
      Nature 253 (1975) 72.

38.   J.A. Kapp, C.W. Pierce and B. Benacerraf.   J. Immunol.
      (1976) In press.

39.   J.A. Kapp, C.W. Pierce, S. Schlossman and B. Benacerraf.
      J. Exp. Med. 140   (1974) 648.

40.   P. Debré, J.A. Kapp and B. Benacerraf.   J. Exp. Med.
      (1976) In press.

41.   P. Debré, M.E. Dorf, J.A. Kapp and B. Benacerraf.
      J. Exp. Med. (1976) In press.

42.   J.A. Kapp, C.W. Pierce and B. Benacerraf.   J. Exp. Med.
      138   (1973) 1107.

43.   J.A. Kapp, C.W. Pierce and B. Benacerraf. J. Exp. Med.
      140 (1974) 172.

DISCUSSION FOLLOWING BARUJ BENACERRAF

SACHS: Your mapping for suppression in the GT system indicate one gene to the right of $I-A$ and one to the left of $I-C$. Could it be that the $I-B$ region controls suppression and if so, might a deletion in this region lead to responsiveness?

BENACERRAF: That possibility is eliminated by the fact that $H-2^b$ is not a suppressor haplotype and the D2.GD strain with the following genotype dd/bbbb is not suppressed by GT immunization.

MOZES: I refer to Dr. Benacerraf's remark that there is a difference between the GLΦ system and the (T,G)-A--L antigenic system in the sense that by studying DNA synthesis by measuring thymidine incorporation in low and high responders to GLΦ, it appeared that the two genes involved in the response to this copolymer are expressed in T cells.

In the case of (T,G)-A--L, it has been shown by Drs. Lonai and McDevitt that T cells of $H-2^k$ mice which produce an active T cell factor, and therefore bear no defect in their helper T cells, do not proliferate as measured by thymidine incorporation. These results are similar to those obtained with GLΦ and we have interpreted them by assuming that while one gene which controls the response to (T,G)-A--L is expressed in the B cell population of $H-2^k$ mice, the second gene may be expressed in either T helper cells, as in the case of SJL low responder mice to (T,G)-A--L, or in a second population of T cells as in the case of $H-2^k$ mice.

BENACERRAF: I agree with Edna Mozes that if one postulates two types of T cells involved in sensitization for blast transformation in culture, the GLΦ system does not differ from the (T,G)-A--L system as far as gene expression of complementing genes where T cells are concerned. The possibility has also to be considered in both systems of the expression of one of both genes in macrophages.

GERSHON: Have you had the chance in the beautiful suppression gene system you described to try some of the standard techniques for alleviating suppression such as adult thymectomy, splenectomy or low dose cyclophospha-

249

mide treatment?

BENACERRAF: We have not carried out such experiments as
yet with the exception of those which Judy Kapp has
carried out in collaboration with you on SJL mice in the
GAT system.   Non-responder SJL mice are rendered responders to GAT by adult thymectomy, as you know; but
that is the only system investigated in this respect.
In these mice, the suppressor phenotype would, therefore, appear to be dominant over the responder phenotype to GAT.

MILLER: You found that GT copolymers do not induce antibody
in most strains of mice with the exception of a few
Swiss strains.   Could this be a reflection of the activation by GT in most strains of a suppressor mechanism
which prevents effective activation of T lymphocytes?
Would it be possible to examine this by pretreating
non-responder strains with agents such as cyclophosphamide known to interfere selectively with the activity
of suppressor T cells, and then to determine, for
example, whether the lymphocytes of the pretreated non-
responder mice can now be stimulated by GT to incorporate thymidine *in vitro?* Alternatively, one could look
for a delayed-type hypersensitivity response to GT using
the radioisotopic assay we developed.

BENACERRAF: We have not used cyclophosphamide in our
experiments.   It is a good idea to try.   However, we
feel sure that these are non-responder haplotypes which
are non-suppressors; that is precisely what we have
demonstrated in the GT system.

[*EDITOR'S NOTE*: Refer to Dr. Miller's paper in this
volume which was presented in a later session of the
conference for a better insight into the background for
the above question - DHK.]

J. KLEIN: At the end of my presentation, I made a remark
which disturbed some people present at this meeting;
namely, that the *Ir* genes may not be terribly specific.
By this statement I meant the following: An *Ir* gene
distinguishing between two related polypeptides such as
GLΦ and GLPro certainly appears very specific.   However,
this apparent specificity may be misleading.   There are
now several instances where the strain distribution
patterns of responsiveness to totally unrelated antigens

(e.g. Thy-1 and ovalbumin) are the same. Although such correlation might be, of course, coincidental, it is also possible that it may reflect a control by the same *Ir* gene. Should this be the case, we could envision that the *Ir* genes recognize, for example, certain short amino acid sequences and thus distinguish closely related antigens but are unable to distinguish some unrelated antigens which happen to share these amino acid stretches. I am inclined to think that there is only a low number of *Ir* genes in the *I* region, that these genes are highly polymorphic, that at least a part of their specificity is generated by gene interaction and that the range of antigenic determinants that they can distinguish is <u>relatively</u> small, certainly smaller than that expected from a true receptor of the type present on a B cell. According to this concept, the *Ir* genes would code for the Ia antigens, would not code for the variable region of the T cell receptor, and would play only an ancillory function in antigen recognition; correspondingly, their range of recognitive capacity would be rather limited.

BENACERRAF: I agree with Jan Klein that the range of specificity encompassed by the Ir gene products is much smaller than that encompassed by immunoglobulins. However, this is only the extent of our agreement. I prefer to consider that the degree of specificity demonstrated by the recognition system coded for *Ir* genes is still considerable and precise and, furthermore, that it implies heterogeneity at the level of the Ir gene product rather than polymorphism at limited number of loci as suggested by Klein. With respect to the same response patterns observed for distant antigens, these are the exception rather than the rule. Moreover, in immunoglobulin idiotypes, Oudin has recently demonstrated common idiotypes in antibodies against widely distinct non-cross-reacting antigens and no one would use this argument to conclude that immunoglobulins are not heterogeneous.

[*EDITOR'S NOTE*: This issue is discussed at considerably greater length in the general discussion in Session VIII-DHK.]

MCDEVITT: There is abundant evidence for *Ir* gene specificity. For TTGG-A--L and G-T-A--L, there is *H-2*-linked *Ir* gene control, while GTTG-A--L and T-G-A--L specified sequence antigens are not under H-2-linked control. Thus, sequence inversions alone are recognized by these genes.

As to the argument that H-2^α and H-2^k control the responses to (H,G)-A--L, BGG and ovomucoid and are, therefore, not specific, I would refer to the Ig idiotype-allotype linkage group. In the latter case, several different idiotypes can be linked to the same constant region allotype, but each idiotype is still highly specific.

BENACERRAF: With McDevitt on my side of the controversy, I do not need a better advocate to defend our position.

RAJEWSKY: I should like to take up Jan Klein's suggestion that the number of different Ir genes in the H-2 complex may be rather small and discuss it together with McDevitt's idiotype argument. In the case of immunoglobulin idiotypes, a given idiotype usually represents only a minor fraction of the total antibody population, which is composed by a large variety of different idiotypes. If there were a similar variety of Ir genes coding for receptors on T cells, it would be difficult to imagine how we could ever find low responder animals, in analogy to the rare occurrence of low responsiveness based on presence or absence of antibody v genes.

McDEVITT: I was using the allotype analogy not to imply that all of the antibody was of a given idiotype, but simply to show that one chromosome could code for several different, highly specific idiotypes and that by analogy one H-2 complex could easily code for response to several different antigens via the possession of several different, highly specific genes which ultimately might be separable by recombination.

RAJEWSKY: I perfectly agree on your point concerning the specificity of Ir gene products. As far as concerns this diversity, the expectation is, I think as Jan Klein does, that it will be restricted as compared to the diversity of antibody combining sites.

BENACERRAF: I have addressed myself to this issue earlier in the discussion and I agree that the dictionary of Ir genes and their products is considerably smaller than the dictionary of specific immunoglobulin specificities coded by v genes.

SELA: When discussing specificity as it relates to the genetic control of immune response, we should distinguish clearly between the specificity of antigen determinants reflected in antibodies and specific receptors on sensitized cells, and the specificity of what I suggest to call "immunogenetic control" determinants. These are chemical structures within the antigenic macromolecules which are responsible for the genetic control of immune responses. Good examples appear to be stretches of L-lysine in strain 13 guinea pigs, stretches of L-proline in SWR mice and stretches of DL-alanine in SJL mice. Another good example is the role of oligotyrosine for the response of SJL mice to the GA polymer. These mice respond well to GA but not to GAT_{10}. Indeed, attaching pentatyrosine to GA abolishes the immune response in SJL mice (unpublished work of Michael Schwartz and Rachel Mizrachi). In all these cases, there is a positive recognition of the immunogenetic control determinants, resulting in no immune response.

BENACERRAF: I agree with Michael Sela.

MAURER: I would agree with the remarks of Dr. Sela. If we put oligopeptides of tyrosine on GA, we can turn off the response of SJL mice to GA. However, if we have the tyrosine present in a limited amount, 5-10% as tyrosyl resides, which I will show later, the response pattern of SJL mice doesn't change. Also, the polymer GAT^4 is immunogenic in SJL mice. The polymer GAT^{10} is a mixture of suppressor and immunogenic molecules.

The question to Dr. Benacerraf. A finding that concerns us as well as you is the positive response to GLΦ of SJL x C57BL/6 mice. Theoretically, those mice have two β genes and no α genes, yet the response is very good. Do you have ideas as to why this occurs?

BENACERRAF: We have investigated the possible complementation for GLΦ responses between two α genes and between β genes. It is clear that α(+)/ α(+) complementation does not work, and we believe that the α genes in $H\text{-}2^a$, and $H\text{-}2^k$ and $H\text{-}2^d$ may very well be identical. With respect to β genes, complementation for GLΦ response has been observed between the β genes of $H\text{-}2^s$ and $H\text{-}2^b$

haplotypes, but this is only observed in the
(SJL x B10)F_{1b} hybrid. It is clear that the β genes of
$H-2^s$ and $H-2^{.b}$ haplotype are different but complement
poorly and that the SJL background plays a role in this
response.

E. MÖLLER: In case you are not going to discuss this on
Friday morning, would you discuss the mechanism for
suppressor cells being relatively ineffective in the
secondary response.

BENACERRAF: Specific suppressor cells can suppress secondary GT responses in $H-2^d$ BALB/c mice. However, this
phenomenon is more difficult to demonstrate than the
suppression of the primary response. To suppress
secondary responses to GT-MBSA, the mice must be preimmunized with GT twice, once before the primary and
once again three days before secondary challenge with
GT-MBSA. This may be due to the poor memory exhibited
by the suppressor T cells and also by the greater
refractoriness of secondary cells to suppression.

E. MÖLLER: But then you have to explain the critical time
interval needed for an effect.

BENACERRAF: There is no critical time interval needed for
suppressive effects. Suppression is observed as early
as 3 days after primary immunization and as late as 28
days. No data exist for secondary immunization with
respect to how long the suppressor effect lasts after
two injections of GT, as revealed by a secondary challenge with GT-MBSA.

GERSHON: I would like to add a comment to support and
amplify Baruj's answer to Erna Möller. It is a general
finding that as T cells differentiate in response to
antigen, they become more and more resistant to suppressor mechanisms and, therefore, it is not surprising
that a secondary response should be harder to suppress
than a primary.

E. MÖLLER: Yes, but those same cells seem to become more
sensitive to other factors, such as helper factor,
during differentiation.

PAUL: The introduction of the concept of immune suppression
(*Is*) genes may provide a mechanism resolving the problem

of dominant genetic control of disease susceptibility.
Thus, disease involving augmented immune responses could
easily be ascribed to a dominant immune response gene.
However, diseases involving diminished immune responses
are much more difficult to relate to immune response
genes. One could anticipate, in such cases, that
disease susceptibility would require homozygosity for a
low responder *Ir* gene. *Is* genes could exert a dominant
depressive ability on human immune responses to agents
of immunopathogenic significance. Furthermore, the two
gene concept of immune suppression could explain the
gene disequilibrium in disease susceptibility because
it would indicate interaction between two genes in the
same haplotype.

BENACERRAF: In the only system which we have investigated
for this question, the GAT system, helper function in
F_1 crosses is phenotypically dominant over suppressor
function. However, the possibility must be entertained
that this is not universally the case and that some
systems may exist where suppression might be dominant.

McDEVITT: Could you give us more detail on situations in
which suppression is dominant over help. We have
always been puzzled by the response of the $H\text{-}2^\alpha$ haplotype to (T,G)-A--L, where the response varies from low
to intermediate to high. This is not due to residual
heterozygosity and might be the outcome of a competition
between helper and suppressor T cells.

BENACERRAF: While we feel, theoretically, that the possibility that suppression may be phenotypically dominant
over helper function must be considered very seriously,
and probably exists in certain genetic combinations, up
to now we have had limited experience. In the GAT
system which was the only one we could study in this
respect to date; the hybrids between non-responder suppressor strains such as SJL ($H\text{-}2^s$) or DBA/1 ($H\text{-}2^q$) with
responder strains behave as responders to GAT. More
experience with other systems is necessary to discovery
situations where suppression may be phenotypically
dominant over helper function.

FUNCTIONAL ANALYSIS OF Ia ANTIGENS
IN RELATION TO GENETIC CONTROL OF THE IMMUNE RESPONSE

HUGH O. McDEVITT

Division of Immunology
Department of Medicine
Stanford University School of Medicine

INTRODUCTION

During the past several years, a considerable amount of evidence has accumulated suggesting that histocompatibility linked specific immune response genes control the recognition of antigen at the carrier, and presumably the T cell, level (1,2). More recently, additional evidence has given indirect support for this concept. Responder and non-responder mouse strains make an equal 19S primary response to aqueous (T,G)-A--L, while only responders show a brisk 7S secondary response. Thymectomy affects the 7S secondary response in the responder strain, but has no effect on the primary response in either strain. These data suggest that the defect in the non-responder strain is in the ability of T cells to induce B cells to make a shift from 19S to 7S antibody production, and/or to generate sufficient numbers of memory B cells of the 7S type (3,4). The demonstration that specific antigen induced tritiated thymidine uptake following immunization was detectable only in responder strains, and was inhibited by exposure to antisera directed against the responder major histocompatibility complex (MHC), also indicated that the non-responder strain was deficient in T cell recognition of specific antigen (5,6,7) and that products of the MHC were involved in this recognition.

Studies of antigen binding T and B cells in (T,G)-A--L responders and non-responders produced several interesting findings. First, the numbers of B antigen binding cells following aqueous (T,G)-A--L immunization rose in the responder strain, but not in the non-responder strain (8). In both strains, antigen-binding B cells following immunization were inhibitable only by anti-IgG antibody, and not by anti-

257

IgM antibody. Thus, B cells in the non-responder have switched from IgM to IgG receptors on their surface, despite the fact that they do not produce significant amounts of serum IgG antibody (9,10). This finding suggests that the non-responder is capable of developing memory B cells, but that sufficient T cell help for triggering these B cells does not exist. It is not clear whether this B cell transition can take place in the absence of T cell help, or whether a specific type of T cell required for helping 7S IgG memory B cells is lacking in the non-responder. These studies also showed that the non-responder strain failed to produce increased numbers of antigen-binding T cells following immunization and boosting. This finding again is compatible with, but does not establish, a defect in the non-responder T cell. In contrast, the number of T antigen-binding cells rose in both the responder and non-responder for an allotype-linked immune response defect, while antigen-binding B cells rose only in the responder (8).

Studies in tetraparental embryo fusion chimeras made between responder and non-responder strains also indicated that there was no defect in the ability of the non-responder B cell to respond to (T,G)-A--L if it was in a histocompatible (tolerant) combination with responder T and B cells (11). At the same time, experiments from other laboratories (12,13) indicated that the defect in C3H mice in their ability to respond to (T,G)-A--L was due to a B cell defect, and that the T cells from the responder and non-responder strains were equally competent. The controversy between these two sets of experimental findings remains to be resolved, and will be referred to below.

The discovery of the immune response associated (Ia) antigens (14) has permitted the first direct identification of an $\underline{I}$ region gene product. Despite the expectation on the part of many investigators that these antigens would prove to be T cell surface antigens related to specific $\underline{Ir}$ gene function, initial evidence indicated that these antigens were found primarily on B lymphocytes (15,16). It was only possible to demonstrate their presence on T lymphocytes by extraordinarily sensitive techniques (17), or indirectly, through the use of T cells as stimulator cells in the mixed lymphocyte reaction (18). The Ia antigens, at present, constitute the $\underline{only}$ known $\underline{I}$ region gene product. While it seems clear that these antigens are responsible for eliciting the mixed lymphocyte reaction and the graft-versus-host reaction (14), and have been implicated as part of specific helper (13) and suppressor (19) factors which can be isolated from sensitized

T cells, direct demonstration of Ia antigens on T cells by cytotoxicity, binding assays, or biochemical extraction (16, 20) have proven negative in our own and other laboratories. I region antigens have also been implicated as the molecules mediating effective collaboration between T cells and B cells in generating a humoral antibody response (21). Because of the difficulty of demonstrating Ia antigens directly on T cell populations, and because of the evidence implicating the Ia antigens in a number of aspects of the cellular and humoral immune response, we have undertaken a systematic analysis of the functions of Ia antigens in B cell and T cell subpopulations.

Ia ANTIGEN EXPRESSION ON B CELL SUBPOPULATIONS

In order to determine whether Ia antigens are expressed on all hapten specific, primary and secondary antibody forming precursor cells (B cells) and whether Ia antigenic expression differentiates between B cell subpopulations, spleen cells from non-immune (primary) and previously immunized (secondary) BALB.K ($H-2^k$) mice were treated with A.TH anti-A.TL antiserum (anti-Ia^k) and complement, or with A.TH normal mouse serum (NMS) and complement. The treated spleen cells were then analyzed for DNP-specific precursor cell activity by an in vitro splenic focus technique for B cell cloning, which maximizes carrier help for B cell stimulation (22). The results of these experiments, carried out by Joan Press and Norman Klinman (23), are shown in Figures 1 and 2.

After pretreatment with normal mouse serum and complement, the average frequency of BALB.K primary DNP-specific precursor cells ranged from 6-10 precursors per 10^6 total cells injected, with an average frequency of 7.6. After pretreatment with anti-Ia^k and complement, the mean clonal precursor cell frequency was lowered to 0.9 per 10^6 injected cells, a reduction in primary precursor cell frequency of 88% (Fig. 1). The majority of primary precursor cells are thus Ia positive, but a small amount of precursor cell activity remains in the spleen cell population after pretreatment with anti-Ia^k and complement. As shown in Figure 2, the mean frequency of normal mouse serum and complement treated DNP-specific secondary precursors is $13.5/10^6$ injected cells. This frequency is reduced 96% (to 0.6 precursor cells/10^6) after pretreatment with anti-Ia^k and complement. Thus, in the secondary response, almost all precursor cells are Ia positive.

259

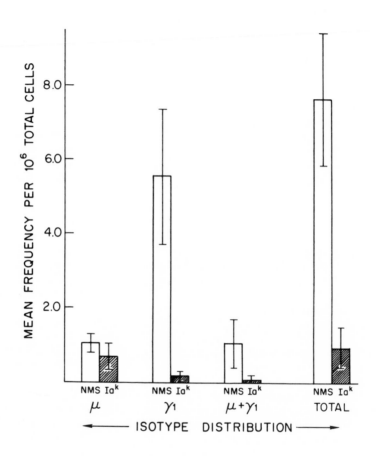

Figure 1. Primary DNP-specific precursor cell frequency per 10⁶ total injectec cells, after pre-treatment with NMS or anti-Ia^k and C'. Error bars represent standard of the mean. Heavy chain class (isotype) of monofocal antibody produced per clone determined by a radioimmunoassay.

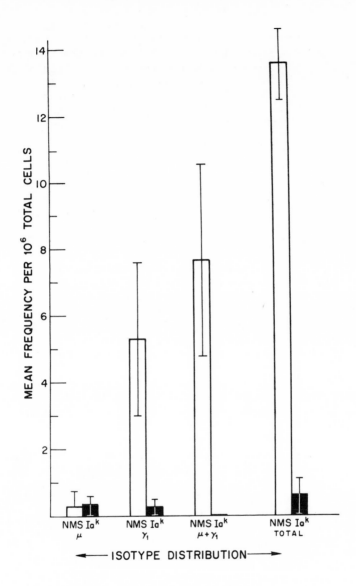

Figure 2. Secondary DNP-specific precursor cell frequency per 10^6 total injected cells, after pretreatment with NMS or anti-Ia^k, and C'. Error bars represent standard of the mean. Heavy chain class (isotype) of monofocal antibody produced per clone determined by a radioimmunoassay.

The mono-focal anti-DNP antibodies produced by primary
and secondary clones derived from anti-Ia^k, or NMS, and complement treated spleen cells were analyzed for immunoglobulin
class distribution by a radioimmunoassay. It is apparent
from Figure 1 that the heavy chain class distribution of antibodies produced by primary clones derived from spleen cells
treated with anti-Ia^k and complement differs from that of the
normal mouse serum and complement treated precursor cells.
Thus, 78% of the Ia "negative" precursor cells gave rise to
clones producing anti-DNP antibody solely of the IgM class, in
contrast to only 14% of the clones in the normal mouse serum
and complement treated group producing solely IgM antibody.
The 88% reduction in the total primary precursor cell frequency is correlated with the marked reduction in the mean
frequency of precursor cells giving rise to IgG$_1$ or to both
IgG$_1$and IgM anti-DNP antibody producing clones. These two
types of clones were reduced by more than 95% and 90% respectively, while the number of clones producing only IgM antibody only did not show a significant reduction. Anti-Ia^k and
complement pretreatment of immunized spleen cells reduced the
frequency of secondary precursor cells giving rise to IgG$_1$
antibody by 95% and to IgG$_1$ and IgM double producing clones
by 100%. The very low frequency of precursor cells giving
rise to clones producing only IgM antibody was not affected.

These results indicate that the expression of Ia determinants delineates at least two subpopulations of primary B
cells. The majority of precursor cells are Ia positive and
can give rise to IgG antibody production. A small subset of
primary precursor cells, however, are Ia "negative" and constitute those B cells which give rise solely to IgM producing
clones (23). Two pieces of evidence suggest that Ia mediates
the specific induction of the B cell switch from IgM to IgG
antibody production. First, the precursor cells which give
rise to IgG antibody producing clones are eliminated by pretreatment with anti-Ia and complement (23). Second, Pierce
and Klinman (24) have demonstrated that 60-70% of primary precursor cells can be stimulated by allogeneic T cells, but then
give rise only to IgM antibody producing clones. This result
occurs only in allogeneic combinations including an I-A and
I-B region difference. (No clones arise from allogeneic
recipients which were not primed with hemocyanin.) Thus, the
I region appears to determine whether allogeneic B cell-T
cell interaction will lead to IgG antibody production (24).
Since the majority of primary precursor cells are Ia positive
and can give rise to IgG production upon stimulation with
syngeneic T cells (23), it would appear that the Ia positive
precursor can give rise either to IgM or to IgG production,

depending on whether or not I region differences exist between the two cell types. Ia recognitive interactions between T cells and B cells, however, are not required for stimulation to IgM production (23). It is not yet clear whether the μ to γ switch is mediated by carrier-specific T cells recognizing B cell Ia antigens, or whether syngeneic T cells permit the isotype switch to occur, but this is somehow prevented by allogeneic T cells which recognize Ia antigens. Nevertheless, the composite data indicate that Ia antigens play a critical role in the induction of the B cell switch from IgM to IgG antibody production in the response to DNP-Hy. It remains to be seen whether this will be true for other antigens which are T cell dependent.

Ia ANTIGEN EXPRESSION ON T CELL SUBPOPULATIONS

As has already been noted, direct demonstration of Ia antigens on T cells by cytotoxicity, binding assays, or biochemical extraction (16,20) have either been negative, or have shown minimal T cell cytotoxicity with anti-Ia and complement (17). However, it is quite possible either that a relatively small percentage of the total T cell population is Ia positive, and/or that these cells express such small amounts of Ia antigens that they are relatively resistant to cytotoxicity mediated by anti-Ia antisera. Small amounts of Ia antigen could be below the level of detection by direct binding assays, or by biochemical extraction. Evidence for the presence or absence of Ia antigens on functional T cell subpopulations was sought by negative selection against a particular T cell function using anti-Ia and complement. The anti-Ia antisera used showed minimal (5-10%) direct cytotoxicity against purified T cell populations, but had high titers of cytotoxicity directed towards B cells, and were capable of killing 85-90% of splenic B cells.

Two T cell manifestations of cellular immunity were studied in experiments performed by Peter Lonai -- the responder cell in the mixed lymphocyte reaction (MLR) and the precursor and effector cell in the cell mediated lympholysis reaction. The results of a typical experiment in which an attempt was made to eliminate MLR responder cells by treatment with anti-Ia and complement serum is shown in Figure 3. In this experiment, B10.A lymphocytes were exposed to B10.S irradiated stimulator cells after treatment with anti-Ia alone, or with anti-Ia and complement. As the figure indicates, treatment with anti-Ia and complement did not significantly reduce the MLR. When the number of Ia negative responder cells was made equal to the number of viable responder

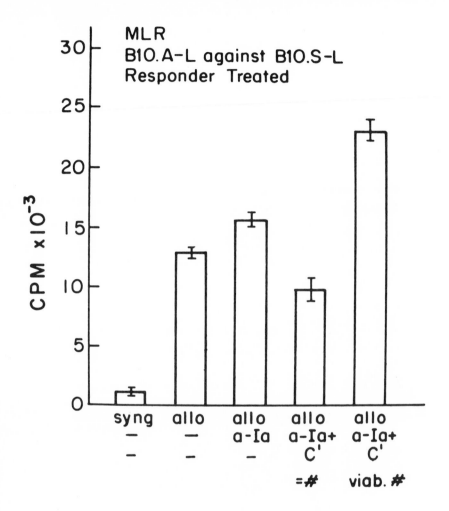

Figure 3. Effect of anti-Ia^k, or anti-Ia^k and complement, on the proliferative response of B10.A lymph node cells to B10.S irradiated stimulator lymph node cells. Syng = syngeneic Allo = allogeneic Viab = viable

cells in the original MLR reaction mixture, the response was potentiated, suggesting that the Ia negative population was enriched for MLR responders. These results are similar to those found by Meo (25; T. Meo, this volume), who also found no effect of anti-Ia antisera on the responder cell in the mixed lymphocyte culture reaction. It therefore appears that the majority of this T cell population is functionally Ia negative by the criterion of anti-Ia and complement mediated cytotoxicity.

The presence or absence of Ia antigens on the precursor cell and the effector cell for cell mediated cytotoxicity was tested in a similar manner. Figure 4 demonstrates the effect of anti-Ia and complement on the precursor cell for cell mediated lympholysis. In this experiment, B10.BR responder cells were treated with anti-Ia^k and complement, following which they were washed and incubated with B10.S stimulator cells. Following five days incubation, sensitized B10.BR cells were then tested for cytotoxicity against ^{51}Cr labeled B10.S PHA blast cells. As the figure indicates, anti-Ia and complement pretreatment had no effect on the development of cytotoxic effector cells during the subsequent mixed lymphocyte reaction. It thus appears that the majority of precursor cells for T cell mediated cytotoxicity are Ia negative. A similar experiment was also carried out for the effector cell for cell mediated cytotoxicity which was generated in the five day mixed lymphocyte reaction. In this experiment, the cells from a mixed lymphocyte reaction between B10.BR responders and B10.S irradiated stimulators were treated with anti-Ia and complement prior to testing for cell-mediated cytotoxicity against ^{51}Cr labeled B10.S PHA blast cell targets. Once again, anti-Ia^k and complement had no effect on the degree of cytotoxicity manifested by this cell population against labeled target cells. Thus, the majority of effector cells in cell mediated cytotoxicity also appear to be Ia negative T cells (26).

Experiments designed to test the presence of Ia antigens on helper T cells and on suppressor T cells were carried out be Drs. Ko Okumura and Donal Murphy in collaboration with Ms. L.A. Herzenberg. The effect of anti-Ia sera on helper T cell activity was tested in a well-characterized (SJL x BALB/c)F$_1$ syngeneic cell transfer system (27) in which DNP-KLH primed B cells depleted of T cells by treatment with anti-Thy-1.2 and complement are injected together with graded and limiting numbers of KLH primed syngeneic spleen cells into an irradiated recipient. The response is assayed by the

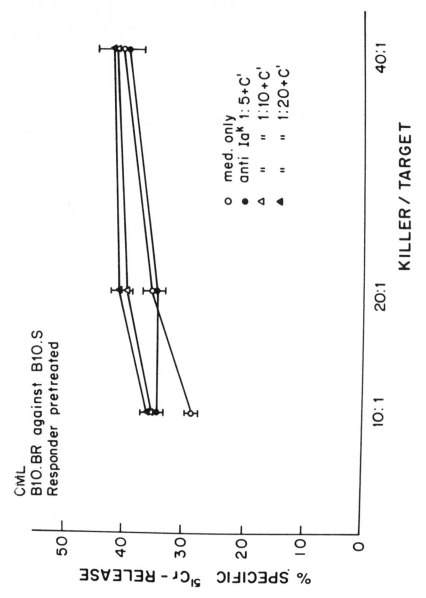

Figure 4. Effect of anti-Ia^k and complement on the ability of <u>in vitro</u> sensitized B10.BR lympho-cytes to lyse ^{51}Cr labelled, PHA stimulated B10.S target cells.

number of DNP-PFC found in the recipient spleen. Several such experiments have been carried out, and the results of one experiment using A.TL anti-A.TH antisera which had been absorbed with either A.TL (cells of the strain producing the antiserum) or A.TH (cells against which the antiserum is produced) are shown in Table 1. DNP-KLH primed B cells gave rise

TABLE 1

EFFECT OF ANTI-Ia ON HELPER CELLS

(SJL x Balb/c)F_1 Spleen
Cells Transferred (x 10^6)[1]

DNP-KLH 1^0 T Depleted[2]	KLH 1^0	Treatment[3]	Indirect DNP-PFC/10^6
4	--	--	218
4	4	NMS	1216
4	4	A.TL anti-A.TH abs. in vitro with A.TL	206
4	4	A.TL anti-A.TH abs. in vitro with A.TH	1021
4	4	A.TL anti-A.TH abs. in vivo with A.TL	513
4	4	A.TL anti-A.TH abs in vivo with A.TH	1231

[1] Balb/c irradiated (600 R) recipients.

[2] Anti-Thy-1.2 plus complement treated.

[3] A.TL anti-A.TH contains anti-Ia^s antibody reactive with (SJL x Balb/c)F_1 (Ia^s/Ia^d). KLH 1^0 spleen (T source) treated with antiserum plus complement. In vitro absorption performed with spleen and lymph node.

to 218 anti-DNP indirect PFC/10^6. The addition of 4 million KLH primed spleen cells treated with normal mouse serum and complement increased this to 1216 anti-DNP-PFC. Treatment with A.TL anti-A.TH absorbed in vitro or in vivo with A.TL caused a marked reduction in the number of anti-DNP-PFC produced, to control levels with in vitro absorbed antisera, and almost to control levels with in vivo absorbed antisera. On the other hand, absorption of the antisera with A.TH completely removed the inhibitory effect of this antiserum on T cell help for the anti-DNP response.

Although these data show that treatment with A.TL anti-A.TH specifically eliminates helper activity, they must be regarded as preliminary. It remains to be demonstrated that I region antibody is responsible. (This antiserum potentially contains antibody against determinants controlled by the I, S, or G regions of the H-2 complex, as well as against determinants encoded by closely linked genes lying outside the complex, e.g. Tla). Using several other cell transfer systems, it has been difficult in the past to show any effect of anti-Ia on T cell helper activity (unpublished observations, 28). This might be due in some instances to failure to establish true limiting conditions for T cell help, or working with sera which do not contain the relevant antibody. The experiments reported here must be repeated with a number of other helper systems and with purified T cells before they can be accepted. In addition, they must be done in strain combinations in which reciprocal antisera can be used as controls, a requirement that is difficult to meet in the strain combination used in these experiments. The conclusion can therefore only be tentative that Ia antigens are present on a subpopulation of T cells which function as helper T cells in inducing a hapten-specific B cell antibody response.

The effect of anti-Ia sera on suppressor T cells was studied by Drs. Okumura and Murphy in the allotype suppression system developed by Lee Herzenberg (27). These experiments have also been carried out a number of times with the same results on each occasion. The results of one experiment using absorbed sera are shown in Table 2. In these experiments, DNP-KLH primed spleen cells are injected into syngeneic irradiated recipients with sufficient numbers of "suppressed" spleen cells (from syngeneic (SJL x BALB/c)F$_1$) to suppress effectively the Ig-1b anti-DNP plaque forming response usually seen following cell transfer and secondary immunization with DNP-KLH. Mice receiving syngeneic DNP-KLH primed spleen cells alone produced 2431 total indirect anti-DNP-PFC, of which 187 were of the Ig-1b class. Animals similarly treated, but also receiving 5 million spleen cells from Ig-1b suppressed syngeneic donors produced 2011 anti-DNP-PFC, of which only 11 were of the Ig-1b class. A.TL anti-A.TH treatment of the suppressor cell population effectively blocked this suppression, either alone, in earlier experiments, or following absorption in vitro or in vivo with A.TL. Absorption of this antiserum with A.TH, the strain against which the antiserum is directed, completely removed the block-

TABLE 2

EFFECT OF ANTI-Ia ON SUPPRESSOR CELLS

(SJL x Balb/c)F_1 Spleen Cells Transferred (x 10^6)[1]			Indirect DNP-PFC/10^6		
DNP-KLH 1^0	Ig-1b[3] Suppressed	Treatment[2]	Ig-1b	Ig-1a	Total IgG
8	--	---	187	196	2431
8	5	NMS	11	201	2011
8	5	A.TL anti-A.TH abs. in vitro with A.TL	139	164	1658
8	5	A.TL anti-A.TH abs. in vitro with A.TH	6	185	2316
8	5	A.TL anti-A.TH abs. in vivo with A.TL	128	174	1869
8	5	A.TL anti-A.TH abs in vivo with A.TH	36	182	1516

[1] Balb/c irradiated (600 R) recipients.

[2] A.TL anti-A.TH contains anti-Ia^S antibody reactive with (SJL x Balb/c)F_1 (Ia^S/Ia^d). Ig-1b suppressed spleen treated with antiserum plus complement. In vitro absorption performed with spleen and lymph node.

[3] Ig-1b suppressed donors had no circulating Ig-1b at time of transfer. These donors were (SJL x BALB/c)F_1 mice exposed perinatally to maternal antibody to Ig-1b (27)

ing activity following absorption either in vivo or in vitro. Similar results were obtained with a second antiserum directed against the I-A and I-B regions of haplotype H-2^S. These experiments indicate that the majority of suppressor T cells are Ia positive and are compatible with similar results obtained in a different system by Hämmerling et al. (28) and with the findings of Tada (19), which indicate that suppressor factors isolated from T cells carry Ia antigenic determinants. These results indicate that allotype specific suppressor T cells, as well as antigen specific suppressor T cells (28), carry Ia antigens on their surface, and are susceptible to cytotoxicity mediated by anti-Ia sera. Whether the target of these two types of suppressor cell are similar is not yet clear. In the allotype suppression system, the suppressor T cells appear to act against allotype

269

specific helper T cells (29) while antigen specific suppressor T cells, at least in some systems (30) appear to be directed against hapten specific B cells.

DISCUSSION

The results of these studies are summarized in Table 3.

TABLE 3

	Cell Population	Ia Status
1)	B cells	
	μ precursors	(−)
	μ + γ precursors	(+)
	γ precursors	(+)
2)	T cells	
	MLC responder	(−)
	CML precursor	(−)
	CML effector	(−)
	Helper T	(+) ?
	Suppressor T	(+)
	(allotype suppression)	

Ia antigens are present on B cells which give rise to IgG, or both IgM and IgG antibody production, and are absent on B cells which give rise solely to IgM antibody (23). These findings,together with the results of experiments by Pierce and Klinman (24) that I region identity determines whether or not primary allogeneic B cell-T cell interactions give rise to IgG production, suggest that Ia antigens play a role in the ability of the precursor cell to switch from IgM to IgG. Although Ia recognitive interactions between B cells and T cells are not required for IgM production, Ia antigens may mediate the signal that results in induction of the μ to γ switch mechanism. Whether this occurs as a function of Ia recognition by T cells, or is a mechanism inherent in the B cell which can be prevented by allogeneic T cells, remains to be resolved.

In the T cell population, MLC responder cells, and precursor and effector cells for cell mediated lympholysis appear to be Ia negative. Helper T cells provisionally appear to be Ia positive, and suppressor T cells in the allotype suppression system are also Ia positive. It thus appears that in the B cell population those cells which are precursors of the IgG antibody producing cells, and in the T cell population those cells which are involved in the regulation (help or suppression) of the B cell response are Ia positive, while those T cells which are involved in direct T cell mediated immunity are Ia negative. This correlation is reminiscent of the well-established finding that IgM responses are usually less T cell dependent than IgG responses, (although the primary IgM monoclonal response to DNP-Hy reported here does require the carrier-primed milieu (23)). It is also reminiscent of the finding that the 19S primary immune responde to (T,G)-A--L, an antigen under H-2 linked Ir gene control, is equal in responder and non-responder strains, while only the responder strain shows a T cell dependent 7S secondary response.

This naturally raises the question of whether the Ia antigens themselves mediate Ir gene effects, as well as effects on T cell-B cell interaction which appear to be a function of the Ia antigens, or whether there is an additional, and as yet undetected gene product which mediates Ir gene effects. While the correlation between the distribution of Ia antigens on B and T cell subpopulations and the expression of Ir gene function suggests that Ia antigens may be the molecules mediating Ir gene effects, it is equally possible that the primary function of Ia antigens is to serve as regulatory signals in the interaction between T cells and B cells and macrophages, and that the Ir genes are separate gene products involved in specific antigen recognition. In this respect, it must be kept in mind that the demonstration of Ia antigens on helper T cells is preliminary and requires confirmation. This is particularly important because in several systems in our own laboratory, as well as others (28), it has previously been difficult to demonstrate Ia antigens on helper T cells.

The mechanism by which Ia antigens function in T cell-B cell interaction is not yet clear. An analysis of specific antibody produced by responder and non-responder B cells in tetraparental chimeras following immunization with (T,G)-A--L indicates that non-responder B cells can interact effectively with responder T cells and/or macrophages across a full H-2 barrier (11). These experiments are carried out in stable, long-term, embryo fusion chimeras. On the other hand, acute mixing experiments of hapten-primed B cells with carrier-primed T cells (for review see 31) indicate that T cells and B cells do not interact effectively across an I region barrier, and that F1 responder T cells cannot interact effectively with non-responder parental B cells. One possible ex-

planation of these conflicting results is that I region identity is not required for efficient T cell-B cell interaction,
but that T cells can interact with B cells of any genotype if
they are in a histocompatible environment, and if they are
exposed to the allogeneic B cell and antigen during the
course of immunization. Alternate possibilities (explored
in more detail by K. Bechtol and J. Press, this volume) must
also be explored.

The resolution of this experimental conflict is vital
for a number of reasons. If it is established that allogeneic T cells and B cells can interact effectively in long-
term chimeras, and if responder T cells can interact effectively with non-responder B cells in this situation as present
results indicate (11, K. Bechtol and J. Press, this volume),
then it would appear that I region identity is not required
for effective T cell-B cell collaboration, and, in addition,
that T cells of responder genotype can interact with B cells
of non-responder genotype. In view of evidence suggesting
that Ir genes may be expressed in both T and B cells (D.H.
Katz, this volume), this result would indicate that there are
strain combinations in which the Ir gene(s) expressed in T
cells may be separate and distinct from the Ir gene(s) expressed in B cells. The resolution of these questions will
require experiments designed to determine the alteration which
occurs in long-term embryo fusion chimeras which permits T
cell-B cell interaction across an allogeneic barrier in a
manner that is not possible in acute, short-term, mixing experiments.

The finding that Ia antigens are also present on suppressor T cells raises a number of important problems. While
it has generally been assumed that Ia antigens on any cell
type are produced by that cell type, this assumption requires
experimental verification. The demonstration of Ia antigens
on suppressor T cells, and in suppressor T cell factors (19)
is compatible with the recent finding that antigen-specific
suppression is under H-2 linked genetic control (Benacerraf,
this volume). Since antigen-induced suppression appears to
be a relatively transient phenomena, it may function as a
transient, regulatory mechanism to regulate and limit the B
cell response to a specific antigen. The possibility must
be explored that suppressor T cells have acquired their Ia
antigens and their antigen specificity as a result of interaction with B cells and/or macrophages and antigen.

In summary, the distribution of Ia antigens on B cell and T cell subpopulations correlates with the B cell types expressing the IgG antibody response, and with the T cell subtypes which are involved in regulating that response. It seems clear that the Ia antigens are part of the mechanism involved in inducing B cells to switch from IgM to IgG specific antibody production, but the precise role which the Ia antigens play in this interaction, and the relationship of Ia antigens to _Ir_ gene effects is not yet clear.

ACKNOWLEDGMENTS

The work reported herein was supported by Grant AI 07757 from the National Institute of Health, and Contract CB 43941 from the National Cancer Institute.

REFERENCES

(1) H.O. McDevitt and B. Benacerraf. Adv. Immunol. 11 (1969) 31.

(2) B. Benacerraf and H.O. McDevitt. Science 175 (1972) 273.

(3) F.C. Grumet and H.O. McDevitt. Transpl. 13 (1972) 171.

(4) G.F. Mitchell, F.C. Grumet, and H.O. McDevitt. J. Exp. Med. 135 (1972) 126.

(5) E.M. Shevach, W.E. Paul, and I. Green. J. Exp. Med. 136 (1972) 1207.

(6) E.M. Shevach, I. Green, and W.E. Paul. J. Exp. Med. 139 (1974) 679.

(7) P. Lonai and H.O. McDevitt. J. Exp. Med. 140 (1974) 977.

(8) G. Hämmerling and H.O. McDevitt. J. Exp. Med. 140 (1974) 1180.

(9) G.J. Hämmerling and H.O. McDevitt. J. Immunol. 112 (1974) 1726.

(10) G.J. Hämmerling and H.O. McDevitt. J. Immunol. 112 (1974) 1734.

(11) K.B. Bechtol, J.H. Freed, L.A. Herzenberg, and H.O. McDevitt. J. Exp. Med. 140 (1974) 1660.

(12) G.M. Shearer, E. Mozes and M. Sela. J. Exp. Med. 135 (1972) 1009.

(13) M.J. Taussig and A.J. Munro. Nature 251 (1974) 63

(14) D.C. Shreffler, and C.S. David. Adv. Immunol. 20 (1975) 125.

(15) D.H. Sachs and J.L. Cone. J. Exp. Med. 138 (1973) 1289.

(16) G.J. Hämmerling, B.D. Deak, G. Mauve, U. Hämmerling, and H.O. McDevitt. Immunogenetics 1 (1974) 68.

(17) J.A. Frelinger, J. Neiderhuber, C.S. David, and D.C. Shreffler. J. Exp. Med. 140 (1974) 1273.

(18) P. Lonai and H.O. McDevitt. J. Exp. Med. 140 (1974) 1317.

(19) T. Tada. Transpl. Rev. 26 (1975) 106.

(20) T. Delovitch and H.O. McDevitt. Immunogenetics 2 (1975) 39.

(21) D.H. Katz and B. Benacerraf. Transpl. Rev. 22 (1975) 175.

(22) N.R. Klinman and J.L. Press. Transpl. Rev. 24 (1975) 41.

(23) J.L. Press, N.R. Klinman, C. Henry, L. Wofsy, T.L. Delovitch, and H.O. McDevitt, in: Membrane Receptors Of Lymphocytes. Proceedings of the International Symposium on Membrane Receptors of Lymphocytes. Eds. M. Seligmann, J.L. Preud'Homme, and F.M. Kourilsky. (North-Holland Publishing Company, Amsterdam, 1975) p. 247.

(24) S. Pierce and N.R. Klinman. J. Exp. Med.,142 (1975) 1165.

(25) C.S. David, J.E. Niederhuber, J.A. Frelinger, E.P. Dugan, T. Meo, D.C. Shreffler. in: Proceedings of the 10th Leucocyte Culture Conference, in press.

(26) P. Lonai and H.O. McDevitt. in preparation.

(27) L.A. Herzenberg, K. Okumura and C.M. Metzler. Transpl. Rev. 27 (1975) 57.

(28) G.J. Hämmerling and S.J. Black, in: Proceedings of the 10th Leukocyte Culture Conference, in press.

(29) K. Okumura, M.H. Julius, C.M. Metzler, T.T. Tsu, L.A. Herzenberg, and L.A. Herzenberg. in preparation.

(30) Dorf, M., J. Kapp, and B. Benacerraf, personal communication.

(31) D.H. Katz and B. Benacerraf. Transpl. Rev. 22 (1975) 175.

DISCUSSION FOLLOWING HUGH McDEVITT

SHEVACH: What is the effect of anti-Ia serum and complement on the specific proliferative T cell?   In the guinea pig where all T cells are Ia-positive, but where all T cells are not killed by anti-Ia serum and complement, treatment of T cells with anti-Ia and complement has no effect on specific T cell proliferation.

McDEVITT: We have not tested the effect of anti-Ia and complement on antigen-induced T cell proliferation.

HÄMMERLING: There are many questions concerning the expression of Ia antigens on functional lymphocyte subpopulations on which Hugh and I completely agree.   However, there are also others on which we disagree.   For instance, we are able to eliminate a primary B cell response by cytotoxic treatment of unprimed B cells with anti-Ia plus complement in an *in vitro* hapten-carrier system.   Secondly, we were not able to eliminate helper T cells by anti-Ia.   On the other hand, with the same batch of anti-Ia serum, suppressor T cells could be eliminated, which is in complete concordance with the results reported by McDevitt on the allotype suppression system (see Hämmerling *et al*, this volume).

McDEVITT: The precursor analysis system of Klinman has several aspects which may make it more sensitive: 1) it is *in vivo*; 2) it employs carrier-primed recipients; and 3) it allows for proliferation of each precursor in a secondary culture to a level of detectable antibody formation.   These factors maximize the chance of detecting precursors of antibody-forming cells.

With respect to helper T cells, I would re-emphasize that these results were obtained in only one of several systems tried and therefore must be regarded as requiring further confirmation.

TAUSSIG: In contrast with Günter Hämmerling, I do not think that Hugh's results mean that the Ia molecules on B cells do not function as acceptors.   The T cell factor may be selecting the B cell precursors which can switch--this would presumably produce IgM first, however.   Also, there are non-Ia mediators of T-B cooperation (Con A factor, for example) which may be the ones which trigger the μ-only B cells.

McDEVITT: Clearly, there are other ways of inducing the
μ→γ switch. Since this effect maps in the I region,
Ia recognition may be one physiologic means of accom-
plishing this.

RAJEWSKY: Your claim that virgin B cells do not express Ia
antigens would imply that in the mouse only a small
fraction of the B cells are virgin since about 90% of
the B cells express Ia--is that correct?

McDEVITT: Ninety percent of B cells express Ia--that is
correct. However, it is quite possible that there are
Ia-negative virgin B cells which make only IgM and Ia-
positive virgin B cells whose progeny can make both IgM
and IgG.

MILLER: Another example of Ia-positive T cells is to be
found in mice sensitized to produce delayed-type hypersensitivity. Lymph node T cells from sensitized mice
can transfer sensitivity to naive mice. Incubating the
cells with appropriate anti-Ia and complement impairs,
though does not totally abolish, this transfer of the
sensitive state.

McDEVITT: This would again indicate that some functional T
cell populations are Ia-positive.

NOSSAL: John Schrader in my laboratory has evidence that B
lymphocytes can "switch" from μ to γ expression in the
absence of T cells and without actually being triggered
to form IgG. This is done by immunizing BALB/c nude
mice, which of course form some IgM but no IgG antibody,
and then infusing carrier-reactive T cells and re-
challenging. These animals are shown to be "ready to
go" for a massive IgG response.

[*EDITOR'S NOTE:* See Schrader, J.W. J. Immunol. 114:
1665, 1975 - DHK.]

McDEVITT: This is similar to the findings of Hämmerling
concerning non-responder antigen-binding B cells with
IgG surface receptors. We are in the process of testing
these mice for memory B cells with (T,G)-A--L·MBSA and
MBSA-primed spleen cells.

PAUL: The concept that T cell collaboration is critical to
the expression of IgG antibodies should not be too

heavily emphasized. There are now several examples of
thymus-independent antigens, including 2,4-dinitro-
phenyl-Ficoll, which cause antibody of the IgG class in
nu/nu mice.* In addition, the experiment alluded to by
Gus Nossal, in which priming of athymic mice with a
thymus-dependent antigen prepares them for an IgG response, if they are subsequently provided with T cells
does not prove that these cells have already switched.
It is quite possible, as Joe Davie and I suggested,*
that proliferation occurs in the absence of T cells and
the μ-γ switch occurs later, when T cells are provided.

*[*EDITOR'S NOTE:* For references to these points, see:
1) Mosier, D.E. *et al* J. Exp. Med. 139:1354, 1974
2) Sharon, R. *et al* J. Immunol. 114:1585, 1975
3) Braley-Mullen, H. J. Immunol. 115:1194, 1975
4) Davie, J.M. and Paul, W.E. J. Immunol. 113:1438,
1974 - DHK]

McDEVITT: T cell help is clearly one way, and perhaps the
most physiologic way, that leads to production of IgG
antibodies. The concept that the μ-γ switch occurs in
the absence of T cell help is based on 1) the findings
of Hämmerling for (T,G)-A--L antigen-binding B cells in
primed non-responders, and 2) the hypothesis that these
non-responders lack (T,G)-A--L helper T cells.

BENACERRAF: I would like to ask Hugh McDevitt if he has
tried to duplicate in his system our GLT experiment
where we showed that (responder x non-responder)F_1 T
cells cooperate only for the DNP-GLT response with anti-
θ-treated DNP-specific responder B cells, whereas this
restriction is not observed with a carrier antigen not
under restricted H-linked *Ir* gene control (Katz, D.H.
et al J. Exp. Med. 138:734, 1973).

McDEVITT: Yes, we have repeated this experiment using
(T,G)-A--L in BALB·B and BALB·K mice. The detailed
results will be presented this afternoon by
Katie Bechtol but are the same as the results which
you obtained and the opposite of the results obtained
in embryo fusion chimeras (see Bechtol and Press, this
volume).

GERSHON: Hugh, is it not correct that Carl Grumet showed an
IgM to IgG switch in non-responders using an allogeneic
effect?

McDEVITT: Yes, that is correct.

KATZ: I think the point Dick Gershon is trying to raise is that in the Ordal and Grumet experiments (Ordal, J.C. and Grumet, C. <u>J. Exp. Med</u>. <u>136</u>:1195, 1972), an allogeneic effect resulted in a YM to YG switch, whereas in the experiment Hugh has presented on the monofocal assay, the transfer of cells into an irradiated allogeneic recipient, a situation which can also lead to an allogeneic effect, fails to result in a YG response.

McDEVITT: The recipients were heavily irradiated (1100 - 1600 R) in order to block the response of the recipient's B cells. We have assumed that this dose of irradiation would also abolish an allogeneic effect, and the results are compatible with this.

GERSHON: I still do not understand the reason for the difference. Surely, Ia identity is not required for an IgM→IgG switch.

McDEVITT: The findings are that Ia-negative cells give rise only to IgM clones, and that in allogeneic combinations only IgM clones are seen. Since this result occurs <u>only</u> with an *I-A* plus *I-B* region difference in the experiments of Pierce and Klinman, it is due to an *I* region difference. We cannot conclude that *I* region identity is required for the IgM to IgG switch. It could also be a requirement merely for Ia recognition, due to previous exposure, by the helper T cell which has been primed by antigen on Ia-positive B cells or macrophages.

SACHS: You mentioned results by Drs. Donal Murphy and Robert Stout indicating that anti-Ia antibodies can inhibit binding to the Fc receptor of T cells. This is something which Drs. Arbeit, Dickler and I have also found using thymocytes and is identical to our previous results on blocking of the B cell Fc receptor. Can you conceive of a mechanism by which one could get such blocking if the Ia antigens were not present on these T cells? Don't you think it more likely that the other methods you (and we) had used previously were just not sensitive enough to detect those antigens?

McDEVITT: That is possible. However, we must keep in mind the possibility that these sera are anti-*I* region sera

and may have antibodies to structures other than what we
now classify as Ia antigens.

NOSSAL: I would like to present data obtained by J.W. Goding
and J.J. Marchalonis in my laboratory. A very strong
anti-Ia serum, prepared in A.TH mice immunized against
A.TL lymph node and thymus cells, was found lightly but
specifically to label at least a subpopulation of A.TL
thymocytes in radioautographic experiments (J.W. Goding
et al J. Immunogenetics 2:9, 1975). Using the same
antisera, it has been possible to isolate small amounts
of Ia antigen from NP-40 extracts of surface radio-
iodinated A.TL thymocytes (Fig. 1). A brief report of
these experiments has recently been published
(J.W. Goding *et al* Nature 257:230, 1975).

The gel patterns raise several important points. Under
the extraction conditions used, cell surface immunoglobulin was not detectable, and thus no preliminary Ig
depletion step was necessary. (Our recent experience
indicates that release by metabolic turnover is the most
reliable extraction procedure for T cell immunoglobulin;
see Haustein *et al*, Biochemistry 14:1826, 1975).

A small but unequivocal peak of radioactivity, corresponding to an apparent molecular weight of approximately
30,000, was seen in the experimental, but not in the
control precipitates. The relative amounts of Ia and Ig
extracted make it unlikely that the Ia detected was
derived from contaminating B cells, since it has been
demonstrated (Vitetta *et al* Immunogenetics 1:82, 1974)
that the TCA precipitable radioactivity incorporated
into Ia following lactoperoxidase catalyzed surface
radio-iodination of B cells is much less than that incorporated into Ig. It is of interest that the mobility
of T cell Ia in SDS gels is similar to the previously
published results for B cells, and that a relatively
sharp peak was obtained. Of course, these experiments
do not address themselves to the important question of
whether molecules coded for by the I region might also
be secreted by T cells. So far, attempts to isolate
molecules bearing Ia determinants from supernatants of
Con A-stimulated T cells have been unsuccessful.

In addition, a peak of radioactivity was seen which
corresponded to a molecular weight of about 45,000. We
have frequently observed this peak in lysates of

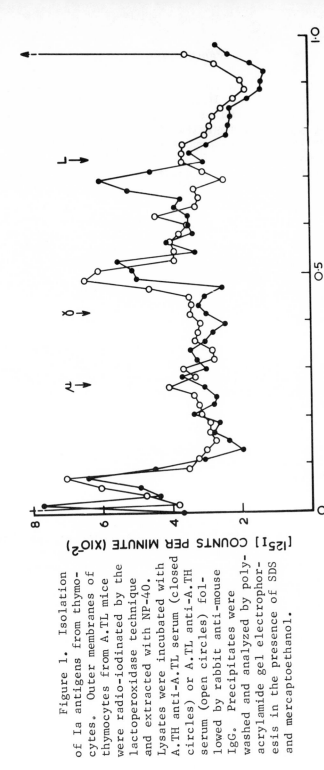

Figure 1. Isolation of Ia antigens from thymocytes. Outer membranes of thymocytes from A.TL mice were radio-iodinated by the lactoperoxidase technique and extracted with NP-40. Lysates were incubated with A.TH anti-A.TL serum (closed circles) or A.TL anti-A.TH serum (open circles) followed by rabbit anti-mouse IgG. Precipitates were washed and analyzed by poly-acrylamide gel electrophoresis in the presence of SDS and mercaptoethanol.

thymocytes, T lymphomas and spleen cells from normal
and athymic mice. It is precipitated in equal amounts
in both control and experimental groups and is also
precipitated by complexes of fowl IgG and anti-fowl IgG.
It may represent a component which binds to antigen-
antibody complexes. It is of interest to note that
NP-40 extracted K and D antigens have a very similar
mobility.

H-2 LINKED IMMUNE RESPONSE GENES: MULTIPLICITY AND FUNCTIONAL COMPLEMENTATION

INGA MELCHERS AND KLAUS RAJEWSKY

Institute for Genetics, University of Cologne

Abstract: Complementation studies indicate that in mice, immune responsiveness to LDH_B is controlled by at least two separate interacting Ir loci in the H-2 complex, one mapping presumably in the I-B region, the other in I-C or S. In addition, the pattern of complementation suggests that either there exist more than two alleles at least at one of the two loci or that more than two loci participate in the control of responsiveness.

The immune response to a variety of antigens is regulated by immune response (Ir) genes in the major histocompatibility complex. It now becomes apparent that at least in several instances more than one Ir gene is involved in the control of the response to a given antigen. This is suggested in particular by the finding of functional complementation between H-linked Ir genes (1-5). In two systems, complementing Ir genes have been separated genetically. Dorf and his colleagues have found that the response of mice to the aminoacid terpolymer GLPhe is controlled by at least two Ir genes, one to the left of the I-C region, the other between I-B and D (3). We have encountered a similar situation in the control of immune responsiveness to porcine lactic dehydrogenase B_4 (LDH_B) by H-2-linked Ir genes (5).

A summary of our findings is given in Table 1. The experimental procedures and most of the data which permit us the construction of this table are

TABLE 1

Functional Complementation of H-2-Linked
Ir Genes in the Response to LDH_B

				F_1-Animals
	Parental Strains			
Strain Designation		H-2 Haplotypes	Responder[1] Classes	Responder[1] Class
CBA/J	x Balb/cJ	k x d	LR x HR	HR
CBA/J	x C57Bl/6J	k x b	"	" [2]
B10.RIII/Sn	x B10.BR/SgSn	r x k	IMR x LR	LR-IMR
C3H.JK/Sn	x B10.BR/SgSn	j x k	"	IMR
B10.SM/Sn	x B10.BR/SgSn	v x k	"	"
B10.PL/Sn	x B10.BR/SgSn	u x k	"	"
B10.HTT	x B10.BR/SgSn	t3 x k	"	"
B10.HTT	x B10.A/J	t3 x a	"	HR
B10.HTT	x B10.A(2R)	t3 x h2	"	"
B10.HTT	x C57BL/10Sn	t3 x b	IMR x HR	SHR
B10.S(7R)	x C57BL/10Sn	t2 x b	HR x HR	" [2]
B10.S(9R)	x C57Bl/10Sn	t4 x b	"	" [2]
Balb/cJ	x C57Bl/6J	d x b	"	HR [2]
C3H.JK/Sn	x B10.RIII/Sn	j x r	IMR x IMR	IMR
B10.PL/Sn	x B10.SM/Sn	u x v	"	"
C3H.JK/Sn	x B10.SM/Sn	j x v	"	HR
B10.RIII/Sn	x B10.SM/Sn	r x v	"	"

1) Responder classes were defined on the basis of mean LDH_B binding capacities in the sera of the experimental animals after standard immunization. Since the mean binding capacities show minor variations from experiment to experiment, at least one established HR and LR strain were included in each experiment. For experimental procedures and data see ref. 5. Abbreviations: LR, low responders. HR, high responders. IMR, intermediate responders. LR-IMR indicates a response level inbetween those of LR and IMR. 2) Unpublished results.

contained in reference 5.

Represented in the table are the levels of responsiveness to LDH_B in various crosses between high responder (HR), intermediate responder (IMR) and low responder (LR) strains. It should be pointed out that the levels of responsiveness in this system appear to be almost exclusively determined by genes in the H-2 complex (5).

Some of the results represented in Table 1 are as expected: We find the familiar dominance of "high" responsiveness over "low" responsiveness in several crosses between HR or IMR and LR. Also, in several instances crosses between parental strains with the same level of responsiveness result in the same response level in the F_1 generation. However, there are many exceptions to this. In one case, the cross between an IMR and a LR leads to a new intermediate level of responsiveness. In addition, in a significant proportion of our crosses functional complementation to higher response levels than those of the parental strains is found. In principle, such complementation can be due to the assembly of (i) different alleles of the same gene or (ii) alleles of different genes in the cells of the F_1 animals. The latter interpretation, which implies the control of responsiveness to LDH_B by at least two separate genes in the H-2 complex, may well hold for all cases of functional complementation in Table 1. It is satisfying in this context that our intermediate responder strains can be tentatively classified into two complementation groups, one comprising $H-2^u$ and $H-2^v$, the other $H-2^j$ and $H-2^r$ bearing animals (animals with $H-2^{t3}$ belonging to either of the two). In one instance, the data unequivocally show control of responsiveness by at least two separate H-2-loci: The recombinant t3 chromosome carries HR s alleles in the K, I-A and I-B regions of H-2, the HR d allele in D and the LR k alleles in I-C and S. Strain B10.HTT which is homozygous for the t3 chromosome is an IMR, in contrast to strains possessing s and/or d alleles in the entire H-2 complex, which are HR. If crossed with LR strains carrying "silent" HR d alleles in the I-C, S and D regions of the H-2 complex (B10.A($H-2^a$/$H-2^a$) or B10.A(2R)

$(H-2^{h2}/H-2^{h2})$), complementation to high responsiveness occurs. The control is a cross between B10.HTT and LR strains with k alleles in the entire H-2 complex, where intermediate responsiveness is observed. Apparently, in this case responsiveness to LDH_B is controlled by at least two loci, one to the left of the crossover in the t3 chromosome (i.e. in K, I-A or I-B) and the other in I-C or S. The former locus may well correspond to the Ir gene previously mapped to the I-B region in our system (6).

It is not yet known whether the two Ir loci in the major histocompatiblity complex defined here exhibit similar or distinct functions in the control of the immune response. If they do, the genetic experiments will be of great help in the elucidation of these functions, as they have already been in the study of Ir control of responsiveness to the amino acid copolymer TG-A-L (4, 7). The overall picture which the results represented in Table 1 suggest is that of a complex control system in which the products of two or more polymorphic genetic loci interact. The assumption of two Ir loci each in two allelic forms is certainly insufficient to explain our data (see for example the equivalence of $H-2^j$ and $H-2^r$ in combination with other IMR H-2 haplotypes, but their non-equivalence if combined with the LR $H-2^k$ haplotype), and we therefore must postulate either a higher degree of polymorphism or the participation of more than two H-2-linked loci in the control of responsiveness to LDH_B.

ACKNOWLEDGEMENTS

This work was supported by the Deutsche Forschungsgemeinschaft through Sonderforschungsbereich 74.

REFERENCES

(1) E. Rüde, E. Günther and E. Liehl. Behring Institute Mitteilungen 53 (1973) 53.

(2) M. Zaleski, H. Fuji and F. Milgrom. Transplant. Proc. 5 (1973) 201.

(3)　M.E. Dorf, J.H. Stimpfling and B. Benacerraf. J. Exp. Med. 141 (1975) 1459.

(4)　A. Munro and M.J. Taussig. Nature 256 (1975) 103.

(5)　I. Melchers and K. Rajewsky. Eur. J. Immunol. 5 (1975) 753.

(6)　I. Melchers, K. Rajewsky and D.C. Shreffler. Eur. J. Immunol. 3 (1973) 754.

(7)　E. Mozes, R. Isac and M.J. Taussig. J. Exp. Med. 141 (1975) 703.

H-3-LINKED UNRESPONSIVENESS TO EA-1 AND H-13 ANTIGENS

DAVID L. GASSER

Department of Human Genetics
University of Pennsylvania School of Medicine

Abstract: A single dominant gene in mice which controls unresponsiveness to Ea-1 erythrocyte antigens is closely linked to H-3 but has been separated from H-3 by recombination. When genetic responders are made tolerant of nonresponder lymphoid cells, they are unresponsive to Ea-1 despite the fact that there is no cross-reactivity between Ea-1 and nonresponder tissue.

Mice possessing the $H-3^b$ allele are poorly responsive to H-13 antigens whereas $H-3^a$ animals are good responders. Heterozygous $H-3^a/H-3^b$ mice respond as poorly to H-13 as the $H-3^b$ parents. $H-3^a$ mice made tolerant of $H-3^b$ antigens are poorly responsive to H-13-incompatible skin grafts.

These results suggest that in both of the H-3-linked immune responses that have been described, the most likely explanation for the unresponsiveness is cross-tolerance.

INTRODUCTION

Previous experiments have demonstrated that a number of genes possessed by various inbred strains of mice can influence the antibody response to Ea-1 erythrocyte antigens (1-4). However, if YBR is crossed with either BALB or CBA the segregation of a single dominant gene for unresponsiveness is observed (1). This gene is an allele of a locus designated Ir-2, which is linked

289

to the agouti locus in the fifth linkage group, or second chromosome (1). Evidence has now been obtained that Ir-2 maps to the right of H-3 and to the left of H-13. It has also been shown that if YBR mice, which are genetic responders, are injected neonatally with spleen cells from (YBR x BALB)F_1 nonresponders, these mice grow up to be unresponsive to Ea-1.

It has been reported that H-3^b mice are unable to produce a normal response to H-13-incompatible tissue grafts (5). This is a quantitative rather than a qualitative difference. We have shown that low responsiveness is inherited as a dominant trait, and that genetic high responders made tolerant of low responder cells respond very poorly to H-13-incompatible grafts.

EVIDENCE FOR THE MAP POSITION OF IR-2

The dominant gene for unresponsiveness to Ea-1 will be designated Ir-2^b and its alternative allele, Ir-2^a. Since most (YBR x B10)F_1 hybrids are responsive to Ea-1 (2), it is obvious that the B10 strain does not have the Ir-2^b allele, but rather possesses Ir-2^a. Several congenic strains of mice having variant H-3 or H-13 alleles on a B10 background have been studied to determine which Ir-2 allele is present in these strains. When 25 (YBR x 30NX)F_1 hybrids were given a primary injection of Ea-1^a cells followed by 10 boosters, 22 were completely unresponsive, suggesting that 30NX possesses the Ir-2^b allele. The 30NX strain so far has been known to differ from B10 only by its possession of the A^w (white-bellied agouti) and H-13^b alleles, which it obtained from CE (6). The fact that it has a dominant nonresponse gene for Ea-1 suggests that it also obtained the Ir-2^b allele from CE. If this is correct, then a recombination event between Ir-2 and H-3 apparently occurred in the derivation of 30NX, as shown in Table 1.

When 15 mice of each of the (YBR x B10.LP)F_1 and (YBR x B10.LP-H-3^b)F_1 generations were tested, all were completely negative for response to Ea-1. This suggests that both B10.LP and B10.LP-H-3^b

possess the Ir-2^b allele , and that crossing-over occured between H-13 and Ir-2 in the derivation of the B10.LP-H-3^b strain, as shown in the table.

The first crossover places Ir-2 to the right of H-3 and the second places Ir-2 to the left of H-13. The distance between agouti and H-13 is about 1 centiMorgan, while that between agouti and H-3 is about 17 centiMorgans (5). There is about 20 ± 7.45% crossing over between agouti and Ir-2 (1). Given the rather large standard errors of these estimates, the only conclusion we can safely draw is that Ir-2 and H-3 are close to one another in a region about 15-20 centiMorgans from the agouti locus. The order shown in the table is based on the evidence from the congenic strains, rather than the crude estimates of the recombination frequency.

UNRESPONSIVENESS OF YBR MICE MADE TOLERANT OF BALB CELLS

The possibility that (YBR x BALB)F$_1$ mice possess antigens that cross-react with Ea-1 was tested by in vivo absorption. An anti-Ea-1^a serum was injected into three unimmunized YBR mice and three previously uninjected (YBR x BALB)F$_1$ recipients. The animals were bled on days 1,4,7 and 10 and tested for anti-Ea-1^a activity. At no time was there a significant difference in the titers, suggesting that nonresponders do not possess antigens which cross-react with Ea-1.

In order to determine whether BALB and (YBR x BALB)F$_1$ mice are unresponsive to Ea-1 because they are cross-tolerant, tolerance to BALB antigens was induced in YBR recipients. Within 24 hours of birth, 15 YBR recipients were given 15 x 10^6 (YBR x BALB)F$_1$ spleen cells each. When they matured, they were given the usual course of immunization for Ea-1, but not one of the 15 produced detectable antibodies.

These results suggest that mice possessing the Ir-2^b allele are cross-tolerant of Ea-1 antigens, despite the fact that there is no detectable cross-reactivity between Ea-1 and non-responder antigens. However, we have not ruled out the possibility that nonresponders produce suppressor cells which dominate the immune systems in the injected animals (7,8).

H-3-LINKED LOW RESPONSE TO H-13 ANTIGENS

The data in Table 2 demonstrate the difference in reactivity of H-3^a and H-3^b mice with regard to H-13-incompatible grafts. The H-3^a mice nearly always rejected very small grafts and could reject 1 cm grafts in about half of the cases. The H-3^b mice rejected some of the small grafts but never rejected 1 cm grafts. Low responsiveness is inherited as a dominant trait since mice of both F_1 hybrid combinations behaved like the low responding parents.

When high responder neonates were made tolerant of low responder bone marrow cells, their response to H-13 was comparable to that of H-3^b animals. For example, not one of seven B10 mice made tolerant of B10.LP-H-3^b cells was able to reject a 1 cm skin graft from 30NX. These results suggest that H-3-linked low responsiveness to H-13 antigens involves cross-tolerance. The fact that this is a quantitative rather than a qualitative difference could be explained if H-13 antigens consisted of several determinants, one of which cross-reacts with H-3^b antigens or with antigens of a closely linked locus. Alternative explanations however, have not been ruled out.

CONCLUSION

Most of the Ir genes which have been described are linked to the major histocompatibility complex (8), but there are a number of these genes which do not map near the MHC. It is important to determine whether the non-MHC-linked Ir genes are fundamentally different from those which are MHC-linked. In the case of two H-3-linked Ir genes, the alleles for unresponsiveness or low responsiveness are dominant, and there is evidence in both cases that cross-tolerance is involved.

Table 1. Recombination events proposed to explain the genotypes of the 30NX and B10.LP-H-3b congenic strains.

Strain	H-3	Ir-2	H-13	Agouti
CE	b	b	b	A^w
B10	a	a	a	a
B10.CE(30NX)	a	b	b	A^w
B10.LP	b	b	b	A^w
B10	a	a	a	a
B10.LP-H-3b	b	b	a	a

Table 2. Rejection of H-13-incompatible skin grafts by mice of various genotypes.

Recipient Strain	H-3	H-13	Donor Strain	H-3	H-13	Size of Graft (mm^2)*	Number Rejected By 100 Days/Total
(a) B10	a	a	30NX	a	b	9	15/17
(b) B10	a	a	30NX	a	b	100	10/21
(c) 30NX	a	b	B10	a	a	9	7/9
(d) 30NX	a	b	B10	a	a	100	7/16
(e) B10.LP	b	b	B10.LP-H-3^b	b	a	9	5/11
(f) B10.LP	b	b	B10.LP-H-3^b	b	a	100	0/10
(g) B10.LP-H-3^b	b	a	B10.LP	b	a	9	3/9
(h) B10.LP-H-3^b	b	a	B10.LP	b	a	100	0/17
(i) (B10 x B10.LP-H-3^b)F$_1$	a/b	a/a	B10.LP	b	b	9	5/21
(j) (30NX x B10.LP)F$_1$	a/b	b/b	B10.LP-H-3^b	b	a	9	4/19

* The 9mm^2 grafts consisted of ear skin while the 100mm^2 grafts were dorsal body skin.

ACKNOWLEDGEMENTS

I am deeply grateful to Dr. Willys K. Silvers for many helpful suggestions, to Miss Ali Winters and Mrs. Brigitte Koeberlein for excellent technical assistance, and to Dr. Ralph Graff for the 30NX mice. This work was supported by grants CA-15146 and CA-15822 from the National Institutes of Health.

REFERENCES

(1)   Gasser, D.L. J. Immunol. 103 (1969) 66.

(2)   Gasser, D.L. J. Immunol. 105 (1970) 908.

(3)   Gasser, D.L. and D.C. Shreffler. Nature New Biol. 235 (1972) 155.

(4)   Gasser, D.L and D.C. Shreffler. Immuno-genetics 1 (1974) 133.

(5)   Snell, G.D., G. Cudkowicz and H.P. Bunker. Transplantation 5 (1967) 492.

(6)   Graff, R.J. and D.W. Bailey. Transplant. Rev. (1973) 250.

(7)   Gershon, R.K., P.H. Maurer and C.F. Merryman. Proc. Nat. Acad. Sci. 70 (1973) 250.

(8)   Kapp, J.A., C.W. Pierce, S. Schlossman and B. Benacerraf. J. Exp. Med. 140 (1974) 648.

(9)   Benacerraf, B. and H.O. McDevitt. Science (Washington) 175 (1972) 273.

IMMUNE RESPONSES OF MICE AGAINST MODIFIED RANDOM POLYMERS OF AMINO ACIDS, AND IMPLICATIONS IN GENE CONTROL

PAUL H. MAURER, CARMEN F. MERRYMAN
AND ALLEN R. ZEIGER

Department of Biochemistry
Jefferson Medical College

Abstract: The introduction of limited amounts (about 5-10%) of amino acids into the nonimmunogenic random copolymer poly(Glu^{60}Lys^{40}), GL, produces conjugates that exhibit variable immunogenicity in all strains of mice. The modified GL derivatives are T cell independent antigens, elicit IgM responses, and are B cell mitogens. Similar modification of the polymers GA, GAL^{10}, GLT^5 and GLØ, the responses against which are under Ir gene(s) control, did not alter the strain distribution patterns (SDP) so as to convert nonresponder mice to responders.

The above observations and the known SDP against a number of GL terpolymers are discussed with speculations to help explain:

1) the immunogenicity of the amino acid modified GL polymer;
2) the nonimmunogenicity of GL in mice;
3) the unique SDP against the GL terpolymers;
4) the divergent immune response data obtained with the same polymer in different laboratories.

INTRODUCTION

One of the perplexing observations associated with studies of immune responses of mice has been the inability to detect significant in vivo responses against the random copolymer poly(Glu^{60}Lys^{40}) (GL) (1) or against haptenic conjugates of the polymer, such as DNP-GL. In contrast to this, the terpolymers of GL and a limited concentration (i.e. 5-10 mol %) of a third α-L amino acid, such as alanine (2),

297

tyrosine (3), phenylalanine (4), proline (5), leucine or serine (6) are immunogenic, and although they exhibit unique strain distribution patterns (SDP) (Table I), most of the antibody is directed against GL. The responses to these

TABLE I

LINKAGE OF RESPONSIVENESS TO GL TERPOLYMERS
WITH H-2 HAPLOTYPE

Terpolymer	Responder H-2 Haplotype	Ir Gene Localization
$GLA^5\text{-}GLA^{20}$	a, d, f, g, j, k, q, r, s	IA
$GLT^5\text{-}GLT^{15}$	d, g, j, ja, q, r	IA + IC
$GL\emptyset^5\text{-}GL\emptyset^{11}$	d, g, j, ja, p, q, r	IA + IC
$GLPro^8$	s	IA - IB
$GLLeu^5$	a, d	IC
$GLSer^7$	a, k	IA

polymers are linked to the major H-2 histocompatibility complex of the mouse and the immune response (Ir) genes controlling responses mapped differently in the I subregions. In the case of the GLØ-GLT terpolymers, at least two complementary dominant genes have been shown to control the responses (7, 8).

RESPONSE TO GL COPOLYMERS MODIFIED WITH VARIOUS AMINO ACIDS

These observations prompted us to prepare derivatives of GL wherein, instead of DNP groupings, limited amounts (about 5 percent) of the amino acids tyrosine, phenylalanine, alanine, leucine, serine or proline were introduced into the amino groups of the side chains of GL. The mice were immunized with 100 μg of polymer as per our usual procedures. Sera obtained about 10 days after the second injection were analyzed for antigen binding capacity using an I^{125} derivative of tyrosylated GL and pools of polyvalent anti-mouse globulins. Table II presents a summary of some of the representative findings with a few derivatives.

TABLE II

RESPONSE TO GL COPOLYMERS MODIFIED WITH VARIOUS AMINO ACIDS[*]

Strain	H-2 Haplotype	Modified Derivative				
		Tyr	Phe	Ser	Ala	Ala-t-boc
A	a	48	39	42	26	66
C57BL/6	b	22	23	27	19	9
BALB/c	d	49	45	42	23	74
ACA	f	58	-	-	6	47
CBA	k	40	18	34	15	40
P	p	42	39	29	26	27
DBA/1	q	45	59	-	52	45
RIII	r	37	78	62	17	25
SJL	s	45	32	19	22	69

[*]Mean % of I^{125} GL(T) bound by 1-2 dilution of serum.

The GL derivatives containing either aliphatic or aromatic amino acids elicited definite immune responses whose SDP were completely different from those obtained against the analogous GL random terpolymer. The poorest responders to the derivatives were the C57BL/6 mice, but even they exhibited significant responses. Some other pertinent observations are as follows:

1. F1 (C57BL/6 x DBA/1) mice of low responder x high responder parents responded as did the high responder parent.

2. Early in our studies we attempted to map the gene controlling the responses by immunizing what we thought at the time to be the informative recombinant inbred strains. As indicated in Table III, the B10.A(1R), (3R), (4R) and (5R) mice all responded.

TABLE III

IMMUNE RESPONSES OF MICE TO GL(T) POLYMER

Strain	% Ag Bound	Strain	% Ag Bound
C57BL/6	27 ± 3	B10.A(1R)	35 ± 11
DBA/1	35 ± 10	B10.A(3R)	27 ± 12
F1(C57BL/6 x DBA/1)	39 ± 8	B10.A(4R)	50 ± 8
		B10.A(5R)	30 ± 4

3.   Nude BALB/c mice, which cannot respond to the terpolymers GLPhe, GLT[5], GLA[5], GLA[20] or GLA[60] (9), responded to
a modified GL(T) preparation with values of 30 ± 5 percent
antigen bound.

4.   The GL(T) and GL(Phe) were B cell mitogens.

5.   Hi line and Lo line mice obtained from Dr. G. Biozzi
were also immunized.   These mice were initially selected for
anti-sheep rbc responses and had different capacities to produce levels of IgM (10).   Although both lines responded to
GL(T), the Hi line mice gave significantly better responses
(i.e. 56 ± 10 vs. 29 ± 9 percent antigen bound).

6.   Finally, as we have recently determined, a significant amount of the antibody produced is of the IgM class.

In summary, the modified GL polymers are immunogenic,
appear to be T cell independent antigens, elicit IgM antibody
and are B cell mitogens.   In contrast to this, the terpolymers which are not B cell mitogens, are T cell dependent antigens, the immune responses are under Ir gene control, and
exhibit unique SDP's.

Because of these findings it was important to determine
whether modifications such as tyrosylation or alanylation
might be a general method for enhancing responses to other
polymers.   The polymers GA and GAL[10], whose responses have
been shown to be under single Ir gene control (11,12), were
modified.   The data presented in Table IV indicate that these
modified polymers neither enhanced the responses in the P and
DBA/1 nonresponder mice, nor reduced the responses of the
responder mice.   However, tyrosylation of the T cell dependent terpolymers GLT and GLØ only changed the immune response
patterns of DBA/1 mice to GLT.

TABLE IV

RESPONSE TO MODIFIED 'GA' AND 'GL' TERPOLYMERS

Strain	GAL^{10} (T)	GA (T)	GLT (T)	GLØ (T)
A	-	95 ± 10	0 ± 0	-
C57BL/6	42 ± 6	-	0 ± 0	-
BALB/c	-	-	62 ± 8	60 ± 5
P	4 ± 2	6 ± 2	0 ± 0	-
DBA/1	9 ± 6	5 ± 4	0 ± 0	76 ± 3
RIII	-	95 ± 0	66 ± 18	-
SJL	-	85 ± 7	-	-

- = Not done

DISCUSSION

From the data presented can one attempt, with some speculations, to explain: 1) immunogenicity of the amino acid modified polymers, 2) non-immunogenicity of GL, and 3) the unique strain distribution pattern of the terpolymers?

1. The modified GL preparations may be immunogenic because of the increased interactions, increased hydrophobicity, or solubility with the "GL" receptors which are present on B cells but not on T cells. Although not presented in detail, t-butyloxylchloride (t-boc) derivatives of the amino acid conjugates enhanced the responses of the poor immunogens (Table II). (We still have no explanation for the nonimmunogenicity of GL-DNP conjugates.)

The B cell mitogenicity may be related to the random introduction of the amino acids into the lysine residues. Theoretically, this could lead to more "repeating" structures in GL(T), GL(Ø), etc. than in GLT^5 or GLØ. The lack of B cell mitogenicity of the modified GL terpolymers may be associated with the introduction of steric factors in the new terpolymer, or possibly with the fact that these polymers are under Ir gene control. From the immune responses obtained, it is evident that the introduced amino acids have not destroyed totally the ability of these modified polymers to react with the T cell receptors. However, the differences in the effect of tyrosylation on the GA vs. the GL terpolymers may be significant, especially as one response appears to be associated with one gene and the other with two gene control. Possibly, the terpolymers whose responses are under Ir gene control do react with receptors on T cells of both responder and (possibly) nonresponder animals so that some suppression of a possible T cell independent response occurs.

2. The nonimmunogenicity in mice of GL might be ascribed both to its inability to react with the GL receptors on B cells (IgM response), or to a lack of a "sufficient cross reaction" with the specific GL terpolymer receptor(s) on T cells. In fact, purified T cells from BALB/c mice immune to GLØ were stimulated 'in vitro' ($3H$-thymidine incorporation) with the homologous GLØ but not with GL or GLA[5].

3. The unique 'in vivo' SDP against the GL terpolymers (Table I) and the specificity of the 'in vitro' incorporation of $3H$-thymidine following stimulation of T cells with the various polymers (unpublished observation), could be interpreted as reflecting the presence of a unique receptor on the T cell for each terpolymer. In fact, Benacerraf and Dorf have suggested that the specific mouse Ir genes controlling responsiveness to different antigens are indeed the products of distinct loci, i.e. each antigen has its own T cell receptor (13). In support of this idea is the knowledge that although 90-95% of the terpolymers contain GL random sequences, the other 5-10 mol % of each individual amino acid can have different effects on the conformational and structural properties of the polypeptides. For example, alanine, leucine and phenylalanine are helix formers; whereas serine, proline and tyrosine can be involved in the formation of nonhelical and pleated sheet structures (14). In addition, each of the "third" amino acids polymerizes at different rates in the terpolymers (15), which is reflected in different primary amino acid sequences, which also influence the secondary and tertiary structures of the polymers.

In spite of the different SDP against the GL terpolymers, and that the Ir genes map in different positions of the I region, the question can still be asked whether each GL terpolymer reacts with its unique T cell receptor(s), or whether the same T cell receptor (the nature of which is not known) recognizes the different terpolymers but reacts with different combining constants. This question cannot be answered at present. Some recent collaborative studies with Drs. Dorf and Benacerraf are important in this regard (16). In our hands, GLT[5] and GLT[15] at pH 7.5 have shown the response patterns in Table I. However, when the same polymer is dissolved in 1% Na_2CO_3 at pH 9.5, changes occur so that these polymers are not immunogenic in F1(A x C57BL/6) and mice of H-2[q] haplotype. This indicates that subtle pH dependent (denaturation) and not so subtle carbonate concentration dependent carbamylation reactions can alter the SDP. Along similar lines, the different amino acids might alter the

---

1. Carbamylation: pH 9.5

$$RNH_2 + CO_3^{=} \rightleftharpoons RN\overset{H}{-}COO^{-}$$

2. 'Cross Linking':

$$RNH-COO^{-} + R'NH_2 \rightleftharpoons RNH-CO-N-R'$$

Figure 1. Carbamate reactions with polymers. The concentrations of 10 mg polymer (RNH_2) per ml 1% Na_2CO_3 corresponds to about 2.5×10^{-4} M polymer and 1×10^{-1}M Na_2CO_3.

---

structural aspects of the GL terpolymer sufficiently so that its interaction with the postulated same T cell receptor(s) in all mice could lead to the observed SDP's. That the responses to GLØ were not altered by this carbonate treatment (16) may also be reflected in the greater stability of GLØ to the tyrosylation reaction which is performed at pH 9 (Table IV).

This chance observation is important in interpreting results obtained with the same synthetic polymer in various laboratories where different degrees of 'tender loving care' are given to the synthetic polymers.

An alternate explanation for the unique SDP's has recently been offered by Klein. He has suggested that "the number of Ir loci may not be extremely large, and that the Ir genes are not so specific. Relative specificity of Ir genes is then accomplished by a combination of multiple allelism at a single locus and polygenic control of the response to a single antigen." (17)

If the 2 Ir gene control which is now known to govern the responses to GLT-GLØ terpolymers becomes more general, it may well be that a small number of loci, each with many alleles, could provide enough different combinations to account for the various SDP's of individual responses.

ACKNOWLEDGMENTS

This study was supported by research grant AI07825 from the National Institute of Allergy and Infectious Diseases and American Cancer Society Grant IM-5D.

REFERENCES

(1)   C.F. Merryman and P.H. Maurer.   Fed. Proc. 32 (1973) 4372.

(2)   P. Pinchuck and P.H. Maurer.   J. Exp. Med. 122 (1965) 665.

(3)   C.F. Merryman and P.H. Maurer.   Immunogenetics 1 (1975) 549.

(4)   C.F. Merryman, P.H. Maurer and D.W. Bailey.   J. Immunol. 108 (1972) 937.

(5)   M.E. Dorf, J.M.D. Plate, J.H. Stimpfling and B. Benacerraf.   J. Immunol. 114 (1975) 602.

(6)   P.H. Maurer and C.F. Merryman.   Immunogenetics

(7)   C.F. Merryman, P.H. Maurer and J.H. Stimpfling.   Immunogenetics 2 (1975) 441.

(8)   M.E. Dorf, J.H. Stimpfling and B. Benacerraf.   J. Exp. Med. 141 (1975) 1459.

(9)   P.H. Maurer and C.F. Merryman.   Unpublished observations

(10)   R. Lieberman, C. Stiffel, R. Asofsky, D. Mouton, G. Biozzi and B. Benacerraf.   J. Exp. Med. 136 (1972) 790.

(11)   P.H. Maurer and C.F. Merryman.   Ann. Immunol. (Inst. Pasteur) 125C (1974) 189.

(12)   C.F. Merryman and P.H. Maurer.   J. Immunol. (Submitted).

(13)   B. Benacerraf and M.E. Dorf.   Progress in Immunology II, 2 (1974) 181.

(14)   G.D. Fasman and P.Y. Chou, in: Peptides, Polypeptides and Proteins, eds. E.R. Blout, F.A. Bovey, M. Goodman and N. Lotan (John Wiley and Sons, 1974) p. 114.

(15)   Y. Shalitin, in: Ring Opening Polymerization, eds. K.D. Frisch and S.L. Reegen (Marcel Dekker, Inc. 1969) p. 114.

(16)   M.E. Dorf, P.H. Maurer, C.F. Merryman and B. Benacerraf. PNAS (Submitted).

(17) J. Klein, in: Contemp. Topics in Immunobiology (1975) Plenum Press In Press .

A POSSIBLE FUNCTION FOR PRODUCTS OF THE MAJOR HISTOCOMPATIBILITY COMPLEX IN HUMORAL IMMUNITY

HARALD von BOEHMER

Basel Institute for Immunology
Basel, Switzerland

Abstract: T-B cell cooperation has been studied in a secondary response to sheep erythrocytes using either syngeneic or allogeneic T- and B-cell combinations. In order to avoid an allogeneic efffect or rejection of B cells by allogeneic T cells T helper cells were prepared from tetraparental bone marrow chimeras (TBMC). T cells primed to SRBC in the chimeric environment cooperated with syngeneic as well as with allogeneic primed B cells carrying the alloantigens to which the T cells had been tolerized. In cell mixing experiments no preference of T cells to cooperate with syngeneic B cells could be demonstrated. In vivo activated T cells were found to be able to induce a switch to IgG secretion in syngeneic as well as allogeneic unprimed B cells.

The data indicate that the presence of differing determinants of the MHC on allogeneic T and B cells does not under any circumstances interfere with T-B collaboration. It will be discussed that the presence of allogeneic determinants of the MHC during T cell priming may be essential in order to obtain allogeneic T-B cell cooperation.

INTRODUCTION

In recent experiments we have shown that stable chimeric mice can be produced by injecting lethally X-irradiated F_1 hybrid mice with bone marrow cells from both parental strains (1). Injection of equal proportions of bone marrow cells from the two different strains resulted in a 50:50 (parent:parent) lymphoid cell chimerism. T cells from such mice were tolerant towards the host's antigens as tested in cell mediated lympholysis as well as in the mixed lymphocyte reaction (1). No indication could be obtained that the tolerance was mediated by suppressor cells or blocking serum factors (2).

Experiments by Katz et al (3) and also by Kindred et al (4) have indicated that allogeneic T and B cells, obtained from strains differing at the I region of the MHC will not cooperate in a secondary humoral immune response. We were interested to see whether this was so also in our chimeric mice or whether allogeneic T and B cells could cooperate in the chimeric environment as postulated by Bechthol et al. (5). For this purpose we have studied and compared the helper activity of primed and activated T cells on syngeneic and allogeneic primed and unprimed B cells.

MATERIALS AND METHODS

Tetraparental bone marrow chimeras (TBMC): The detailed experimental protocol has been reported (1).

T helper cells from TBMC: TBMC were given an intraperitoneal injection of 0.1 ml 25% SRBC suspension 4 months after irradiation and injection with bone marrow cells. 1-2 months after immunization T cells were prepared from lymph node cells, thoracic duct lymphocytes and spleen (6). T helper cells carrying antigens from one parental strain only were obtained by killing cells of the other parental type with anti-H2 sera and complement.

Activated T cells: In order to obtain activated T cells 5×10^7 spleen cells from TBMC were transferred with 5×10^8 SRBC into lethally irradiated F_1 hybrids which were syngeneic to the hosts used for preparation of TBMC. After 7 days the spleens were taken out and T cells were prepared (6).

The preparation of B cells, the adotpive transfer system as well as the plaque assay have been described previously (6).

RESULTS

Titration of CBA T helper cells from TBMC with a constant number of allogeneic and syngeneic primed B cells

TBMC prepared by injecting (CBA/J x DBA-2/J)F_1 hybrids with bone marrow cells from both strains were used. All mice showed an approximately 50:50 (parent:parent) lymphoid cell chimerism.

Various numbers of SRBC-primed CBA T cells derived from TBMC were transferred with primed CBA or DBA-2 B cells into lethally X-irradiated (CBA x DBA)F$_1$ recipients. As shown in Fig. 1, 2 x 10^6 T cells argumented the IgG-PFC response of either syngeneic or allogeneic B cells by a factor of 10.

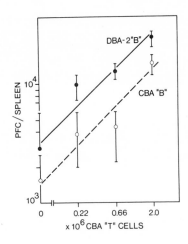

Figure 1. Titration of primed CBA T cells from TBMC with allogeneic and syngeneic primed B cells.

The helper effect of T cells from TBMC on a mixed population of B cells from TBMC

TBMC were prepared by injecting (C3H x SJL)F$_1$ hybrids with bone marrow cells from both parental strains. The mice were primed with SRBC and used 1 months later for the transfer experiments: After preparation of T and B cells one group of X-irradiated (C3H x SJL)F$_1$ recipients received 2 x 10^6 T cells from the TBMC together with 6 x 10^6 B cells from TBMC. (Control groups received either T or B cells alone). A second group of recipients received 2 x 10^6 C3H T cells (prepared from TBMC by treatment with anti-SJL serum) together with 6×10^6 C3H and SJL B cells from TBMC. Seven days after priming with SRBC, PFC were determined and their origin was tested with anti-C3H and anti-SJL sera. It would be expected that if the C3H T cells cooperated more efficiently with syngeneic than with allogeneic B cells then the proportion of C3H-PFC would be higher in the recipients receiving C3H helper T cells compared with those recipients receiving a mixed population of C3H and SJL helper T cells ($\sim 1:1$). As shown in Table I this was not observed indicating that there was no preferential cooperation of C3H T cells with syngeneic C3H B cells.

Table I

Helper effect of SRBC primed T cells from TBMC for a mixture of allogeneic and syngeneic B cells from TBMC

Cells injected		Proportion of T cells killed by		PFC IgG	Proportion of	
T cells	B cells	αC3H serum	αSJL serum		C3H PFC	SJL PFC
2×10^6 T	6×10^6 B	58%	<5%	3,124(3,845-2,539)	29.8%	64.0%
2×10^6 T	-	58%	<5%	36(54-24)	ND	ND
-	6×10^6 B	-	-	305(373-244)	ND	ND
2×10^6 T anti SJL treated	6×10^6 B	98%	-	3,044(3,939-2,352)	30.4%	70.1%

Ability of "activated" T helper cells to "switch" syngeneic and allogeneic unprimed B cells into IgG secretion:

5×10^7 spleen cells from a TBMC, prepared by reconstitution of (C3H x SJL)F1 hybrids with bone marrow from both parental strains, were transferred into lethally irradiated (C3H x SJL)F1 mice with 5×10^8 SRBC. After 7 days C3H T cells were prepared and injected with either 5×10^6 syngeneic or allogeneic unprimed B cells into a second (C3H x SJL)F1 host together with 5×10^8 SRBC. As shown in Table II C3H T helper cells transferred with either syngeneic or allogeneic tolerated SJL B cells significantly augmented their IgG-PFC response.

DISCUSSION

Our experiments together with those reported recently by Waldmann et al. (7) using a hapten carrier system, seem to indicate that the presence of determinants coded for by the MHC does not, under any circumstances, prevent T-B cell cooperation. Among several possibilities, which have been discussed elsewhere (2) to explain the different outcome of ex-

Table II

| Cells injected | | IgM-PFC | IgG-PFC |
T cells	B cells		
Chimera C3H T (3 x 10^6)	C3H (5 x 10^6)	315(920-235)	1841(3733-898)
Chimera C3H T (3 x 10^6)	SJL (5 x 10^6)	832(1388-498)	4597(9491-2226)
Chimera C3H T (3 x 10^6)	-	2	3
-	C3H (5 x 10^6)	25(75-8)	247(429-142)
-	SJL (5 x 10^6)	176(362-85)	354(791-158)

periments using TBMC as opposed to those reported by Katz et al., (3) one possibility should be discussed in more detail.

Erb and Feldmann (8) have shown in recent experiments that antigen or antigen fragments may become associated with structures coded for by the I region of the MHC. This complex seems to be essential for the induction of T helper cells. According to these experiments one might postulate that there is associated recognition by T cells of antigen specific as well as I region specific determinants. This postulate seems to be in accordance with experiments by Rosenthal et al. (9) demonstrating a genetic restriction of recognition by primed T cells of antigen pulsed macrophages. If T cells recognize antigenic determinants as well as determinants coded for by the I region (possibly with different portions of the receptor) one might expect the "T cell helper product" to be of the same specificity. Since I region determinants are present on B cells as well as antigenic determinants bound by Ig receptors, the T cell product may have an appropriately high affintiy to trigger a secondary immune response only if the two determinants are identical to those which induced the T helper cell. Therefore a T cell primed by antigen 1 (ag 1) in association with I region product 1 (Ip 1) will not easily help primed B cells carrying ag 1 and Ip 2. Thus primed T cells from one strain will not effectively cooperate with B cells from another strain. Semiallogeneic T and B cells will cooperate because they share I region products. T cells primed in a chimeric environment will according to this speculative hypothesis be primed

311

to ag 1 and Ip 1 as well as ag 1 and Ip 2 and therefore cooperate with syngeneic as well as with allogeneic B cells. The concept of associated recognition of antigen and I-region products by T helper cells is very similar to the concept of Zinkernagel and Doherty (10) who showed associated recognition of antigen and K and D region products by killer cell precursors and killer cells.

REFERENCES

(1) H. von Boehmer, J. Sprent and M. Nabholz. J. Exp. Med. 141 (1975) 322.

(2) H. von Boehmer and J. Sprent. Tranplantation Reviews Vol. 29 (1976) in press.

(3) D.H. Katz, T. Hamaoka and B. Benacerraf. J. Exp. Med. 137 (1975) 1405.

(4) Kindred, B. Cell. Immunol. 17 (1975) 277.

(5) Bechthol, R.B., J.H. Freed, L.A. Herzenberg and H.O. McDevitt. J. Exp. Med. 140 (1974) 1660.

(6) H. von. Boehmer, L. Hudson and J. Sprent. J. Exp. Med. 142 (1975) 989.

(7) H., Waldmann, H. Pope, and A.J. Munro. Nature (1976) in press.

(8) Erb, P. and Feldmann, M. J. Exp. Med. 142 (1975) 460.

(9) Rosenthal, A.S. and Shevach, E.M. J. Exp. Med. 138 (1973) 1194.

(10) R.M. Zinkernagel and P.C. Doherty. J. Exp. Med. 141 (1975) 1427.

IMMUNE RESPONSE (*Ir*) GENE SYSTEMS

Michael Sela, Chairman

van ROOD: I would like to address a comment to Ira Green. Ira, you could find out whether the response is linked to *HLA* by doing "partial" family studies. If you could persuade the sibs of your volunteers to participate in this study and could immunize them, you could end up with the following six groups:

EXPECTED RESPONSE

	Sibs of Responders	Sibs of Non-Responders
HLA-identical	high	low
HLA-haploid	lower	higher
HLA 2 haplotype different	Partial low	Partial high

You could then analyze these groups to determine whether they show significant association with *HLA*.

NOSSAL: I would like to mention work by Claude Bernard showing that the *H-2* exerts a strong influence on the susceptibility to Experimental Autoimmune Encephalomyelitis. Experimental autoimmune encephalomyelitis (EAE) was induced in inbred and congenic strains of mice by injection of mouse spinal cord homogenate (MSCH) in Freund's complete adjuvant (FCA) with pertussis vaccine (Bernard, C.C.A. and Carnegie, P. J. Immunol. 114: 1537, 1972).

The inbred strains SJL/J ($H-2^s$) and C57BL/6 ($H-2^b$) were susceptible to EAE, whereas mice carrying other $H-2$ alleles such as $H-2^d$ and $H-2^k$ were non-susceptible despite full immunization with MSCH, FCA and pertussis.

The failure of non-susceptible animals to develop EAE in response to encephalitogenic challenge cannot be attributed readily to an absence of a relevant antigen in the target tissue (brain) because the inciting

molecule, basic protein of myelin purified from BALB/c
(H-2^d) brain was found to be encephalitogenic for SJL/J
mice. When F_1 hybrids between the susceptible SJL/J and
several resistant strains were compared with each of the
parental strains, it appeared that susceptibility to EAE
was inherited as a dominant trait. This dominant inheritance was also observed in F_1 animals obtained by crossing the susceptible SJL/J and resistant BALB/c in
either direction, indicative of an absence of maternal
effects. The number of loci determining susceptibility
was examined in F_2 and backcross animals. Most of the
F_2 mice from SJL/J and BALB/c matings were susceptible
whereas only 29% of the F_1 backcrosses to resistant
parents developed EAE, suggesting that susceptibility to
EAE is inherited as a polygenic trait. The fact that
susceptibility in F_1 x BALB/c animals was significantly
associated with the H-2^s allele of the susceptible
parent indicated that one of the genes responsible for
susceptibility to EAE was closely associated with the
H-2 region (Table I).

TABLE I

Incidence of clinical and histological EAE in parental, hybrid and backcross mice
injected with mouse spinal cord

Strain	H_2 genotype	No. of mice with EAE
SJL/J	s	10/10
BALB/c	d	0/10
(SJL/J x BALB/c)$_{F_1}$	s/d	10/10
(SJL/J x BALB/c)$_{F_2}$	s/s	5/6
	s/d	9/9
	d/d	3/4
(SJL/J x BALB/c)$_{F_1}$ x BALB/c	s/d	5/8
	d/d	1/13

Additional evidence for an H-2 linkage was obtained by
testing various strains of mice derived from recombinants involving the H-2 allele of the susceptible
strains. By the use of the A.SW mice possessing the
H-2^s of the SJL/J strain, but on the different resistant background, it was clear that the relevant genetic
region was within the H-2 region or closely linked to
it. Further definition of the genetic locus involved
was made by testing intra-H-2 recombinant mice. It was

found that strains bearing either K or the K and I region derived from a responder chromosome, were susceptible to EAE, implying that the $H-2$ gene control of susceptibility to EAE is located on the centromeric left side of the $H-2$ complex (Table II).

TABLE II

Incidence of clinical and histological EAE in H-2 recombinant strains of mice injected with mouse spinal cord

Strain	H-2 type	Composition of H-2 region						No. of mice with EAE
		K	IA	IB	IC	S	D	
SJL/J	s	s	s	s	s	s	s	12/12
A. SW/Sn	s	s	s	s	s	s	s	18/20
A. TH	th	s	s	s	s	s	d	15/15
A. TL	tl	s	k	k	k	k	d	14/14
C57Bl/6	b	b	b	b	b	b	b	5/5
B.10.A	a	k	k	k	d	d	d	0/6
B.10.A (2R)	h-2 Sg	k	k	k	d	d	b	0/4
B.10.A (4R)	h-3 Sg	k	k	b	b	b	b	0/10
B.10.A (5R)	i-2 Sg	b	b	b	d	d	d	5*/7

* Mild clinical and histological disease.

The B10.A(4R) strain, which shares the $I-B$, $I-C$, S and D region with C57BL/6, failed to develop EAE, indicating that the genetic locus involved is not to the right of the $I-B$ region, but is either in the K or $I-A$ region. Also, the A.TL strain which bears the $H-2K$ region of $H-2^s$ was highly susceptible, further suggesting that one of the relevant genes is closely associated with the K locus. An alternative possibility would be that the locus for EAE lies to the left of the $H-2K$ region. Mice with EAE developed cell-mediated immune responsiveness to basic protein of myelin as judged by the macrophage migration inhibition assay, using peritoneal exudate cells; this was not observed with mice of resistant strains (Table III). However, the migration of peritoneal exudate cells of both susceptible and resistant strains was significantly inhibited in the presence of purified protein derivative (PPD) of *M. tuberculosis*. Thus, the gene(s) involved in the control of susceptibility to EAE also influence T cell responsiveness to BPM. Antibody to BPM, as judged by radioimmunoassay, was detected in susceptible and resistant strains but there was no correlation between the presence or levels of antibody and susceptibility or resistance to EAE (Table III). It is suggested that resistance to EAE is associated with failure to recognize and/or respond to the encephalitogenic determinant of the BPM molecule.

TABLE III

Immunological response to mouse basic protein of myelin (BPM) in susceptible and resistant strains of mice injected with mouse spinal cord.

Mouse strain	H-2 type	No. of mice tested	Immune response - BPM	
			CMI[1]	Antibody[2]
SJL/J	s	8	34.1 ± 4.2	0.32
A. SW	s	6	76.8 ± 6.8	0
BALB/c	d	22	98.0 ± 13.8	0
CBA/J	k	13	108.7 ± 11.2	0.48
(SJL/J x BALB/c)$_{F_1}$	s/d	15	31.1 ± 6.2	0.15

1   MIF assay; Migration with PPD (all strains)   25-56%

2   Antigen binding capacity by radioimmunoassay

NOSSAL: Another approach to the study of lymphocyte responses against antigens of the *I* region has been described by J.W. Goding and N.L. Warner. The experimental system concerns the ability of congenic resistant strains of mice to reject T cell lymphomas derived from strains of mice differing only at the *I* region. In all, 14 tumors have been studied with 2 pairs of strain combinations. A.TL mice uniformly rejected 4 different A.TH tumors, and A.TH mice similarly rejected all 3 A.TL tumors, whereas all tumors grew in syngeneic and (A.TH x A.TL)F_1 hybrids. In contrast, 3 T lymphomas of B10.A(2R) origin, and 4 T lymphomas of B10.A(4R) origin all grew successfully in both B10.A(2R) and B10.A(4R) mice.

The particular point of interest in relation to the present session is that rejection of tumors bearing allogeneic Ia antigens occurred in one strain combination but not in the other. Although various possibilities have been discussed to explain these observations (Goding, J.W. and Warner, N.L. J. Exp. Med. 142:536, 1975; Warner, N.L. and Goding, J.W., in Membrane

316

<u>Receptors of Lymphocytes</u>, ed. M. Seligmann,
J. Preud'Homme and F. Kourilsky; Elsevier), the two
possibilities of particular interest are:

1) That the ability to respond to a particular Ia
determinant is itself under Ir region genetic control,
and

2) That the rejection of tumors between A.TH and A.TL
strains is not induced by any known serologically
defined I region antigen, but may represent a histocompatibility type I region locus that is capable of
only inducing T cell-mediated responses. In this
regard, it is interesting to note that the tumors bear
extremely little serologically detectable Ia antigen.

SHEARER: Very preliminary data, which will have to be
verified, concerned with attempts to map the Ir gene
controlling response potential to TNP-modified $H-2D^d$
products using A.TL spleen cells suggest that this gene
may map to the left of $I-A$, possibly in the K region.

Is it possible that the K-region-associated $H-2$-linked
genetics associated with response to EAE reactivity
does not involve an Ir gene function, but is attribu-
table to basic protein-modified K-region products involved in the formation of a new altered autologous
antigen?

NOSSAL: I am happy to hear that your postulated level of
control is also at or near the K-region. I think the
fact that basic protein of myelin from BALB/c mice is
encephalitogenic in SJL mice is adequate to prove that
the effect is on responsiveness, not on antigenic structure.

KATZ: Gus, in your backcross analysis of susceptibility to
EAE, you observed 75% incidence of disease in the d/d
serotyped F_2 progeny; this obviously indicates the
existence of two genes involved in the disease susceptibility. Are you saying that both of these genes are
to the left of $I-A$?

NOSSAL: We know there is more than one gene, but the numbers of F_2 and backcross mice is not yet large enough
for us to determine the exact number of genes. The
only one that has been mapped is the $H-2$-associated one,

317

which appears clearly to be on the left of *I-A*.

GERSHON: In studying a problem such as EAE one must consider not only production of immunity but other factors.
For example, we have shown that delayed type hypersensitivity (DTH) depends to some extent on mast cell and
vasoactive amine activity, so that even when immune T
cells are present DTH may be lacking. We have also
shown (Askenase, P., Waksman, B., Metzler, C. and
Gershon, R.K. manuscript in preparation, 1975) that EAE
can be abolished or at least diminished in immune rats
by depletion of vasoactive amines. Differences in mast
cells between mice strains might be responsible in part
for some of your findings. I don't know about SJL but
C57BL/6 are high in mast cell number or activity.

NOSSAL: I think the experiments on MIF production answer
your objection. Basic protein of mouse myelin inhibits
macrophage migration in all susceptible strains, but
not in resistant strains. However, migration of PEC
was significantly inhibited in resistant strains by
PPD--a good specificity control.

McDEVITT: Have you looked at various backgrounds and the
effect of the genetic background on EAE induction?

NOSSAL: So far, the strains found to be resistant include
CBA/J and BRVR (H-2^k), BALB/c and NZB and NZC (H-2^d),
A/J and B10.A (H-2^a), as well as the recombinant
strains shown on Table 2. The susceptible strains,
apart from the recombinants, were SJL/J and A.SW/Sn
(H-2^s) and C57BL/6 (H-2^b). The other strains you mentioned have not yet been tested.

SELA: In studies which were recently published (Mozes et
al., *J. Exp. Med.*, 140, 349, 1974) we have shown that
the tetrapeptide TyrTyrGluGlu is the major determinant
of (T,G)-A--L. The low response to TyrTyrGluGlu-A--L
may be corrected with MBSA, suggesting that the correction of the low response to (T,G)-A--L with MBSA
occurs really through an increase of the response to
its major determinant (M. Schwartz, E. Mozes and M.
Sela, unpublished data). Comparison of the structure
of the various antibodies by means of isoelectrofocusing, making use of ^{131}I-tagged (T,G)-A--L and TyrTyr-
GluGlu-A--L, showed that antibodies are discrete and
almost identical in high responders and in low

responders corrected with MBSA (M. Cramer, M. Schwartz, E. Mozes and M. Sela, unpublished data). The affinities are also in both cases very similar.

GERSHON: Excuse me if I missed something; your plaque-forming cell (PFC) assay vs. antibody response suggest a significant difference in affinity since you can show PFC without demonstrable antibody activity. This might indicate multivalency of low affinity antibody producing plaques on RBC with lots of attached antigen which would have insufficient affinity to be measured as antibody in solution.

SELA: Presence of plaque-forming cells in the absence of detectable antibodies in the serum may indeed reflect the low affinity of the antibodies made by these cells. In the comparison I discussed, the similar affinities were in high responders and low responders corrected with MBSA. When the low responders are not thus corrected, the affinity is indeed much lower.

PAUL: Michael, what was the antibody class of the PFC you were discussing.

MOZES: The hemolytic plaque forming cells measured in high and low responders to (T-T-G-G)-A--L were of the IgM class. The avidity of these plaques was studied and the avidity of the low responder's plaques was much lower than that of the high responders.

MUNRO: As we describe elsewhere in this book we have found that certain low responder strains to (T,G)-A--L become high responders in F_1 hybrids. The low responder strains which show this complementation were selected with knowledge of the nature of the defect in the response to (T,G)-A--L in these strains, in particular B10.M ($H-2^f$) mice which have a defect in an acceptor for the T,G-A--L-specific T cell factor and B10.BR ($H-2^k$) and I/St ($H-2^j$) mice which fail to make active T-cell factor for (T,G)-A--L. These experiments rely on differences in IgM plaque-forming cells in high and low responder strains. Dr. McDevitt has repeatedly suggested that the IgM response to T,G-A--L is a poor indication of the responder status of mice. While Dr. Mozes, in at least secondary responses, finds marked differences in IgM response between high and low responder strains. We have found that an intraperitoneal

injection of 10 μg of T,G-A--L in Freund's complete
adjuvant produces clear differences in direct PFC
(Table IV) all of which are inhibited by the incorporation of anti-μ serum in the plaque assay. The strains
in Table IV are congenic for the *H-2* complex. Although
this does not completely prove that these observed differences in primary IgM response are controlled by *Ir-1*
genes, it would seem reasonable to conclude so. Using
this assay clear complementation is seen with the B10.M
strain crossed with B10.BR and I/St (Table V). The
B10.M mice in these experiments were obtained from Dr.
Archer working in Dr. A. Davis' laboratory at Searle,
High Wycombe, England.

The differences in these experiments and those reported
below by Dr. McDevitt are probably in part due to technical differences and in part due to different source
of critical B10.M(H-2^f) strains.

Table IV

Primary PFC Responses of High (B10) and Low (B10.BR)
Responder Strains to (T,G)-A--L

		Day 7	Day 15	Day 21
B10	Direct	100	25,000	200
	Indirect	0	2,500	1,500
B10.BR	Direct	50	100	100
	Indirect	0	0	0

Table V

Primary PFC Responses to (T,G)-A--L at 14 Days of
Various Low Responder Strains and F_1 Recombinants

Strain	Haplotype	PFC/Spleen
I/St	H-2^j	50
B10.BR	H-2^k	20
B10.M	H-2^f	10
I/St x B10.M	H-$2^{j/f}$	7,500
B10.BR x B10.M	H-$2^{k/f}$	19,500
B10	H-2^b	14,500

[*EDITOR'S NOTE:* Following the preceding presentation by Allan Munro, Hugh McDevitt described results from his laboratory on the same topic - his commentary follows below - DHK.]

COMMENTARY

HUGH O. McDEVITT

Division of Immunology
Department of Medicine
Stanford University School of Medicine

Dan Meruelo in our laboratory has spent considerable time attempting to confirm the results reported by Alan Munro and Michael Taussig. Using factor prepared from educated thymocytes, or from spleen cells of animals immunized five to six days earlier with (T,G)-A--L 1383 in compete Freund's adjuvant, we have found that the results are variable, and that it is difficult to get consistently reproducible results. The numbers of direct PFC per spleen are much smaller than those reported by Taussig and Munro, and only direct plaques are obtained even when injecting factor with previously immunized anti-θ treated spleen cells, rather than factor with non-immunized bone marrow. We do find some potentiation of the numbers of direct PFC per spleen, but so far our results are so variable that it is difficult to draw any definite conclusions.

For these reasons, and because Taussig and Munro have reported a difference between B10 and B10.BR mice in the number of direct PFC per spleen at day 14 following immunization with 10γ (T,G)-A--L 1383 in complete Freund's adjuvant, we decided to repeat these *in vivo* experiments. We were particularly stimulated to do this because our earlier studies showed very little difference in the numbers of direct PFC per spleen in the C3H (low-responder) versus C3H.SW (high-responder) strains following *in vivo* immunization. This was in direct contrast to the results of Taussig and Munro, who found a large difference in the number of direct PFC per spleen in B10 (responder) versus B10.BR (low-responder) strains. In addition, Taussig and Munro have reported that F_1 hybrid mice derived from a cross between B10.M ($\underline{H-2}^f$ (T,G)-A--L low-responder) and B10.BR ($\underline{H-2}^k$, (T,G)-A--L low-responder) were high responders in terms of the numbers of direct PFC detected at day 14 following *in vivo* immunization with 10γ (T,G)-A--L 1383 in complete Freund's adjuvant. This has been interpreted as two gene complementation in the immune response to (T,G)-A--L. If this result is correct and is determined by Ir-1A, it would predict that this F_1 would also show complementation for the IgG secondary response to (T,G)-A--L. This is an important point, and one that has perhaps not been sufficiently emphasized in interpreting these results. As I mentioned earlier, in all of our results, the major difference between a high-responder and a low-responder strain to (T,G)-A--L is in the secondary IgG response. Whether the animals are immunized with (T,G)-A--L in complete Freund's adjuvant or in aqueous solution, there is very little, and for some preparations of (T,G)-A--L, no difference in the primary response, while there is a very large difference in the secondary antibody response, which is mostly IgG. If the gene complementation reported by Taussig and Munro does indicate the necessity for two genes to develop the responder phenotype to (T,G)-A--L, and if these genes control the same process originally assigned to Ir-1A$^{(T,G)-A--L}$, then one would expect complementation to be more pronounced in the IgG secondary than in the IgM primary, since it is in the IgG secondary that the main difference between high-responder and low-responder is observed.

The first figure shows the results obtained by Beverly Deak for immunization of B10, B10.BR, B10.M, B10.WB, (B10.M x B10.BR)F_1, and (B10.M x B10.WB)F_1 mice with 10γ (T,G)-A--L 52 in complete Freund's adjuvant, as determined by our standard antigen binding assay. The B10 strain is H-2^b and a high-responder to (T,G)-A--L. The other three strains are low responders to (T,G)-A--L, and the two F_1 hybrids are crosses involving H-2 types (H-2^f and H-2^k, and H-2^f and H-2^j) which have been shown by Taussig and Munro to complement for the direct PFC response following in vivo immunization with (T,G)-A--L 1383. In the top figure, the percent antigen bound values for primary and secondary sera at a 1/50 dilution are broken down into total and 2 mercaptoethanol resistant (IgG) values. In the lower part of the figure, serum dilution 1/250, there is very little detectable 2-Me sensitive antibody activity so only total antibody titers are plotted. The results show the usual large difference in response between the high-responder B10 strain and the low-responder strains. In addition, neither the (B10.M x B10.BR)F_1 or the (B10.M x B10.WB)F_1 hybrid shows any complementation in either the primary or secondary IgM or IgG response to 10γ of (T,G)-A--L 52. If anything, the response of the F_1 hybrids is lower than that of the B10.M parental strain.

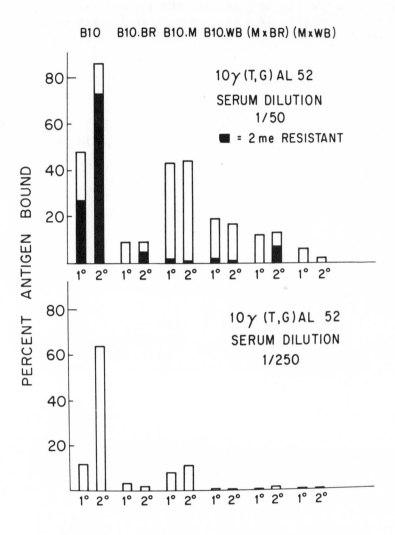

Figure 1. Primary and secondary serum antibody response to 10γ (T,G)-A--L 52 in CRA, determined by our standard antigen binding assay.

Because we were dealing with a different preparation of (T,G)-A--L, these studies were repeated by Meruelo and Deak following, as nearly as possible, the immunization regimen employed by Taussig and Munro. These results are shown in the second figure. Mice were immunized with 10γ (T,G)-A--L

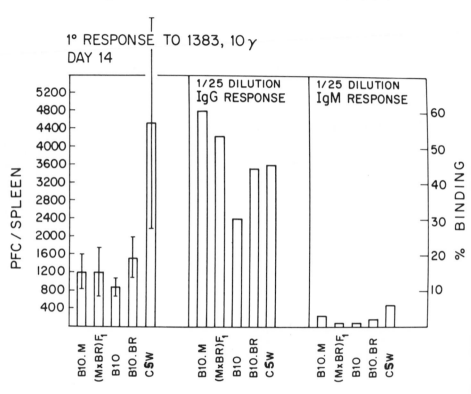

Figure 2. Day 14 primary response immunization with 10γ (T,G)-A--L 1383 in CFA. PFC response was determined with (T,G)-Pro--L tagged SRBC. Serum antibody was determined by standard antigen binding assay in which IgG is assumed to be 2-Me resistant antibody and IgM total antibody minus 2-Me resistant antibody

1383 in complete Freund's adjuvant and sacrificed on day 14, at which time the number of direct PFC per spleen were determined using sheep red cells sensitized with (T,G)-Pro--L (the same assay employed by Taussig, Munro and Mozes). Serum antibody titers were also determined. B10.M, (B10.M x B10.BR)F$_1$ B10 and B10.BR strains showed similar numbers of direct PFC per spleen, and similar levels of serum antibody, which are variable, mostly IgG, and dependent on the day after immunization. It is clear that there is no complementation for the direct PFC per spleen in the (B10.M x B10.BR)F_1.

To ascertain that our results and those of Taussig and Munro were not due to differences in the kinetics or dose dependency of the response, we have followed the direct and indirect plaque forming response and the serum antibody titers throughout the primary response and the secondary response to (T,G)-A--L 52 and to (T,G)-A--L 1383. It is clear that in the primary response there is considerable day-to-day variability in the direct PFC response to (T,G)-A--L in complete Freund's adjuvant, but at no time is there a marked difference between the high-responder and low-responder strains. Clear differences are readily seen in the secondary response. Because of the scarcity of animals, we were able to repeat the studies using a higher dose of (T,G)-A--L 1383 (50γ) only in B10, B10.BR, and (B10.M x B10.WB)F_1 strains. These studies also failed to show any complementation for the primary or the secondary response in the (B10.M x B10.WB)F_1 strain.

These results raise two separate problems. The first is the direct conflict between our results (as well as those of Edna Mozes) and the results of Alan Munro and Michael Taussig in the numbers of direct PFC per spleen found when high-responder and low-responder strains are immunized with 10γ (T,G)-A--L 1383 in complete Freund's adjuvant and plaqued at day 14 with (T,G)-Pro--L sensitized sheep red cells. We find little or no difference between high-responder and low-responder strains, whereas Taussig and Munro find a distinct and very large difference. This must be due to a difference either in antigen, assay technique, or in the animals themselves. We can certainly resolve these differences by an exchange of animals, antigens, and techniques.

A more important problem is the failure to find complementation for an IgG secondary response, which defines the major difference between high-responder and low-responder strains to either (T,G)-A--L 1383 or (T,G)-A--L 52 in F_1 hybrids which have been reported by Taussig and Munro to show complementation for the IgM primary response. Benacerraf and Dorf (this volume) have shown that there are some F_1 hybrids in which complementation is not observed though it would be expected on the basis of results in other F_1 hybrids or in H-2 recombinants. While this might be an explanation for the failure to detect complementation in the IgG secondary response to (T,G)-A--L, I think this is unlikely since

Taussig and Munro have reported complementation in (B10.M x B10.BR)F$_1$ for the _in vivo_ primary direct PFC response. It therefore seems clear that we are dealing with a strain combination which has been shown to complement _in vivo_, and, the evidence would certainly predict that some degree of complementation should be detected in the _in vivo_ secondary response. This is clearly not the case. While we will certainly go on to test other combinations which have been reported to complement by Taussig and Munro, such as (I/St x B10.M)F$_1$, alternative explanations should also be sought. One possible explanation which has occurred to us is that the factor detected by Taussig and Munro is not a helper factor, but is, rather, a suppressor factor of the type already described by Tada (this volume). Tada has described strains which can produce a suppressor factor, but whose B cells cannot be suppressed by that factor. This is similar to the T cell factor, B cell acceptor difference described by Taussig and Munro. It is possible that this factor is a suppressor factor, that it is produced by both high-responder and low-responder strains, and that the responder strains (all _H-2_^{b}) as well as strains carrying _H-2_^{f} are the only strains which possess the B cell acceptor for this suppressor factor, which is, therefore, unable to affect low responder B cells such as B10.BR (_H-2_^{k}). If this were the case, injection of bone marrow cells plus antigen and factor might lead to suppression of the IgG response only in _H-2_^{b} and _H-2_^{f} strains, or their F$_1$ hybrid. Suppression of the IgG response might then result in a reciprocal augmentation of the IgM direct PFC response.

Certainly other possibilities should be kept in mind. The appeal of this explanation is that it has experimental precedent and that it is directly testable. It would predict that (B10.M x B10.BR)F$_1$ hybrids should develop suppressor T cells following immunization with aqueous (T,G)-A--L which could inhibit the subsequent response to (T,G)-A--L complexed with methylated bovine serum albumin, a result that we have been unable to obtain in standard low-responder strains such as C3H (_H-2_^{k}).

SELA: I think that it is cogent at this moment that
probably for very good reasons, we have meticulously
avoided until now to ask the central question, namely:
what do we mean by genetically controlled?

PAUL: I would like to briefly mention some data which
Ronald Schwartz and I have obtained on the T-lymphocyte proliferative response to (T,G)-A--L. We have examined the activity of T-lymphocytes purified from
peritoneal exudates and have mapped the Ir gene involved as to the left of $I-B$, which is precisely where
the genes had been mapped by measuring antibody responses. In particular, mice of the $H-2^k$ haplotype,
including B10.BR, AKR and C3H, which are classified by
Taussig and Munro as T-cell factor producers, do not
make proliferative responses. Of course the failure of
T-lymphocyte proliferation can be reconciled with success in factor production but at least some T-cell
functions in $H-2^k$ mice are grossly abnormal.

In preliminary experiments, we observe that (B10.BR x
B10.M) F_1 T cells do respond to (T,G)-A--L with proliferation - whether this is complementation or not
still needs to be proven.

MEO: Can we interpret DNA synthesis as a response equivalent to antibody production? The discrepancy between
the success of Dr. Schwartz's in $vitro$ experiment
(mentioned by Dr. Paul) and the failure of Dr. McDevitt
to show complementation in the $H-2^k$ x $H-2^f$ heterozygote
could be explained by the fact that the response in the
latter system is a measure of the (T-G)-A--L immunogenicity, and in the first system also of mitogenicity.
Shouldn't we also include as control the unimmunized
F_1?

PAUL: Tommy, we are quite confident that we are not
measuring a mitogenic activity of the synthetic antigens. In our system, virtually no B lymphocytes are
present and the response to "authentic" B mitogens is
quite minimal. Furthermore, all the antigens have been
tested on cells from mice immunized with Freund's adjuvant only and have proved not to be mitogenic.

McDEVITT: It should be noted that in the Schwartz and
Paul's system $H-2^d$ shows a strong proliferative response to (T,G)-A--L, so that proliferative response and

antibody response may not always be correlated.

BENACERRAF: I would like to ask Dick Gershon whether suppressor cells work as well on IgM responses as well as
on IgG responses.

GERSHON: Thymus-dependent IgM is very susceptible to suppressor T cell activity. The question of whether thymus-independent immune responses are also susceptible
to suppressor T cell activity is less clear. In my
analysis, this point has not been clearly shown. IgG
antibodies and in particular high affinity antibodies
are clearly more easily suppressed than IgM.

BENACERRAF: In reference to the gene complementation observed by Munro and Taussig with (T,G)-A--L, we feel
that their system is operationally and phenomenologi-
cally different from the complementation in the GLΦ
system. The Munro and Taussig system resembles more
the gene complementation in the suppressor system we
have investigated. The evidence for this statement
stems from the genetic restriction in the effectiveness
of suppressive factor in recipient mice. This will be
discussed by Judith Kapp tomorrow (see Kapp, et al,
this volume).

TAUSSIG: Three comments. First on whether the *Ir-1* gene
controls the IgM response, Edna Mozes has shown clearly
that there are good differences in the IgM response to
(T-T-G-G)-A--L in *H-2* congenic mice. The *Ir-1* gene
most probably controls the level of response to both
IgM and IgG. Secondly, the fact that low responder T-
cells may make factor yet not proliferate *in vitro*,
could be because the acceptor defect-demonstrable for B
cells-is also present on T cells. Finally, I am not
convinced that the two-gene model of a factor and a
corresponding acceptor, is not applicable to GLΦ. If
both the α and β genes contributed to an acceptor,
present on both T and B cells, the results described by
Dr. Benacerraf for GLΦ could be explained. The *cis-
trans* effect could perhaps be accounted for by allelic
exclusion of certain Ia products, and the requirement
that both functional genes be expressed in the same
cell.

MOZES: There are differences in the number of IgM plaques
of high and low responder mice to either (T-T-G-G)-A--L

328

or (T,G)-A--L in a secondary response.

J. KLEIN: I would like to ask those involved in the controversy whether they H-2-typed their B10.M mice to be sure that these mice carry the H-2^f haplotype.

McDEVITT: We've just gotten the antisera and are in the process of checking this.

SACHS: I would like to ask Alan Munro whether the observation that there is a B cell acceptor defect, which in your published paper was shown in C3H/HeJ, has been found in any other H-2^k haplotype strain?

MUNRO: Yes, it has been shown in the B10.BR congenic strain as well.

GREEN: Is complementation due at all to the increased complexity of GLΦ or (T,G)-A--L as compared to simple antigens such as PLL?

BENACERRAF: We feel that the gene complementation is a general phenomenon in H-linked Ir gene control systems. It was discovered most easily with the GLΦ system because in this system the two complementary genes are separated by the length of the I region and therefore permits recombination to be observed. The *cis-trans* preference for gene complementation is another explanation for the difficulty in observing frequent complementation.

van ROOD: Could the "H-2" people explain to the "HLA" workers whether the gene complementation data provide us with an explanation for the existence of linkage disequilibrium in man?

McDEVITT: I think that the two-gene complementation result, and especially the finding of the *cis-* versus *trans*-effect, is the best reason found to date for the linkage disequilibrium seen in the HLA system. This is especially true after hearing from Shearer that there may be Ir genes controlling the response to modified K or D genes, and the report by Nossal that EAE induction maps in the H-$2K^s$ region. These results taken together indicate that certain *cis*-combinations of certain alleles at the HLA A, B, C, and D loci could be expected to confer distinct selective advantages.

van ROOD: This thus implies that we have to look in man
    for complementary immune response genes in the *La*[*A*]
    locus region.   In this context, the B cell determinants
    which are coded for by the *La*[*A*] region in man (see
    Amos, this volume) and Balner (*Nature*, submitted) might
    be relevant.

STROMINGER: I would like to point out that since the Ia
    antigen is probably composed of two polypeptide chains,
    the two gene effect could be the result of expression
    of structures on two different polypeptides.   However,
    Baruj points out to me that this explanation does not
    take account of the *cis-trans*-effect which would imply
    that both genes have their effect on one polypeptide.

SELA: Before closing the general discussion, I would like
    to make one final comment.   This session was devoted to
    immune response gene systems, within a meeting con-
    cerned with the role of products of the histocompatib-
    ility gene complex in immune responses.   We should not
    forget, nevertheless, that some immune response gene
    systems are not linked to histocompatibility, but to
    such other properties as sex or allotype.   They may be
    also relevant and important for health and disease.
    Now, I would like to give Morten Simonsen a few moments
    to present some interesting data.

SIMONSEN: I wish to show a single slide which summarizes
    the findings of my colleague Claus Koch who has studied
    the genetics of the (T,G)-A--L response in chickens.
    The (T,G)-A--L was provided by Edna Mozes.   The inbred
    chicken strains B1 and B2 were imported from Drs.
    Schierman and McBride in New York, the outbred White
    Leghorns (W.L.) were of outbred commercial stocks.   The
    titrations shown were performed with iodinated (T,G)-
    A--L after a standard immunization schedule with (T,G)-
    A--L in Freund's adjuvenate.   We earlier found B1 to be
    low and B2 to be high responders (Fig. 3).

    The first 3 columns show that the response in an F_2
    population segregated with the MHC alleles so that
    those typing $B^1/1$ were all low, while $B^2/2$ were high,
    with one exception in the $B^2/2$ group which may pos-
    sibly have been a crossing-over.

    The birds in the following two columns were F_1 crosses
    of inbred $B^1/1$ and $B^2/2$ with outbred WL's which had

330

been typed by me with respect to the allo-aggression
(*AA*) locus which forms part of the MHC (Simonsen, M.:
Alloaggression in Chickens, Identification of the Major
Genetic Locus. *Acta Path. Microbiol. Scandinav.* Sect.
C, 83:1-14, 1975). They were selected for

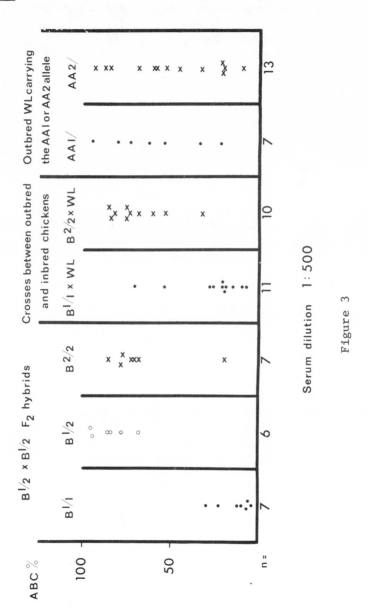

Figure 3

absence of both the *AA1* and *AA2* alleles of the two inbred strains. Hence the F_1 offspring would contain one
of these alleles, inherited from the inbred parent. It
is seen that the hybrids with $B^1/1$ were low responders
with the exception of 2 animals. These, however, became low responders when the titrations were repeated
with (T,G)-Pro--L instead of (T,G)-A--L, whereas the
others showed unchanged ABC. Hence these 2 birds must
have formed antibodies which were predominantly of
specificities other than TG. The hybrids with $D^2/2$
were high responders, again with one exception.

The two last columns are the important ones in the context of this session. They show the data from wholly
outbred WL's which I had typed as containing either
AA1 or *AA2*, indistinguisable both by serology and by
GVH-inhibition from the alleles of the inbred birds.
As you see, there is just no correlation at all here
between the *AA* genes and the antibody response to
(T,G)-A--L. The message is, therefore, that whether a
high responder owes this property to MHC-linked genes
which provide the right helper T cells or, alternatively, to the lack of genes which provide the right suppressor cells, these genes are not in fact the same as
the allo-aggression genes. They are merely linked to
AA genes as seen in the family studies, but nevertheless disassociate in the outbred populations.

Genetic Control of Cell Interactions

WILLIAM PAUL, CHAIRMAN

MACROPHAGE-T LYMPHOCYTE INTERACTION: THE CELLULAR BASIS FOR GENETIC CONTROL OF ANTIGEN RECOGNITION

ALAN S. ROSENTHAL AND ETHAN M. SHEVACH

Laboratory of Clinical Investigation
and Laboratory of Immunology
National Institute of Allergy and Infectious Diseases
National Institutes of Health

Abstract: Macrophage function in antigen recognition by
T lymphocytes is reviewed both with respect to antigen
handling, interactions with lymphocytes, and their
role in the regulation and genetic control of immune
responsiveness. These studies support the concept
that at least one functional expression of the immune
response genes *(Ir)* is at the level of the macrophage.
The cellular and molecular basis by which such an *Ir*
gene product might function is discussed.

I. MACROPHAGE FUNCTION IN ANTIGEN SPECIFIC T CELL ACTIVATION

Although it is generally recognized that macrophages
facilitate a variety of *in vitro* thymus-dependent immunological phenomena in the mouse, guinea pig, and man (1),
only recently have we begun to analyze the precise cellular
and molecular events which underlie their function. It is
clear, for example, that antigen-specific activation of
mediator production and clonal expansion by T lymphocytes
requires the presence of macrophages and that the effects
of macrophages in such activation extend beyond maintenance of *in vitro* culture conditions. Indeed in the
guinea pig, one can clearly demonstrate that recognition
of soluble protein antigens by the T lymphocyte requires
an initial uptake of antigen by the macrophage (2).

The biologic constraints inherent in such a two-cell
immunogenic recognition unit are clear. It is therefore
necessary to define both the cellular and immunological

specificity of this requirement for macrophages. In the
simplest experiments, the proliferative capacity of populations of lymphoid cells depleted of macrophages are
restored by macrophages but not by lymphocytes, granulocytes, or fibroblast (3). This requirement for macrophages
in T cell antigen recognition is not predicated upon or
restricted by the immune state of the animal from which the
macrophage was obtained, although as will be described
later, macrophages and lymphocytes must share genetic
identity at some portion of the major histocompatibility
complex (MHC) for successful detection of the antigenic
signal bourne by the macrophage.

Is macrophage-lymphocyte interaction a general
requirement for all T cell activation or do these associations function solely in the recognition of cell bound and
soluble protein antigens? The response of T lymphocytes to
the non-specific plant mitogen, PHA, also requires accessory
cells but unlike the macrophage requirement for soluble
protein antigen recognition, their function can be replaced
by fibroblast or increased cell density suggesting that the
interaction between antigen and macrophage is not a simple
event (Table I) (4).

TABLE I

*Comparison of the Specificity of the ACcessory Cell Require-
ment for Antigen and Mitogen-Induced T-Cell Proliferation*

Accessory Cells	Lymph Node Lymphocyte DNA Synthesis	
	KLH (100 µg/ml)	PHA (1.0 µg/ml)
	^{3}H-thymidine incorporation (Δ cpm/culture)	
None	16	135
PEC	8293	127,943
Fibroblasts	17	45,147

Thus it becomes crutial to establish the nature of the
antigen uptake process and the physical state of macrophage-
associated antigen. The uptake of protein antigens,
assessed functionally, occurs at 4° via an initial binding
step not requiring the expenditure of metabolic energy
followed by a second temperature dependent event. When this
latter step is carried out in a glucose free media, uptake
of immunological activity is reduced by the combined effects
of sodium azide and 2-deoxyglucose, agents which inhibit
aerobic and anaerobic metabolism, respectively, to a level

equal to but not below that observed at 4° (1). Cytochalasin B, an agent active against a variety of membrane functions and which blocks classic pinocytosis, does not effect uptake of immunologically relevant protein (1). Trypsinization of macrophages pulsed with antigen at 4° removes all immunologically activity without altering the ability of such macrophages to take up new antigens. If, however, trypsinization is progressively delayed by prior culture at 37°, macrophages pulsed with antigens at 4° become progressively resistant to the effects of trypsinization such that by 120 minutes the macrophage's immunological potential is unaltered (5). In addition, antibody against antigens (as high 0.5 mg/ml) does not effect the ability of antigen-pulsed macrophages to initiate T cell proliferation (6).

The immunologic potential of macrophage-bound antigen decays in a linear fashion (1/2 maximal, 1.5 days) when they are cultured for extended times prior to mixing with specifically immune lymphocytes. No concordant decrease in cell associated protein antigen was noted by quantitation of the amount ^{125}I-labelled antigen remaining after the initial 24 hours of preculture. At a minimum, one must conclude that these data are inconsistant with a passive role for the macrophage in which there is a free and random distribution of antigens on the macrophage membrane as originally proposed for antigen handling in the mouse (7).

II. HOW DO MACROPHAGES INTERACT WITH LYMPHOCYTES?

Macrophage-lymphocyte interaction may occur either indirectly via the secretion of antigen complexed to soluble macrophage products cytophilic for lymphocytes or alternatively by direct cell interaction. Evidence for the first exists for generation of specific helper T cell activity in mouse (8). However, soluble macrophage products have not been found which generate antigen specific lymphocyte proliferation in the guinea pig. Instead at least two types of physical interactions have been shown to take place. The first occurs rapidly, is independent of the presence of antigen, and is without immunologic commitment. This step requires active macrophage, but not lymphocyte, metabolism, divalent cations and involves a trypsin-sensitive macrophage site. This binding does not distinguish T or B lymphocyte and is reversible such that at any given time binding represents an equilibrium between cellular association and dissociation (9). When this step has brought specifically immune lymphocytes into apposition with antigen-bearing macrophages, a second type of binding results. This latter phenomenon is dependent upon the presence of antigen and a sharing on lymphocyte and macrophage of histocompatibility linked gene products. This association is not easily reversed and eventuates in proliferation of the bound lymphocyte (10).

Data supporting the linkage between physical and functional macrophage-lymphocyte interaction in the antigen recognition process has been obtained using cytochalasin B, a reagent which inhibits recognition of antigen specific signals by T lymphocytes without effecting lymphocyte responsive to mitogenic signals such as PHA (11). Cytochalasin B inhibited antigen-initiated lymphocyte proliferation and antigen dependent lymphocyte-macrophage interaction when added immediately to culture but was progressively ineffective when added later in culture. This indicated to us that cytochalasin B acts selectively on an early event in antigen specific proliferation since it does not interfere with uptake of antigen by macrophages nor inhibit PHA-induced proliferation. Thus antigen recognition itself rather than the machinery of DNA synthesis are perturbed. In fact, cytochalasin B under certain conditions has been noted to enhance the proliferative response of lymph node lymphocytes to PHA and Con A (12). Lastly, cytochalasin B also inhibits antigen initiated production of macrophage migration inhibition factor by immune lymphocytes if added at the initiation of culture but not if addition is delayed as little as 2 hours indicating a similar role for macrophage-lymphocyte interaction in non-proliferative T cell activation phenomenon (13).

We would conclude that the effects of cytochalasin B result solely from its inhibition of antigen-independent phase of macrophage-lymphocyte interaction (14). Inhibition of this step would preclude the development of subsequent antigen dependent interactions assayed both physically and functionally. Alternatively, cytochalasin B might have a second mode of action and directly inhibit antigen dependent physical and functional interaction either by perturbing the macrophage's antigen display mechanism or by interfering with the reception of the antigenic signal, but not mitogenic signals, by the T lymphocyte. In either event, these observations emphasize

the close relationship between physical macrophage-
lymphocyte interaction and antigen mediated activation of
immune T lymphocytes.

III. IMMUNE RESPONSE GENE FUNCTION IN MACROPHAGE-T LYMPHOCYTE INTERACTION

The use of antigens under control of dominant H-linked
genes and specific alloantisera which recognize cell-
associated antigenic determinants which are also products
of H-linked genes provide useful biological probes of the
function and cellular location of molecules which play
critical but incompletely defined roles in the T lymphocyte
antigen selection or activation process. Alloantisera
block the antigen response controlled by an *Ir* gene linked
to the gene coding for the alloantigen, but had little
effect on the antigen response controlled by an *Ir* gene
which is the product of the opposite haplotype (20,21).
One interpretation of such findings is that *Ir* genes
produce a cell surface associated product and that this
product plays a role in the mechanism of antigen recognition by the T lymphocyte. The inhibitory activity of the
alloantisera was initially presumed to be directed solely
against the proliferating T lymphocyte. However, the
central role of the macrophage in the activation of T cell
proliferation, suggests that an alternative site for the
inhibitory effect of the alloantisera might be on the
macrophage itself by blockade of the physical and/or
functional interaction of the macrophage and T cell.
Unfortunately experiments which attempt to define the
cellular site of action of the alloantisera using combinations of antigen-pulsed macrophages and T cells are not
possible because efficient interaction of macrophage-
associated antigen and T cell is only seen when the
macrophage and T lymphocyte share identity of gene products
linked to the guinea pig MHC (22). It is unlikely that the
histocompatibility restrictions observed for macrophage-T
cell interaction was the result of an active process of
"rejection" that occurred whenever histoincompatible cells
were mixed together as significant T cell proliferation was
observed when F_1 macrophages were added to parental T cells
and vice versa.

There are, however, a number of conditions in which a
macrophage may "paradoxically" induce allogeneic lymphocyte
proliferation. These circumstances are rather revealing
situations in that they clearly show that the failure to

recognize soluble protein antigens bound to allogeneic
macrophages is not a primary inability of such cells to
present signals but may instead reflect a basic feature of
antigen handling by macrophages.

Recently both human (15) and guinea pig (16) macrophages have been shown to be very effective stimulators of
allogeneic lymphocyte proliferation. In the guinea pig
mixed leukocyte reaction, little stimulatory activity can be
attributed to T lymphocytes although in the mouse, both B
cells (17) and macrophages (18) are effective stimulators.
Guinea pig B lymphocytes have also been found to initiate an
MLR even though they are less stimulatory than equivalent
numbers of macrophages (Greineder, Lipsky and Rosenthal,
unpublished observation). Thus soluble proteins may be
displayed in an immunologically relevant fashion only on
syngeneic or semi-syngeneic macrophages; whereas in the
MLR, it is the histoincompatible macrophage that induces T
cell proliferation again suggesting that the critical
difference lies in the display of alloantigen as opposed to
that of foreign proteins.

In another model system, chemical alteration of either
macrophage-depleted lymphocyte or macrophage plasma membrane glycoproteins by treatment with either sodium
metaperiodate or neuraminidase-galactose oxidase generates
free aldehyde groups on different terminal sugar group (19).
Subsequent and rather massive lymphocyte proliferation will
ensue if and only if modified lymphocyte is combined with
unmodified macrophages or modified macrophages are combined
with unmodified lymphocytes. Moreover proliferation
will occur irrespectively of the histocompatibility difference between the macrophage and lymphocyte and upon
mixing modified and unmodified cells a striking clustering
of lymphocytes about macrophages is also observed. These
latter observations have led us to suggest that immune
recognition may in fact consist of at least two separate,
but linked, events (1). The first phase of this interaction
involves the selective binding of antigen-specific T cells
by macrophages bearing that antigen. The second or
"activation" phase of macrophage-lymphocyte interaction is a
relatively non-specific event which follows as a consequence
of stabilization of physical macrophage-lymphocyte interaction initiated by the antigen specific selection process.

We can assess, at a functional level, the site of
action of alloantisera in these two situations where

allogeneic macrophages are capable of activating T cell proliferation. Thus, the MLR between the two inbred strains is markedly inhibited by an alloantiserum directed against the stimulatory macrophage, while the same serum has no effect on the responding lymphocyte (Table II). In a similar fashion, when T lymphocytes are treated with sodium periodate and mixed with untreated macrophages, the resultant stimulation is markedly inhibited by an allo-antiserum directed against the macrophage, but not the proliferating T cell (Table III). Although these studies do not define the site of action of the alloantisera for soluble protein antigen-induced proliferation, they do suggest that certain T cell proliferative responses can be markedly inhibited by alloantisera acting solely on the stimulatory macrophage.

TABLE II

Alloantiserum Induced Inhibition of the MLR

Target Macrophage	Strain 2 T Cells		Strain 13 T Cells	
	NGPS	13 Anti-2	NGPS	13 Anti-2
	^{3}H-thymidine incorporation (Δ cpm/culture)			
Strain 2	6,509	356	351,368	157,162
Strain 13	72,857	186,423	4,689	3,471
(2x13)F_1	87,886	85,154	292,144	135,455

TABLE III

Alloantiserum Induced Inhibition of the Proliferative Response of $NaIO_4$ Treated T Cells

Macrophage	Strain 2 T Cells		Strain 13 T Cells	
	NGPS	13 Anti-2	NGPS	13 Anti-2
	^{3}H-thymidine incorporation (Δ cpm/culture)			
Strain 2	105,557	5,348	129,697	8,757
Strain 13	53,991	48,240	58,235	49,533
(2x13)F_1	44,878	28,622	37,846	36,029

An alternative approach to localizing the site of alloantisera blockade is to directly examine the effect of alloantisera on antigen-induced macrophage-lymphocyte interaction. Binding of lymph node cells by antigen pulsed macrophages was determined after 20 hours of culture at 37°C. Anti-2 serum completely inhibited the binding of strain 2 lymphocytes to strain 2 macrophages pulsed with DNP-GL to a greater extent than to PPD (Table IV). This result suggests that the inhibition of T cell proliferation observed by measurement of ^{3}H-thymidine incorporation is secondary to a blockade of the physical interaction of macrophage and T cell, rather than to an interference with T cell proliferation subsequent to antigen specific binding. The cellular site of action of this inhibition of antigen specific binding cannot be determined. One can, however, examine the binding of strain 13 lymphocytes to strain 2 neuraminidase galactose-oxidase treated macrophages. In such experiments, aldehyde-dependent binding is completely inhibited by an alloantiserum directed solely at the macrophage (Table V).

TABLE IV

The Effect of Alloantisera on Antigen-Specific Binding of Strain 2 Lymphocytes to Strain 2 Macrophages

Experiment	Serum	Antigen-Specific Binding	
		PPD	DNP$_{22}$-GL
		Δ Lymphocytes/100 Macrophages	
1	NGPS	81	41
	13a2	79	0
	2a13	102	54
2	NGPS	102	65
	13a2	46	0
	2a13	155	64

IV.   GENETIC ANALYSIS OF DETERMINANTS MEDIATING MACROPHAGE-T-LYMPHOCYTE INTERACTION.

An additional restriction on the interaction of antigen-pulsed macrophages with immune T cells was observed when macrophages were obtained from a parental animal that lacked a given *Ir* gene were pulsed with an antigen controlled by that gene and then mixed with (non-responder X responder) F_1 T cells (Table VI). Thus, macrophages from non-immunized strain 2 and (2x13)F_1 guinea pigs pulsed with DNP-GL (an antigen the response to which is controlled by a

2-linked *Ir* gene) activate immune F_1 T lymphocyte proliferation equally, while the magnitude of stimulation
observed when strain 13 DNP-GL pulsed macrophages were used
is approximately 1/10 that seen when strain 2 or $(2x13)F_1$
macrophages are used (23).

TABLE V

*Effect of Alloantisera on the Binding at 1 and 20 Hours of
Strain 13 Lymphocytes to Neuraminidase-Galactose Oxidase
Treated Strain 2 Macrophages*

Experiment	Aldehyde Modification	Serum	Binding At:	
			1 Hour	20 Hours
			Lymphocytes/100 Macrophages	
1	–	NGPS	52	11
	–	13a2	29	16
	+	NGPS	321	423
	+	13a2	363	258
2	–	NGPS	17	9
	–	13a2	17	2
	+	NGPS	153	325
	+	13a2	222	193

TABLE VI

*Activation of $(2x13)F_1$ T Cells by Parental Antigen
Pulsed Macrophages*

Antigen	Lymphocyte DNA Synthesis		
	$(2x13)F_1$ Mφ	Strain 2 Mφ	Strain 13 Mφ
	^{3}H-thymidine incorporation (Δ cpm/culture)		
PPD	28,117	21,919	28,048
DNP-GL	14,539	23,402	2,992

One possible explanation for the failure of the non-
responder macrophage to activate the (non-responder X
responder) F_1 T cell is an intrinsic defect in *Ir* gene
product function in the non-responder macrophage. The most
direct approach to the analysis of the determinants mediating macrophage-T lymphocyte interaction would be to study
the macrophages and/or T cells derived from an animal which

bears a recombinant chromosome in which the genes which code for the alloantigens and *Ir* gene products have been separated. Unfortunately, in the offspring of $(2x13)F_1$ X parental animals we have not observed such a recombinant chromosome. As an alternative, we have used outbred animals where relationships exist between *Ir* genes and alloantigens which differ from those found in the inbred populations (24). In inbred strain 2 and in the progeny of $(2x13)F_1$ X 13 animals the gene controlling responsiveness to the random copolymer L-glutamic acid, L-alanine (GA) is linked to the genes controlling the 2 histocompatibility antigens. Outbred animals have been identified which are 2^-GA^+. We have evaluated the capacity of macrophages from this group of 2^-GA^+ animals to activate T cell proliferation in cells derived from 2^+GA^+ inbred strain 2 animals and vice versa (Table VII). Macrophages derived from animals that bear the GA *Ir* gene but lack the 2 alloantigens were incapable of activating T cell proliferation in cells derived from 2^+GA^+ donor; similarly, inbred strain 2 macrophages were incapable of activating T cell proliferation in cells derived from 2^-GA^+ animals. These results suggest that sharing the *Ir* gene product alone is not sufficient for macrophage-T cell interaction.

TABLE VII

Activation of T Lymphocytes From 2^+GA^+ and 2^-GA^+ Animals By GA Pulsed 2^+GA^+ and 2^-GA^+ Mφ

Responder Status of Mφ Donor	2^+GA^+ T Cells	2^-GA^+ T Cells
2^+GA^+	93 ± 8*	10 ± 3
2^-GA^+	3 ± 2	85 ± 14

* Percent stimulation compared to syngeneic Mφ's

We have also examined the situation where macrophages bear the alloantigen in the absence of the linked *Ir* gene. In inbred strain 13 and in the progeny of $(2x13)F_1$ X 2 animals the genes that control responsiveness to the copolymer L-glutamic acid, L-tyrosine (GT) and to the 2,4-dinitrophenyl derivative of guinea pig albumin (DNP-GPA) are linked to the genes controlling the 13 alloantigens. However, a small number of $13^+GT^-DNP\text{-}GPA^+$ and $13^+GT^+DNP\text{-}GPA^-$ animals have been observed in a number of outbred colonies. When macrophages from these animals were pulsed

344

with GT or DNP–GPA and mixed with immune strain 13 T cells, the macrophages from the $13^+GT^-DNP-GPA^+$ donor were incapable of activating strain 13 cells when pulsed with GT but functioned normally when pulsed with DNP–GPA; in similar fashion, macrophages from $13^+GT^+DNP-GPA^-$ animals failed to activate inbred strain 13 cells when pulsed with DNP–GPA, but functioned relatively normally when pulsed with GT (Table VIII).

TABLE VIII

Activation of Strain 13 T Cells by Antigen Pulsed Macrophages

Responder Status of Macrophage Donor	Percent Syngeneic Stimulation when pulsed with	
	GT	DNP–GPA
$13^+GT^+DNP-GPA^+$	95 ± 9	100 ± 6
$13^-GT^-DNP-GPA^-$	8 ± 4	17 ± 9
$13^+GT^-DNP-GPA^+$	12 ± 3	90 ± 11
$13^+GT^+DNP-GPA^-$	75 ± 14	8 ± 4

The results of these experiments superficially appear to demonstrate that sharing of the alloantigen is not sufficient for effective macrophage–T lymphocyte interaction. However, more detailed studies of the $13^+GT^-DNP-GPA^+$ and the $13^+GT^+DNP-GPA^-$ populations has shown that both populations of animals appear to lack one of the alloantigens identified by 2-anti-13 serum. Furthermore, by specific immunization and absorption experiments, it has been shown that the 13 antigen associated with the GT gene is distinct from the 13 antigen associated with the DNP–GPA *Ir* gene. One must conclude from these experiments that macrophage–T lymphocyte interaction is highly specific and requires identity between macrophage and T cell at the specific alloantigen linked to the *Ir* gene under investigation. Activation will not occur even if macrophage and T cell share a portion of the alloantigen haplotype required for interaction, but not that associated with the *Ir* gene under study.

V. ROLE OF MACROPHAGE–ASSOCIATED ANTIGEN IN THE REGULATION OF GENETIC CONTROL OF THE IMMUNE RESPONSE.

Based on the results of studies described, models for the role of the macrophage in genetic control of T cell

responses to soluble protein antigens must consider:
1) an antigen specific receptor on the T lymphocyte,
2) cellular interaction structures identical to or closely
linked to the alloantigens, 3) the *Ir* gene product functioning either as the specific T cell receptor or as an
auxillary antigen recognition molecule on the macrophage,
and/or T cell, 4) antigen bound to metabolically intact
macrophages in a form resistant to proteolytic treatment and
located in a cellular site not available to specific antibody, and 5) a macrophage associated non-specific membrane
trigger site or secretory product as suggested by the
activation of aldehyde treated lymphocytes by normal
macrophages.

We had previously postulated that macrophage associated
antigen was randomly distributed on the surface of the
macrophage and bore no specific relationship to alloantigen
(23). During immunologically relevant macrophage T
lymphocyte interaction the two cells came into close
functional contact in areas of shared histocompatibility.
Furthermore, the *Ir* gene controlled antigen recognition
structures on the T cell must be physically related to the
sites for macrophage-T lymphocyte binding specified in the
same haplotype. Macrophages from the non-responder parent
function poorly because the recognition sites for antigen
on the T cell are spacially related to the macrophage-T
lymphocyte binding site of the responder parent while the
main contacts between the cells are at the non-responder
binding sites. Unfortunately, this model has become
progressively less attractive.

Another possible interpretation of our experimental
results can be derived from studies in the mouse which have
demonstrated that T cells sensitized to haptens (25) or
viruses (26) are primarily cytotoxic for targets which are
H-2D or H-2K compatible. The explanation offered for those
results was that T cells were sensitized to a new antigenic
determinant or *NAD*, in the form of hapten or virus altered
"self". These altered self antigens are the products of
the H-2K, H-2D or closely linked genes. Although the
products of the I-region appear to play no role in the
specificity of the T cell cytotoxicity, the explanation
offered for the results may have relevance for our understanding of the requirements for macrophage-T lymphocyte
interaction in induction of T cell proliferation. One
might postulate that the T cell is incapable of recognizing
"native" antigen and can only be sensitized to antigen

346

altered self; the failure of interaction between allogeneic macrophage and T cell can be regarded as a failure of recognition rather than interaction. The strain 13 macrophage pulsed with PPD fails to activate immune strain 2 T cells because the strain 2 animal has never seen PPD, but rather during the primary immunization, has been sensitized to "PPD altered self"; in our experiments the "self" antigens appear to be the products of the I-region of the guinea pig MHC (24).

Unfortunately, the antigen-altered self hypothesis does not explain the restriction observed in the studies where antigen-pulsed non-responder macrophage fail to activate (responder X non-responder)F_1 T cell. T cells derived from an immunized F_1 animal should be equally stimulated with the antigen altered *Ia*-complex of both parental haplotypes and should respond equally well to antigen pulsed macrophages of either parent. Indeed, such a response is observed when F_1 immune T cells are mixed with parental macrophages pulsed with PPD an antigen not under unigenic control. In order to explain the defect in the non-responder macrophage and be faithful to the "antigen altered self" or *NAD* hypothesis, one must postulate that the non-responder macrophage lacks the Ia antigen which can be altered by the antigen under study.

Additional limitations of the *NAD* model for cellular selection in recognition of soluble protein antigens is the difficulty from a chemical point of view of postulating a family of proteins or glycoprotein whose plasticity is such that a sufficient range of conformational changes can be induced in them by binding antigens to explain the exquisite specificity of the T cell recognition process. Finally, a *NAD* thesis implies that some of the antigenic determinant recognized by the T cell are exclusive, since antibody maintains the ability to directly interact with antigen in free solution, i.e. out of context of self, while the T cell receptor should not recognize antigen except in the context of self.

We would therefore favor a simpler and perhaps more unifying hypothesis which states that a given macrophage's repretoir of *Ir* gene products function to specify determinant selection (*SDS*). Possible mechanism by which the interaction of antigen with the *Ir* gene product could select determinant specificity are as follows:

1) *Enzymatic* - the *Ir* gene product is an enzyme of relative broad specificity such as a proteinase which destroys only those polypeptide sequence towards which it has reactivity.

2) *Conformational* - This mechanism is the converse of the *NAD* model in that the interaction of antigen with the Ir gene product alters the tertiary structure of the antigen itself so as to display selected regions of the polypeptide to the T cell.

3) *Receptor Presentation* - This would require that certain similar existing amino sequences or conformations in a complex antigen be recognized by *Ir* gene products. Such receptor molecules would possess specific binding properties akin to that of the binding site of a proteolytic enzyme but would differ from the enzymatic model in that no selective degradation of the antigen occurs. The function of such class specific antigen binding molecules would be to orient or display those regions of the polypeptide antigen not bound to the receptor.

The *SDS* model readily explains genetic control of the immune response to antigens of limited diversity in that the appropriate *Ir* gene product is lacking in the non-responder macrophage. However, the *SDS* model must also explain the histocompatibility restrictions observed for macrophage-T lymphocyte interaction with multi-determinant antigens. To do so, one would postulate the existence of distinct MHC linked cellular interaction structures which differ between the two inbred strains. These cellular interaction structures would then be identical with the serologically identifiable *Ia* antigens and the *Ir* gene product is serologically silent. However, it is important to note that the *SDS* model does not require the existence of MHC linked cellular interaction structures if major differences exist in the repretoire of *Ir* gene products in the two inbred strains. In this latter instance the failure of interaction would be regarded as a failure of recognition in that the determinants selected for presentation would differ appreciably between the two strains.

REFERENCES

(1) Rosenthal, A.S. and Shevach, E.M., in *Contemporary Topics in Immunobiology*, Edited by W. Weigle, Plenum Press, New York, in press.

(2) Waldron, J.A., Horn, R.G., and Rosenthal, A.S., J. Immunol., *111:* 58, 1973.

(3) Rosenstreich, D.L. and Rosenthal, A.S., J. Immunol., *112:* 1085, 1974.

(4) Lipsky, P.E., Ellner, J.J., and Rosenthal, A.S., J. Immunol., in press.

(5) Waldron, J.A., Horn, R.G., and Rosenthal, A.S., J. Immunol., *112:* 746, 1974.

(6) Ellner, J.J. and Rosenthal, A.S., J. Immunol., *114:* 1563, 1975.

(7) Unanue, E.R., Adv. in Immunol., *95:* 15, 1972.

(8) Erb, P. and Feldmann, M., J. Exp. Med., *142:* 460, 1975.

(9) Lipsky, P.E. and Rosenthal, A.S., J. Exp. Med., *138:* 900, 1973.

(10) Lipsky, P.E. and Rosenthal, A.S., J. Exp. Med., *141:* 138, 1975.

(11) Rosenthal, A.S., Blake, J.T., and Lipsky, P.E., J. Immunol., *115:* 1135, 1975.

(12) Yoshinaga, M., Yoshinaga, A., and Waksman, B., Proc. Nat. Acad. Sci. (USA), *69:* 3251, 1971.

(13) Ben Sasson, S.A. and Rosenthal, A.S., J. Immunol., *115:* 1140, 1975.

(14) Lipsky, P.E. and Rosenthal, A.S., J. Immunol., *115:* 440, 1975.

(15) Rode, H.N. and Gordon, J., Cell. Immunol., *13:* 87, 1974.

(16) Greineder, D.K. and Rosenthal, A.S., J. Immunol., *114:* 1541, 1975.

(17) Fathman, C.G., Handwerger, B.S. and Sachs, D.H., J. Exp. Med., *140:* 853, 1974.

(18) Schirrmacher, V., Pena-Martinez, J. and Festenstein, H., Nature, *255:* 155, 1975.

(19) Greineder, D.K. and Rosenthal, A.S., J. Immunol., *115:* 932, 1975.

(20) Shevach, E.M., Paul, W.E. and Green, I., J. Exp. Med., *136:* 1207, 1972

(21) Shevach, E.M., Green, I. and Paul, W.E., J. Exp. Med., *139:* 679, 1974.

(22) Rosenthal, A.S. and Shevach, E.M., J. Exp. Med., *138:* 1194, 1973.

(23) Shevach, E.M. and Rosenthal, A.S., J. Exp. Med., *138:* 1213, 1973.

(24) Shevach, E.M., Lee, L. and Ben-Sasson, S.Z., in *Immune Recognition,* Edited by A.S. Rosenthal, p. 627, Academic Press, New York, 1975.

(25) Shearer, G.M., Rehn, T.G. and Garbarino, C.A., J. Exp. Med., *141:* 1348, 1975.

(26) Zinkernagel, R.M. and Doherty, P.C., J. Exp. Med., *141:* 1427, 1975.

DISCUSSION FOLLOWING ALAN ROSENTHAL

GREEN: If antigen is not on the surface of macrophages (as judged by the results of your own study), what specific entity on the surface of macrophages interacts with the antigen-specific T lymphocytes?

ROSENTHAL: A number of possibilities exist to explain this apparent paradox. First, antigen-independent macrophage-lymphocyte interaction might induce an antigen display event such that the T cell now has access to previously unavailable antigen. Alternatively, antigen display may occur normally through a process akin to exocytosis, a process described to occur in macrophages by Calderon and Unanue*. Lastly, antigen may simply exist normally on the cell surface, complexed to or altered by self components, in a trypsin-resistant, antibody-inaccessible site.

*[EDITOR'S NOTE: See Calderon, J. and Unanue, E.R. J. Immunol. 112:1804, 1974 - DHK.]

UHR: My remark is a follow-up of Ira Green's question and bears on the problem of not finding antigen on the macrophage surface at the time of specific binding of lymphocytes by antigen-pulsed macrophages. Ben-Sasson and Mary Lipscomb in my department have confirmed Rosenthal's studies on the binding and selection of lymphocytes by antigen-pulsed macrophages. The kinetics of binding obtained are different from those you have shown and the difference may be an attractive one from your point of view. Thus, they have observed maximal specific binding in 1 hour. At this time, surface antigen is present. You could postulate then that lymphocyte binding at this time prevents removal of surface antigen. This situation would then make your fourth model (SDS) a viable one.

ROSENTHAL: Well, I believe that the studies you refer to must be re-examined in light of the fact that the investigators to whom you refer use macrophages from immunized guinea pigs and these are coated with cytophilic antibody. As such, the binding observed early in co-culture may simply reflect an enhanced clustering due to immune complex and not that due to antigen-specific T cells.

I think it is also important to point out that the kinetics observed in any binding assay is, to a large degree, constrained by the geometry of the assay system and to cell density, or more precisely to the frequency of antigen-specific cells. Peritoneal exudate lymphocytes (used by Ben-Sasson) and those by our laboratory (Lipsky and Rosenthal) differ in their frequency of antigen-reactive cells.

UHR: I do not think that the issue of the kinetics is a trivial one. If specific binding occurs immediately, it must be due to antigen and the stabilization of the binding may be under I region control. This view contrasts with the one you presented based on the kinetics you observed.

ROSENTHAL: I agree it is not trivial. Unfortunately, as I have pointed out, the systems being used are not identical with respect to important but merely technical aspects of the assay. I think it more important to note that both groups are in agreement as to the existence of antigen-specific clustering of lymphocytes about macrophages as an important early event in the T cell antigen recognition process.

KAPP: Your interpretation of the periodate experiment is that periodate stabilizes interaction of macrophages and lymphocytes and that activation is due to maintaining these cells in close contact rather than to the recognition of neoantigens. If that is so, can you inhibit this response by the incorporation of excess-free aldehyde in the medium?

ROSENTHAL: No, you cannot. Interestingly, all of us routinely culture lymphoid cells in media rich in free aldehydes; that is the sugar glucose.

PAUL: The observation that free aldehydes do not block activation or rosette formation should not be regarded as too serious an objection in view of the inability to block T lymphocyte activation with excess-free ligand in any system of which I am aware.

CUNNINGHAM: It is not clear to me what you think periodate is doing.

ROSENTHAL: It sticks the two cells together non-specifically. Activation of lymphocyte proliferation is viewed as a non-specific consequence of such physical interaction.

CUNNINGHAM: Do alloantisera block this interaction and block stimulation?

ROSENTHAL: Yes

CUNNINGHAM: Treatment of the macrophage alone with periodate is sufficient for stimulation. Is that correct?

ROSENTHAL: No. Treatment of <u>either</u> macrophage or lymphocyte will give proliferation upon mixing modified macrophage with unmodified lymphocyte or by mixing modified lymphocyte with unmodified macrophage. What's critical is that you need both macrophage and lymphocyte.

MUNRO: Do inhibitors of protein synthesis effect the antigen-dependent clustering?

ROSENTHAL: We have not examined this question.

NOSSAL: I wonder whether Dr. Rosenthal could say a little about macrophage-B cell interactions. There are two perspectives of interest to me. First, there are now good methods of purifying hapten-specific B cells operationally; this would provide a system where antigen-dependent clustering would far outweigh numerically the reversible non-antigen dependent clustering. Secondly, John Schrader has some preliminary evidence to suggest that antigen presented to syngeneic (but not allogeneic) nude spleen cells on macrophages can trigger antibody formation *in vitro*.

ROSENTHAL: Peter Lipsky in my laboratory has recently examined this question. Interestingly, antigen-bearing macrophages are not effective at inducing B lymphocytes proliferation from specifically immunized guinea pigs while those same macrophages are extremely efficient at inducing T cell proliferation. Despite this, the clustering of lymphocytes about macrophages does distinguish between T and B lymphocytes.

GENETIC CONTROL OF LYMPHOCYTE INTERACTIONS AND DIFFERENTIATION

DAVID H. KATZ AND BARUJ BENACERRAF

Department of Pathology
Harvard Medical School

The phenomena of cell interactions in the development and regulation of immune responses have been extensively investigated during the past 7-8 years. As a result, much has been learned about the importance of such cell interactions in regulating the immune system and, although not yet precisely delineated, about the mechanisms involved in these interactions. In recent years, much evidence has been obtained to indicate a very important role for gene products of the major histocompatibility complex (MHC) in controlling interactions between T and B lymphocytes (1-4) and between macrophages and lymphocytes (5, 6) resulting in the hypothesis that there are cell interaction (CI) genes located in the MHC that code for molecules responsible for mediating cell-cell interactions (2, 3, 7-9). This notion has been strengthened by the recent demonstrations that certain biologically active T cell factors derived from antigen-activated T cells bear determinants of gene products known to map in the MHC of the mouse, and more specifically, in the I region of $H-2$ (10-16). On the other hand, certain observations in systems employing tetraparental mice (17, 18) and long-term radiation bone marrow chimeras (19) have quite recently provided additional constraints upon the aforementioned hypothesis which justifiably merits a thorough re-evaluation of the basic underlying concept.

In this presentation, we will review the data and systems that have been utilized in the development of the hypothesis concerning CI genes and will discuss some very recent findings on the involvement of immune response or Ir genes in cell-cell interactions. Moreover, we will analyze the seemingly conflicting observations obtained in other systems and attempt to integrate the latter findings into a working model concerning lymphocyte differentiation. Finally, we will present some very new and preliminary data which may provide an explanation for the observed differences in the requirements for identity of certain MHC genes in cell-cell interactions depending on the system utilized for study.

EVIDENCE FOR GENETIC RESTRICTIONS IN COOPERATIVE T-B CELL INTERACTIONS

The evidence for the existence of genetic restrictions in T-B cell interactions can be succinctly summarized as follows: Under conditions in which syngeneic lymphoid cells interact together to develop humoral immune responses, cells lacking certain critical identities in MHC genes fail to interact successfully (1-4, 7-9). Based on these observations, we proposed that genes in the *H-2* complex coded for products involved in the development of effective cell-cell interactions in the immune response (2, 3, 7).

Even before experiments were performed to investigate the question directly, observations from studies concerning the nature of T-B cell cooperative responses indicated that surface histocompatibility molecules might be involved in such interactions. To understand this reasoning, one must recall that essentially two diverse types of experimental models have been employed in the study of immunocompetent cell interactions. The first type is what we refer to as a "physiologic" model in the sense that experiments of this type presumably duplicates what occurs in the cooperative responses between isogeneic cells in the intact individual. The second model is non-physiologic in the sense that although the regulatory events appear to be identical to physiologic responses, the model is established in relatively artificial conditions. The prime example of the latter model is the "allogeneic effect", the phenomenon in which regulatory influences are exerted by allogeneic T cells interacting with histoincompatible T or B lymphocytes at the cell surface histocompatibility antigens (20). Analysis of the information obtained from studies with these two seemingly diverse model systems indicates that the following remarkable parallels can be drawn between them insofar as their characteristics features:

1) The regulation by T cells is manifested on both T and B lymphocytes.
2) The net consequences of such regulation spans an

entire spectrum of immunological balance ranging from enhancement at one end to suppression at the other.

3) The initial cellular events occur at very definite surface membrane sites coded for by genes in the major histocompatibility complex.

It was the obvious importance of the third point above in the very potent regulatory influence exerted by the allogeneic effect, a phenomenon constituted by allogeneic cells interacting at histocompatibility antigens on the cell surface, which prompted us to explore the possibility that these histocompatibility molecules were indeed integrally involved in mechanisms of physiologic cell-cell interactions. A system was, therefore, devised to test mixtures of T and B lymphocytes from various origins, possessing known MHC gene identities and/or differences, for their capacities to engage in cooperative interactions (2, 3).

Initially, experiments were planned by taking advantage of the *in vivo* radioresistance of primed carrier-specific T cells (21, 22). According to the simplest approach, allogeneic hapten-specific B cells could presumably be safely transferred to carrier-primed irradiated recipients to investigate T cell-B cell interactions. However, in our first experiments, we made the unexpected observation that a heavily irradiated mouse (600 R) possesses sufficient numbers of active residual T cells to exert this effect on a small population of adoptively transferred histoincompatible primed B lymphocytes (23). The central problem was, therefore, to design an experimental scheme that specifically circumvented the possible contribution to the results of a complicating allogeneic effect. This was accomplished for *in vivo* cell transfer studies by using an F_1 hybrid as the recipient of T and B cells from the respective parental strains against which the semiallogeneic host would be genetically incapable of reacting.

The protocol is schematically illustrated in Fig. 1 (2). Fifty x 10^6 spleen cells from either bovine gamma globulin (BGG)-primed or normal parental donor mice are injected intravenously into non-irradiated, unprimed (A x B) F_1 hybrid recipients. Twenty-four hours later, when the transferred cells have migrated to the lymphoid organs, these mice are irradiated (600 R) and then injected intravenously with a second cell inoculum consisting of 20 x 10^6 DNP- keyhole limpet hemocyanin (KLH)-primed B lymphocytes derived from the same or the other parental strain. The

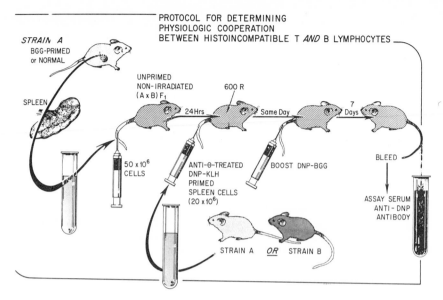

Figure 1.   See text for explanation (Ref. 2).

latter cells are depleted of T lymphocytes by treatment with
anti-θ serum and complement prior to transfer to eliminate
development of a fatal graft-versus-host reaction in the
irradiated F_1 recipient.   Immediately thereafter, secondary
challenge is performed with 50 μg of DNP-BGG intraperitoneally in saline and the mice are bled 7 days later.   This
type of experiment is always performed in a simultaneously
symmetrical fashion to alleviate potential variability
between different pools and strain origins of carrier-primed
and DNP-primed donor cells.

This protocol takes advantage of the fact that:
1) primed mature mouse T lymphocytes are relatively radioresistant when they are subjected to X-irradiation *in situ*
after adoptive transfer and a suitable period for migration
to the recipient lymphoid organs has elapsed (22); and
2) semi-allogeneic recipients are genetically incapable of
reacting against histocompatibility specificities of either
parental strain lymphocytes.   Since the F_1 host is genetically incapable of reacting against either parental donor
cell population, and since the irradiated carrier-primed
parental cells are present in restricted numbers, the
allogeneic effect has been avoided.   This is true for both
enhancing and suppressive influences of the allogeneic

effect. Furthermore, the fact that the transferred parental DNP-specific B cells in the F_1 recipient, which would be the potential target for the allogeneic effect, constitutes but a small proportion of the cells against which the T cells from the second parent can react in the F_1 environment is an additional argument for the absence of allogeneic effects in this experimental design. Finally, it should be noted that certain of our experiments were performed utilizing an *in vitro* system in which similar precautions were established to avoid a complicating allogeneic effect (2, 24, 25).

In Fig. 2, we have compiled most of our results to date which have been designed to localize the gene(s) involved in controlling optimal T-B cell interactions. Such *CI* genes have been mapped within the *H-2* gene complex, and more specifically, to the *I-A* and/or *I-B* subregions, by utilizing mixtures of T and B lymphocytes from appropriate inbred and recombinant strains of mice with known identities and differences at various *H-2* regions and subregions. Thus, the capacity to obtain responses in cell combinations 1 and 2, but not in 3 and 4, demonstrate that *CI* genes are, indeed, in the *H-2* complex since identities and differences at *H-2* determine the outcome of responses between such mixtures; non-*H-2* or background genes are not involved. The positive response in cell combination 5 reflects the capacity of reciprocal mixtures of parental and F_1 hybrid T and B cells to effectively interact in the system when conventional antigens to which responses not restricted by immune response or *Ir* genes are employed. This is an important point since cell-cell interactions in parent-F_1 mixtures rule out the existence of 1) non-specific blocking phenomena due to presence of foreign alloantigens (from the other parent) on the cell surface, and 2) non-specific suppression due to an allogeneic cell interaction.

The data from cell combinations 6 through 15 in Fig. 2 illustrate the manner in which *CI* genes have been mapped to *I-A* and/or *I-B* subregions by these studies. This conclusion follows from the fact that in all combinations tested, effective cooperative interactions have been obtained whenever gene identities in *I-A* and/or *I-B* exist, and conversely T and B cell mixtures that have differed in these two subregions have failed to display cooperative responses. The presence or absence of gene identities in other regions or combinations of regions of *H-2*, such as *K*, *I-C*, *S*, *G* or *D* does not appear to play a determining role.

MAPPING OF *CI* GENES CONTROLLING T-B CELL
COOPERATIVE RESPONSES WITHIN THE *H-2* GENE COMPLEX

● GENE IDENTITIES ○ GENE DIFFERENCES

| CELL COMBINATION | BACKGROUND GENOTYPE | H-2 REGIONS AND SUB-REGIONS | | | | | | | COOPERATIVE RESPONSE |
| | | | I | | | | | | |
		K	I-A	I-B	I-C	S	G	D	
1	●	●	●	●	●	●	●	●	YES
2	○	●	●	●	●	●	●	●	YES
3	○	○	○	○	○	○	○	○	NO
4	●	○	○	○	○	○	○	○	NO
5		%	%	%	%	%	%	%	YES
6		●	●	●	●	●	●	○	YES
7		●	●	●	●	○	○	○	YES
8		●	●	●	○	○	○	○	YES
9		●	●	●	○	○	○	●	YES
10		○	●	●	○	○	○	●	YES
11		○	●	●	●	●	●	●	YES
12		○	○	○	○	○	○	●	NO
13		○	○	○	●	●	●	●	NO
14		●	○	○	○	○	○	●	NO
15		●	○	○	○	○	○	○	NO

Figure 2. This figure represents a
composite of all results from a series of studies
performed both *in vivo* and *in vitro* with combinations of T and B cells from various inbred and
recombinant inbred strains of donor mice. The
presence of gene region identities and differences
among the cell combinations studied and the capacity of such combinations to manifest a cooperative
response are illustrated. (Compiled from data presented in Refs. 2, 3, 7, 9, 11, 12, 24 and 25).

Further definition of the genetic mapping of *CI* genes
has been recently completed in our laboratory and is illustrated by the experiment summarized in Fig. 3 (26). The
left side of the figure depicts the protocol and various
combinations of cell mixtures analyzed for cooperative responses to DNP-KLH. The gene regions of the *H-2* complex
(*K*, *I-A*, *I-B*, *I-C*, *S*, *G*, *D*) are symbolized in brackets for
each strain and the gene region differences among the
various combinations are summarized. The relevant data are

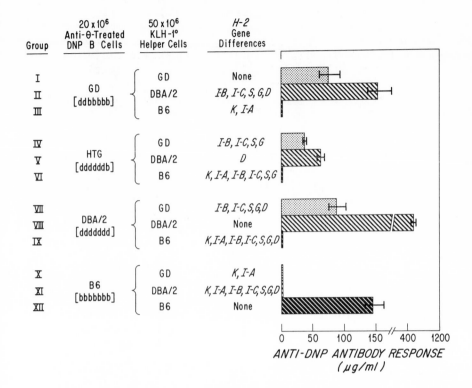

Figure 3. Mapping of *CI* genes in the *I-A* subregion of *H-2*. Recipients for all cell combinations were (B6 x A)F$_1$ hybrids. KLH-primed helper cells were transferred intravenously into non-irradiated recipients on day 0; 24 hours later all recipients were irradiated and anti-θ serum-treated spleen cells from DNP-fowl gamma globulin-primed donors were transferred. Secondary challenge was performed intraperitoneally with 25 μg soluble DNP-KLH immediately thereafter. Combinations, strain origins and specificities of T and B cells are indicated. Mean serum anti-DNP antibody levels of groups of 5 mice on day 7 after secondary challenge are illustrated. Horizontal bars represent ranges of the standard errors (Ref. 26).

summarized on the right side of Fig. 3 and demonstrate that the *CI* genes involved in cooperative responses to a conventional hapten-carrier conjugate, DNP-KLH, are located in the *I-A* subregion. This conclusion derives from the fact that: 1) B cells and T cells from GD mice cooperate reciprocally with T and B cells from DBA/2 mice which are identical at *I-A* but differ at *I-B* and *I-C* (groups II and VII); 2) B cells from HTG mice are effectively helped by GD carrier-specific T cells in a similar mixture where identities exist at *I-A* but differences exist at *I-B* and *I-C* (group IV); and 3) B cells and T cells from GD mice fail to cooperatively interact in reciprocal mixtures of T and B lymphocytes from B6 donors which differ at *I-A*, and despite identities at *I-B* and *I-C* (groups III and X). Since gene differences in the *K*, *S*, *G* and *D* regions do not appear to be involved (Fig. 2), these results localize the *CI* genes in the *I-A* subregion, at least with respect to responses to this complex conventional antigen. A similar conclusion has been recently reached by Janeway and Paul in a comparable system (27).

There are several possible explanations for the failure of physiologic T-B cell cooperation to occur across the major histocompatibility barrier. Certain of these possibilities which appear to be quite unlikely include the following:

1) Failure of transferred T and B cells to migrate to appropriate sites in the lymphoid organs *in vivo*, and/or rejection of one or the other cell type. These possibilities have been eliminated by using the F_1 recipient as a neutral host environment in which very good cooperative interactions could be obtained between *H-2*-identical cell mixtures and, moreover, by the corroboration of these data in a fully *in vitro* system (2).

2) A "block" of some sort to cell-cell interaction by the presence of a foreign major histocompatibility specificity on the cell surface of one or the other of the lymphocyte classes. This has been ruled out in our initial experiments which demonstrated highly effective cooperation between reciprocal combinations of parental F_1 hybrid T and B lymphocytes and provided that the carrier antigen employed is one to which both parental strains involved are genetic responders (2). These findings demonstrate, moreover, that the existence of one common major *H-2* haplotype is sufficient for effective interaction to occur between two cell

populations even though the F_1 cells also possess a set of foreign H-2 specificities.

3) Ineffective or inefficient macrophage-lymphocyte interaction due to major histocompatibility differences. This possibility plays little, if any, significant role in these particular experiments since the major macrophage component for the secondary response is most likely provided by the irradiated F_1 host. The latter not only share a common haplotype with both parental H-2 specificities but also support good cooperative responses between adoptively transferred syngeneic T and B cells.

4) Non-specific suppressive influences exerted by the adoptively transferred allogeneic T cells on the DNP-specific B cells. This seems remote since, as discussed above, non-specific enhancement, rather than suppression, due to allogeneic effects was the major difficulty to overcome in developing the system (23). Moreover, primed parental T cells were shown to serve as effective helper cells for F_1 B cells under circumstances where comparable suppressive effects, had they existed, might be expected to manifest themselves (2). Finally, in an experiment designed to test this possibility directly, proof has been obtained that no appreciable non-specific suppressive influence exists to explain the absence of cooperative responses between histoincompatible T and B cells (28). Thus, concomitant transfer of histoincompatible carrier-primed T cells does not appreciably diminish the cooperative response between isogeneic T and B cells. Likewise, it should be pointed out that in a detailed analysis of the appropriate conditions to conduct these experiments, we were unable to obtain physiologic cooperation between histoincompatible T and B cells over a very wide range of cell doses.

This reasoning has led us to conclude, therefore, that the genetic restrictions for physiologic cooperation between T and B cells in secondary immune responses concern the actual cooperative interaction between these cells. It should be emphasized, however, that the system employed in the aforementioned experiments was designed to analyze secondary responses between previously primed populations of T and B lymphocytes. The studies described above provide clear evidence that the relevant CI gene or genes controlling the interactions between primed T and B lymphocytes are located in the I region of the H-2 gene complex.

It is relevant to point out that the *I-A* and *I-B* sub-regions where the *CI* genes appear to be mapped by our studies (Figs. 2 and 3) are precisely the subregions where the majority of all known immune response or *Ir* genes have been mapped (29, 30). However, as discussed at length elsewhere (8) and below, while this suggests an association between Ir and CI gene products in lymphocyte function, it does not imply that these are necessarily products of the same gene(s).

EVIDENCE FOR FUNCTIONAL INTERRELATIONSHIPS BETWEEN *CI* AND *Ir* GENES

The close functional association between Ir and CI gene products in T-B cell cooperative interactions is per-haps most strikingly illustrated by the following experiment. By taking advantage of our previous demonstration of highly effective cooperation between reciprocal combinations of parental and F_1 hybrid T and B lymphocytes when the carrier molecule employed is one to which both parental strains are genetic responders (2), an experiment was designed to deter-mine whether F_1 carrier-primed T cells can serve as helper cells for either or both parental B cells when: a) the response to the carrier molecule employed is under genetic control such that one parental strain is a responder and the other is a non-responder, and b) the determinant specificity of the parental B cells being assessed is not under genetic control and bears no relationship to the specificity of the carrier molecule (31). The experimental system utilized *Ir* genes controlling responses to the terpolymer L-glutamic acid-L-lysine-L-tyrosine (GLT) to which A strain mice ($H\text{-}2^a$) are non-responders whereas BALB/c ($H\text{-}2^d$) and (BALB/c x A)F_1 hybrids (CAF_1) are responders.

As shown in Fig. 4, BALB/c (Group II) and A/J (Group VIII) DNP-specific B cells are effectively "helped" by KLH-specific F_1 T cells in response to DNP-KLH. Similar-ly, GLT-primed CAF_1 T cells cooperate very well with B cells from BALB/c donors in response to either soluble or macro-phage-bound DNP-GLT (Groups IV and VI). In marked contrast, however, these same GLT-specific F_1 T cells fail to serve as helper cells for DNP-specific B cells from A/J donor mice irrespective of whether soluble or macrophage-bound DNP-GLT is employed for secondary challenge (Groups X and XII). These results demonstrate, therefore, that GLT-primed CAF_1 T cells can provide for responder BALB/c, but not for non-responder A/J, the required stimulus for the anti-DNP

364

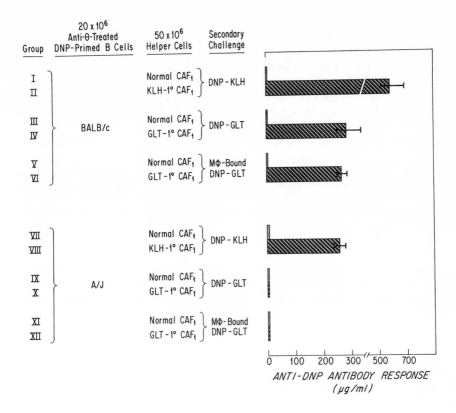

Figure 4. Involvement of *Ir* gene in control of T and B lymphocyte interactions. Recipients for all cell combinations were CAF_1 hybrids. The transfer scheme is described in the text. Combinations, strain origins and specificities of T and B cells are indicated. Secondary challenge was performed intraperitoneally with either 20 µg of soluble DNP-KLH or 100 µg of soluble DNP-GLT or intraveneously with 10^7 F_1 macrophages (MΦ) containing 2.4 µg DNP-GLT per mouse as indicated. Mean serum anti-DNP antibody levels of groups of 5 mice on day 7 after secondary challenge are illustrated. Horizontal bars represent ranges of the standard errors. (Taken from Ref. 31).

responses of DNP-specific B cells of these respective parental strains to the DNP conjugate of GLT (31).

As discussed at length elsewhere (29), the number of specific H-linked *Ir* genes that have been identified and the specific manner in which they permit immune responses to distinct antigens to take place, particularly at the T cell level, has suggested that they are somehow involved in either the specificity or the function of the T cell antigen receptors and may, therefore, be clonally expressed in this class of lymphocytes.

The implications of the preceding experiment on the F_1-parent cooperative response to DNP-GLT have been discussed by us (7, 8, 31) to mean either: 1) that *Ir* genes may also be expressed, and non-clonally, in B cells of responder animals, and/or 2) that the activation of the Ir gene product determines in turn the activation of the molecules involved in T-B cell interactions coded for by the same haplotype. According to the latter alternative, there would be no requirement for the <u>functional</u> expression of the Ir gene product in the B cell but only a requirement for the Ir gene product or associated *I* region gene product(s) from the T cell to govern the interaction with the B cell at the histocompatibility "acceptor" or CI site on the B cell surface. This alternative is schematically depicted in Fig. 5.

The fact that both *Ir* and *CI* genes are located in precisely the same region of the genome and the close functional interrelationship between them, as illustrated by the preceding experiment, raises the interesting possibility that the apparently distinct functions governed by these genes (i.e. antigen recognition and cell interactions) reflect the activities of product(s) of identical genes, or, alternatively, that multiple genes that have remained closely linked are responsible for these effects. For many years, it was thought that individual *Ir* genes controlled the responses to specific antigens (29, 32). Recently, however, immune responses to certain antigens have been found to be controlled by two distinct H-linked *Ir* genes. The most extensively studied example is the *Ir* gene-controlled response of inbred mice to the linear synthetic terpolymer of L-glutamic acid, L-lysine and L-phenylalanine (GLΦ). Thus, Dorf *et al* previously demonstrated (33, 34) that F_1 hybrids derived from the matings of selected non-responder parental strains (i.e. strains previously believed to be lacking the *Ir-GLΦ* gene) were phenotypic responders to

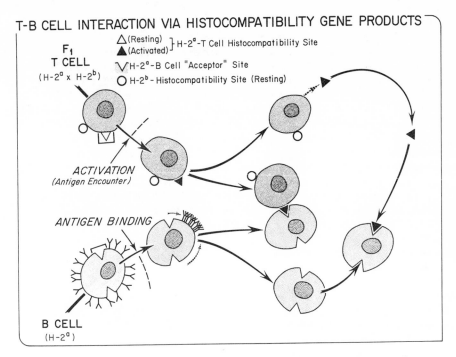

T-B CELL INTERACTION VIA HISTOCOMPATIBILITY GENE PRODUCTS

F_1
T CELL
($H-2^a$ x $H-2^b$)

△(Resting)
▲(Activated) } $H-2^a$-T Cell Histocompatibility Site

$\vee H-2^a$-B Cell "Acceptor" Site

○ $H-2^b$-Histocompatibility Site (Resting)

ACTIVATION
(Antigen Encounter)

ANTIGEN BINDING

B CELL
($H-2^a$)

Figure 5. This is a schematic depiction of how activation of the Ir gene product(s) may determine in turn the activation of molecules involved in T-B cell interactions coded for by the same haplotype. The T cell derives from a responder ($H-2^a$) x non-responder ($H-2^b$) F_1. As shown starting at top left, activation of the T cell specific for the antigen results in functional expression of CI molecules corresponding only to the $H-2^a$ responder haplotype (solid triangle); this permits these T cells to interact only with primed B cells (lower left) of the $H-2^a$ haplotype either by direct membrane-membrane contact (center) or via released molecules (lower right). Although not shown, in the case of F_1 cells specific for antigens not restricted by Ir gene control, CI molecules of both $H-2^a$ and $H-2^b$ (circle) haplotype would be expressed functionally thereby permitting interactions with primed B cells of both parental origins.

GLΦ. Moreover, selected recombinant strains derived by cross-over events between non-responder parental strains were also found to be GLΦ responders (33). These observations demonstrated: 1) the existence of two genetically separable loci controlling responses to GLΦ; 2) that the non-responder phenotype may reflect the absence of only one or both of the *Ir-GLΦ* genes; and 3) that complementation of two non-responder alleles can occur to result in the responder phenotype when the genes are located in either the *cis-* or *trans-* position. The two *Ir-GLΦ* genes have been tentatively designated α and β with their respective alleles termed α(+), α(-) and β(+), β(-) (33). The β genes have been mapped in the *I-A* subregion and the α genes have been tentatively mapped in a new subregion of *I* termed *I-F* located to the right of *I-C* (34).

Taking the aforementioned information collectively, one immediate question raised by the 1) close interrelationship between *Ir* and *CI* genes, and 2) the involvement of separable genes in the control of responses to a single defined antigen is the possibility that one gene is responsible for governing events in the T cell and the other gene is predominantly concerned with B cell function. This possibility has been recently speculated upon by others (35). If this were the case, then appropriately designed experiments should demonstrate selective functional defects in one or the other lymphocyte class depending on the presence or absence of the α and β *Ir-GLΦ* genes. Thus, one can ask whether a (non-responder x non-responder)F_1 hybrid, itself a phenotypic GLΦ responder as a result of gene complementation, can provide GLΦ-specific helper T cell function for DNP-specific B cells of one or the other, or neither, of the non-responder parents in response to DNP-GLΦ. Likewise, in principal, the reciprocal question can be asked by determining whether either one of the non-responder parents can provide GLΦ-specific T cell helper function for the DNP-specific B cells of the F_1 hybrid. If each of the *Ir-GLΦ* genes were predominantly concerned with the function of one of the two lymphocyte classes, then one would predict that F_1 T cells would provide helper function for B cells of parent #1 but not of parent #2 and, reciprocally, T cells from parent #2 might provide GLΦ-specific helper function for F_1 B cells whereas T cells from parent #1 would be unable to do so.

The experiment presented in Fig. 6 illustrates the basic design used to answer part of the question posed above (36). The left side of the figure depicts the

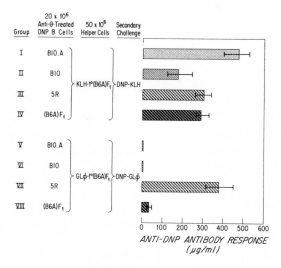

Strain	H-2 HAPLOTYPE							Ir-GLϕ		
	K	I-A	I-B	I-C	S	G	D	Genotype α β		Phenotype
B10.A	K	K	K	D	D	D	D	+	−	Non-Responder
B10	B	B	B	B	B	B	B	−	+	Non-Responder
5R	B	B	B	D	D	D	D	+	+	Responder
(B6 x A) F$_1$	B/K	B/K	B/K	B/D	B/D	B/D	B/D	−/+	+/−	Responder

Figure 6. Failure of $(H\text{-}2^b \times H\text{-}2^a)\text{F}_1$ T cells to provide GLϕ-specific helper function for B cells of either parental strain and demonstration that the most efficient T-B cell interactions occur when the α and β Ir-GLϕ genes are located in the cis- position. The protocol of the adoptive transfer system is described in the text of the paper. The recipients for all cell combinations were (B6A)F$_1$ hybrids. Combinations and strain origins of T and B cells, the specificities of helper cells employed in various groups and the antigen used for secondary challenge are indicated on the left. The genotypes and phenotypes of the strains employed are summarized beneath the protocol and data. Mean serum levels of anti-DNP antibody of groups of 5 mice on day 7 after secondary challenge with DNP-KLH or DNP-GLϕ are illustrated. Horizontal bars represent ranges of standard errors. Statistical comparison between the relevant groups yielded the following results: Groups V, VI and VIII versus Group VII had P values less than 0.001 in all cases. (Taken from Ref. 36).

protocols and various combinations of cell mixtures
analyzed for cooperative responses to DNP-KLH and DNP-GLΦ.
The *H-2* gene regions and *Ir-GLΦ* genotypes and phenotypes
are summarized at the bottom of the figure for convenience.
Before discussing the data shown in Fig. 6, it is pertinent
to cite the following data from control groups included in
the experiment but not shown in the figure: 1) All of the
DNP-primed spleen cell populations were capable of developing good secondary adoptive anti-DNP responses to the
immunizing antigen, DNP-fowl gamma globulin (FγG), in
parallel transfers utilizing spleen cells not treated with
anti-θ serum. 2) Anti-θ serum treatment in the conditions
employed effectively abrogated the capacity of such cells to
mount an *in vivo* response in the absence of additional
carrier-primed cells. 3) The substitution of normal cells
for carrier-primed cells failed to permit development of
responses to DNP-KLH or DNP-GLΦ.

The relevant results are presented on the right side
of Fig. 6. Groups I and IV demonstrate the capacity of
semi-syngeneic KLH-primed (B6A)F_1 T cells to provide
excellent helper activity for the DNP-specific B cells of
both parental strains, the 5R recombinant and the syngeneic
F_1 hybrid donors in response to DNP-KLH within the environs
of (B6A)F_1 irradiated recipients. In contrast, GLΦ-primed
F_1 T cells fail to cooperatively interact with B cells from
either B10.A or B10 parental donors in response to DNP-GLΦ
(Groups V and VI). This is not a reflection of defective
GLΦ-specific T cell function on the part of the GLΦ-primed
F_1 cells as evidenced by the capacity of these cells to
provide substantial helper activity for DNP-specific B cells
from the 5R recombinant strain donors in both experiments
(Group VII). An unexpected result in this experiment is
illustrated by Group VIII in which GLΦ-primed F_1 T cells
provided only low helper activity for DNP-specific B cells
from syngeneic F_1 donors in response to DNP-GLΦ. These
results cannot be explained on the basis of defective B
cell function on the part of the F_1, B10.A or B10 donor B
cells since the same pools of cells were used for Groups I,
II and IV in which good antibody responses were elicited.
The difference in magnitude of the F_1 B cell response to
DNP-GLΦ compared to that observed with 5R B cells was highly
significant (P = 0.0032) and cannot be attributed to a
lower general responsiveness on the part of F_1 B cells since
the magnitude of cooperative response of 5R and (B6A)F_1 B
cells with F_1 KLH-specific T cells to DNP-KLH were quite
comparable (cf. Groups III and IV, Fig. 6). These data

suggest a substantial difference in efficiency of T-B cell
interactions when the *Ir* genes involved in the B cells are
located in the *cis-* versus the *trans-* position (36).

Attempts to demonstrate GLΦ-specific helper T cell
function in either of the non-responder parental strains
were likewise unsuccessful as shown by the experiment in
Fig. 7 (36). In this experiment, spleen cells from GLΦ-
primed B10.A, B10, 5R and (B6A)F_1 donors were tested for
helper T cell activity with DNP-primed B cells from (B6A)F_1
donor mice in response to DNP-GLΦ in the same type of adoptive transfer system utilized in the preceding experiments.
In addition to the controls described in the preceding
section, the population of DNP-primed (B6A)F_1 B cells
employed in this experiment were capable of responding to
DNP-KLH when admixed with KLH-primed helper T cells from
B10.A, B10, 5R and (B6A)F_1 donor mice (data not shown).

As shown in Fig. 7, neither B10.A nor B10 donors
were capable of providing detectable GLΦ-specific helper
activity for (B6A)F_1 B cells in response to DNP-GLΦ. In
contrast, GLΦ-primed T cells from 5R donors provided helper
function for DNP-specific F_1 B cells. A meager degree of
helper activity was also obtained with (B6A)F_1 GLΦ-primed
T cells, although this was substantially less than that
observed with the 5R donor cells, a result which once again
suggests the greater efficiency of the two *Ir-GLΦ* genes when
located in the *cis-* position in the responding T cells.
Nevertheless, the demonstration of GLΦ-specific helper
activity in 5R and F_1 donors and the absence of detectable
activity in the case of either parental donor strongly
indicates that both genes must be expressed for specific
T cell helper function to be successfully generated.

Thus, these observations demonstrate that the functions of T lymphocytes and B lymphocytes and the cooperative
interactions between T and B cells require the presence of
both α and β *Ir-GLΦ* genes in each respective cell type.

The unexpected observations in these experiments was
the relative inefficiency of F_1 GLΦ-primed T cells in providing helper functions for F_1 B cells in response to DNP-
GLΦ. This result cannot be explained on the basis of a
relatively weak GLΦ-specific F_1 helper cell population since
these cells provided quite adequate helper activity for B
cells from 5R recombinant donors. Indeed, the substantial
difference observed between F_1-5R and F_1-F_1 T and B cell

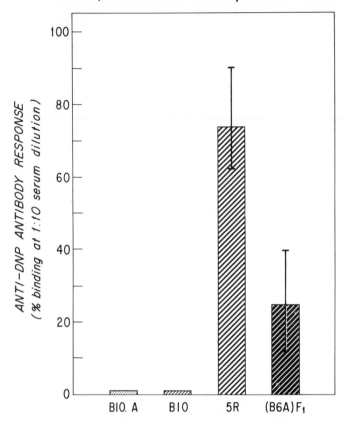

(B6A)F₁ ANTI-θ-TREATED DNP-FγG-PRIMED B CELLS

DONORS OF GLφ – PRIMED T CELLS

Figure 7. Failure of non-responder parental T cell to provide helper function for (non-responder x non-responder)F₁ B cells. The same type of adoptive transfer protocol used for the experiments in Figs. 1 and 2 was employed. The responses to DNP-GLΦ of mixtures of GLΦ-primed T cells from the various donor strains indicated with DNP-primed (B6A)F₁ B cells in (B6A)F₁ recipients are illustrated. The data are presented as mean serum levels of anti-DNP antibody of groups of 5 mice on day 11 after secondary challenge. The % binding of 1 x 10⁻⁸ M (³H)-DNP-ε-amino-N-caproic acid by 1:10 dilutions of sera were recorded. Vertical bars represent ranges of standard errors. Statistical comparison of responses obtained with 5R helper cells with B10.A and B10 T cells yielded P values less than 0.001 in both cases; comparison of 5R and (B6A)F₁ GLΦ-specific helper activity yielded P = 0.028. (Taken from Ref. 36).

interactions suggests the preferential efficiency of a *cis*-chromosomal relationship of the $\alpha(+)$ and $\beta(+)$ alleles in the respective interacting lymphocyte classes. It should be pointed out, however, that we cannot rule out the possibility that these effects may be the result of gene dosage as discussed elsewhere (37).

Several examples of more effective *Ir* gene complementation in antibody responses of intact animals to GLΦ in the *cis*- rather than *trans*- position have been presented and discussed previously (37) and elsewhere in this volume (see Benacerraf *et al*) for haplotypes other than $H-2^a$ and $H-2^b$. It is of interest that the exception to the *cis-trans*-phenomenon were the comparable anti-GLΦ responses observed in B10.A(5R) and in (C57BL/6 x A/J)F$_1$ mice. However, as shown by the experiments in Figs. 6 and 7, when passive transfer experiments involving a limited number of cells are carried out, the presumed *cis*- or F$_1$ effect can also be demonstrated with the α and β genes of the $H-2^a$ and $H-2^b$ haplotypes.

In addition to the *cis-trans*- effect, several important issues raised by these and previous experiments with systems under Ir gene control need to be clarified to permit a definitive understanding of the genetic control of T and B cell interactions:

1) Are the primed F$_1$ B cells resulting from the interactions with parental T cells restricted, or preferentially conditioned, to interactions with helper T cells from the same parental origin as compared with helper T cells bearing the other parental haplotype, a phenomenon which we term "haplotype preference?"

2) Are hapten-specific memory B cells selected to interact best in the secondary response with helper T cells specific for the carrier used in the primary response?

THE CONCEPTS OF "ADAPTIVE DIFFERENTIATION" AND "HAPLOTYPE PREFERENCE"

The basic observation that the most efficient T-B cell cooperative interactions occur between lymphocytes derived from histocompatible donors has been analyzed most extensively in secondary responses to hapten-protein conjugates utilizing the systems described in the preceding sections. In addition to work performed in our laboratory, several other investigators have made comparable findings with somewhat different systems. Thus, Kindred and Shreffler reported that successful thymus implant reconstitution of humoral anti-SRBC responses in nude mice required that the thymus donor was H-2-compatible (1). Likewise, Toivanen and co-workers have elegantly demonstrated the requirement for histocompatibility in thymus-bursa cooperative anti-SRBC responses in chickens (4, 38). Recent studies of Janeway and Paul have corroborated the requirement for identity of genes in the I-A subregion for cooperative secondary responses to hapten-protein conjugates in mice (27).

However, recent observations of other investigators appear to be discordant with the aforementioned results and require, therefore, careful scrutiny. Two notable examples in which successful interactions appear to occur between histoincompatible T and B lymphocytes to produce responses of the IgG antibody class have been reported. The first of these were studies by Bechtol et al (17, 18) in which allophenic or tetraparental mice, produced by fusion of embryos of strains which were responders and non-responders, respectively, to the synthetic polypeptide antigen (T,G)-A--L, produced anti-(T,G)-A--L antibodies of both responder and non-responder immunoglobulin allotype. The possibility of a complicating allogeneic effect that may have contributed to these results was avoided in the experimental design, and the authors, therefore, concluded that production of non-responder allotype (T,G)-A--L-specific antibodies by such tetraparental animals was an indication of successful cooperation between responder T cells and non-responder B cells (18). This is, of course, precisely the reverse of our findings in the adoptive secondary response system to hapten-protein conjugates and, in particular, to the findings described above with the Ir-GLT and Ir-$GL\Phi$ gene systems (31, 36). A remote alternative explanation for the data obtained in allophenic mice is that the T cells of the non-responder haplotype convert somehow to responder status, a possibility which we view quite unlikely.

The second notable example of apparent successful interaction between histoincompatible T and B cells was reported recently by von Boehmer et al (19). These investigators prepared allogeneic bone marrow chimeras by transferring equal numbers of anti-θ serum-treated bone marrow cells from each parent strain into lethally irradiated F_1 recipients. After sufficient time for lymphoid reconstitution, such chimeras were shown to possess approximately 50-50 mixtures of lymphoid cells from the respective parental haplotypes and, moreover, that a state of stable mutual tolerance existed among the chimeric T cells (39). The latter was shown by an inability of chimeric T cells to respond to *H-2* determinants of the host in mixed lymphocyte reactions (MLR) or cell-mediated killing (39). Utilizing an adoptive secondary anti-SRBC response system, von Boehmer *et al* have shown that primed chimeric T cells bearing *H-2* determinants of only one parental strain, provided comparable helper activity for both syngeneic B cells and allogeneic B cells of the same *H-2* haplotype to which the T cells had been tolerized in the chimeric environment. These results prompted the authors to conclude that the capacity of histoincompatible T and B cells to cooperatively interact was determined by unknown determinants which under normal circumstances prevented such interactions, whereas in conditions of mutual tolerance this interference is circumvented (19). This interpretation may be correct; however, von Boehmer *et al* failed to control for a possible allogeneic effect by including unprimed chimeric T cells in their adoptive transfer system, and until such controls have been performed, one must reserve conclusions in these studies. The absence of detectable MLR activity as measured by ^{3}H-thymidine incorporation is no criterion upon which to rule out possible allogeneic effects as very clearly illustrated by our own experience with irradiated histoincompatible recipients exerting a potent allogeneic effect on transferred allogeneic B cells (23). A third example of apparent physiological interactions between allogeneic T and B cells reported by Heber-Katz and Wilson (40) in rats was restricted to primary *in vitro* responses of the IgM antibody class. We believe that the basic observations of Bechtol *et al* (17, 18) and von Boehmer *et al* (19) are indeed correct--namely, that under conditions of long-term cohabitation, lymphocytes of disparate *H-2* haplotype origins may effectively interact in a manner indistinguishable from that normally occurring between syngeneic T and B cells. The interpretation of these observations may not, however, be as readily apparent as it may seem. On the one hand, it may be tempting to conclude that existence of mutual tolerance between the two classes of lymphocytes may result in successful interactions as a consequence of removal of determinant(s) interfering with such interactions in mixtures of non-tolerant histoincompatible lymphocytes; these putative interfering determinants would have to be something other than the major histocompatibility antigens, since lymphocytes in tolerant bone marrow chimeras retain their respective surface *H-2* antigens (19). This explanation does not, however, easily account for the reciprocal F_1-parent cooperation obtained with conventional DNP-protein conjugates or the capacity of (responder x non-responder)F_1 T cells to provide helper activity for B cells of the responder parent but not the non-responder parent in cooperative responses to DNP-GLT.

There is an interesting alternative possibility that could explain the observations discussed above. This possibility stems from the fact that in both the allophenic mice and bone marrow chimera studies the circumstances existed in which the T and B lymphocyte populations being analyzed had differentiated within the same genetic environment and, moreover, appear to be mutually, and specifically, tolerant with respect to one another. One might ask, therefore, what the influence of the genetic environment may be on subsequent properties of lymphocytes having undergone primary differentiation within that environment. Recently, a second type of radiation bone marrow chimera studies were performed by Urso and Gengozian (41, 42), and although not originally designed to approach this particular question, their observations provide some revealing insights into the apparently contradictory findings described thus far. Their chimeras were made by transplanting totally allogeneic bone marrow cells into lethally irradiated recipients (in contrast to parent→F_1 combinations used by von Boehmer *et al*). This difference is important because the majority of surviving long-term chimeras prepared in this way tend to be immunologically deficient in terms of their capacity to mount humoral antibody responses to SRBC. Their studies were designed to analyze the basis for the immunological deficiency in such chimeras and the points germane to this discussion can be summarized in general as follows (41, 42):

1) The immunological deficiency in long-term radiation bone marrow chimeras can be either a T cell or B cell defect depending on the genetic combinations employed to prepare the chimera.

2) In either case, the deficiency can be corrected by reconstitution with the appropriate reciprocal lymphocyte class--provided the reconstituting cell population is syngeneic with the chimeric host; cells syngeneic with the donor cell type do not reconstitute, despite the fact that 90-95% of the lymphoid cells in the chimeric host are of donor origin.

These striking observations, taken collectively with the tetraparental data (17, 18) and the von Boehmer experiments (19), suggest to us the possibility that the process of differentiation of stem cells may be critically regulated by histocompatibility molecules on cell surfaces, and that such differentiation may be "adaptive" to the environment in which it takes place. In other words, "adaptive differentiation" results in preferential interactions with cells which have undergone their differentiative process in the same (or similar) genotypic environment; the latter phenomenon we consider under the generic term of "haplotype preference", of which other examples will be discussed below.

Recently, we have been performing experiments to ascertain the validity of the adaptive differentiation concept. We elected initially to test what effects varying the host genotypic environment would have on B cell differentiation during primary immunization with respect to subsequent responsiveness and interaction capacities of such B cells. In other words, if a B cell from strain X undergoes primary differentiation in the lymphoid environment of strain Y, will the "haplotype preference" for secondary interactions remain with T lymphocytes of their haplotype of origin (strain X) or manifest genotypic preference for functional interactions with T lymphocytes of the host environment haplotype (strain Y)?

A schematic version of the type of protocol designed to approach this question is shown in Fig. 8 (43). The protocol involves successive adoptive transfers of B lymphocytes into various strains of irradiated, carrier-primed host recipients. Thus, spleen cells from unprimed (A x B)F$_1$ hybrid donors are treated with anti-θ serum plus complement to remove T lymphocytes. The peripheral B lymphocytes obtained in this manner are transferred into irradiated carrier (KLH)-primed recipients of various haplotypes (*i.e.* [A x B]F$_1$, parent A, parent B and unrelated strain C) and into irradiated unprimed syngeneic (A x B)F$_1$ recipients. All animals are immunized with DNP-KLH; 7-8 days later, the animals in each group are sacrificed, their spleen cells obtained and pooled, and a portion assayed for IgM and IgG DNP-specific PFC. The remaining cells (untreated or anti-θ serum-treated) from each group of primary recipients are then injected into 5 groups of secondary recipients. The latter correspond to the same 5 groups utilized in the first transfer except that a different protein (FγG) was used for carrier priming. The second transfer multiplies 5 times

PROTOCOL FOR DETERMINING ADAPTIVE DIFFERENTIATION
(HAPLOTYPE PREFERENCE) OF B LYMPHOCYTES

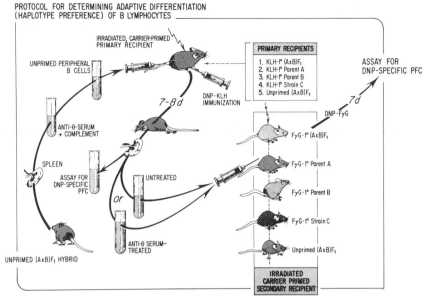

Figure 8. See text for explanation (Ref. 43).

that of the first transfer since each of the 5 primary transfer cell populations are transferred into 5 groups of secondary recipients. All groups are then challenged with DNP-FγG and their spleens analyzed for DNP-specific PFC 7 days later. Although not depicted on this scheme, additional successive transfers can be performed, or other modifications of the basic plan made as will be described below.

Only a few experiments of this type have been performed thus far, and so we consider these observations to be preliminary and far from conclusive. There are indications, however, from the preliminary data which merit some discussion. One such experiment in which CAF_1 B cells were the primary donor inoculum is presented in Fig. 9. The full protocol and data from transfer I is depicted on the left side of Fig. 9. The primary PFC responses in transfer I demonstrate a substantially higher response in KLH-1^O CAF_1 recipients (Group I) than the other 4 groups. It is pertinent to point out that the CAF_1 donor B cells were subjected to an allogeneic effect in the parental BALB/c and A/J recipients as well as the unrelated B6 recipients. This follows from our previous experience in irradiated histoincompatible recipients of DNP-primed B cells discussed above (23). It is impossible to deduce to what extent suppression or enhancement is reflected in the magnitude of responses observed in these three groups (II-IV) as compared to unprimed controls (Groups V). It should be recalled that there is much evidence demonstrating suppressive influences of the allogeneic effect on <u>unprimed</u> lymphocyte populations (20).

The data from the second transfer of this experiment is summarized on the right side of Fig. 9. Note that in every case the maximum response was obtained in the strain identical to the primary recipient haplotype. Whereas it could be tempting to interpret these results as demonstrating a clear example of adaptive differentiation, there is a considerably more complex aspect of this system that makes a simple interpretation virtually impossible. First, it is fair to assume that, just as in the case of transfer I, there are potential allogeneic effects operating in certain of the transfer II recipient groups. If this is the case, it is quite interesting that some form of selective advantage has been imparted to each donor cell inoculum from transfer I in relation to the haplotype in which such cells resided in the primary transfer. For example, when B cells primed in BALB/c primary recipients are transferred to BALB/c secondary recipients, a clearly higher response is obtained than when such cells are transferred to A/J or B6 secondary recipients (cf. Groups II B, C and D), despite the fact that the latter strains are genetically capable of inducing some form of allo-geneic effect on the transferred B cells. These differences may reflect either selection during priming in the first recipient of a B cell subpopulation particularly susceptible to an enhancing allogeneic effect in the BALB/c environment or, alternatively, selection of a subpopulation particularly sensitive to suppressive allogeneic effects exerted by haplotypes other than BALB/c (i.e. A/J and B6 in this case).

It is not possible to determine from the above data what may be occurring, but the crucial point is that something has clearly transpired in the course of priming which appears to dictate the "haplotype preference" of the cell population for secondary cell interactions. It is now necessary to delineate the various aspects of these phenomena, such as whether the apparent adaptation is a reflection of an antigen-driven differentiation process and/or whether cell surface molecular changes can be demonstrated to accompany such events. It is perfectly conceivable that the presentation of antigen by macrophages plays a critical role in determining the haplotype preference displayed by primed T and/or B cells in subsequent interactions; this notion is supported by 1) the original observations of Rosenthal and Shevach (5) on the critical role of histocompatibility molecules in antigen

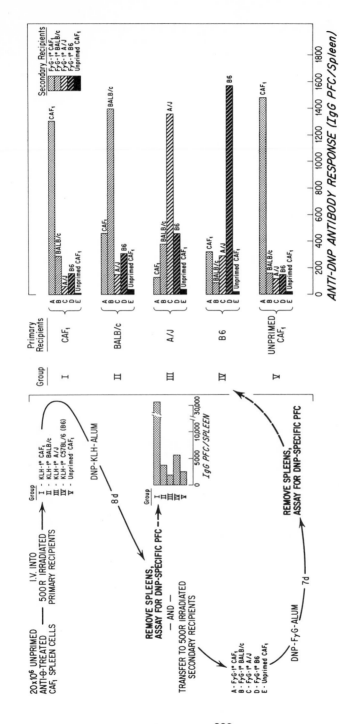

Figure 9. See text for explanation. Data are presented in mean IgG DNP-specific plaque-forming cells per spleen of groups of five mice. (Ref. 43).

presentation by macrophages for stimulation of *in vitro* DNA synthesis by primed guinea pig T lymphocytes (reviewed in this volume); 2) unpublished work of Zinkernagel (44) and Miller (45) on priming of F_1 T cells in irradiated parental hosts in which such cells subsequently manifest haplotype preference for interacting with primed B cells of the corresponding parental haplotype; 3) the studies of Erb and Feldmann (6, 46) demonstrating the importance of gene identities in the *I* region between macrophages and T lymphocytes for efficient priming of mouse helper T cells *in vitro*; and 4) the observations of Pierce *et al* (in this volume) demonstrating the capacity of antigen-bearing allogeneic macrophages to prime animals for subsequent responses in which preference is manifested for antigen on the same allogeneic macrophages rather than on syngeneic macrophages. On the other hand, it is also conceivable that interactions between histoincompatible T and B lymphocytes during very early stages of differentiation result in inductive events that determine the ultimate haplotype preference expressed by such cells in subsequent interactions. The nature of such inductive events, the level at which they may occur and the expression of their consequences at the molecular level are questions that we can now begin to explore.

CONCLUSION

The histocompatibility gene complex has been among the most fascinating and thoroughly studied gene systems in mammals over the past two decades. During this time, it has become increasingly clear that the molecules coded by genes in this complex play varied and integral roles in the functions of the immune system. One cannot help feeling that we are but at the proverbial "tip of the iceberg" at the present time, and there exist many new avenues to explore and delineate about the biological importance of histocompatibility gene products.

The studies summarized herein have focused on the importance of histocompatibility molecules in lymphoid cell interactions and lymphocyte differentiation, a subject also discussed in other papers in this volume. We believe that such observations have provided strong evidence for the involvement of the histocompatibility gene complex in regulatory events controlling certain aspects of the immune system. It is particularly germane to bear in mind the important differences between cells at various stages of differentiation in terms of their relative genetic restrictions in this

regard. Hence, it might be a tempting assumption that interactions between lymphoid cells very early in ontogeny will
promote adaptive changes in one or both cell types to permit
successful interactions between them at later stages of
development, a model which we have suggested in this paper.
The genetic restrictions observed in our studies have been
demonstrated to occur in mixtures of T and B lymphocytes
which have been previously primed by antigen and, thereby,
perhaps irretrievably "locked" into set phenotypic expres-
sion(s) of the functional cell surface molecules required for
successful cell interactions. In addition, the role of Ia
antigens in differentiation of B cells of various immunoglobulin classes and subclasses, as described by McDevitt
et al in this volume, requires further detailed exploration
in order to gain greater insight into these questions.

In any event, the cumulative evidence obtained in many
laboratories over the years has left little doubt that the
regulatory role of T cells in immune responses is one of the
control of differentiation events in other lymphocytes of
both T and B classes. The observations presented here provide strong evidence that the molecules involved in this
differentiation process are gene products of the major histocompatibility complex which appear to be phenotypically
interrelated on the surface membranes of such cells. Moreover, the broad implication of this concept is that control
of cell differentiation processes may be a major function of
histocompatibility molecules even in cell systems beyond the
scope of the lymphoid system.

ACKNOWLEDGMENTS

We are indebted to our colleagues who have participated
in various aspects of the studies discussed herein. In
particular, we wish to cite the close collaboration of
Drs. Toshiyuki Hamaoka and Martin Dorf and the skilled
technical assistance of Henry DiMuzio, Nomi Eshhar,
Mary Graves, Lee Katz, Mercy Koshy and Jeanne McDonald. We
also thank Charlene Small and Deborah Maher for excellent
secretarial assistance in preparing the manuscript. The
studies reported here were supported by Grants AI-10630 and
AI-09920 from the National Institutes of Health.

REFERENCES

(1) B. Kindred and D.C. Shreffler. J. Immunol. 109 (1972) 940.

(2) D.H. Katz, T. Hamaoka and B. Benacerraf. J. Exp. Med. 137 (1973) 1405.

(3) D.H. Katz, T. Hamaoka, M.E. Dorf and B. Benacerraf. Proc. Nat. Acad. Sci. U.S.A. 70 (1973) 2624.

(4) P. Toivanen, A. Toivanen and O. Vainio. J. Exp. Med. 139 (1974) 1344.

(5) A.S. Rosenthal and E.M. Shevach. J. Exp. Med. 138 (1973) 1194.

(6) P. Erb and M. Feldmann. Nature. 254 (1975) 352.

(7) D.H. Katz and B. Benacerraf, in: The Immune System: Genes, Receptors, Signals. eds. E.E. Sercarz, A.R. Williamson and C. Fred Fox. (Academic Press, New York, 1974) p. 569.

(8) D.H. Katz and B. Benacerraf. Transpl. Rev. 22 (1975) 200.

(9) D.H. Katz, M.E. Dorf, D. Armerding and B. Benacerraf, in: "Molecular Approaches to Immunology" – Miami Winter Symposia, Vol. 9. eds. E.E. Smith and D.W. Ribbons. (Academic Press, New York, 1975) p. 211.

(10) D. Armerding, D.H. Sachs and D.H. Katz. J. Exp. Med. 140 (1974) 1717.

(11) D.H. Katz and D. Armerding, in: Immune Recognition – Proceedings of the Ninth Leukocyte Culture Conference. ed. A.S. Rosenthal. (Academic Press, New York, 1975) p. 727.

(12) D.H. Katz and D. Armerding, in: "Cellular and Soluble Factors in the Regulation of Lymphocyte Activation" – FASEB Symposium, April, 1975. Fed. Proc. In press.

(13) A.J. Munro, M.J. Taussig, R. Campbell, H. Williams and Y. Lawson. J. Exp. Med. 140 (1974) 1579.

(14) M.J. Taussig, A.J. Munro, R. Campbell, C.S. David and N.A. Staines. J. Exp. Med. 142 (1975) 694.

(15) T. Tada, M. Taniguchi and T. Takemori. Transplant. Rev. 26 (1975) 106.

(16) T. Takemori and T. Tada. J. Exp. Med. 142 (1975) 1241.

(17) K.B. Bechtol, T.G. Wegmann, J.H. Freed, F.C. Grumet, B.W. Chesebro, L.A. Herzenberg and H.L. McDevitt. Cell. Immunol. 13 (1974) 264.

(18) K.B. Bechtol, J.H. Freed, L.A. Herzenberg and H.O. McDevitt. J. Exp. Med. 140 (1974) 1660.

(19) H. von Boehmer, L. Hudson and J. Sprent. J. Exp. Med. 142 (1975) 989.

(20) D.H. Katz. Transpl. Rev. 12 (1972) 141.

(21) D.H. Katz, W.E. Paul, E.A. Goidl and B. Benacerraf. Science. 170 (1970) 462.

(22) T. Hamaoka, D.H. Katz and B. Benacerraf. Proc. Nat. Acad. Sci. U.S.A. 69 (1972) 3453.

(23) T. Hamaoka, D.P. Osborne, Jr. and D.H. Katz. J. Exp. Med. 137 (1973) 1393.

(24) D.H. Katz, M.E. Dorf and B. Benacerraf. J. Exp. Med. 140 (1974) 290.

(25) D.H. Katz, M. Graves, M.E. Dorf, H. DiMuzio and B. Benacerraf. J. Exp. Med. 141 (1975) 263.

(26) D.H. Katz, D. Armerding, M.E. Dorf, Z. Eshhar and B. Benacerraf, in: Proceedings of the Tenth Leucocyte Culture Conference. eds. V.P. Eijsvoogel, D. Roos and W.P. Zeylemaker. (Academic Press, New York, 1975).

(27) C.A. Janeway, Jr. and W.E. Paul. Manuscript in preparation, 1975.

(28) D.H. Katz, T. Hamaoka, M.E. Dorf and B. Benacerraf. J. Immunol. 112 (1974) 855.

(29) B. Benacerraf and H.O. McDevitt. Science. 175 (1972) 273.

(30) B. Benacerraf and D.H. Katz, in: Immunogenetics and Immunodeficiency. ed. B. Benacerraf. (Medical and Technical Publishing Co., Ltd., London, 1975) p. 117.

(31) D.H. Katz, T. Hamaoka, M.E. Dorf, P.H. Maurer and B. Benacerraf. J. Exp. Med. 138 (1973) 734.

(32) B. Benacerraf and D.H. Katz. Adv. Cancer Research. 21 (1975) 121.

(33) M.E. Dorf, J.H. Stimpfling and B. Benacerraf. J. Exp. Med. 141 (1975) 1459.

(34) M.E. Dorf and B. Benacerraf. Proc. Nat. Acad. Sci. U.S.A. 72 (1975) 3671.

(35) A.J. Munro and M.J. Taussig. Nature 256 (1975) 103.

(36) D.H. Katz, M.E. Dorf and B. Benacerraf. Manuscript submitted for publication, 1975.

(37) M.E. Dorf, P.H. Maurer, C.F. Merryman and B. Benacerraf. Manuscript submitted for publication, 1975.

(38) P. Toivanen, A. Toivanen and T. Sorvari. Proc. Nat. Acad. Sci. 71 (1974) 957.

(39) H. Von Boehmer, J. Sprent and M. Nabholz. J. Exp. Med. 141 (1975) 322.

(40) E. Heber-Katz and D.B. Wilson. J. Exp. Med. 142 (1975) 928.

(41) P. Urso and N. Gengozian. J. Immunol. 111 (1973) 712.

(42) P. Urso and N. Gengozian. J. Immunol. 113 (1974) 1770.

(43) D.H. Katz. Manuscript in preparation.

(44) R. Zinkernagel. Personal communication.

(45) J.F.A.P. Miller. Personal communication.

(46) P. Erb and M. Feldmann. J. Exp. Med. 142 (1975) 460.

DISCUSSION FOLLOWING DAVID KATZ

SHEARER: In the interest of completion of the list of those
    examples in which allogeneic T and B cells cooperate
    for antibody production, I would like to mention that
    Edna Mozes, Michael Sela and I reported some years ago
    allogeneic T and B cell transfers involving several
    strain combinations and with a number of synthetic poly-
    peptide immunogens in which good cooperation appeared to
    be obtained. These experiments were carried out in
    high and low responder strains and involved immunogens
    under *H-2*-linked *Ir* gene control. They included
    studies with (T,G)-Pro--L, (Phe,G)-A--L, (T,G)-A--L,
    loop-A--L, loop-Pro--L and (Phe,G)-Pro--L. These allo-
    geneic transfer experiments were controlled for optimal
    cell interactions by the use of innocent bystander
    immunogens or determinants, the latter two of which
    were a part of the immunogenic macromolecule. No evi-
    dence was observed for either suboptimal or superoptimal
    (allogeneic effect) interaction using the bystander
    antigens. The result obtained for those antigenic
    determinants under Ir gene control have been published
    and will not be discussed here.* They, in fact, have
    been exactly predictive for the findings of Mozes,
    Taussig and Munro using specific T cell factors. It is
    unlikely that such concordance of results obtained in
    our allogeneic transfers and in the factor experiments
    could be due to coincidence.

    *[*EDITOR'S NOTE:* For references to these points, see:
    1) J. Immunol. 111:1429, 1973
    2) J. Exp. Med. 135:1009, 1972
    3) Eur. J. Immunol. 4:430, 1974
    4) Proc. Nat. Acad. Sci. 71:1574, 1974 - DHK.]

KATZ: I think you are making a perfectly valid point. I
    am very sorry for my oversight in not referring to your
    earlier work.

GERSHON: The host obviously contributes something important
    to the reactivity of the B cell or which modifies its
    ability to interact with other cells. It would be in-
    teresting to modify the host by such maneuvers as thy-
    mectomy or splenectomy or some such thing to see what
    host factor is altering the B cell.

KATZ: I think that is a very good point. You are suggesting that in the adaptive differentiation experiment
where something in the host is clearly influencing the
primary differentiation of the transferred B cells, we
might learn a great deal about what this may be by
treating the host in the ways you mentioned. Certainly
we should be able to determine whether host T lymphocytes are relevant in this regard by using thymectomy
or ALS pre-treatment; it is perfectly conceivable that
host macrophages or other non-lymphocytic cells may be
most important here, although I am inclined to favor
the T lymphocyte as playing the central role.

McDEVITT: What you have shown in your adaptive differentiation protocol is that CAF_1 B cells primed in various
hosts then respond best in the host in which they were
primed. This could be, and may well be, due to an
allogeneic effect. Have you tried this with allo-reactive (for CAF_1)-depleted, carrier-primed helper T cells
in an F_1 recipient?

KATZ: As I pointed out in my presentation, there is little
doubt at all, in my mind, that some type of allogeneic
effect is occurring in this type of protocol. I gather
that you are suggesting that we take B6 T cells, deplete
them of allo-reactivity against CAF_1 alloantigens, then
prime them to a carrier, eg. KLH, in an irradiated CAF_1
recipient and then test these cells for cooperation
with DNP-specific B cells from B6, CAF_1, BALB/c and
A/J. This is certainly a feasible experiment and may
provide information on adaptive differentiation of T
cells.

McDEVITT: Have you looked at the passaged CAF_1 B cells
from the various hosts to see if they carry new antigenic determinants?

KATZ: No, we have not done this as yet. However, in the
final stages of an experiment that is currently underway, we are planning to analyze the B cells recovered
from the various host haplotypes for their capacities
to stimulate mixed lymphocyte reactions (MLR) with
effector cells derived from all of the appropriate
haplotypes. I should say, however, that after thinking
about it, I feel that serological analyses will not be
revealing of "new" antigenic determinants because:
1) there are many data in chimeric animals which show

that donor cells can be detected by appropriate alloantisera directed against the donor haplotype; and 2)
the population of cells affected in this type of experiment may only be the DNP-specific B cells which would
comprise but a small subpopulation of the original donor
inoculum. I am hoping, therefore, that if such changes
do occur in cell surface determinants of the affected
cells, they will be demonstrable in MLR analyses.

PAUL: David, in the last experiment you showed, there was
one unprimed group which was included as a primary response. The magnitude of that primary was equivalent to
most of the secondary responses raising an important
question as to the significance of the secondary responses in the experimental groups.

KATZ: You are absolutely correct in your interpretation of
the data that was shown. I failed to point out that the
magnitude of the response in the unprimed recipients in
the first transfer corresponds to a background level of
response in CAF_1 animals. What you are alluding to is
affected, in the second transfer, by the fact that the
secondary recipients are receiving lower numbers of B
cells in view of the need to divide the cells obtained
from the primary recipients into five times as many
secondary hosts. In other words, the magnitudes of the
primary and secondary responses in this experiment
should not be compared.

PAUL: I have another question which deals with the relative
activities of DNP-FYG versus DNP-GLΦ-primed F_1 B cells
when mixed with GLΦ-primed F_1 T cells. In the experiment you showed, it was demonstrated that F_1-F_1 cooperation was substantially better when the F_1 B cells came
from DNP-GLΦ-primed donors. One, of course, would be
interested in knowing whether you are dealing with
conjugate-specific B cells, that is, cells which recognize a determinant to which GLΦ makes a substantial
contribution; then, one might ask whether or not this
explains the inferior behavior of F_1 cells as compared
to the 5R recombinant cells in cooperative responses to
DNP-GLΦ.

KATZ: I think that this is certainly a valid possibility
for explaining the data we now have.

BENACERRAF: I would just like to point out that the experiment showing that DNP-KLH primed 5R B cells cooperate better than (a x b)F$_1$ B cells with GLΦ T cells remain valid as an example of *cis-trans* preference in the a x b haplotypes.

STIMULATION OF ANTIBODY RESPONSES IN VITRO BY ANTIGEN-BEARING SYNGENEIC AND ALLOGENEIC MACROPHAGES

CARL W. PIERCE, JUDITH A. KAPP AND BARUJ BENACERRAF

Department of Pathology
Harvard Medical School

Abstract: The ability of antigen-bearing syngeneic and allogeneic peptone-induced peritoneal exudate macrophages
to support development of primary and secondary antibody responses to a T cell-dependent antigen by murine
lymphoid cells *in vitro* has been investigated. Syngeneic and allogeneic macrophages support development of
comparable *primary* antibody responses. Immunized
spleen cells, however, develop *secondary* antibody responses preferentially when stimulated *in vitro* with
antigen on macrophages syngeneic to the macrophages
used to immunize the spleen cells *in vivo*. The genetic
restrictions governing effective macrophage-lymphoid
cell interactions in secondary antibody responses appear to be operative at the level of the immunized T
cell. The implications that sensitized T cells selectively recognize antigen presented in the context of
the macrophage membrane-antigen complex which sensitized the T cells initially are considered.

INTRODUCTION

Interactions among at least three distinct types of
cells in the immune system, macrophages (Mϕ), thymus-derived
cells (T cells) and precursors of antibody-producing cells
(B cells), are required for development of optimal antibody
responses to complex multi-determinant antigens (1). Experiments probing the mechanisms of interactions among T
cells and B cells necessary for development of antibody responses in mice have shown that these cells must share membrane molecules encoded by the I region of the H-2 complex
for efficient physiologic interactions to occur (2). This

genetic restriction is addressed in detail by other contributors to this volume.

By contrast, genetic restrictions similar to those governing T cell-B cell interactions have not been shown to be operative in interactions among Mφ and lymphoid cells (T cells and B cells) in the development of antibody responses by murine cells *in vitro* (3). Several investigators have demonstrated that lymphoid cells develop comparable antibody responses when incubated with antigen and syngeneic or allogeneic Mφ (4-10). However, the generation of carrier-specific helper T cells *in vitro* appears to require that the T cells and Mφ share membrane molecules encoded by the *I* region of the *H-2* complex (11). Thus, the lack of genetic restrictions governing interactions among Mφ and lymphoid cells in antibody responses may not be absolute.

In another experimental system, combinations of immunized guinea pig lymphocytes and Mφ must be syngeneic for successful development of DNA synthetic responses to the immunizing antigen *in vitro* (12). The differences in requirements for syngenicity between Mφ and lymphoid cells may be explained by species differences; however, this seems unlikely in the light of Erb and Feldmann's data (11). These differences may, more realistically, depend on whether a T cell or B cell response is being measured and the sensitivity of the precursor cell to activation. For example, successful generation of murine helper T cells or DNA synthetic responses by guinea pig lymphocytes may require that T cells and Mφ share molecules encoded by the major histocompatibility complex of the species. Similarly, syngenicity in the *I* region of the *H-2* complex may be required for interactions between T cells and B cells which effectively stimulate B cells for antibody responses. However, allogeneic Mφ may be able to activate T cells sufficiently for their effective interaction with B cells in antibody responses.

We have been investigating the apparent lack of genetic restrictions among Mφ and lymphoid cells in the development of antibody responses *in vitro* for several years. In this brief communication, we will compare the ability of syngeneic and allogeneic Mφ to support development of primary and secondary antibody responses *in vitro*.

EXPERIMENTAL SYSTEM

In the experiments to be described, the antigen was the synthetic terpolymer of L-glutamic acid[60]-L-alanine[30]-L-tyrosine[10] (GAT). Antibody responses to GAT are controlled by an autosomal dominant, H-2-linked, immune response (Ir) gene; mice of the H-$2^{a,b,d,f,j,k,r,u,v}$ haplotypes are "responders" (2). Spleen cells from these mice develop IgG GAT-specific PFC responses when stimulated with GAT in Mishell-Dutton cultures (13). Spleen cells from mice of the H-$2^{n,p,q,s}$ haplotypes fail to respond to GAT and are "non-responders". Mφ and T cells are required for development of antibody responses to GAT by responder B cells in $vitro$, and the defect in non-responder mice is not in the Mφ population (9). Mφ in peptone-induced peritoneal exudate bind GAT and Mφ-bearing nanogram quantities of GAT (quantitated with ^{125}I-GAT) stimulate PFC responses by responder lymphoid cells comparable to those stimulated by microgram quantities of soluble GAT (9,10,14). The basic experimental design was to incubate spleen cells or lymphoid cells (separated from spleen cells by adherence techniques 9,10) from responder C57BL/6 (H-2^b) mice with syngeneic or allogeneic Mφ bearing nanogram quantities of GAT for 5 days under Mishell-Dutton conditions and compare the IgG GAT-specific PFC responses stimulated by the two types of Mφ.

ABILITY OF SYNGENEIC AND ALLOGENEIC MACROPHAGES TO SUPPORT DEVELOPMENT OF PRIMARY ANTIBODY RESPONSES
IN VITRO

Our previous experiments demonstrating that lymphoid cells develop comparable antibody responses when incubated with syngeneic or allogeneic Mφ (9,10) have been criticized on several grounds. The experiment shown in Table I and related summarized experiments were carried out to answer these criticisms.

Lymphoid cells from virgin C57BL/6 (H-2^b) mice were incubated with graded numbers of GAT-bearing syngeneic C57BL/6 (H-2^b) or allogeneic P/J (H-2^b) Mφ (P/J mice are non-responders to GAT). These Mφ from peptone-induced peritoneal exudate were pulsed with GAT (14) either immediately before addition to the cultures (Day 0) or 24 hrs previously (Day-1) and incubated to allow release of irrelevant GAT. Syngeneic and allogeneic Mφ of the same age ($i.e.$, Day 0 or Day-1) stimulated comparable GAT-specific PFC responses; Day-1 Mφ, with approximately tenfold less GAT than Day 0 Mφ, stimulated

only slightly lower responses. Allogeneic and syngeneic
Mφ aged for seven days after pulsing retained approximately 0.1 ng GAT/10^5 cells, and stimulated comparable PFC responses to GAT not unlike those stimulated by Day-1 Mφ.

TABLE I

ABILITY OF SYNGENEIC AND ALLOGENEIC MACROPHAGES
TO STIMULATE A PRIMARY RESPONSE TO GAT

10 X 10^6 Lymphoid Cells C57BL/6 (*H-2^b*)	Day 5 IgG GAT-Specific PFC/Culture	
	C57BL/6 Mφ (*H-2^b*)	P/J Mφ (*H-2^b*)
GAT-Mφ Pulsed on Day 0*		
7 X 10^4	905	710
3.5 X 10^4	410	520
1 X 10^4	230	360
GAT-Mφ Pulsed on Day-1**		
7 X 10^4	470	660
3.5 X 10^4	345	240
1 X 10^4	45	180
No Mφ - 5 μg GAT	<10	

Mφ = peptone-induced peritoneal exudate macrophages

* C57BL/6 Mφ had 2.25 ng GAT/10^5 cells
   P/J Mφ had 1.78 ng GAT/10^5 cells

** C57BL/6 Mφ had 0.20 ng GAT/10^5 cells
    P/J Mφ had 0.13 ng GAT/10^5 cells

This experiment demonstrates again that syngeneic and
allogeneic macrophages support development of comparable primary antibody responses *in vitro* and answers some criticisms
of previous experiments. First, during the 24 hr incubation
after pulsing with GAT, approximately 90% of the GAT initially associated with Mφ is released into the medium; further
incubation results in minimal release. Since aged allogeneic
Mφ function as well as aged syngeneic Mφ, the possibility
that GAT is transferred from allogeneic Mφ to syngeneic Mφ
contaminating the lymphoid cells and that the latter actually
stimulate the antibody response is unlikely. Second, in
previous experiments, the allogeneic Mφ used shared specificities encoded by the *I* region of the *H-2* complex and thus

were not strictly allogeneic. The H-2^p Mφ used in this experiment, to our knowledge, share no known specificities with the H-2^b lymphoid cells. Identical results to those in Table I have also been obtained using allogeneic Mφ sharing various I region specificities with the lymphoid cells. One last objection has been that allogeneic Mφ may stimulate a mixed lymphocyte response with resultant release of allo-geneic effect-like factors which stimulate antibody responses (2). DNA synthetic responses have been measured in the same cultures used to assess antibody responses; 7 X 10^4 allo-geneic Mφ have never stimulated significant DNA synthetic responses in cultures of 10^7 C57BL/6 lymphoid or spleen cells (E/C <1.5). Further, medium from these cultures has not been shown to contain allogeneic effect-like factors.

ABILITY OF SYNGENEIC AND ALLOGENEIC MACROPHAGES TO SUPPORT DEVELOPMENT OF SECONDARY ANTIBODY RESPONSES *IN VITRO*

Although genetic restrictions governing interactions among Mφ and lymphoid cells in primary antibody responses *in vitro* were not identified, genetic restrictions governing Mφ-T cell interactions exist for generation of helper T cells in mice (11) and for DNA synthetic responses to antigen by guinea pig lymphocyte (12). We have observed that lymphoid cells from mice immunized with GAT developed secondary PFC responses to GAT only when incubated with GAT-bearing syn-geneic macrophages. The results of experiments investigating this phenomenon in detail are shown in Table II.

C57BL/6 mice were immunized by intraperitoneal injection of 4 X 10^6 GAT-bearing or normal Mφ from the indicated mouse strains 28 days before the experiment. Spleen cells from these mice were incubated with graded numbers of freshly pre-pared GAT-bearing syngeneic C57BL/6 (H-2^b) or allogeneic DBA/1 (H-2^q) Mφ or 5 μg soluble GAT. Normal DBA/1 Mφ (2.5 X 10^4) were added to some cultures for control purposes. Spleen cells from mice immunized with GAT-C57BL/6 Mφ devel-oped secondary antibody responses when incubated with soluble GAT or GAT-C57BL/6 Mφ, but not when incubated with allogeneic GAT-DBA/1 Mφ (A). By contrast, spleen cells from mice im-munized with GAT-DBA/1 Mφ developed secondary antibody re-sponses when incubated with GAT-DBA/1 Mφ, but not when incu-bated with soluble GAT or GAT-C57BL/6 Mφ (B). Spleen cells from mice immunized with GAT-C57BL/6 and GAT-DBA/1 Mφ devel-oped secondary antibody responses when stimulated with soluble GAT, GAT-C57BL/6 Mφ, or GAT-DBA/1 Mφ (C).

TABLE II

ABILITY OF SYNGENEIC AND ALLOGENEIC MACROPHAGES
TO STIMULATE A SECONDARY ANTIBODY RESPONSE
TO GAT BY SPLEEN CELLS PRIMED WITH GAT-MACROPHAGES

10 X 10^6 C57BL/6 Spleen Cells ($H-2^b$)		Day 5 IgG GAT-Specific PFC/Culture		
Primed with GAT-Mφ**	GAT-Mφ/ Culture	C57BL/6 Mφ ($H-2^b$)*	DBA/1 Mφ ($H-2^q$)*	5 ug GAT
(A) C57BL/6 ($H-2^b$)	5 X 10^4	425	<10	
	2.5 X 10^4	265	<10	680
	2.5 X 10^4‡	420	–	
(B) DBA/1 ($H-2^q$)	5 X 10	20	1020	
	2.5 X 10	30	760	<10
	2.5 X 10‡	30	–	
(C) C57BL/6 + DBA/1	5 X 10	1510	850	
	2.5 X 10	1040	910	1270
	2.5 X 10 ‡	1020	–	
(D) C57BL/6 + Normal DBA/1	5 X 10^4	355	<10	1020
	2.5 X 10^4	840	<10	
	2.5 X 10^4‡	350	–	

Mφ = peptone-induced peritoneal exudate macrophages

* C57BL/6 Mφ had 2.78 ng GAT/10^5 cells
   DBA/1 Mφ had 3.15 ng GAT/10^5 cells

** C57BL/6 mice were immunized 28 days previously by
   intraperitoneal injection of 4 X 10^6 of the indicated
   Mφ. C57BL/6 Mφ had 33.5 ng GAT/10^6 cells; DBA/1 Mφ
   had 27.0 ng GAT/10^6 cells.

‡ 2.5 X 10^4 normal DBA/1 Mφ **were** added to these cultures.

To evaluate possible effects due to sensitization of C57BL/6
spleen cells with allogeneic DBA/1 Mφ, mice were immunized
with GAT-C57BL/6 and normal DBA/1 Mφ. Spleen cells from
these mice developed secondary antibody responses to soluble
GAT and GAT-C57BL/6 Mφ, but not to GAT-DBA/1 Mφ (D). Further,
responses in cultures with GAT-C57BL/6 and normal DBA/1 Mφ
provide critical control information. Normal DBA/1 Mφ had no
significant effect on responses stimulated by GAT-C57BL/6 Mφ
in cultures of spleen cells from mice immunized with

GAT-C57BL/6 Mφ (A), GAT-C57BL/6 and GAT-DBA/1 Mφ (C), and
GAT-C57BL/6 and normal DBA/1 Mφ (D). These observations indicated that DBA/1 Mφ were not stimulating a suppressive
effect on responses of appropriately immunized spleen cells
stimulated by GAT-C57BL/6 Mφ. Further, DBA/1 Mφ added to
spleen cells from mice immunized with GAT-DBA/1 Mφ (B) did
not stimulate a response to GAT-C57BL/6 Mφ. This suggested
that allogeneic Mφ were not stimulating a non-specific enhancing effect and that any transfer of GAT from C57BL/6 to
DBA/1 Mφ was insufficient to stimulate a secondary antibody
response.

Comparable results have been obtained when lymphoid
cells from immunized mice were substituted for spleen cells
and when P/J (H-2^b) or BALB/c (H-2^a) Mφ were substituted for
DBA/1 Mφ throughout the experiment. Lastly, significant DNA
synthetic responses (E/C <1.5) were not detected in cultures
of spleen cells from mice immunized with allogeneic Mφ and
H-2 identical allogeneic Mφ.

Thus, in the development of secondary antibody responses,
genetic restrictions govern effective interactions among Mφ
and lymphoid cells. Secondary antibody responses develop
preferentially in the presence of GAT-Mφ syngeneic with those
used for immunization. Preliminary data localize this genetic restriction to the H-2 complex. A preliminary experiment investigating whether this genetic restriction is operative at the level of the T cell or B cell is shown in Table
III.

Lymphoid cells from normal and GAT-primed C57BL/6 mice
were passed over a column of insoluble rabbit anti-mouse Fab
to deplete B cells (15). The recovered T cells were incubated with normal C57BL/6 B cells (lymphoid cells treated
with anti-Θ serum + C) and graded numbers of GAT-C57BL/6 or
GAT-DBA/1 Mφ. Combinations of normal C57BL/6 T cells and B
cells developed comparable primary PFC responses to GAT when
incubated with syngeneic GAT-C57BL/6 or allogeneic GAT-DBA/1
Mφ. However, T cells from GAT-primed animals (GAT-C57BL/6
Mφ) and normal B cells developed PFC responses to GAT preferentially in cultures stimulated with GAT-C57BL/6 Mφ. The
experiment in Table III has been repeated once with T cells
from animals immunized with allogeneic GAT-Mφ with similar
results. Other very preliminary data show that immunized B
cells develop comparable secondary antibody responses when
incubated with normal T cells and syngeneic or allogeneic
GAT-Mφ.

TABLE III

ABILITY OF SYNGENEIC AND ALLOGENEIC MACROPHAGES TO
STIMULATE ANTIBODY RESPONSES TO GAT IN
CULTURES OF GAT-PRIMED T CELLS AND NORMAL B CELLS

10 X 10^6 Normal B Cells C57BL/6 (H-2^b)		Day 5 IgG GAT-Specific PFC/Culture	
5 X 10^6 T Cells	GAT-Mφ/ Culture	C57BL/6 Mφ* (H-2^b)	DBA/1 Mφ* (H-2^q)
Normal	7 X 10^4	1270	1075
Normal	3.5 X 10^4	1100	785
Primed**	7 X 10^4	1410	165
Primed	3.5 X 10^4	1005	<10

B Cells + 5 μg GAT	<10
Normal T Cells + 5 μg GAT	<10
Primed T Cells + 5 μg GAT	<10

Mφ = peptone-induced peritoneal exudate macrophages.

*   C57BL/6 Mφ had 1.50 ng GAT/10^5 cells
    DBA/1   Mφ had 0.70 ng GAT/10^5 cells

** Primed T cells were obtained from C57BL/6 mice immunized
    35 days previously with 10 μg GAT in Maalox.

DISCUSSION

These experiments illustrate three major points concerning genetic restrictions governing efficient Mφ-lymphoid cell interactions in the development of antibody responses *in vitro*. First, in the *primary* antibody response, no genetic restrictions have been demonstrated; allogeneic and syngeneic Mφ support development of comparable responses. Second, in the *secondary* antibody response, genetic restrictions are operative; immunized spleen cells develop antibody responses preferentially with antigen-bearing Mφ syngeneic to those used during the immunization process. Third, these genetic restrictions appear to operate at the level of the T cell, although restrictions at the level of the B cell have not been rigorously excluded.

The observations that secondary antibody responses by immunized spleen cells develop preferentially in the presence of Mφ syngeneic with those used with immunization and, more specifically, that immunized T cells appear to be the site of this restriction, provide an explanation for genetic restrictions in Mφ-lymphocyte interactions observed in DNA synthetic responses to antigen by guinea pig cells (12). The lymphocytes in those experiments were from animals immunized with syngeneic Mφ. The fact that those lymphocytes develop DNA synthetic responses preferentially in the presence of syngeneic Mφ is entirely consistent with the present findings. Moreover, it emphasizes the critical nature of the Mφ-antigen complex in sensitizing T cells and eliciting subsequent responses by sensitized T cells.

The present findings appear to be in conflict with observations that helper T cells develop *in vitro* only in the presence of Mφ sharing antigens encoded by the *I* region of the *H-2* complex with the T cells (11). However, in the assay of helper T cell activity, Mφ syngeneic with the T cells, but not Mφ syngeneic with those used to generate the helper T cells, have been employed. On the basis of the present findings, we would predict that, if Mφ syngeneic with those used to generate helper T cells were used in the assay, the helper T cells would function preferentially with these Mφ.

Katz and Unanue (8) found no genetic restrictions governing Mφ-lymphoid cell interactions in development of secondary antibody responses to hapten-protein conjugates by immune lymphoid cells *in vitro*. However, the strain combinations used in these experiments, BALB/c and A/J, share specificities encoded by the *H-2* complex to the right of and including the *I-C* region. Our preliminary data suggests that the observed genetic restrictions are governed by molecules encoded by the *H-2* complex; their data suggests that molecules encoded by genes in the *I-C* region or to the right thereof govern these interactions.

The observations that specifically sensitized T cells respond preferentially when confronted with the same Mφ-antigen complex used for immunization have considerable implications for the understanding of fundamental mechanisms in immune responses to T cell-dependent antigens. It is conceivable that immune T cells, although capable of recognizing specific antigen alone, selectively or preferentially recognize that antigen when it is presented on Mφ membranes in the same context of membrane molecules originally presented to sensitize the T cells. Whether or not Mφ-membrane molecules are modified in some way when presenting antigen is not known. Nevertheless, the Mφ-antigen complex involved in stimulating T cells may be analogous to the hapten-carrier complex involved in stimulating B cells, *i.e.*, Mφ-membrane molecules may function as a "carrier" for T cell antigen recognition. If the genetic restrictions governing Mφ-lymphoid cell interactions in secondary antibody responses are determined by molecules encoded by the *H-2* complex, these phenomena may represent an expanded capacity of T cells to recognize antigens encoded by the *H-2* complex, analogous to the mixed lymphocyte reaction. From an evolutionary point of view, T cell recognition of histocompatibility antigens is a primitive mechanism. It is possible that during evolution, T cells have expanded the library of antigens which they recognize by "seeing" these antigens displayed on Mφ membranes in the context of histocompatibility antigens.

ACKNOWLEDGEMENTS

This investigation has been supported by U.S.P.H.S. Research Grants AI-09897 and AI-09920 from the National Institute of Allergy and Infectious Diseases. C.W.P. is the recipient of a U.S.P.H.S. Research Career Development Award 5-K04-AI-70173 from the National Institute of Allergy and Infectious Diseases. We thank Ms. Sharon Smith for secretarial assistance in preparation for the manuscript.

REFERENCES

1. Pierce, C.W., Peavy, D.L., and Tadakuma, T., Ann. N.Y. Acad. Sci., 256:365, 1975.

2. Benacerraf, B. and Katz, D.H., Adv. Cancer Res., 21: 121, 1975.

3. Pierce, C.W. and Kapp, J.A., in The Role of Macrophages in Immunobiology, Edited by D.S. Nelson, Academic Press, New York, in press.

4. Hartmann, K.-U., Dutton, R.W., McCarthy, M., and Mishell, R.I., Cell. Immunol., 1:182, 1970.

5. Haskill, J.S., Byrt, P., and Marbrook, J., J. Exp. Med. 131:57, 1970.

6. Shortman, K. and Palmer, J., Cell. Immunol., 2: 399, 1971.

7. Cosenza, H. and Leserman, L.D., J. Immunol., 108: 418, 1972.

8. Katz, D.H. and Unanue, E.R., J. Exp. Med., 137:967, 1973.

9. Kapp, J.A., Pierce, C.W., and Benacerraf, B., J. Exp. Med.,138:1121, 1973.

10. Pierce, C.W., Kapp, J.A., Solliday, S.M., Dorf, M.E., and Benacerraf, B., J. Exp. Med., 140:921, 1974.

11. Erb, P. and Feldmann, M., J. Exp. Med., 142:460, 1975.

12. Rosenthal, A.S. and Shevach, E.M., Contemp. Topics Immunobiol., in press.

13. Kapp, J.A., Pierce, C.W., and Benacerraf, B., J. Exp. Med., 138:1107, 1973.

14. Pierce, C.W., Kapp, J.A., Wood, D.D., and Benacerraf, B., J. Immunol., 112:1181, 1974.

15. Kapp, J.A., Pierce, C.W., Schlossman, S.F., and Benacerraf, B., J. Exp. Med., 140:648, 1974.

H-2 LINKED *Ir* GENE REGULATION OF DELAYED-TYPE HYPERSENSITIVITY IN MICE

J.F.A.P. MILLER, M.A. VADAS, ALISON WHITELAW
AND JENNIFER GAMBLE

Experimental Pathology Unit
Walter and Eliza Hall Institute of Medical Research

INTRODUCTION

Many T cell activities are regulated by genes of the major histocompatibility complex (MHC). These include lysis of virus-infected (1) or chemically modified (2) target cells and cooperative interactions between T and B lymphocytes (3) and between T lymphocytes and macrophages (4). Since delayed-type hypersensitivity (DTH) is a T cell-dependent inflammatory response, we were interested in exploring to what extent genes of the MHC might influence the capacity of lymphoid cells to be involved in DTH responses. We examined this using two systems: (1) the adoptive transfer of DTH by sensitized lymphocytes between congenic strains of mice and (2) the DTH response to antigens known to be under Ir gene control in inbred strains of mice.

METHODS

Mice of various strains were sensitized to protein antigens, such as fowl gamma globulin (FGG) or to dinitro-fluorobenzene (DNFB). Lymph node cells from sensitized donors were taken at the peak period of sensitivity and injected intravenously into normal mice. These were immediately challenged with the appropriate antigen to test for the transfer of the sensitive state. The test used has been described in detail elsewhere (5, 6). It depends on labelling replicating cells by ^{125}I-UdR (iododeoxyuridine) and quantifying the influx of labelled cells into a defined site where antigen has been deposited. Ten µl of the appropriate concentration of FGG was injected intradermally in the left pinna and a control solution in the right. Ten hours later,

403

0.1 ml of 1 mM solution of 5-fluorodeoxyuridine was injected
intraperitoneally (in order to block subsequent I-UdR incorporation into de novo nucleotide synthesis and thus increase
labelling efficiency for cells in DNA synthesis) and 20
minutes later 2 μCi of ^{125}I-UdR in 0.1 ml saline (specific
activity 90-110 μCi/μg) was given intravenously. After a
further 16 hours (i.e. 26 hours after antigen challenge), the
mice were killed, the pinnae cut off at the hairline, counted
in a Packard Gamma Spectrometer and checked histologically
for mononuclear cell infiltration. The results are expressed
as the ratio of the radioactivity in the left ear to the
radioactivity in the right ear (L/R ^{125}I-UdR uptake). It is
unusual to obtain a ratio greater than 1.2 in naive mice not
receiving sensitized cells. In previous work (5, 6), evidence was obtained to show that this test measures the extent
of DTH in mice since (1) the ear reaction is not apparent at
6 hours but is so at 24 and 48 hours; (2) it is associated
with a mononuclear cell infiltration (predominantly monocytic)
in which the cells are labelled in autoradiographs; (3) it is
T cell-dependent since it fails to occur in athymic nu/nu
mice or in normal mice immunized with antigens known not to
activate T cells; and (4) it can be transferred to naive mice
by purified T cells, not by lymphoid cells depleted of T
cells nor by serum antibody.

RESULTS AND DISCUSSION

Lymph node cells from mice sensitized to FGG were injected into recipient mice which were then challenged in the
ear and tested for DTH. Maximal responses occurred in syngeneic and minimal or no response in allogeneic recipients
(Table I). The reaction in semi-allogeneic recipients of 8
million cells was of an intermediate degree (Fig. 1).
Similar results were obtained following transfer of DNFB-
sensitized lymph node cells (Table I).

To determine whether transfer of DTH is linked to the
MHC, congenic strains of mice with recombinant chromosomes
were used. Adoptive transfer of DTH from CBA to B10.BR
(which have the same genes at the MHC but different backgrounds) was successful. On the other hand, transfer was not
possible from C57BL to B10.BR; these strains have similar
backgrounds but different MHC (Table II). The next set of
transfer experiments indicated that identity at the K-end
(K, I-A and I-B), but not at the D-end (I-C, S, D), was
sufficient for successful transfer (Table III). A further
set of transfer experiments showed that identity only at the

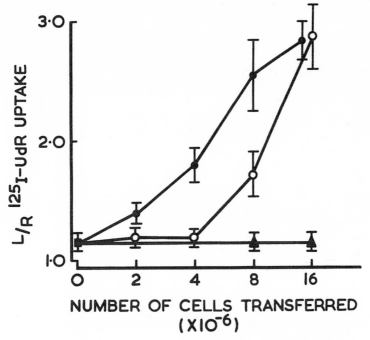

Figure 1. DTH response in naive CBA (●),
(CBA x BALB/c)F_1 (o) and BALB/c (▲) recipients
of various doses of FGG-sensitized CBA lymph
node cells.

H-2D or only at the H-2K region of the MHC did not allow
successful transfer (Table IV), and a final set indicated
that transfer was possible with identity in the I region,
and strongly suggested that identity at the I-A region was
necessary and sufficient (Table V). In the case of DNFB-
sensitized lymph node cells, adoptive transfer of DTH was
also possible between strains identical at the I-region but
not at the H-2K or H-2D regions (Table VI). Whether identity
only at H-2K or H-2D is sufficient to allow transfer of DTH
to DNFB is being examined.

The inability to transfer DTH between strains of mice
incompatible at some regions of the MHC is believed not to
result from rejection of the injected cells, recruitment of
the cells out of the circulation, nor engagement in a mixed
lymphocyte reaction (MLR). For example, the experiments with
F_1 cells or F_1 hosts (Table I and Fig. 1) tend to exclude
rejection, recruitment or engagement in a MLR. The results

TABLE I

EFFECT OF H-2 INCOMPATIBILITY ON ADOPTIVE TRANSFER OF DTH TO FGG AND DNFB

Antigen Sensitization	Source of Sensitized Cells	DTH Response in following recipients		
		CBA	(CBA x C57BL)F_1	C57BL
FGG	CBA	2.62 $\pm$ 0.20	2.14 $\pm$ 0.13	0.96 $\pm$ 0.08
FGG	(CBA x C57BL)F_1	1.56 $\pm$ 0.25	2.04 $\pm$ 0.15	1.78 $\pm$ 0.22
FGG	C57BL	1.03 $\pm$ 0.11	1.58 $\pm$ 0.08	2.96 $\pm$ 0.23
DNFB	CBA	2.06 $\pm$ 0.10	1.68 $\pm$ 0.30	1.33 $\pm$ 0.10
DNFB	(CBA x C57BL)F_1	1.74 $\pm$ 0.27	2.96 $\pm$ 0.22	2.94 $\pm$ 0.46
DNFB	C57BL	1.19 $\pm$ 0.12	2.14 $\pm$ 0.31	4.69 $\pm$ 0.36

Five mice per group. Values given in this and other tables are arithmetic mean $\pm$ one SEM.

TABLE II

CONTROL OF ADOPTIVE TRANSFER OF DTH TO FGG BY MHC

Donors of FGG Sensitized Lymph Node Cells	Recipients	MHC of Recipient						L/R ^{125}I-UdR Uptake
		K	I-A	I-B	I-C	S	D	
CBA	CBA	k	k	k	k	k	k	1.99 ± 0.15
CBA	B10.BR	k	k	k	k	k	k	2.05 ± 0.11
CBA	C57BL	b	b	b	b	b	b	1.11 ± 0.08
None	CBA	k	k	k	k	k	k	1.10 ± 0.05
C57BL	C57BL	b	b	b	b	b	b	4.78 ± 0.45
C57BL	CBA	k	k	k	k	k	k	1.05 ± 0.01
C57BL	B10.BR	k	k	k	k	k	k	1.04 ± 0.08
None	C57BL	b	b	b	b	b	b	1.03 ± 0.08

Five mice per group.

407

TABLE III

IDENTITY AT THE K-END BUT NOT AT THE D-END OF THE MHC ALLOWS SUCCESSFUL TRANSFER OF DTH TO FGG

Donors of FGG Sensitized Lymph Node Cells	Recipients	MHC of Recipient						L/R ^{125}I-UdR Uptake
		K	I-A	I-B	I-C	S	D	
CBA	CBA	k	k	k	k	k	k	2.31 ± 0.17
CBA	B10.A	k	k	k	_d_	_d_	_d_	2.78 ± 0.18
BALB/c	BALB/c	d	d	d	d	d	d	3.53 ± 0.34
BALB/c	B10.A	_k_	_k_	_k_	d	d	d	1.15 ± 0.09
—	CBA							1.10 ± 0.05
—	BALB/c							1.15 ± 0.03
—	B10.A							1.14 ± 0.10

Five mice per group. Region of difference between donor and recipient mice is underlined.

TABLE IV

IDENTITY ONLY AT THE H-2D OR ONLY AT THE H-2K REGIONS OF THE MHC DOES NOT ALLOW SUCCESSFUL TRANSFER OF DTH TO FGG

Donors of FGG Sensitized Lymph Node Cells	Recipients	MHC of Recipient						L/R ^{125}I-UdR Uptake
		K	I-A	I-B	I-C	S	D	
C57BL	C57BL	b	b	b	b	b	b	2.67 ± 0.26
C57BL	CBA	k	k	k	k	k	k	1.09 ± 0.08
C57BL	B10.A(2R)	k	k	k	d	d	b	1.12 ± 0.03
CBA	B10.A(2R)	k	k	k	d	d	b	2.45 ± 0.31
A.SW	A.SW	s	s	s	s	s	s	1.63 ± 0.15
A.SW	A/J	k	k	k	d	d	d	1.01 ± 0.15
A.SW	A.TH	s	s	s	s	s	d	1.76 ± 0.16
A.SW	A.TL	s	k	k	k	k	d	1.15 ± 0.07

Five mice per group. Region of difference between donor and recipient is underlined.

TABLE V

IDENTITY AT THE I-A REGION OF THE MHC IS SUFFICIENT FOR ADOPTIVE TRANSFER OF DTH TO FGG

Donors of FGG Sensitized Lymph Node Cells	Recipients	MHC of Recipient						L/R ^{125}I-UdR Uptake
		K	I-A	I-B	I-C	S	D	
CBA	CBA	k	k	k	k	k	k	2.24 ± 0.21
CBA	A.TL	s	k	k	k	k	d	2.22 ± 0.10
CBA	A.TH	s	s	s	s	s	d	1.08 ± 0.03
CBA	B10.A(2R)	k	k	k	d	d	b	2.45 ± 0.31
CBA	B10.A(4R)	k	k	b	b	b	b	2.52 ± 0.35
B10.A(4R)	B10.A(4R)	k	k	b	b	b	b	2.04 ± 0.10
B10.A(4R)	A.TL	s	k	k	k	k	d	1.54 ± 0.07
B10.A(4R)	A.TH	s	s	s	s	s	d	0.95 ± 0.08
B10.A(4R)	CBA	k	k	k	k	k	k	1.69 + 0.11

Four to five mice/group. Region of difference between donors and recipient mice is underlined.

TABLE VI

IDENTITY AT THE I-REGION OF THE MHC IS SUFFICIENT FOR ADOPTIVE
TRANSFER OF DTH TO DNFB

Donors of DNFB-Sensitized Lymph Node Cells	Recipients	MHC of Recipients						L/R ^{125}I-UdR Uptake
		K	I-A	I-B	I-C	S	D	
CBA	CBA	k	k	k	k	k	k	2.06 ± 0.10
CBA	A.TL	s	k	k	k	k	d	2.72 ± 0.21
CBA	A.TH	s	s	s	s	s	d	1.07 ± 0.10
CBA	B10.A(2R)	k	k	k	d	d	b	2.86 ± 0.62

Five mice per group. Region of difference between donor and recipient mice is underlined.

411

are taken to indicate that effective interaction between
sensitized lymphocytes and cells presenting antigens
(presumably macrophages) are governed by cell surface structures coded by genes of the MHC. Thus, identity at the I-A
region may be necessary to allow optimal physical contact
between lymphocytes and macrophages as a prelude to lymphocyte triggering so that mediators can be released to induce
the mononuclear cell infiltrate and hence the DTH lesion. By
contrast, identity at the K or D region of the MHC is essential for lysis of target cells by cytotoxic lymphocytes (1,
2). These differences may indicate that precursors of killer
T cells and of T cells responsible for the transfer of DTH
may belong to two distinct functional subsets. In fact, it
has been shown that cytotoxic T lymphocytes are $Ly-2,3^+$ (7)
whereas T cells involved in adoptive transfer of DTH are
$Ly-1^+$ (Table VII).

   The immune response of mice to lactic dehydrogenase B
(LDH_B) is under H-2-linked genetic control (8). Thus, for
example, BALB/c mice, but not CBA mice, could be effectively
immunized to produce antibody or helper cells to LDH_B. The
DTH response to LDH_B in CBA and BALB/c mice sensitized to
20 µg of antigen in complete Freund's adjuvant is shown in
Fig. 2. A good response was obtained in BALB/c mice when
challenge was performed at 14 and 21 days after sensitization.
By contrast, very poor responses were seen in CBA mice when
tested at any time after sensitization. When the mice were
pretreated with 200 µg/kg cyclophosphamide 2 days before
sensitization, responses in BALB/c mice were marked as early
as 5 days. Of great interest was the finding that cyclophosphamide pretreated "nonresponder" CBA mice could respond
to LDH_B. The response, in contrast to that of BALB/c, was
short lasting, reaching a maximum at 7 days and disappearing
by 14 days. Responsiveness could be transferred to naive
mice by lymphoid cells. In the case of CBA mice, adoptive
transfer of DTH by 15×10^6 lymph node cells was not possible
If, however, the naive recipients were T cell depleted or
pretreated with cyclophosphamide 8 days before receiving
transferred cells, an adoptive response was obtained
(Table VIII). These results strongly suggest that, in this
system, the T cells of "nonresponder" mice can be involved
in DTH reactions, but that a cyclophosphamide-sensitive
suppressor mechanism normally operates and overrides the
capacity to respond. Further studies are in progress to
determine whether a similar suppressive mechanism exists in
the case of other antigens, the response to which is under
H-2-linked genetic control and to elucidate the nature of
the suppressive influences and of their targets.

TABLE VII

T CELLS RESPONSIBLE FOR THE TRANSFER
OF DTH ARE Ly-1 CELLS

Treatment of Sensitized Lymph Node Cells Prior to Transfer	L/R ^{125}I-UdR Uptake in Naive Syngeneic Recipients
Complement alone	2.11 ± 0.16
Anti-Ly 1.1 and Complement*	1.24 ± 0.03
Anti-Ly 2.1 and Complement	2.04 ± 0.35

Five mice per group.
*We thank Dr. I.F.C. McKenzie for a gift of the anti-Ly sera.
The same anti-Ly 1.1 serum effectively killed helper T cells
but not suppressor T cells in other experiments.

SUMMARY

Sensitized lymphocytes can transfer a state of delayed
type hypersensitivity (DTH) to soluble protein antigens in
naive mice only if donor and recipient share the I-A region
of the H-2 gene complex. It is suggested that this restriction reflects a requirement for an Ir gene controlled
mechanism which governs effective interaction between sensitized T lymphocytes and antigen presented on the surface of
macrophages. The DTH responsiveness of CBA and C57BL mice
to lactic dehydrogenase B (LDH$_B$) is under H-2-linked Ir gene
control, BALB/c mice responding well and CBA mice being
unable to respond. If, however, CBA mice were pretreated
with cyclophosphamide, they became capable of mounting an
effective but short-lasting DTH response to LDH$_B$. It is
concluded that a suppressor mechanism, sensitive to cyclophosphamide, operates to prevent T cell responsiveness in
the "non-responder" strains.

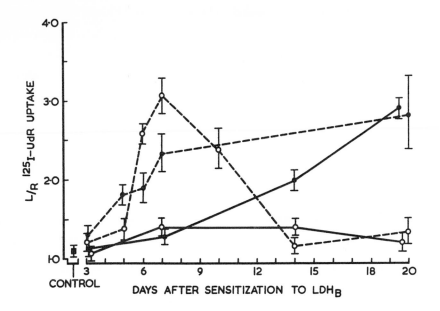

Figure 2. DTH response in BALB/c (●) and CBA (o) mice sensitized with 20 µg of LDH$_B$ in complete Freund's adjuvant. (——) indicates response in mice not pretreated with cyclophosphamide; (---) indicates response in mice given 200 µg/kg cyclophosphamide 2 days before sensitization. ▓ = control non-sensitized mice.

REFERENCES

(1) R.M. Zinkernagel and P.C. Doherty. J. Exp. Med. 141 (1975) 1427.

(2) G.M. Shearer, T.G. Rehn and C.A. Gabarino. J. Exp. Med. 141 (1975) 1348.

(3) D.H. Katz, M. Graves, M.E. Dorf, H. DiMuzio and B. Benacerraf. J. Exp. Med. 141 (1975) 263.

(4) P. Erb and M. Feldmann. J. Exp. Med. 142 (1975) 460.

(5) M.A. Vadas, J.F.A.P. Miller, J. Gamble and A. Whitelaw. Intern. Arch. Allergy Appl. Immunol. 49 (1975) 670.

TABLE VIII

ADOPTIVE DTH RESPONSE TO LDH_B IN "NON-RESPONDER"
CBA MICE

Donors Sensitized to LDH_B	Recipients	L/R ^{125}I-UdR Uptake
None	Naive CBA	1.13 ± 0.08 (8)
Cyclophosphamide-pretreated CBA	Naive CBA	1.10 ± 0.04 (6)
Cyclophosphamide-pretreated CBA	Cyclophosphamide-pretreated naive CBA	1.58 ± 0.09 (5)
Cyclophosphamide-pretreated CBA	Adult thymectomized, irradiated, marrow protected, naive CBA	1.33 ± 0.10 (5)

Number of mice per group is shown in brackets.

(6) J.F.A.P. Miller, M.A. Vadas, A. Whitelaw and J. Gamble. Intern. Arch. Allergy Appl. Immunol. 49 (1975) 693.

(7) H. Cantor and E.A. Boyse. J. Exp. Med. 141 (1975) 1390.

(8) I. Melchers, K. Rajewsky and D.C. Shreffler. Eur. J. Immunol. 3 (1973) 754.

DIFFERENTIAL EXPRESSION OF Ia ANTIGENS ON SUPPRESSOR T CELLS, HELPER T CELLS AND B PRECURSOR CELLS

G.J. HÄMMERLING, K. EICHMANN AND C. SORG

Institute for Genetics, University of Cologne
and
Universitäts-Hauptklinik, Münster

Abstract: The present communication describes
the detection of Ia antigens on unprimed
and primed antibody forming precursor cells.
Moreover, also suppressor T cells could be
eliminated by cytotoxic treatment with anti-
Ia serum, whereas, helper cells were negative
under identical conditions. No evidence was
obtained that stimulation of lymphocytes with
either PPD or ConA leads to active secretion
of products bearing Ia determinants.

The immune response region of the mouse H-2
complex appears to be of prime importance for
many immunological phenomena such as genetic control of the immune response, mixed lymphocyte reaction, T - B cell interaction etc. (reviewed in
1). Because many of these reactions are based on
cellular interactions of various types, probably
mediated by cell surface components, the recently
discovered Ia antigens which are coded by the
immune response region (1) are of particular interest. Therefore, the tissue distribution and cellular expression of Ia antigens has been extensively studied.

The results summarized in Table 1 show that
Ia antigens can be readily detected on mature B
lymphocytes utilizing various serological techniques (2, 3). Double fluorescence experiments

417

with rhodamine and fluoresceine conjugated antibodies indicated that not all but approximately 90%
of Ig positive splenic lymphocytes express Ia antigens whereas about 10% of Ig positive cells appear
to lack Ia determinants.

TABLE I
Tissue Distribution of Ia Antigens

Bone Marrow	5-20	Macrophages	10-50
Splenic B	90	Epidermal Cells	20-50
CRL	90	Erythrocytes	0
LPS Blast	90	Brain	0
Thymus	0	Kidney	0
Cort.Res.Thy	5-10	Liver	0
Splenic T	0-5	Muscle	0
T-TDL	0	Fibroblasts	0
Con A Blast	20-30	Spermatocytes	20-50
PHA Blast	5-15	Teratocarcinoma	20-60

Summary of cytotoxicity, fluorescence and absorption data. Values given in percent positive
cells. CRL = Lymphocytes with complement receptor.

Under identical conditions only small subpopulations of T lymphocytes, notably Concanavalin A
induced blast cells (4), show significant reaction
with anti-Ia serum. Among cell types of other than
lymphoid origin Ia determinants are detectable on
macrophages, epidermal cells, spermatocytes (5),
and primitive teratocarcinoma cells of the OTT6050
line (Hämmerling and Kapp, in preparation). The
anti-Ia sera used throughout these studies (A.TH
anti-A.TL = anti-Ia^k andA.TL anti-A.TH = anti-Ia^s)
are polyspecific and contain activity against several different Ia antigens specified by all three
major subregions I-A, I-B and I-C of the I-region.

Although negative serological reactions do not
necessarily imply complete absence of Ia antigens,
these data clearly demonstrate that T as well as B
cell populations are heterogeneous with respect to
the expression of Ia antigens. Therefore, we
attempted to investigate whether lymphocyte subpo-

pulations with defined functions such as primed and unprimed B precursor cells or helper and suppressor T cells would display differential expression of Ia antigens. For this purpose in vivo and in vitro hapten-carrier systems were employed. Some experiments are described in the following section.

Ia ANTIGENS ON FUNCTIONAL LYMPHOCYTE SUBPOPULATIONS

Graded numbers of T-cells enriched by nylon wool fractionation of spleen cells from A/J mice primed with Group A streptococcal vaccine (Strep.A) as a source of helper cells were mixed in in vitro microcultures with spleen cells from normal A/J mice as a source of primary PFC precursors. 4 days after challenge with TNP-Strep.A conjugate exclusively primary (IgM) TNP specific plaque forming cells were found.

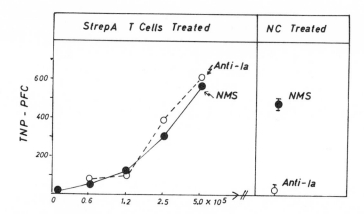

Figure 1. Left part: Graded numbers of nylon wool purified T cells from Strep.A primed A/J mice were treated with antisera plus C' and cultured with 1×10^6 normal A/J cells. Right part: Normal A/J spleen treated with NMS or A.TH anti-A.TL plus C' were cultured with 0.5×10^6 Strep.A primed T cells. The mixtures were challenged with Strep.TNP in microcultures and after 4 days the primary anti-TNP response was plaqued. Mean of 8 cultures.

As depicted in Fig. 1 treatment of helper cells with anti-Ia serum plus guinea pig complement did not influence the helper activity whereas anti-Thy-1.2 serum completely eliminated helper cells. On the other hand when the normal cell population was treated with anti-Ia serum plus complement all B cells which gave raise to primary PFC responses were eliminated.

Similar studies were performed utilizing in vivo adoptive secondary cell transfer experiments. Again carrier primed helper cells could not be removed by treatment with anti-Ia plus C'. In contrast, all hapten primed antibody forming precursor cells were sensitive to such treatment. In previous studies it was observed that PFC are also Ia positive (2). Thus, it appears that all immunocompetent cells of the B cell lineage, unprimed (virgin) B cells, primed (memory) B cells and PFC are Ia positive. It can be concluded from these data that the fraction of Ig^+ Ia^- splenic lymphocytes has not reached its full immunocompetence suggesting that for successful induction of both primary and secondary antibody formation in T cell dependent immune responses Ia determinants have to be present on B cell surfaces. This interpretation is in accordance with recent results of Munro and Taussig (6) who suggest on the surface of primary B cells the existence of Ia structures which act as acceptor sites for antigen specific T cell products.

A system in which suppressor cells can be identified is the following one: Anti-idiotypic antibody was raised in guinea pigs against anti-Strep.A antibody of the A5A clone produced by A/J mice. Upon injection of anti-idiotype of the IgG2 class A/J mice are rendered specifically tolerant in a way that after challenge with Strep.A no antibody of the A5A clone is observed whereas the response of other Strep.A reactive B-cell clones is normal (7). This tolerance can be actively transferred by spleen cells from tolerant mice into irradiated (200 r) recipients.

As shown in Fig. 2 treatment of spleen cells from suppressed mice before transfer with either

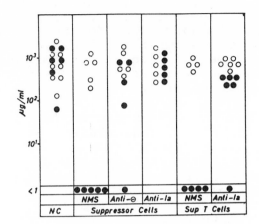

Figure 2. 1 x 10^6 cells from A/J mice
suppressed with anti-A5A-Id2 were transferred into 200 r A/J mice. 6 weeks later
they were challenged with Strep.A and then
the total anti-carbohydrate titer (O) and
the titer of the specific A5A idiotype (●)
were measured. Titer of individual mice
are shown. NC = normal cells.

anti-Thy-1.2 or anti-Ia serum plus C' eliminates
suppression of the A5A clone. Furthermore, treatment of nylon wool purified T cells from tolerant
mice with anti-Ia also abolishes suppression.
These data clearly indicate that in this system
tolerance is mediated by Ia positive suppressor T
cells. Equivalent observations have been made in
an independent system in which the IgG response of
Balb/c mice to pneumococcal polysaccharide type
SIII is suppressed by suppressor cells. Again suppressor cells could be eliminated by treatment with
either anti-Thy-1.2 or anti-Ia sera (S. Segal and
G.J. Hämmerling, in preparation).

Altogether these data clearly demonstrate that
suppressor T cells and helper T cells can be easily distinguished by the amount of Ia antigens they
express on their surfaces. Meanwhile other investigators came to identical conclusions (M. Feldmann,

L. Herzenberg, personal communication). In this context it is of interest to note that Taniguchi et al. (8) described a T cell suppressor factor bearing Ia determinants. This factor is not secreted by the suppressor cells whereas helper cells appear to secret upon stimulation with antigen specific helper cell replacing factors which carry Ia determinants (6).

ARE Ia ANTIGENS SECRETED BY ACTIVATED LYMPHOCYTES?

Up to here the expression of Ia antigens on cell surfaces was discussed. There are also reports that lymphocytes stimulated in allogeneic reactions secrete Ia positive factors with the ability to substitute for T cells in in vitro antibody forming responses (9). These observations prompted us to ask the question whether appropriately activated lymphocytes would in general produce soluble mediators with relationship to Ia antigens. This problem was approached with a very sensitive double labelling technique. Lymph node cells of tuberculin sensitive C3H mice ($H-2^k$) were labelled in culture with ^3H leucine and stimulated simultaneously with either PPD or Concanavalin A. Unstimulated control cultures were labelled with ^{14}C leucine. After incubation for 24 hours the cells were separated from the supernatants and the membranes solubilized by the nonionic detergent NP-40. After precipitation with normal mouse serum and rabbit anti-mouse Ig aliquots were incubated with A.TH anti-A.TL serum and A.TL anti-A.TH as a negative control and precipitated with rabbit anti-mouse Ig. Analysis of precipitates in 8% SDS-polyacrylamid gels demonstrated the presence of large amounts of Ia antigens (Mw 30,000 and 60,000 daltons) with very high specific radioactivity in all cell extracts. Mixing of supernatants from stimulated and unstimulated cultures before analysis by sephadex filtration or in SDS gels of various concentrations provides information which products are synthesized de novo or in increased amounts by stimulated cells. Within a molecular weight range of 10,000-200,000 daltons no molecules with Ia determinants were found in the supernatants of either stimulated or unstimulated cell cultures. The effectivity of the method employed was demonstrated by the easy detection of migration inhibition factor (Mw 40,000) in stimulated cell cultures under identical conditions thus making a relationship of Ia antigens with migration inhibition factor very unlikely. While it is not clear if this chemical approach is sensitive enough to detect products secreted in small amounts by a few clones only these results suggest that Ia antigens are not actively produced in large quantities by activated lymphocytes. These results are in agreement will those of Hübner et al. (10) who failed to absorb ConA induced T cell replacing factors (RTF) by anti-H-2 or anti-Ia sera.

ACKNOWLEDGEMENTS

We wish to express our thanks to Ms. M. Schöld for expert technical assistance and to Ms. Å. Böhm for preparing this manuscript.

This work was supported by Sonderforschungsbereich 74.

REFERENCES

(1) D.C. Shreffler and C.S. David. Adv. Immunol. 20 (1975) 125.

(2) G.J. Hämmerling, B.D. Deak, G. Mauve, U. Hämmerling and H.O. McDevitt. Immunogenetics 1 (1974) 68.

(3) D.H. Sachs and J.L. Cone. J. Exp. Med. 138 (1973) 1289.

(4) H. Wagner, G.J. Hämmerling and M. Röllinghoff. Immunogenetics 2 (1975) 257.

(5) G.J. Hämmerling, G. Mauve, E. Goldberg and H.O. McDevitt. Immunogenetics 1(1975) 488.

(6) A.J. Munro and M.J. Taussig. Nature 256 (1975) 103.

(7)   K. Eichmann. Eur. J. Immunol. 5 (1975) 511.

(8)   M. Taniguchi, K. Hayakawa and T. Tada. J. Exp.
      Med., in press.

(9)   D. Armerding, D.H. Sachs and D.H. Katz. J.
      Exp. Med. 140 (1974) 1717.

(10) L. Hübner, G. Müller, A. Schimpl. and
      E. Wecker. Z. Immun.-Forsch. 150 (1975) 210.

EFFECTIVE ALLOGENEIC T CELL-B CELL INTERACTION
IN CHIMERIC MICE

KATHLEEN B. BECHTOL AND JOAN L. PRESS

Division of Immunology
Department of Medicine
Stanford University School of Medicine

INTRODUCTION

In order to examine the cellular expression of antigen-specific immune (Ir) response genes, and the mechanism of interaction between T cells and B cells, a number of laboratories have used several rather diverse experimental systems to analyze the interactions of T cells and B cells derived from mice of different genotypes. The results obtained in these disparate experimental systems have generated conflicting interpretations of the requisites for cellular interactions and the mechanism of Ir gene expression. In this report, two different experimental systems were used to analyze the site of expression of the Ir-1A gene, which controls the immune response to the synthetic polypeptide (T,G)-A--L.

RESULTS

This laboratory has previously demonstrated that when tetraparental mice are constructed from an Ir-1A low-responder genotype embryo (C3H) and a homozygous Ir-1A high-responder genotype embryo (C57 or CWB), then immunized to (T,G)-A--L in complete Freund's adjuvant (CFA), and challenged with (T,G)-A--L in aqueous solution, the antibodies elicited are comprised of the immunoglobulin (Ig) allotypes of both of the input genotypes(1,2). In other words, anti-(T,G)-A--L antibody is produced by the B cells of both the high- and low-responder genotype. In these experiments, antigenic stimulation, T cell-B cell interaction, and subsequent antibody production occurred in a tetraparental milieu between strains which are histoincompatible. Katz and his co-workers have shown that under conditions where T cells are reacting against allogeneic target B cells, these B cells

425

can be stimulated to produce antibody (3). It is possible
that in the aforementioned tetraparental experiments, the
low-responder genotype B cells were subjected to a similar
type of "allogeneic effect", hence produced antibody to
(T,G)-A--L.

In order to rule out the possibility of an "allogeneic
effect" as the causal mechanism for stimulation and production of anti-(T,G)-A--L antibody by low-responder genotype
B cells in tetraparental mice, two other types of tetraparental mice were constructed, immunized, and analyzed for their
antibody response. In the first situation, tetraparental mice
were constructed from C3H, low-responder genotype embryos
($\underline{H-2}^k$, $\underline{Ir-1A}$ low/low, and $\underline{Ig}^{a/a}$) and congenic (CKB x CWB)F_1
high-responder genotype embryos ($\underline{H-2}^{k/b}$, $\underline{Ir-1A}$ low/high, and
$\underline{Ig}^{b/b}$). The high-responder embryo is heterozygous and shares
with the low-responder embryo the entire $\underline{H-2}$ complex, including $\underline{Ir-1A}$. Thus, the low-responder B cells should not
be targets for allogeneic stimulation. The low- and high-
responder B cells differ in immunoglobulin allotype ($\underline{a}$ and
$\underline{b}$, respectively), so that allotype composition of the total
serum and the specific anti-(T,G)-A--L antibody response can
be measured.

Four (C3H x CWB)F_1 ($\underline{Ig}^{a/b}$) mice were also analyzed. Here
the B cell expresses either the $\underline{Ig}^a$ or $\underline{Ig}^b$ allotype, due to
allelic exclusion. All cells are $\underline{H-2}^{k/b}$ and express the
$\underline{Ir-1A}^{low/high}$ genotype. The F_1 mice define the pattern of
allelic mixtures of Ig allotype which would result from stimulation of the immune system in the absence of possible
effects of the $\underline{H-2}$ complex on T cell-B cell interactions. As
shown in Figure 1, the C3H ↔ (CKB x CWB)F_1 tetraparental
mice produced high-titered anti-(T,G)-A--L antibody responses
which had the same distribution of $\underline{Ig}^a$ ($\underline{Ir-1A}$ low-responder)
and $\underline{Ig}^b$ ($\underline{Ir-1A}$ high-responder) allotype antibodies as did
the response of the control, (C3H x CWB)F_1, $\underline{Ig}^{a/b}$ heterozygous mice. Thus, under histocompatible conditions where
there should be no "allogeneic effect" against the low-responder genotype B cells, the $\underline{Ir-1A}$ high- and low-responder
genotype B cells of these tetraparental mice respond in equal
fashion to antigenic stimulation, to produce anti-(T,G)-A--L
antibodies.

In the second experimental situation, tetraparental mice
were constructed from the input embryos of two histoincompatible, low-responder genotype strains, C3H.Q ($\underline{H-2}^{q/q}$,
$\underline{Ir-1A}^{low/low}$, and $\underline{Ig}^{a/a}$) and CKB ($\underline{H-2}^{k/k}$, $\underline{Ir-1A}^{low/low}$, and

Ig$^{b/b}$). If a histoincompatibility reaction were occurring in tetraparental mice sufficient to stimulate low-responder genotype B cells, it might be expected that some of the chimeric C3H.Q↔CKB tetraparental mice would produce increased anti-(T,G)-A--L antibody responses. Of the eleven tetraparental mice constructed, four mice were shown to be chimeric in Ig^a and Ig^b allotype in their serum IgG1 and IgG2a. All eleven tetraparental mice were clearly low-responders in their antibody response to (T,G)-A--L. In the previous studies of low-responder↔high-responder tetraparental mice with homozygous H-2 differences (C3H↔C57 and C3H↔CWB), eight of the thirteen high-responding chimeras tested produced significant a allotype antibody responses to (T,G)-A--L. None of the four chimeric low-responder↔low-responder (C3H.Q↔CKB) tetraparental mice produced detectable anti-(T,G)-A--L antibody in either immunoglobulin allotype class. These results indicate that even when tetraparental mice are constructed such that a complete histocompatibility difference exists between the input genotypes, there is insufficient histoincompatibility reaction in these chimeric mice to cause an increase in the antibody response to (T,G)-A--L.

The finding that low-responder genotype B cells can be stimulated in the tetraparental milieu of high- and low-responder genotype B and T cells to produce IgG anti-(T,G)-A--L antibody is at variance with the findings of Katz and co-workers, that low-responder B cells cannot interact with (high-responder x low-responder genotype)F$_1$ T cells to produce an anti-DNP antibody response when challenged with DNP on a carrier antigen under Ir-gene control (4). Since the experimental system employed by Katz was markedly different from the experimental system using tetraparental mice, it was of interest to determine whether low-responder genotype B cells could be stimulated by F$_1$ T cells in an acute adoptive secondary response, when the antigen in question was (T,G)-A--L, and the H-2 haplotypes employed were the same (H-2^k and H-2^b) as those used in the tetraparental mice experiments.

BALB.B (H-2^b) and BALB.K (H-2^k) mice were immunized with 0.1 mg of DNP$_9$-BGG in CFA 2-4 months prior to use. (BALB.K x BALB.B)F$_1$ mice were immunized with 10 μg of (T,G)-A--L or 0.1 mg of hemocyanin (Hy) in CFA 2 months prior to use. The experimental protocol entailed transferring 25 x 10^6 (anti-Θ and complement treated) spleen cells from DNP-BGG primed BALB.B or BALB.K mice, along with 50 x 10^6 spleen cells from F$_1$ mice primed to either (T,G)-A--L or Hy, into 600 r

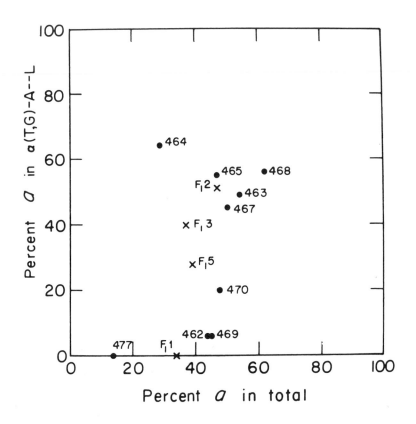

Figure 1. Allotype composition of specific anti-(T,G)-A--L antibody response related to total serum allotype mixture for C3H ↔ (CKB x CWB)F₁ tetraparental mice and (C3H x CWB)F₁ mice.

irradiated F₁ recipients. The recipient mice were then challenged either with 34 µg of DNP₅-(T,G)-A--L, or with 50 µg of DNP₉-Hy, in aqueous solution. Serum anti-DNP antibody was measured 7 days later by a modified Farr assay. The results are presented in Figure 2. When DNP-BGG primed spleen

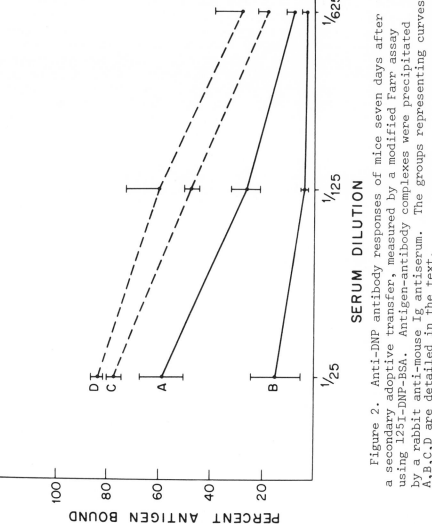

Figure 2. Anti-DNP antibody responses of mice seven days after a secondary adoptive transfer, measured by a modified Farr assay using 125I-DNP-BSA. Antigen-antibody complexes were precipitated by a rabbit anti-mouse Ig antiserum. The groups representing curves A,B,C,D are detailed in the text.

cells from either BALB.B (curve C) or BALB.K (curve D) were transferred with spleen cells from F_1 mice primed to Hy, and secondarily challenged with DNP-Hy, both parental B cells were capable of mounting a high-titered anti-DNP antibody response. When DNP-primed BALB.B spleen cells were transferred with (T,G)-A--L-primed F_1 spleen cells (curve A) and challenged with DNP-(T,G)-A--L, a good adoptive secondary response was also obtained. In contrast, however, BALB.K DNP-primed spleen cells gave only a weak anti-DNP antibody response when transferred with (T,G)-A--L-primed F_1 spleen cells (curve B). The results of this experiment confirm the original observation of Katz and co-workers (4) and indicate that under conditions of an acute, adoptive secondary response, low-responder genotype B cells cannot interact sufficiently with heterozygous (high-responder x low-responder genotype)F_1 T cells to generate an anti-hapten antibody response when the carrier antigen is under Ir gene control. Thus, when two different experimental systems are used, albeit with the same antigen and the same H-2 haplotypes, quite distinct and contradictory results are obtained.

In the experimental system using tetraparental mice, chimerism has been established during embryogenesis and is long-term. The interacting cells are therefore presumably mutually tolerant and have been immunized and boosted in situ. In contrast, the test system of Katz and co-workers (4), as well as the one described in this report, employs an acute adoptive secondary transfer into irradiated recipients, where the B cells and T cells are primed in separate environments and asked to interact in a secondary host. This type of test system could conceivably be influenced by the presence of residual, alloreactive T cells not eliminated by anti-θ and complement.

Several recent findings support the results of the tetraparental experiments and indicate that effective B cell-T cell interaction can occur across homozygous major histocompatibility differences. The results of Heber-Katz and Wilson(5) demonstrating cooperation between allogeneic T cells and B cells when alloreactive T cells have been removed from the population suggest that allogeneic cells can interact to generate a T-dependent primary IgM antibody response. Pierce and Klinman (6) have also demonstrated that primary precursor cells can be stimulated by allogeneic T cells, but that the antibody response obtained is primarily IgM. Stimulation to IgG antibody production occurs only when there is homology in the I region of H-2.

Additional confirmation of the tetraparental results comes from the studies of von Boehmer et al., (7) who constructed long-term stable chimeras by transferring T cell-depleted bone marrow from two H-2 different parental mouse strains into a lethally irradiated F1 host. These stable chimeras were immunized 3-4 months after reconstitution, then the B cells and T cells of each H-2 type were separated, recombined in allogeneic combinations, and secondarily challenged with antigen. Under these conditions, a secondary IgG antibody response to SRBC could be obtained from the interaction of chimeric but allogeneic B and T cells.

Several mechanisms can be postulated to explain the results obtained in the tetraparental-chimera systems: (1) Low-responder genotype B cells are fully competent, and high-responder genotype T cells are capable of interacting with them. However, under certain experimental conditions, e.g., acute cell transfers into irradiated recipients, this interaction is blocked or suppressed. (2) Low-responder genotype B cells are competent, and in stable chimeric situations, low-responder genotype T cells become competent to interact in high-responder fashion with the low-responder B cells. (3) Low-responder B cells are competent, and high-responder genotype T cells acquire the ability to interact with low-responder genotype B cells in the tetraparental milieu. (4) In stable chimeras, the low-responder genotype B cell is altered to become competent to stimulation. In all except the fourth possibility, the site of Ir gene action in this system would be in a cell type other than the B cell, presumably in the T cell. The second, third, and fourth mechanisms would necessitate some form of information exchange, perhaps by exchange of genetic information or cell surface molecules. Alternatively, the ability of tetraparental B and T cells to interact effectively could reflect a specificity of antigen recognition determined at the time of primary immunization by the specific combination of antigen and cell surface molecules in a manner analogous to the specificity of cytotoxic T cells induced by virus-infected allogeneic cells (8). Experiments are in progress to resolve these issues.

ACKNOWLEDGMENTS

We would like to thank Ms. Mary Vadeboncoeur and Ms. Karla Spangenberg for their technical assistance.

This work was supported by NIH Grants AI 07757 and AI 11313. Dr. Bechtol was a Junior Dernham (J-197) postdoctoral fellow of the American Cancer Society, California Division, and Dr. Press is an Arthritis Foundation postdoctoral fellow.

REFERENCES

(1) K.B. Bechtol, T.G. Wegmann, J.H. Freed, F.C. Grumet, B.W. Chesebro, L.A. Herzenberg, and H.O. McDevitt. Cellular Immunology 13 (1974) 264.

(2) K.B. Bechtol, J.H. Freed, L.A. Herzenberg, and H.O. McDevitt. J. Exp. Med. 140 (1974) 1660.

(3) D.H. Katz. Transplantation Reviews 12 (1972) 141.

(4) D.H. Katz, T. Hamaoka, and B. Benacerraf. J. Exp. Med. 137 (1973) 1405.

(5) E. Heber-Katz and D.B. Wilson. J. Exp. Med. 142 (1975) 928.

(6) S. Pierce and N.Klinman. J. Exp. Med., in press.

(7) H. von Boehmer, L. Hudson, and J. Sprent. J. Exp. Med. 142 (1975) 989.

(8) R.M. Zinkernagel and P.C. Doherty. J. Exp. Med. 141 (1975) 1427.

GENERAL DISCUSSION - SESSION IV

GENETIC CONTROL OF CELL INTERACTIONS

William Paul, Chairman

PAUL: The observation that optimal activation of primed
         guinea pig T lymphocytes by antigen-pulsed macrophages
         and that optimal collaboration between primed mouse T
         and B lymphocytes requires that the interacting cell
         types share certain histocompatibility antigens is one
         of the most provocative findings to be made in the
         fields of cellular interaction and immunogenetics. In
         opening the discussion on this topic, I can suggest
         four types of explanations which require consideration.

1. "Allogeneic Suppression"
Cell types not identical in all or part of their MHC's
fail to collaborate because their differences stimulate
mixed lymphocyte responses and some type of allogeneic
effect which suppresses physiologic collaboration. The
most powerful arguments against this as a general mechanism to explain all forms of genetic restriction in
macrophage-T lymphocyte and in T-lymphocyte-B lymphocyte collaboration derive from the finding that primed
parental guinea pig T lymphocytes can be specifically
stimulated by antigen-pulsed F_1 macrophages but not by
antigen-pulsed macrophages derived from the alternative
parent and that primed parental T lymphocytes can efficiently collaborate with primed F_1 B lymphocytes but
not with primed B lymphocytes derived from the alternative parent. In this instance, opportunity for inhibition of physiologic collaboration because of recognition of histocompatibility differences exist equally
between parent and F_1 and between allogeneic cells.
However, only when one haplotype is shared does efficient interaction occur. This does not exclude the possibility that allogeneic suppression may explain certain instances in which collaboration is not observed.

2. "Self Recognition"
Interacting cell types have properties of self recognition. Activation depends on a dual recognition system,
one recognition structure being specific for self and
the other for antigen. Experiments indicating that
distinct sets of F_1 T cells preferentially collaborate
with cells derived from each parent can best be

433

explained by proposing that interacting cells display allelic exclusion for cellular interaction structures. To explain results obtained from studies of T cell mediated cytotoxicity, both allelic and genic exclusion must be postulated. Alternatively, a phenotypic restriction occurring after activation, fixing a relation between the two types of recognition structures could be invoked.

3. "Selective or Adaptive Mutual Recognition"

Interacting cell types use a dual recognition system, one which recognizes antigen and the other recognizing a cellular interaction structure. However, it is not necessary that the cells participating in the collaboration be syngeneic, only that the cell combination used in the primary and the secondary stimulation be the same. This requires that an individual possesses cellular recognition structures specific for each of the interaction structures of all other members of the species. Individual cells might be specialized for recognizing individual interaction structures prior to first experience with collaborating cells; the appropriate specialized cell might be selected and then expand as a result of such recognition. Alternatively, a cell might be initially pluripotential in its collaborative ability and, after priming, become phenotypically restricted to interact only with the cell types with which they initially interacted.

4. "New Antigenic Determinant or Selective Presentation"

This thesis holds that there is no cellular interaction structure *per se* but that the antigen presenting cell (macrophage or B lymphocyte) bears a structure (H antigen or Ir gene product) which interacts with antigen, perhaps with a degree of specificity. This interaction might then lead to the generation of a new determinant which could be either an altered histocompatibility antigen (altered self), a new antigenic determinant created by apposition of histocompatibility antigen (or gene product) with conventional antigen or a modification of conventional antigen induced by the histocompatibility structure.

In an effort to determine the nature of the mechanism(s) underlying the genetic control of specific cellular interactions, I think that we should carefully examine all of our experimental data in the light of these suggestions. Moreover, we should consider the design of experiments which could aid in the choice between these various proposals to explain the observed phenomena. Finally, we should bear in mind the possibility that these observations are reflective of mechanisms involved in a wide variety of interactive phenomena among cells which do not directly participate in immune responses.

GERSHON: Bill, which experiments that have been presented today do you take to rule out the possibility that some form of suppression could account for all the cooperative failures and peculiarities of histoincompatible cells we have heard about today?

PAUL: I think it highly unlikely that all genetic control of specific intereactions can be mediated by suppressor mechanisms based on allogeneic interactions. One of the most important reasons for thinking this are the experiments of David Katz which indicate that the ability of F_1 T lymphocytes to collaborate with parental macrophages and/or lymphocytes also displays apparent regulation, and that independent populations of primed F_1 cells collaborate with B cells from each parent.

GERSHON: In order to demonstrate parental T cooperation with F_1 B cells some maneuver (i.e. irradiation) is required to rule out allogeneic effects. Couldn't that also knock out suppression?

KATZ: The question Dick Gershon has raised concerns the possibility that in the mixture experiments in which parental carrier-primed T cells were shown to provide helper function for F_1 B cells in responses to conventional DNP-proteins, how can one conclusively exclude the possibility of a complicating allogeneic effect? My answer to this is that there is no absolute evidence that some allogeneic effects are not contributing to the response. However, this is an irrelevant point in view of the fact that the appropriate controls for the involvement of allogeneic effects -- namely, using normal, unprimed parental T cells admixed with F_1 DNP-specific B cells -- were always included and were uniformly negative in many such experiments. Thus, irrespective of the potential contribution of allogeneic effects, it can be clearly stated that 1) such effects

435

were negligible, and 2) the demonstrable response was surely a reflection of physiologic, carrier-specific T cell-B cell interactions.

GERSHON: My point, David, is not that you have not eliminated the allogeneic effect; rather that the technique you used to do so may have also affected a possible suppressor mechanism.

KATZ: I assume you mean that the technique we use, namely to subject the carrier-primed cells (and the normal cell controls for the carrier-specific population) to x-irradiation *in situ* 24 hrs after transfer to an F_1 recipient, may have eliminated detectable manifestations of an enhancing allogeneic effect but, nevertheless, either left or induced a suppressor mechanism. This is certainly possible -- one could even argue that eliminating the enhancing allogeneic effect has, in fact, unmasked a suppressor mechanism that would have otherwise been subliminal in the system. If this is the case, however, it would represent a unique example of a suppressor system that is less radiosensitive than a helper system; usually, to my knowledge, just the reverse is true.

But for the sake of putting this in proper perspective, let us assume that what you are suggesting is, indeed, happening. This would leave us in a remarkable paradox in terms of what the data tell us. This paradox stems from the observations that 1) concomitant transfer of BALB/c and A/J carrier-primed cells does not interfere with the cooperative interactions of either one of these populations with its respective histocompatible B cell partner (Katz et al. *J. Immunol.* 112: 855, 1974), a situation certainly conducive to expression of a suppressor mechanism exerted by the histo-incompatible cell population, if this occurs; and 2) parental carrier-primed T cells provide excellent helper activity for B cells of F_1 hybrid donors. Now, as Bill Paul stated a few minutes ago, it is very difficult to conceive of why, if a suppressor mechanism was operating in this system, it is manifested in such a highly selective manner -- namely, that it operates in mixtures between totally histo-incompatible T and B cells but not in mixtures of semi-histoincompatible cells. Certainly, the foreign alloantigens on A/J B cells recognized by BALB/c T cells, and which would presumably constitute the inciting force to a suppressor event, are also present on $(BALB/c \times A/J)F_1$ B cells; consequently, the latter cells should be similarly suppressed if this were a contributing feature to explain our observations on failure of effective interactions between primed histoincompatible T and B cells. In view of the fact that this does not occur -- in other words, good cooperation occurs between parent and F_1 -- I consider it highly likely that our original interpretation of these findings is still the correct one, and that the failure of primed histoincompatible T and B cells to interact is a reflection of dissimilarity in H-linked CI molecules required for the mediation of such interactions.

TAUSSIG: I would like to ask David Katz to comment on an apparent paradox, namely that cell interactions mediated by soluble factors do not show the histocompatibility restrictions you have found with viable T and B cells, even though the factors are I-region products. This seems to suggest that the effects you observe may be peripheral to the delivery of a signal to the B cell -- perhaps due rather to some special requirements of cell - cell contact, suppressive interaction, etc.

KATZ: On the contrary, Michael, I believe that the lack of genetic restrictions observed with some, but not all, of the soluble factors (remember, Tomio Tada's suppressive factor shows absolute genetic restrictions) suggests that certain of the effects of the T cell factors may, in fact, be peripheral to the way Nature has designed these systems. I am glad that you brought the matter up because I want to emphasize my personal conviction that cell interactions that occur physiologically in the intact individual are mediated by membrane-membrane contact between the involved cells. This is not to say that all of our soluble factors are mere artifacts, but rather that what we observe with such molecules is only a portion of reality. This is my feeling about our own AEF as well as factors studied by you, Tomio, Edna and so on. The point is that the manner in which a molecule may act when situated within and/or on the plasma membrane, influenced as it may be by its own orientation and by structures contiguous to it, could be strikingly different from the way the same molecule may function once removed from the cell membrane -- A good example of this is the fact that certain bacterial cell wall polysaccharides exhibit potent mitogenic properties when isolated and purified, whereas these molecules have no such properties when they are still an integral part of the bacterial cell membrane.

So, I would urge some caution in attempting to draw absolute parallels from what we observe with our biologically active factors -- which are, indeed, beautiful molecular handles to study -- and the actual physiologic interactions themselves, because, in my view, when the book is closed on this area we will have found that membrane-membrane contact is occurring between such interacting cells.

BENACERRAF: I would like to correct Dr. Taussig's statement that I region-specific factors have no genetic restrictions because they do indeed. From Dr. Taussig's own work with the helper factor, and from Dr. Tada and our own experiments there is clear evidence that factors are genetically restricted in their effectiveness as predicted by the genetic Ir or Is gene defects of the recipient animals.

McDEVITT: I agree with Baruj. AEF, suppressor factors, and the Taussig factor all show some degree of strain specificity. In fact, if a mix of supernatant factors from lymphocytes shows non-specificity, that might be due to lymphokines plus antigen, while genetic restrictions on cell interactions are much more likely to exhibit meaningful cell surface antigenic specificity and genetic restrictions.

TAUSSIG: I agree my generalization was too sweeping. However, the paradox remains.

KATZ: I don't wish to belabor the point further, but I think it should be brought out that your factor is seemingly less restricted genetically than one would expect on the basis of our CI gene hypothesis, but you are looking at its effects on primary IgM responses; perhaps if you could get it to work on secondary IgG responses you would find a considerably greater degree of genetic restriction than you do at present. We are presently analyzing AEF in this regard and should know shortly what the relative genetic restrictions may be of its biological effects on primary versus secondary responses.

PAUL: Michael, one could just as validly suggest as David,
in fact, was doing a moment ago, that it is in the interaction of intact cells, that physiologically important constraints are likely to operate.

WILSON: David, in your experiments (employing Strain A
primed T cells transferred into $(AxB)F_1$ animals which
are then inactivated, then given also Strain B primed
B cells) there are two sources of T cells which could
generate allo-aggressive effects. These allo-aggressive effects could diminish collaboration as a secondary event. The T cell sources are: radioresistant T
cells from the Strain A donor and low theta-bearing T
cells from the B donor. A sensitive assay for allo-
aggressive T effects is the inactivated F_1 animal
model. If these reconstituted animals are left to
their own resources, what is their fate, do they die?

KATZ: No, they do not die -- in fact in certain instances
where we, for one or another reason (usually oversight),
have not disposed of animals in a given experiment
shortly after its completion, we have found all of the
F_1 recipient mice alive and perfectly healthy many
months later. This is, indeed, a strong point in favor
of our own position -- now that you mention it -- that
I had not thought about in this context previously.
This is not surprising, however, in view of: 1) the
fact that T cells in the carrier-primed parental population are transferred in limited numbers and then irradiated, thereby abrogating any further proliferative
capabilities; and 2) the fact that, although low density theta-positive cells in parental B cell population
might escape complement-mediated cytolysis *in vitro*,
most residual theta-positive T cells in this population
should be opsonized and cleared by the reticuloendo-
thelial system of the irradiated recipient host within
minutes after intravenous transfer.

SACHS: I wonder if Dr. Pierce would care to comment on the
differences between his results and those of Dr.
Feldmann regarding the histocompatibility requirements
of macrophage-lymphocyte interactions.

PIERCE: Erb and Feldmann have reported that helper T cells
develop *in vitro* only in the presence of syngeneic

macrophages or macrophages from mice sharing specificities of the *I* region of the *H-2* complex with the T
cells. However, in the assay to evaluate helper T cell
activity, only macrophages syngeneic with the T cells,
and not macrophages syngeneic with those used to generate the helper T cells, have been used. Our results
demonstrate that primed lymphoid cells, and more specifically primed T cells, preferentially develop secondary antibody responses in the presence of antigen on
macrophages syngeneic with those used for priming.
Based on these results, we would predict in the Erb and
Feldmann system, that helper T cells generated *in vitro*
would function preferentially in test cultures with
macrophages syngeneic to those used to generate the
helper T cells. In fact, probably no differences exist;
we are only projecting a prediction onto the data of
Erb and Feldmann.

GERSHON: My understanding of the Feldmann system is that
syngeneic macrophages are needed for T-T immunization
and that syngeneic macrophages (or indeed any macrophages) are not needed for T-B interactions in the secondary response. Therefore, it may not be that the
helper cells have to see antigen altered by *I* region
antigens in the secondary response. On the other hand
my recollection may be faulty.

NOSSAL: In the Feldmann system, no *extra* macrophages are
added in the *second* stage of the culture. The splenic
cells acting as the B cell source have enough macrophages for antibody-formation to take place. However,
a curious thing is that the initial activation *in vitro*
of T lymphocytes to become helper cells requires an extraordinarily large number of macrophages -- more than
are present in a normal spleen (Erb and Feldmann, *Cellular Immunol.* in press, 1975).

GREEN: What do the phenomena discussed by Drs. Rosenthal
and Katz, in regard to recognition of soluble protein
antigens and synthetic antigens, have to do with the
recognition of antigens on the surface of stimulator
cells in the MLR?

BACH: Except for one small part of your question, I am
afraid that no critical answers are available. Adherent
cells are required to allow an MLC reaction to take
place. Beyond that, Barbara Alter and I, as well as

many others, have shown that allogeneic macrophages will also permit a proliferative response to take place. However, it is difficult to analyze this critically. It is possible that the allogeneic macrophages actually stimulate lymphocytes; that the lymphocytes consequently produce a factor and the reaction is allowed to proceed in that manner. This is just very difficult.

SESSION V

Idiotypic Determinants on T Cell Receptors

DAVID H. KATZ, CHAIRMAN

T LYMPHOCYTE RECEPTOR ANALYSIS
BY ANTI – IDIOTYPIC STIMULATION

K. RAJEWSKY, G.J. HÄMMERLING, S.J. BLACK
C. BEREK AND K. EICHMANN

Institute for Genetics
University of Cologne

Abstract: Idiotype-bearing murine B and T lymphocytes can be efficiently sensitized by the
IgG_1 fraction of anti-idiotypic antibody
(a̱-Id1) raised in guinea pigs. A dose-response and kinetic analysis of the sensitization process shows that ng doses of a̱-Id1
are required for sensitization in both the
T and B cell compartment and that sensitization is detectable as early as five days after injection of the antibody.

Genetic evidence supports the notion
that the idiotypic determinants on T helper
cell receptors and on immunoglobulin molecules are controlled by the same genes in
the heavy chain linkage group.

INTRODUCTION

The variable portions of antibody molecules
are distinguished from each other serologically by
their idiotypic specificity which is defined by
anti-idiotypic antibodies (a̱-Id). Idiotype-anti-
idiotype reactions are exquisitely specific: A
given a̱-Id will react with the particular antibody
species (the idiotype) against which it has been
raised but not with most other antibodies. In addition, in many instances idiotypes have been found
to be strain-specific and to represent genetic
markers for genes in the heavy chain linkage group

coding for variable portions of immunoglobulin heavy chains (V genes) (reviewed in reference 1).

It is clear, therefore, that anti-idiotypic antibodies should be useful if one wants to investigate whether humoral antibodies and receptors for antigen on the lymphocyte surface carry the same variable portions – a problem which is still very much debated in the case of T lymphocytes.

We have used in our studies idiotypic markers of immunoglobulin molecules which specifically bind Group A streptococcal carbohydrate (A-CHO). The first is the A5A marker, carried by a single antibody species which is a major component of the antibody population elicited in A/J mice by immunization with Group A streptococcal vaccine (Strep.A) (1). The second idiotypic marker, called S117 is carried by antibodies to A-CHO of Balb/c mice immunized with Strep.A (Berek et al., in preparation). It is defined by anti-idiotypic antibody against the S117 myeloma protein, which is secreted by the Balb/c plasmacytoma S117 and which specifically binds N-acetyl-glucosamine, the major antigenic determinant of A-CHO. The expression of both the A5A and the S117 marker is under the control of genes in the Ig-1 complex and follows strain specific patterns which are different for the two idiotypes (1).

Our idiotypic receptor analysis has its basis in the finding that under suitable conditions anti-idiotypic antibody can sensitize idiotype-bearing T and B lymphocytes (2-5). Similar observations have been made by Trenkner and Riblet (6, and personal communication). In the present article we explore the dosage requirements for efficient sensitization of T and B lymphocytes by anti-idiotypic antibody and the tempo of sensitization in the two cellular compartments. In addition, we review experimental evidence in favour of the view that the same genes in the heavy chain linkage group code for variable regions of T and B cell receptors for antigen.

SENSITIZATION BY ANTI-IDIOTYPIC ANTIBODY

Anti-idiotypic antibodies to the A5A and the S117 protein were raised in guinea pigs and separated into the IgG_1 ($\bar{a}$-Id1) and IgG_2 ($\bar{a}$-Id2) fractions. In order to establish whether $\bar{a}$-Id is able to sensitize idiotype-bearing lymphocytes, the following experimental protocol was adopted: Mice received a single intravenous or intraperitoneal injection of $\bar{a}$-Id. 6 weeks later spleen cells from these animals were transferred into sublethally irradiated syngeneic hosts, together with spleen cells from animals primed with a hapten(4-hydroxy-5-iodo-3-nitro-phenacetyl; NIP) conjugated to chicken gamma globulin (CG). The hosts were then injected with a NIP-Strep.A conjugate, bled 9-12 days later and the sera were titrated for antibodies to A-CHO and NIP, and for idiotype. This system permits us to detect sensitization of idiotypic B cells and of Strep.A specific T helper cells by $\bar{a}$-Id. If B cell sensitization occurs, we expect a secondary response to A-CHO upon stimulation with the NIP-Strep.A complex, and the anti-carbohydrate antibody should consist exclusively of idiotype-bearing molecules. Sensitization in the T helper cell compartment can be detected in our system, since the anti-NIP response relies on the presence of T helper cells with specificity for Strep.A. The details of the experimental procedure have been published (2).

In unpublished experiments it was found that over a wide dose range $\bar{a}$-Id2 was unable to sensitize B or T helper cells in our system, which is not surprising in view of the suppressive activity of this class of $\bar{a}$-Id (7). In contrast, a dose of 100 ng idiotype binding capacity (IBC) of $\bar{a}$-Id1 induced efficient immunity to Strep.A in both B and T helper cells. At least in the B cell compartment sensitization was restricted to idiotype-positive cell, since in the adoptive secondary response all antibodies to group A carbohydrate carried the idiotype (2). In Fig. 1 we present a detailed dose-response analysis of B and T helper cell priming by $\bar{a}$-Id1. It can be seen that priming appears to follow the same dose-response pattern in the B and T cell system. Detectable pri-

447

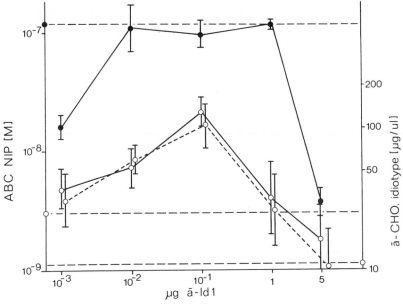

Figure 1. T and B cell sensitization
by anti-idiotypic antibody: dose response
analysis. A/J mice were primed with various
doses of ā-Id1 with specificity for the A5A
idiotype (abscissa; doses refer to the IBC
of ā-Id1). 6 wk later spleen cells (25×10^6
cells/host) from these animals were transferred into irradiated syngeneic hosts together with spleen cells (22×10^6 cells/host)
sensitized to NIP-CG. Hosts were injected
with 1×10^9 NIP-Strep.A particles and bled
10 days later. Sera were titrated for antibodies to NIP (left ordinate; molar NIP
binding capacity) and A-CHO (right ordinate),
and for the A5A idiotype (r.o.). Filled
circles: anti-NIP response; open circles,
solid line: response to A-CHO; open circles,
broken line: A5A idiotypic response. Also
shown are (i) the level of a presumably maximal anti-NIP response in the system (secondary stimulation with 0.2 ug NIP-CG; broken horizontal line on top) and (ii) the
response to NIP and A-CHO in the absence of
cells primed with ā-Id1 (the two lower broken horizontal lines). Further experimental
details in ref. 2.

ming occurs upon injection of as little as 1 ng
IBC of a̅-Id1, optimal sensitization requires $10-10^3$
ng and 5 ug IBC of the antibody preparation
appear to paralyze the system. Note that as expected, the titers of antibody to A-CHO and of idiotype are indistinguishable in all instances. This
is in sharp contrast to the situation observed
upon priming with Strep.A, where only approximately
25% of the resulting antibody carry the idiotype
(2). It should also be noted that the pattern in
Fig. 1 is probably misleading in that the response
to A-CHO depends largely on the presence of specific helper cells as is the case for the anti-NIP
response. Thus, the high dose of a̅-Id1 may well
selectively paralyse T helper cells, and from previous experiments we have indeed reason to believe
that at this dose B cell sensitization still takes
place (7).

Sensitization by a̅-Id1 is a rapid process.
The data represented in Fig. 2 show that sensitization by an optimal dose of a̅-Id1 (100 ng IBC) is
detectable as early as 5 days after injection of
the antibody. At this point in time the effect is
clearly seen at the helper cell level, whereas the
B cell response is still very weak. We can not decide whether this reflects a more rapid response
of T helper cells to anti-idiotypic stimulation or
merely a difference in sensitivity of our detection methods.

In summary, the data described in this section show that efficient and rapid specific sensitization of B lymphocytes and T helper cells can
be achieved by minute doses of a̅-Id1. The kinetics
of sensitization resemble those described for a
variety of conventional antigens. Unfortunately,
we have been unable so far to find conditions for
a selective priming of T helper cells by anti-
idiotypic antibody.

HELPER CELLS INDUCED BY ANTI-IDIOTYPIC ANTIBODY
BEAR IDIOTYPIC RECEPTOR MOLECULES

Our in vivo experiments have shown that a̅-Id1
sensitizes idiotypic B cells and T helper cells
which exhibit specificity for the same antigen as

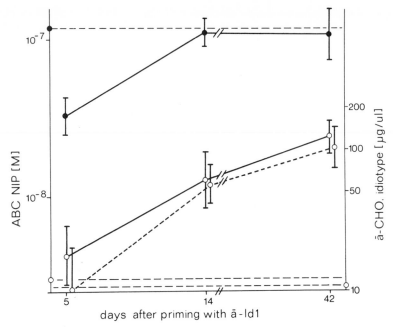

Figure 2. T and B cell sensitization
by anti-idiotypic antibody: kinetic analysis. A/J mice were primed with 100 ng IBC
of ā-Id1 with specificity for the A5A idiotype. Five, 14 and 42 days after priming
spleen cells from such animals were analysed for responsiveness to Strep.A in the
adoptive transfer system as described in
the text and in the legend to Fig. 1. Symbols as in Fig. 1.

the idiotype. This suggests that T helper cells as
well as B cells express idiotype-bearing receptor
molecules.

We have attempted to establish this important
point in a more direct way. For this purpose an
in vitro system was developed in which an anti-
hapten (trinitrophenyl; TNP) plaque-forming
response was induced in spleen cell populations by
addition of a TNP-Strep.A conjugate (TNP-Strep.A).
The TNP response in this system was dependent on
the presence of helper T cells with specificity
for Strep.A (3, 4).

In contrast to the in vivo experiments, the
in vitro system permits a detailed analysis of T
helper cell receptor specificity. It was found
(3, 4) that the function of helper cells from animals primed with ā-Id1 could be specifically and
efficiently inhibited by including small doses of
either A-CHO or ā-Id into the cell culture system.
As far as we can see, this demonstrates convincing-
ly that the T helper cells induced by ā-Id1 carry
functional receptor molecules with similar or identical antigen-binding and idiotypic specificity as
the idiotypic immunoglobulin. It may be noted in
passing that these results also prove the existence
of helper cells with specificity for a carbohydrate
antigen.

Our results point to a striking structural
similarity of T and B cell receptors for antigen.
Other workers have independently reached the same
conclusion by showing that T cell receptors for
histocompatibility antigens and alloantibodies specific for the same structure share idiotypic determinants (8-10). The question of whether the variable portions of T and B cell receptors are
identical at the molecular level can only be answered definitively by chemical analysis. However, since idiotypes are markers for V genes in
the heavy chain linkage group, we can also approach
this question by genetic means and ask whether
idiotypic determinants on immunoglobulins and T
cell receptors are controlled by the same gene(s).

As mentioned above, both the A5A and the S117
idiotype are strain-specific markers, the strain
distribution of which is different for the two
idiotypes. We have determined responsiveness of T
helper cells to anti-idiotypic stimulation in a
large panel of mouse strains which either express
or do not express the corresponding idiotype at
the immunoglobulin level and in addition carry a
variety of different H-2 haplotypes. The H-2
complex deserves particular attention in the context of these experiments, since immune response
(Ir) genes in the I region of H-2 specifically
control T cell responsiveness to a variety of antigens, and indeed T cells appear to produce antigen-
binding factors carrying I region controlled Ia

antigens (11, 12).

A summary of the results of our genetic analysis which employed anti-idiotypic antibodies to
both the A5A and the S117 marker appears in Table
1. Inspection of the Table reveals a perfect and
striking correlation between helper cell responsiveness to a-Id1 and the presence of the corresponding idiotype in the immunoglobulins. In idiotype-positive strains T helper cells always
respond to anti-idiotypic stimulation, in idiotype-negative strains they never do so.

In contrast, helper cell responsiveness is
not restricted to any particular H-2 haplotype.
Note that in some cases responder and non-responder strains carry the same H-2 haplotype in their
genome (Table 1: A/J and B10.A, DBA/2 and B10.D2,
A.SW and B10.S(7R). In the latter combination the
two strains possess identical K, I and S regions
in H-2).

Of crucial importance is the finding that in
all cases helper cell function could be specifically inhibited by the same and only the same anti-
idiotype which had been used for sensitization.
This indicates that as a rule helper cells induced
by anti-idiotypic stimulation express idiotypic
determinants on their functional receptors.

We conclude from our data that anti-idiotypic
antibody will induce idiotypic T helper cells only
and invariably when the animals express in the Ig-1
complex a V gene coding for the corresponding immunoglobulin idiotype. This strongly suggests that
the same genes in the Ig-1 complex code for variable portions of both antibody molecules and antigen-binding receptors on the T cell surface.

We are aware, however, that our genetic data
do not so far formally prove the point. As an alternative interpretation, one might imagine that
the presence of immunoglobulin idiotype in the environment (e.g. on idiotypic B cells) is a prerequisite for the anti-idiotypic stimulation of T
helper cells. If this were the case, idiotypic T
helper cells would appear in our system under the

TABLE 1

Strain Distribution of Helper Cell Responsiveness to Anti-Idiotype

Strain	H-2	Ig-1 Ig-1	Complex A5A	S117	Helper Cell Stimulation with[2] $\bar{a}$-A5A	$\bar{a}$-S117
DBA/2	d	c	cr[1]	cr	+	+
RF	k	c	cr	cr	+	+
A/J	a	e	+	−	+	−
A.SW	s	e	+	−	+	−
Balb/c	d	a	−	+	−	+
129	b	a	−	+	−	+
BAB14	d	b	−	+	−	+
C57Bl/10Sn	b	b	−	−	−	−
B10.A	a	b	−	−	−	−
B10.S(7R)	th	b	−	−	−	−
B10.D2	d	b	−	−	−	−
B10.BR	k	b	−	−	−	−
AKR	k	d	−	−	−	−

1) Strain expresses idiotypes which are cross reactive but clearly distinct from A5A and S117.

2) Mice were primed with 100 ng IBC of $\bar{a}$-Id1 with specificity for either A5A ($\bar{a}$-A5A) or S117 ($\bar{a}$-S117). 3-6 wk after priming, spleen cells from these animals were stimulated in vitro with TNP-Strep.A and direct anti-TNP plaque forming cells (PFC) were counted 4 days later. The TNP response depends on helper cells with specificity for Strep.A. + indicates a response with 100-500 anti-TNP PFC per culture. − indicates a response with 2-30 anti-TNP PFC per culture. Helper function could in all cases be specifically inhibited by the corresponding $\bar{a}$-Id. In all strains represented in the table Strep.A-specific helper function could be induced by sensitization with strep.A itself. Further details in references 3-5.

control of the heavy chain linkage group, yet
their receptors could be coded for by other genes,
the Ir genes in the I region of H-2 being the obvious candidates. This would imply that a variety
of H-2 haplotypes (c.f. Table 1) could code for
A-CHO specific receptor molecules which exhibit
idiotypic cross reactions with the A5A and/or the
S117 markers. We consider this possibility unlikely because of the extreme specificity of idiotype-
anti-idiotype reactions (see also our discussion
in ref. 5).

It appears, therefore, that genes in the
Ig-1 complex code for variable portions of both
immunoglobulin molecules and T cell receptors.
We do not yet know whether these receptors are
produced by the cells which carry them. Also, it
would appear likely that additional genes participate in the specification of T cell receptors
as is the case for immunoglobulin molecules.
Those additional genes may well be different in
the two systems.

ACKNOWLEDGEMENTS

We thank Ms. G. von Hesberg, Ms. M. Schöld
Ms. H. Wirges-Koch and Ms. C. Brenig for able
technical help.

This work was supported by the Deutsche Forschungsgemeinschaft through Sonderforschungsbereich 74.

REFERENCES

(1)   K. Eichmann. Immunogenetics. In press.

(2)   K. Eichmann and K. Rajewsky. Eur. J. Immunol.
      5 (1975) 661.

(3)   S.J. Black, K. Eichmann, G.J. Hämmerling and
      K. Rajewsky, in: Membrane Receptors of
      Lymphocytes. eds. M. Seligmann, J.L. Preud'-
      homme and F.M. Kourilsky. (North-Holland
      Publishing Co., Amsterdam, New York, 1975)
      p. 117

(4) S.J. Black, G.J. Hämmerling, C. Berek, K. Ra-
     jewsky and K. Eichmann. J. Exp. Med. Sub-
     mitted for publication.

(5) G.J. Hämmerling, S.J. Black, C. Berek,
     K. Eichmann and K. Rajewsky. J. Exp. Med.
     Submitted for publication.

(6) E. Trenkner and R. Riblet. J. Exp. Med.
     142 (1975) 1121.

(7) K. Eichmann. Eur. J. Immunol. 4 (1974) 296.

(8) H. Binz and H. Wigzell. J. Exp. Med. 152
     (1975) 197.

(9) T.J. McKearn, Science (Wash.) 183 (1974) 94.

(10) H. Ramseier. Cell Immunol. 8 (1974) 177.

(11) A.J. Munro, M.J. Taussig, R. Campbell,
     H. Williams and Y. Lawson. J. Exp. Med.
     140 (1974) 1579.

(12) T. Tada, M. Taneguchi and T. Takemori.
     Transplant. Rev. 26 (1975) 106.

DISCUSSION FOLLOWING KLAUS RAJEWSKY

E. MÖLLER: Would Dr. Rajewsky please make a drawing on the
blackbroad indicating how he visualizes the action of
the anti-idiotype antibody on T cells and for the induction of B memory cells?

RAJEWSKY: I would make a drawing showing a lymphocyte with
its receptor and the anti-idiotype binding to it. It
is, of course, clear, however, that the process must be
more complex, since mere binding of an antigen to the
receptor does not suffice in general to trigger the
cell. What we know about the processes of sensitizing
B and T cells with anti-idiotype is that: 1) IgG_1 but
not IgG_2 will sensitize; 2) in both cases, sensitization
occurs very rapidly and in the absence of detectable
antibody formation; and 3) minute doses of anti-idiotypic antibody are sufficient and no artifically introduced adjuvant is required.

The most interesting question in this context is, I
think, whether indeed different Ig classes exert distinct functions in idiotype regulation under physiolog-
i/ .l conditions. It will be important to define such
functions for the various classes of <u>autologous</u> anti-
idiotypic antibody in order to get more insight into
the regulation of the immune system by idiotype-anti-
idiotype interactions. If, indeed, such interactions
are crucial for the regulation of the immune system as
Niels Jerne has proposed, then it may well be that a
number of the phenomena which have been encountered in
the study of induction of immunity and tolerance by
antigens will reveal there is physiological significance
only in the context of the idiotypic network.

ARMERDING: Are there any other differences between IgG_2
and IgG_1 anti-idiotypic antibodies other than the
observed suppressing or enhancing properties, such as
affinity, specificity, etc.? Do both classes of anti-
idiotypic antibodies recognize different antigenic
determinants?

RAJEWSKY: IgG_1 and IgG_2 antibodies differ in a number of
"effector" functions such as binding to macrophages
(IgG_2 positive, IgG_1 negative), binding of complement
(IgG_2 positive, IgG_1 negative) and probably others.
There also seems to be differences in the flexibility

of the two types of molecules. On the other hand, I consider it very unlikely that anti-idiotypic antibodies of the two classes should differ in affinity for the idiotype or with respect to the determinants which they recognize. However, we do not have data on these points. It is important to stress that although we find the stimulatory activity in the IgG_1 fraction, we do not know for sure whether the stimulating material is IgG_1 itself. In fact, there is some indirect evidence from immune elimination experiments that this may not be the case. In addition, we have found that our IgG_1 preparations (but not IgG_2) contain some idiotype-binding IgM ($\sim$ 1% of the total idiotype-binding capacity).

BENACERRAF: Did you try F(ab)$'_2$ from guinea pig γ_2 and γ_1 to explain the difference in the ability of the classes to trigger T cell helper activity specific for the carbohydrate?

RAJEWSKY: This has so far not been done.

SACHS: Your strain distribution studies indicate linkage of the T helper-cell idiotype to allotype and not to H-2 One might then ask is that idiotype produced by the T cell itself or has it come from a B cell. Have you tried incubating T cells from a strain not expressing the idiotype (eg. BALB/c) with antibody from an idiotype producer (eg. CAL-20) to see whether helper cells can then be generated by anti-idiotype?

RAJEWSKY: Günter Hämmerling should answer this question.

HÄMMERLING: We have not done this experiment (that is, to take strep A-primed T cells from an idiotype-negative strain); however, we incubated unprimed T cells from idiotype-positive A/J mice with anti-strep A antibody of the A5A clone. These cells did not display helper cell function.

WILSON: Klaus, as I understand it, you can induce positive responses by priming with anti-idiotype and boosting with strep A, but not with a) strep A priming and anti-idiotype, or b) priming with anti-idiotype and boosting with anti-idiotype. Can you speculate why this is so? In a perhaps over-simplified comparison, it seems to violate one of the generalizations we considered

457

earlier, namely, that T cells like to see the same
immunogen for boosting that they saw during priming.

RAJEWSKY: What you say, Darcy, is absolutely correct, and
I find the phenomenon most interesting. Klaus Eichmann
and I have, in fact, started our experiments on idiotype stimulation by a long series of unsuccessful
attempts to induce idiotypic responses in cells primed
with streptococcal vaccine. The sensitized cells were
transferred to irradiated hosts which were then boosted
with anti-idiotypic antibodies of the IgG_1 and/or IgG_2
class, sometimes specifically purified on idiotype
immunoadsorbents in a large dose range and with or without addition of IgG-specific helper cells or allogeneic
cells. Idiotypic responses were either not detectable
or very weak in these experiments. The same was true
when cells from donors primed with anti-idiotypic antibody were transferred. Also, in animals primed with
anti-idiotypic antibody, we usually find no or only
little idiotype in the serum. I do not really understand why all this is so. However, if one envisages
that a conformational change in the B cell receptor
molecules is necessary in order to induce certain (but
not all) B cell functions, namely in particular, its
differentiation into an antibody-producing cell, then
one might entertain the idea that the anti-idiotypic
antibody may be not an ideal inducer of this differentiation since at least a large fraction of it presumably
binds to determinants in the vicinity of the antigen-
binding site, but not to the antigen-binding site
itself.

PAUL: Since anti-Fab antibodies are poor stimulants of
immunoglobulin synthesis of B lymphocytes, it does not
seem at all surprising that anti-idiotype does not
activate strep A-primed B cells.

RAJEWSKY: I think that it is an interesting problem why
antibodies to Fab do not stimulate. However, in the
case of anti-idiotypic antibodies, our failure is much
more surprising, I think, since 1) the antibody is
strictly directed to the variable portion of the Ig
receptor molecule and 2) we did provide a "second
signal" by introducing into the system either helper
cells specific for guinea pig Ig or allogeneic cells.

UNANUE: Klaus, what percentage of the T cells bind to the anti-idiotype?

RAJEWSKY: An important question which we cannot yet answer.

IDIOTYPIC RECEPTORS FOR ANTIGEN ON T LYMPHOCYTES

HANS WIGZELL AND HANS BINZ

Department of Immunology
Uppsala University Medical School

Abstract: It is possible to use the antigen-binding receptors on T lymphocytes as immunogen, thereby inducing
anti-T idiotypic antibodies. A convenient way to do
this is to use F_1-hybrid animals between two inbred
strains as recipients of T lymphocytes from one of the
parental strains. Such F_1-hybrid animals will then
frequently produce anti-idiotypic antibodies specific
for T cell receptors on the inoculated cells having
specificity for the major histocompatibility locus
antigens of the other parent. We have used such an
approach in inbred rat strains differing at the *Ag-B*
locus. Antibodies induced in such a manner against T
receptors for antigen cross-react completely with idiotypes present on IgG antibodies directed against the
same antigen as the T receptors. Thus, antigen-binding
receptors of T and B lymphocyte type express shared
idiotypes indicating the use of common genetic material
in the generation of their respective receptors. It is
possible to directly visualize the idiotype-positive T
cells by the use of anti-idiotypic antibodies. In the
present system between 5-6% of normal T lymphocytes
express idiotypic receptors signifying immune reactivity across the *Ag-B* locus barrier. Proof for actual
linkage between idiotype and specific immune potential
came via affinity chromatography of idiotype-positive
cells using anti-idiotype antibodies, whereby close to
"pure" idiotype-positive T cells could be demonstrated
to express highly restricted immune reactivity against
the relevant *Ag-B* antigen only. Such a high figure of
idiotype-positive cells suggested the presence of
"natural" antibody-like molecules to be present in
normal serum from adult rats due to membrane turnover
or shedding. It was possible to demonstrate and

461

actually isolate such molecules being present in very
low concentration in serum as well as in urine. Analysis as to molecular characteristics of the natural
antibodies in serum revealed two dominant groups of
molecules, both expressing idiotypic markers and
antigen-binding capacity. One, around 150,000 daltons,
and one with a molecular size of around 35,000 daltons.
The smaller molecules were also found in the urine.
When analyzed as to cellular origin the large molecules
were found to be produced by B lymphocytes, whereas the
smaller ones were a product of T cells.

INTRODUCTION

Little doubt exists that T lymphocytes as well as B
lymphocytes express their specific immune competence via
actively produced receptors for antigen. However, the nature
of these receptors as far as the T cells are concerned have
for a long time constituted a major enigma to immunologists.
We have approached the T lymphocyte receptors for antigen via
the use of anti-idiotypic antibodies specifically induced
against T cell receptors with specificity for a given antigenic determinant. Such an approach was initially suggested
some time ago (1) and evidence for the success of this system
have been forthcoming during the last few years (2-5). In
the present article we will deal with the use of anti-
idiotypic antibodies in the analysis of the relationship
between B and T cell receptor molecules with specificity for
the same antigenic determinant (6-9). Furthermore, the distribution of idiotype in normal T and B lymphocyte populations will be described and discussed with regard to theoretical implications. Physical isolation of idiotype-positive
cells by the use of affinity chromatography using anti-
idiotype columns demonstrates a most clearcut positive relationship between the presence of an idiotypic marker on a T
lymphocyte and its potential immune capacity. Preliminary
data on the isolated T cell receptor for antigen as to
physicochemical characteristics will be presented.

The present experimental systems involve the use of
inbred strains of rats and the measurements of reactivity
across the MHC complex of the rat; the $Ag-B$ locus. We have
accordingly used the strains Lewis, DA, BN and AUG (all
differing with regard to the $Ag-B$ locus (10) and their corresponding F_1 hybrids. Anti-idiotypic antibodies have been
produced by the inoculation of parental T lymphocytes into
adult F_1 hybrids (6). Measurements of the activity of such

anti-idiotypic antibodies involve radioimmunoassays using normal T or B lymphocytes from different strains as targets and ^{125}I-labelled rabbit-anti-rat IgG or protein A from Staphylococcus aureus as indicators of anti-idiotype binding (6).

Furthermore, as indicated in the respective sections a variety of immunological techniques have been applied to study the effect and specificity of these anti-idiotypic antibodies in various experimental systems.

DEMONSTRATION OF ANTI-IDIOTYPIC ANTIBODIES REACTIVE WITH BOTH T AND B RECEPTORS FOR THE SAME ANTIGENIC DETERMINANTS

Using the inoculation of parental T lymphocytes into F_1-hybrids between two inbred strains of rats we have been able to induce high titered anti-idiotypic antibodies directed against the receptors on those inoculated cells, which carry reactivity for Ag-B antigens of the other parental strain (8). Thus, such antisera, in the presence of complement, will selectively deplete the relevant parental T lymphocytes of their capacity to react against the Ag-B antigens intact. This was shown to be true for both MLC and GVH reactivity (6) (see Table I). These data show the anti-idiotypic nature of our anti-T cell reactive sera. At the

TABLE I

Specificity of reactions of anti-T idiotypic sera induced by injection of F_1-hybrid rats with parental T lymphocytes

<u>Antiserum</u>: (Lewis x DA)F_1-anti-Lewis T

<u>Binding to cells</u>: Positive with Lewis T and B. Negative with (Lewis x DA)F_1 T + B or DA T + B.

<u>Inactivation of T cell function</u>: Absence of complement: No inhibition of GVH or MLC

Presence of complement: Inhibition of Lewis-anti-DA reactivity measured by GVH or MLC. No inhibition of Lewis-anti-BN or Lewis-anti-August reactivity.

<u>Binding of IgG molecules</u>: Positive with IgG Lewis-anti-DA Negative with Lewis-anti-BN.
(for details see 6)

same time we could demonstrate that these anti-T idiotype
sera would also react with IgG antibodies reactive against
the same antigenic determinants as would the T cell receptors
(6). This could be shown via indirect hemagglutination
assays using IgG coated sheep erythrocytes (11) and in a few
cases also by gel diffusion experiments. The idiotypic
nature of the antisera with regard to these IgG molecules was
thus established. It was thus clear that despite the fact
that these anti-idiotypic antisera were induced against T
cell receptors for antigen they could also be shown to react
with B cell products, in this case highly purified IgG antibodies with relevant antigen-binding capacity. To prove
identity between the anti-T and anti-B idiotype reactive
antibodies, immunoadsorbents with relevant IgG antibodies
were prepared. Anti-T receptor-induced antisera were filtered through such columns. It could thus be shown that columns coated with pure IgG antibody molecules carrying the
relevant idiotypic determinants could completely remove all
anti-idiotypic activity against the idiotype-positive T cells.

TABLE II

Anti-T cell idiotypic antibodies react with idiotypic IgG
molecules

Antiserum: (Lewis x DA)F_1-anti-Lewis T

IgG-Lewis-anti-DA Sepharose: Passage through this Sepharose
        will remove all anti-Lewis T anti-DA activity as
        measured in Table I. Acid elution will recover all
        anti-T idiotypic activity.

IgG-Lewis-anti-BN Sepharose: Passage will not remove any
        anti-Lewis T antibodies.

IgG-Lewis normal serum Sepharose: Like for IgG-Lewis-anti-
        BN Sepharose.

(for details see 6)

Such removed activity could be recovered via acid elution from the relevant columns. We would thus conclude that anti-idiotypic antibodies induced against T cell receptors for antigen show complete cross-reaction with IgG antibody molecules produced in the same strain of rats that produced the T cells and with specificity for the same antigen. However, we are not ready as yet to state that the opposite is true (3,6). It is thus possible that anti-idiotypic antibodies induced against B cell receptors for antigen (Ig molecules) may contain additional anti-idiotypic antibodies reactive with unique B idiotypes not to be found on T receptors for the same antigen. The complete cross reaction found between T and B cell receptors for antigen using anti-T idiotypic sera (found so far in three different anti-idiotypic systems) does, however, suggest identity (or close to identity) with regard to at least one part of the antigen-combining areas of T and B cell receptors reactive with the same antigenic determinant.

VISUALIZATION: FREQUENCY-DETERMINATION AND PHYSICAL ISOLATION OF IDIOTYPE POSITIVE T LYMPHOCYTES

Actual visualization of antigen-binding T cells is difficult. The actual relevance of such binders as to function is largely undecided. The approach using anti-T idiotypic antisera allows an actual direct visualization of idiotype positive T (as well as B) lymphocytes using fluorescent antibody techniques or autoradiography (7, 12). Previously, reactions across the MHC barrier have been demonstrated by several workers (using functional activation as measured by MLC or GVH reactions) to involve several percent of normal T lymphocytes (13, 14). We could directly confirm via the use of anti-idiotypic antibodies that indeed several percent (5-6%) of normal T lymphocytes from a given rat strain display idiotypic markers signifying reactivity against a certain Ag-B antigen(s) (7). Significantly lower frequency figures (around 1%) were obtained for B lymphocytes. The failure to detect any conventional Ig markers on T lymphocytes and the capacity to remove via trypsin treatment from such T cells the idiotypic molecules with subsequent recovery during overnight incubation at 37°C largely exclude cytophilic antibody B cells as a possible cause of error in the present system. Furthermore, as will be presented later in this talk, we have actually been able to directly mark such T idiotypic molecules via internal labelling procedures and show them to be distinct entities from idiotype-positive molecules produced by B lymphocytes.

465

Purification of idiotype-positive T lymphocytes was subsequently attempted to further prove the relationship between presence of this marker and the expected specific immune competence of the cell. This was performed using two or three step procedures involving sequential passages through anti-Ig columns (7, 8). For instance, Lewis normal T lymphocytes were produced by filtration through anti-Ig columns. Subsequently, these cells were incubated with anti-(Lewis-anti-BN) idiotypic antibodies [produced in (Lewis $\times$ BN)F$_1$-hybrids by inoculation of Lewis T cells (7)]. Mere incubation with anti-idiotypic antibodies has been shown not to involve any reduction of the immune capacity of such coated T cells (6, 8). The cells were washed and put through a second anti-Ig column, now removing the anti-idiotype-coated cells but letting the rest pass through. The retained cells could be mechanically eluted and tested for function. The passed cells were either tested for function or incubated with a second anti-idiotype serum; this time with anti-Lewis-anti-DA reactivity and the procedures were repeated once more. The various cell populations were subsequently tested for GVH reactivity against DA, BN and AUG antigens using the local popliteal lymph node assay. The results were very clearcut (8) and are summarized in Table III. It could be

---

TABLE III

Purification or depletion of immunocompetent T cells using anti-idiotypic antibodies and anti-Ig columns

	LxBN^x	LxDA^x	LxAUG^x
PI	0.64	-0.04	-0.06
EI	-0.61	0.76	0.65
PII	0.63	0.80	-0.07
EII	0.74	-0.70	0.55

PI = passed anti-Ig column after incubation with anti-(Lewis-anti-BN) antibodies.

EI = bound and eluted from anti-Ig column after incubation with anti-(Lewis-anti-BN) antibodies.

PII = PI cells passed anti-Ig column after incubation with anti-(Lewis-anti-DA) antibodies.

TABLE III cont.

EII = PI cells bound and eluted from anti-Ig column after incubation with anti-(Lewis-anti-DA) antibodies.

(for details see ref. 8)

[x]Popliteal lymph node GVH assay. Figures denote $\log_{10}$ mean of weight of lymph nodes inoculated with control Lewis T cells divided by the weight of nodes inoculated with experimental cells as indicated. Mean of three to ten nodes in each group. Doubly underlined figures = reduced GVH reactivity of experimental cells (figures below 0.50 indicate no detectable GVH reactivity). Singly underlined figures = highly significant increase in GVH reactivity.

---

shown that the procedure functioned according to expectation. Thus, cells incubated with anti-Lewis-anti-BN antibodies and subsequently passed through an anti-Ig column would show no demonstrable reactivity against BN but normal against DA and AUG. Conversely, the cells retained on the column and subsequently eluted showed exclusive reactivity against BN but no detectable activity against DA nor AUG. Corresponding analogous data were obtained when using the second anti-idiotype serum. T cells with different idiotype receptors can thus be sorted out from a normal population by anti-idiotype antibodies and shown to display different, highly restricted immune competence in line with their idiotypic markers. In fact, in the present strain combinations we were unable to detect any significant cross-reactivity using the present approach. This is in contradiction to the results of other workers studying cross-reactivities in reactions across the MHC barrier but admittedly using other means for selecting out their reactive (or unreactive) cells (15).

A SPECULATIVE DISCUSSION OF THE FREQUENCY OF IDIOTYPE-POSITIVE LYMPHOCYTES

A high proportion of normal T lymphocytes express idiotypic markers signifying reactivity across a certain MHC barrier. How could this high frequency be explained? First, it should be recalled that in most of these systems more than one idiotype is involved but the exact number is unknown but is most likely quite limited. It would thus seem clear that rat anti-*Ag-B* antibodies frequently express remarkable

467

homogeneity. Thus, in the combination AS-anti-AUG there is a single very dominating clone of antibodies being produced (16) whereas in the Lewis-anti-BN or -DA system single lines of identity within each idiotype system have been observed when testing several individual anti-idiotype sera in gel diffusion (17). Evidence for limited heterogeneity in the rat anti-*Ag-B* system does also stem from the observation that during hyperimmunization there is frequently an induction of auto-anti-idiotypic antibodies reactive with a dominating clone in the early anti-*Ag-B* sera but not with late anti-*Ag-B* sera (11). This limited heterogeneity is, of course, also a necessary prerequisite for functional elimination via the use of anti-idiotypic antibodies to occur at any appreciable frequency. More relevant to the matter of frequency of the idiotypic T cells is the suggestive evidence that the anti-T idiotype antibodies seemingly react with single chain idiotypic determinants. The hypothetical reasoning of single chain determined idiotypic determinants may also explain why the frequency of idiotypic B cells is lower than that of the T cells in the present system (7). This, one could explain on the basis that it is well known that a combination of two chains may lead to blocking of determinants otherwise expressed on the single chains (18). Conversely, anti-idiotypic antibodies induced against B cell products in the present system have already been shown to react well with the idiotype positive B cells with reactivity against Ag-B antigens, but less well with T cells of corresponding specificity (3). This is exactly what one would expect if the anti-B idiotype antisera mostly react with idiotypic determinants of a composite type (= dependent on the presence of both a heavy and light chain in combination) with only a few antibodies being directed against single chain determined idiotypes.

PRESENCE OF IDIOTYPIC MOLECULES WITH ANTI-AG-B ACTIVITY IN SERUM AND URINE OF NORMAL ADULT RATS

The finding of a high percentage of idiotype-positive lymphocytes with markers indicating reactivity across the MHC barrier of the species (12, 7) suggested that due to membrane turnover or shedding such material might be recovered from the sera of normal individuals. Using Lewis adult rats as donors of serum, we demonstrate the actual presence of such "natural" antibodies as measured by their capacity to cause specific inhibiton of anti-idiotypic antibodies binding to the corresponding Lewis T lymphocytes (9). These natural antibodies could be shown to be present in very low concentration in comparison to immune sera but would seemingly occur spontaneously and could be recovered from the sera of Lewis rats brought in from rat colonies devoid of other rat strains. When analyzed as to molecular size we could demonstrate the existence of two dominant groups of molecules in these sera. One group of molecules had a size similar to 7S IgG or somewhat larger, whereas another group of molecules demonstrated a molecular weight around 35,000 or somewhat smaller than ovalbumin. The lower molecular weight component could also be recovered from the urine of these normal rats. Table 4 gives a summary of the behaviour and characteristics

TABLE IV

Characteristics of natural idiotypic, antigen-specific molecules with anti-*Ag-B* reactivity found in serum or urine of adult rats.

Molecular size	160,000	35,000
Serum	+	+
Urine	–	+
Idiotypes	+	+
Antigen-binding capacity	+	+
Resistance to reduction	–^{x}	+

(for further details see 9)

+ = present   – = absent

^{x}treatment with 0.2 M 2-mercaptoethanol and 0.1% SDS reduce this molecule into two subunits with the approximate size of 50,000 and 25,000 daltons.

of these molecules. Reduction, alkylation and SDS-polyacrylamide electrophoresis of the high molecular weight molecules turns the molecules into two groups; with the size of conventional Ig heavy and light chain molecules (17). The class connection(s) of the heavy chain molecules is so far undecided. Similar treatment of the low molecular weight component will lead to no reduction in size, thus suggesting a single chain structure of these molecules.

As both groups of naturally occurring molecules express idiotypic markers as well as antigen binding characteristics we would conclude that they indeed represent a kind of natural antibodies. It would seem clear that the low molecular weight component in this regard must be considered an unorthodox-sized molecule to express this behaviour.

DEMONSTRATION OF CELLULAR ORIGIN OF NATURALLY PRODUCED, IDIOTYPE-POSITIVE MOLECULES WITH REACTIVITY AGAINST *Ag-B* ANTIGENS

It was then considered important to establish the cellular origin of production of these naturally occurring antibody-like structures. Accordingly, B and T lymphocytes were purified from normal Lewis spleen and lymph nodes followed by incubation overnight at 37°C in the presence or absence of tritiated amino acids. Supernatants were subsequently collected, dialyzed and tested for antigen binding capacity. Using unpurified, internally-labelled material no significant difference in binding capacity to syngeneic or allogeneic cells could be demonstrated. However, if the supernatants were purified over specific anti-idiotype columns (making a purification step in the order of 10,000), the subsequently bound and eluted material could be shown to express specific binding capacity to the relevant *Ag-B* containing cells. This was true for supernatants obtained from either T, T+B or only B cell supernatants. We could thus conclude that it was indeed possible by direct internal labelling procedures to extract labelled material from T or B lymphocytes with both idiotypic and antigen binding characteristics. Analysis of such supernatant material as to behaviour in polyacrylamide electrophoresis was then carried out using either internally or externally labelled material after anti-idiotype immunosorbent purification. No difference was seen whether material was labelled by external or internal means. Fig. 1 shows that "purified B cell" supernatant only contains the large sized molecules whereas supernatant from T cells contained the low molecular weight molecules. We could thus conclude that the idiotypic, antigen-binding material in normal serum was produced by B and T lymphocytes, whereas the T receptor material was the dominating one to be found in the urine of these normal individuals.

It should be noted that we are not prepared to state that the structure of the T cell receptor whilst situated on the membrane of the T lymphocytes has the same build up as

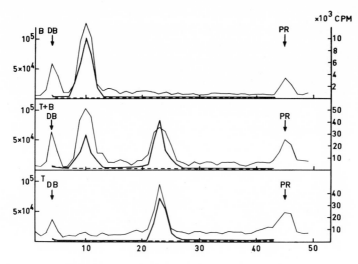

Figure 1. Production of idiotypic, antigen-binding molecules from normal Lewis T and B lymphocytes: Measurements of molecules present in supernatant fluid of lymphocytes grown for 12 hours *in vitro* using RPMI 1640,5% FCS and a cell concentration of 2×10^7 cells/ ml. Supernatants were purified over anti-idiotype immunosorbents (see ref. 9) and B and T cells according to ref. 6. Material purified over anti-idiotype columns were labelled with ^{125}I using chloramine-T technique and separated over Sephadex G-200. Total radioactivity = thin line, radioactivity indicating specific antigen-binding capacity of material (= to BN cells) (see ref. 9) = thick line, radioactivity indicating non-specific binding (= binding to Lewis cells) = dotted line. Total radioactivity = left axis. Specific or non-specific activity = right axis. DB = blue dextran. PR = phenol red.

the molecule which is found in the supernatant, serum or urine. Preliminary data using detergent-solubilized cell-membranes suggest that the T cell receptor for antigen when located in the membrane is larger than the around 35,000 daltons unit found in the released form. Our preliminary data on this matter does not allow us, however, to state in a productive way the exact relationship between the larger

471

sized molecules on the membrane and the 35,000 component. It should be emphasized, however, that even when using NP-40 solubilized idiotypic material from normal T lymphocytes the 35,000 component is still the dominating molecule to be found. We have so far been unable to detect any molecules of conventional heavy or light chain Ig type in our material extractable from the T lymphocytes.

SPECULATIONS AS TO THE STRUCTURE OF
THE T CELL RECEPTOR FOR ANTIGEN

Some seemingly safe conclusions can be drawn as to the antigen-binding receptor on T lymphocytes in comparison to the antigen-binding Ig molecules produced by B cells. One major conclusion would be that at least part of the antigen-binding receptors on the two types of receptors are coded for by genes of similar if not identical composition. This is stated due to the capacity of highly purified idiotypic IgG used as immunosorbent to completely remove the anti-T idiotypic antisera from reacting with the idiotype-positive T lymphocytes. As we have been unable so far to demonstrate any soluble T cell receptor with characteristics of IgG molecules we consider it very unlikely that such IgG immunosorbents could be contaminated with T cell molecules carrying hypothetical, "T unique" determinants. Complete overlap with regard to idiotypic determinants would argue against that these are coded for by two distinct genetic systems. We would thus suggest identity to at least one part of the variable region determined gene products in the two lymphocyte groups. It should be realized, however, that final proof for identity would require actual isolation and sequence analysis of T and B cell receptors with the same idiotypic determinants and antigen-binding capacity.

Our present data do not allow us to state the nature of the genes coding for the variable regions of the T cell receptor in relation to those of the B cell immunoglobulin molecules. In the system of Eichmann and Rajewsky (19) where anti-idiotypic antibodies can be used to specifically induce antigen-specific helper T cells it has been possible to link this capacity of the T lymphocytes to become stimulated to presence or absence of a given heavy chain allotype. Positive allotypes were exactly those which were known to contain v genes coding for the relevant idiotype in IgG antibody molecules. This would suggest that T and B cells in their receptor for antigen may use the same v_H chain genes. The authors, however, do also stress the need of

472

caution as in their system they have no actual proof that the
T cells themselves produce such antigen-binding and idiotypic
receptors. In the present system, experiments are on the way
to analyze for the possible linkage of T cell idiotypes to
allotypes of heavy or light chain type. In two preliminary
experiments we have also used idiotypic IgG molecules or
their respective heavy or light chains as inhibitors in a
radio-immunoassay using anti-T idiotypic antibodies and idiotype-positive T cells as target antigens. In these two experiments a quite high inhibitory capacity of the isolated
heavy chains was noted indicating shared idiotypic determinants between the heavy chains of IgG antibody molecules and
T cell receptors. Further experiments, however, are necessary before any firm conclusions can be drawn as to the significance of these preliminary observations.

T lymphocytes are capable of expressing sophisticated
discriminatory power as to cognition of foreign material,
and it is debatable whether B or T lymphocytes differ in this
regard. It is generally accepted that the capacity of B
lymphocytes to recognize antigen of widely varying configura-
tions to a large extent can be explained on the build-up of
their antigen-binding molecules, namely their use of a combination of two different variable polypeptide chains in the
creation of the antigen-binding area. It would be reasonable
to assume that the T cell receptor for antigen would use a
similar mechanism in the production of its antigen-combining
sites. The present results that the idiotypic 35,000 dalton
molecules from T lymphocytes express specific antigen-binding
capacity do not argue against this. Although these molecules
under the present experimental conditions behave like single
chain molecules with a capacity to react to MHC-determined
antigens in a specific manner, this may only indicate a
"framework specificity" of these idiotypic T cell molecules
for MHC determinants. Additional heterogeneity may thus reside within each idiotype-positive T cell group as to the
further "fine" specificity of the T receptor. But more important, it is also quite likely as mentioned earlier that
the T cell receptor for antigen whilst located on the membrane is a more composite molecule with two different polypeptide chains participating in the construction of the receptor. One of these chains would be a yet undefined chain,
whereas the other one would be the 35,000 dalton molecule described in the present article. Serological and biochemical
characterization of such membrane-attached T cell receptors
is now required to validate or disprove the above reasoning.

REFERENCES

(1)   H.R. Ramseier and J. Lindenmann. J. Transplant. Rev. 10 (1972) 57.

(2)   H. Binz and J. Lindenmann. J. Exp. Med. 136 (1972) 872.

(3)   H. Binz, J. Lindenmann and H. Wigzell. J. Exp. Med. 140 (1974) 731.

(4)   P. Joller. Nature New Biol. (Lond.) 240 (1972) 214.

(5)   M.V. Elves. Transplantation 16 (1973) 403.

(6)   H. Binz and H. Wigzell. J. Exp. Med. 142 (1975) 197.

(7)   H. Binz and H. Wigzell. J. Exp. Med. 142 (1975) 1218.

(8)   H. Binz and H. Wigzell. J. Exp. Med. 142 (1975) 1231.

(9)   H. Binz and H. Wigzell. Scand. J. Immunol. 4 (1975) 591.

(10)   J. Palm and J. Black. Transplantation 11 (1971) 184.

(11)   T.J. McKearn. Science 183 (1974) 94.

(12)   H. Binz, T. Bachi, H. Wigzell, H. Ramseier and J. Lindenmann. Proc. Nat. Acad. Sci. (U.S.A.) 72 (1975) 3210.

(13)   D.B. Wilson, J.L. Blyth and P.C. Nowell. J. Exp. Med. 128 (1968) 1157.

(14)   W.L. Ford, S.J. Simmonds and R.C. Atkins. J. Exp. Med. 141 (1975) 682.

(15)   J. Howard and D.B. Wilson. J. Exp. Med. 140 (1974) 660.

(16)   K. Welsh. Personal communication.

(17)   H. Binz. Unpublished experiments.

(18) W.V. Epstein. Science 148 (1965) 1591.

(19) K. Eichman and K. Rajewsky. Eur. J. Immunol. 5
      (1975) 661.

ACKNOWLEDGEMENTS

H.B. was supported by a fellowship by European
Molecular Biology Organization. H.W. was supported by NIH
contract NOI-CB-33859 and Swedish Cancer Society.

DISCUSSION FOLLOWING HANS WIGZELL

KATZ: Hans, I know that many of us here would benefit if
you would summarize the following points: First, the
molecular properties of the serum versus the urine
factors, including a) how many chains?; b) what is the
evidence for single versus multiple chains? and c) what
linkage group does the single chain belong to?

WIGZELL: As stated, the naturally-occurring idiotypic
material in the serum is constituted by two major groups
of molecules. The large (around 150,000 daltons) unit
is, we believe, made up of 7S IgM-like molecules.
Reduction and alkylation leads to typical single chain
molecules of heavy and light Ig chain types. The low
molecular size group of molecules retain their size
under similar conditions and would thus seem to be a
single chain.

As to linkage groups, we have no direct linkage data.
Judging from the data of Eichmann and Rajewsky in
conjunction with our preliminary inhibition experiments
using dissociated heavy and light Ig chains, we believe
the linkage group to be that of the heavy chain Ig gene
group.

KATZ: Secondly, how do you explain the high frequency of
idiotype-positive cells?

WIGZELL: We believe the dominating T cell idiotypic determinants to represent single chain-determined idiotypes.
Thus, the frequency may represent germ line v gene
frequencies. The lower frequency of idiotypic B cells
versus T cells in the present system could be explained
using the following reasoning: our anti-T idiotype
antisera might react with idiotypic determinants that
can be shielded by, eg., the variable light chain
region of the B cell. This would reduce the detectable
number of idiotype-positive B cells.

KATZ: Third, would you reiterate the differences between
free and cell-bound idiotype-positive material?

WIGZELL: No major difference is seen between the B cell
idiotype material whether free or cell-bound. With
regard to T cell idiotypic molecules, this does not
seem to be true. In preliminary experiments carried

out by Hans Binz, the 30–50,000 molecular weight idiotypic molecules does still constitute a major component
of detergent-solubilized material. However, molecules
of a large size can also be found. The exact relationship between these two groups of molecules is not clear.

KATZ: Finally, do you believe the idiotype-positive cells
which may be specific for other antigens represent distinct clones of cells or cells with multiple receptor
specificities?

WIGZELL: As to your question on restrictions of specificity
of our idiotype-positive T cells: we are convinced by
our fractionation experiments that the single idiotypic
T lymphocyte is very restricted in its immune specificity. It remains to be established whether within each
idiotype-positive group of cells there exists additional
heterogeneity with regard to receptor specificity. We
attempted to analyze this using highly purified idiotype-positive T lymphocytes obtained by affinity
chromatography for their helper activity against
various defined antigens.

SIMONSEN: Hans, you have been very open yourself to the
possible source of error in your system that may be
explained by antigen-antibody complexes. I am not sure
whether you have performed a crucial experiment to
exclude this possibility. For example, with your
strongest antibody--the anti-(Lewis anti-DA)--have you
tried to determine whether you can absorb it with a
BN anti-DA antibody, which would remove the antigen if
it is present?

WIGZELL: No, we have not done that experiment, but we have
done the following experiment: We can take glutaraldehyde polymerized Lewis anti-DA antibody and use this as
a perfectly good inducer of anti-idiotype antibodies in
guinea pigs tolerized to rat gamma globulin--now it is
difficult to imagine that antigen-antibody complexes
could be involved in this. But you are making a
perfectly valid point about the possibility of antigen-
antibody complexes in the situation of inducing anti-
idiotype by injecting parental cells into F_1 hybrids.
Nevertheless, I think the other observations such as
the one just cited argue strongly that the effects we
see are due to the activities of anti-idiotypic antibodies and not due to antigen-antibody complexes.

477

SHEVACH: What percent of conventionally raised alloantibodies contain activity directed against the idiotype
represented on the donor strain for the responder
strain?

WIGZELL: There exist data in the rat that antibodies
against the rat MHC antigens display restricted heterogeneity. Thus, Ken Welsh has found that AS-anti-Aug
antisera frequently are composed of a single, dominant
clone of alloantibodies against which anti-idiotypic
antibodies can be made. Similarly, we have found
dominating clones of alloantibody molecules in Lewis-
anti-DA and Lewis-anti-BN combinations. Data of
McKearn *et al* have demonstrated the existence of a few
clones in a similar strain combination. I can thus not
give you actual average percent values, but I would
prefer to put emphasis on this reduced heterogeneity
found in several combinations. This would, to my mind,
constitute a basic requirement if successful depletion
of function using anti-idiotypic antibodies would occur.

KUNKEL: There are a few points that I would like to raise
concerning Dr. Wigzell's findings which are based on a
rather long experience with conventional idiotypic
systems. The first concerns the concept that you are
suggesting, namely, that a piece of heavy chain may be
involved in the T cell receptor and in producing your
idiotypic antiserum. If this were indeed the case, one
would expect chain specificity for the v regions, that
would not be absorbed out with whole alloantibody molecules; the light chain variable regions are known to
cover antigens of the heavy chain hypervariable areas
involved in the idiotypic system. The fact that the
whole alloantibody molecule absorbs out all your idiotypic activity might argue against your concept,
although I do not feel it is a strong argument. Related
to this point is the possibility that your absorption
experiments with isolated heavy chains do not rule out
idiotypic specificity for a combined H-L unit. In conventional idiotypic studies where the idiotypic antibody is made against whole Ig molecules, similar findings might well be obtained. In our hands, light
chains never remove the idiotypic antibodies but purified heavy chains frequently do. The latter findings
may sometimes be due to some contaminating whole molecules which are always difficult to remove entirely
from heavy chain preparations.

I would like to support your suggestion that you might be dealing with antibodies to a special v region subgroup rather than to the hypervariable regions involved in conventional idiotypic antibodies. Recent evidence from a number of laboratories, including our own, indicate an association of certain framework residues with particular idiotypes and antibody combining sites, although there are some results opposing this view. In the case of the Pr cold agglutinins, a new v region subgroup has turned up associated primarily, but not entirely, with this type of antibody. This may be the case with your system, and if this were so, the quantitative problem that you have been struggling with for the T cell receptor dictionary would be alleviated.

WIGZELL: We are quite willing to accept the possibility that our T cell idiotypes may, in fact, represent v subgroup markers rather than "true" idiotypes. Accordingly, we are thus planning the experiments looking for helper activity against conventional antigens using T cells purified with regard to idiotype as alluded to in my answer to David Katz.

As to the single chain inhibition experiments, I would stress their preliminary nature. Still, the inhibitory activity of the isolated heavy IgG chains when using anti-T idiotype sera is surprisingly high in comparison to most conventional anti-B, Ig idiotypic systems. We, thus, believe the present heavy chain inhibitory capacity to be much larger than could be simply explained away on the basis of contaminating H-L units and would use these findings as further support for the single chain nature of the 30-35,000 T idiotype-positive molecules.

PAUL: Since it is possible from your data that the T cell receptor is a single chain and that the idiotype may be expressed solely on this chain and on the H chain of the alloantibody, one would anticipate that isolated H chains from alloantibody should have substantial antigen-binding activity and that the fine specificity of such H chains should resemble that of T cells.

WIGZELL: Yes, such an assumption would follow, should the constant region of the soluble T cell receptor molecule turn out to be like conventional Ig regions. However, it is not excluded that this T region contains sites that may add in a secondary "non-specific" manner to the specific binding of the receptor to the relevant allo-antigeneic determinants.

BACH: How do you measure a 1% cross-reactivity in a GVH reaction and how many antisera and strains have you tested?

WIGZELL: We have tested Lewis for reactivity against the DA, BN and Aug strains. Three different anti-idiotypic antisera have been used with anti-(Lewis-anti-DA) or anti-(Lewis-anti-BN) specificity. By the combined comparison of enriched, specific GVH reactivity and respective depletion of a given cell population as demonstrated in our fractionation experiments, we are actually able to reach such a cut off level figure.

BENACERRAF: What is your feeling about the relative absence of reactivity of your anti-idiotype antiserum with thymocytes in view of the ability of these cells to bind antigen and to react with these cells?

WIGZELL: Anti-idiotypic antisera in our system bind very poorly to thymocytes. That reactivity would seem to be in the order of a few percent of the reactivity found against normal peripheral T lymphocytes. Although we have no proof for this, I would assume these few idiotype-positive thymocytes to be analogous to the medullary, cortisone-resistant T lymphocytes found in a mouse thymus.

ROSENTHAL: Alloantisera block functions of guinea pig T cells *in vitro* without the addition of complement. Why does the suppression of the MLC by anti-idiotypic antibodies require that you kill the T cell by addition of complement?

WIGZELL: I believe this is due to the fact that multivalent antigenic determinants are very difficult to inhibit using bivalent ligands. Furthermore, we know that membrane turn-over of the idiotypic T cell receptor would seem to be a quite rapid process.

MILLER: Can you enrich for idiotype-positive T cells by activating parental thymus cells in an irradiated F_1 hybrid? What is then the percentage of such idiotype-positive cells in the progeny of the activated T cells?

480

WIGZELL: T cells selected via MLC against the relevant alloantigen display highly increased percent idiotype-positive cells. In some work by Hans Binz together with Pekka Häyry using surgical sponges infiltrated with allogeneic fibroblasts as allografts, around 50% of the infiltrating aggressive cells could be shown to carry the relevant idiotype(s).

ARMERDING: Do the serum and urine factors exhibit binding activity to the respective antigens?

WIGZELL: Both the serum and urine idiotype-positive material exhibit antigen-binding specificity. The low molecular serum and urine factor are probably identical.

SACHS: The hybrid histocompatibility system (Hh), in which hybrid animals reject parental lymphoid cells, has been well-documented by Cudkowicz and others in the mouse. However, in that system the rejected cells can be lymph-oid tumors which presumably would not possess the kind of clonally expressed receptors which you have made antibodies against. Have you tried or do you plan to try to immunize F_1 rats with a parental lymphoid tumor or other immunologically non-competent cell type to determine whether such cell types can also lead to "anti-idiotypic" antibodies?

WIGZELL: It would be very useful to find lymphoid tumor cells carrying idiotype-positive receptors. As to immunization, we already know that even idiotype-positive parental B cells normally fail to induce anti-idiotypic antibodies if injected into F_1 hybrids. IgG molecules cross-linked or in adjuvant are more effi-cient. The reason why idiotype-positive parental T cells constitute such a good immunogen in F_1 hybrids we consider to reside in the capacity of these cells to induce an allogeneic effect reaction functioning as a powerful adjuvant.

SIMONSEN: If B cells fail to work because of the absence of an enhancing   allogeneic effect, this defect could probably be overcome by injecting T cells of the one parent simultaneously with B cells of the other. Have you tried this?

WIGZELL: I think your assumption is perfectly true; we have not tried this as yet.

481

KATZ: Before closing this session, I would just like to
state my strong feelings about the immense practical
importance of what Hans Binz and Hans Wigzell have so
tirelessly been working on. I think that some of the
questions and comments following Hans Wigzell's presentation make it clear that the definitive proof on the
mechanism(s) of these phenomena has yet to be obtained
and that, moreover, we may all be surprised when we
learn what it is. Nevertheless, irrespective of what
the mechanism(s) turn out to be, the fact that Binz and
Wigzell have isolated a material from normal urine
which can be used to immunize the individual from which
it was derived to make auto-anti-idiotypic antibodies
thereby specifically abrogating the capacity of the
individual to react against a foreign tissue graft of
defined allospecificity has implications which are
extremely far-reaching. As such, I think it would be
justified to consider this to be potentially among the
most important observations in basic immunology to have
foreseeable therapeutic implications for man.

Properties of Histocompatibility Gene Products Involved in Regulation of Immune Responses

G. J. V. NOSSAL, CHAIRMAN

THE NATURE OF ANTIGEN SPECIFIC T CELL FACTORS INVOLVED IN THE GENETIC REGULATION OF IMMUNE RESPONSES

EDNA MOZES

Department of Chemical Immunology
The Weizmann Institute of Science

Abstract: We have studied the properties of antigen specific
T-cell factors which are capable of replacing T cells
in T-dependent antibody responses. The specificity of
these factors was found to resemble that of humoral
antibodies although it is not identical with antibody
specificity. Thus, there is cross reaction in the
helper effect of factors produced using the synthetic
polypeptides (T,G)-A--L, (Phe,G)-A--L and (H,G)-A--L.
However, a (T,G)-A--L specific factor will not cooperate with B cells in producing antibodies to (T,G)-Pro--
L, although anti-(T,G)-A--L antibodies cross react with
(T,G)-Pro--L as well as with the synthetic polypeptides
derived from A--L.

Attempts were made to characterize T cell specific
factors using Sephadex columns as well as by ion exchange chromatography. A major step of purification
was achieved when the (T,G)-A--L specific T cell
factor was recovered from an antigen-immunoadsorbent.
The eluate was found to be as active as the whole T
cell supernatant in helping B cells to mount an immune
response to (T,G)-A--L. Antiserum prepared against
the eluate inhibited over 90% of the cooperative activity of the factor. On SDS polyacrylamide gels, the
eluate appeared to possess two major peptide chains of
molecular weights of 45,000 and 70,000.

The T cell factor specific for (T,G)-Pro--L to which
the immune response was previously found not to be H-2
linked was found to be similar in its nature to the
(T,G)-A--L specific factor. Thus, the activity of a
factor produced with (T,G)-Pro--L was removed by an

antigen-coated column, whereas its activity was not reduced after transfer through an anti-immunoglobulin immunoadsorbent. This factor was found to be absorbed by I region specific antisera suggesting that it is a product of I region genes. Experiments in which the immune response of F_1 hybrids between two low responder mouse strains to (T,G)-Pro--L was tested indicated the existence of two genes regulating this response. Thus, the response potential to (T,G)-Pro--L is controlled by an H-2 linked Ir gene and by a second gene which is not linked to H-2.

The antigen specific T cell factors affect the levels of splenic cyclic AMP in high responder mice. This assay provides a convenient system for measuring T cell factor activity. In addition, these studies will hopefully contribute to the understanding of the mechanism of B cell activation by T cell signals.

INTRODUCTION

One of the central functions of thymus derived (T)-cells in the immune system is their collaboration or helper effect in the process of antibody production by bone marrow derived (B) cells to a variety of antigens (1-3). However, the precise mechanism of T cell interaction with antibody forming cell precursors is still undefined. It has been demonstrated that binding of antigens by T cells (4,5) or the specificity of the helper effect (6) is as diverse as that of soluble antibodies or B cells, nevertheless, the identity of the molecule(s) carrying this specificity on T cells is still unknown.

Recently, it has been demonstrated that T cells helper effect can be replaced by soluble factors produced by these cells. The T cell factors fall into two major categories: non-specific and specific. Non-specific factors have been found to be produced by either mitogen activation (7) or allogeneic stimulation (8). These factors replace T cells in restoring anti-erythrocyte and anti-nonrelated antigens responses in T cell deprived in vitro systems. Antigen specific factors generated by treating educated T cells with antigen have been found to replace T cells in eliciting antibody responses to the stimulating antigen either in vitro (9) or in-vivo (10). In one of these systems the specific T cell factor was characterized as an immunoglobulin (11) whereas in another system the specific T cell factor was found to bear

no antigenic relationship to immunoglobulin, but to react
with antisera directed against the major histocompatibility
(H-2) complex of the strain in which it was produced (12,13).
Furthermore, the activity of this T cell factor was removed
by immunoadsorbents coated with anti Ia antisera (14) suggesting that this T cell specific factor is a product of I region
genes. The latter T cell factors have been successfully
utilized in studying the cellular basis of the genetic
controls of immune responses to multichain synthetic polypeptide antigens, since they can be used for measuring
directly T and B cell function (15-17). It has been found
using T cell factors specific to two synthetic polypeptides,
poly(LTyr,LGlu)-poly (DLAla)--poly(LLys) designated (T,G)-
A--L and poly(LTyr,LGlu)-poly(LPro)--poly(LLys) designated
(T,G)-Pro--L, that genetic defects can be expressed in B
cells which are not stimulated by the T cell product, in T
cells which are not capable of producing the enhancing factor,
or in both cell types (15-17).

An important feature of these T cell factors is their
antigen specificity. The specificity of a T cell factor
produced to (T,G)-A--L was demonstrated by the removal of its
activity on specific antigen-Sepharose columns (12) and also
by demonstrating that the in vivo helper effect was specific
to the antigen used in the T cell education (10). It is very
likely that the specific T cell factor represents the molecular recognition component of T cells, namely, the T-cell
receptor. If this is the case, the molecular identification
and characterization of the T cell factor may solve one of
the most controversial topics in immunology.

This paper reports attempts to purify and characterize
the properties of this antigen specific T cell mediator.

SPECIFICITY OF T CELL FACTORS

If the specific T cell factors are either shed-off or
secreted T cell receptors involved in the process of T-B cell
cooperation, it is important to establish the degree of
specificity of such factors and to find out how far the binding sites of these factors resemble that of humoral antibody,
as far as their specificity is concerned.

T cell factors to four multichain synthetic polypeptides,
(T,G)-A--L, poly(LPhe,LGlu)-poly(DLAla)--poly(LLys), (Phe,G)-
A--L, poly(LHis,LGlu)-poly(DLAla)--poly(LLys), (H,G)-A--L and
(T,G)-Pro--L, were prepared as described (10,15). Briefly,

487

irradiated recipient mice were injected with 10^8 thymocytes and 10 µg antigen in complete Freund's adjuvant. Seven days later, the spleens of these mice which contained educated T cells, were cultured for 6 hours in serum free medium containing 2 µg/ml of antigen. The cell cultures were centrifuged and the supernatants were used as the T cell factors, and were analyzed for their cooperative activity with 10^7 B cells in adoptive transfer experiments. The mice were injected with either (T,G)-A--L, (Phe,G)-A--L, (H,G)-A--L or (T,G)-Pro--L. The B cells and recipient mice for these experiments were chosen according to their response potential to the above antigens. The recipients were bled 12 days following cell transfers and their sera were checked for antibody responses using the passive microhemagglutination assay. The specificity of the factors as measured by their helping effect is shown in Table 1. There is a complete "cross-cooperative" effect between factors to (T,G)-A--L, (Phe,G)-A--L and (H,G)-A--L. When a factor to (T,G)-A--L was injected together with either (T,G)-A--L, (Phe,G)-A--L or (H,G)-A--L, a significant immune response was obtained for the three antigens. Similarly, the factor to (Phe,G)-A--L was as active in eliciting immune response to either (Phe,G)-A--L or (T,G)-A--L and a T cell factor produced with (H,G)-A--L cooperated efficiently with B cells to elicit an immune response to the 3 synthetic polypeptides built on A--L: (H,G)-A--L, (T,G)-A--L and (Phe, G)-A--L. In contrast, a factor to (T,G)-A--L failed to cooperate with B cells to provoke an immune response to (T,G)-Pro--L and vice versa, a factor produced with (T,G)-Pro--L did not trigger B cells to produce (T,G)-A--L specific antibodies. It is noteworthy that antibodies to (T,G)-A--L cross react with (Phe,G)-A--L, (H,G)-A--L and with (T,G)-Pro--L. However, antibodies to (T,G)-Pro--L do not cross react with (T,G)-A--L since they are directed exclusively to the Pro--L moiety of the polypeptide (18).

The specificity of T cell factors produced with (T,G)-A--L and (T,G)-Pro--L was further analyzed using immunoadsorbents of antigens coupled to Sepharose. As can be seen in Table 2, the (T,G)-A--L factor lost its cooperative activity after passage on immunoadsorbents of either (T,G)-A--L or (Phe,G)-A--L. An immunoadsorbent of (T,G)-Pro--L Sepharose failed to reduce the activity of the factor produced with (T,G)-A--L. No reduction in the helper activity of the (T, G)-A--L factor was detected after chromatography on an immunoadsorbent of multichain poly-DL-alanine (A--L), indicating that the cross-reactivity in the specificity of the factor between (T,G)-A--L, (Phe,G)-A--L and (H,G)-A--L is not due to

Table 1

SPECIFICITY OF T CELL FACTORS[a]

Cells and factors transferred into irradiated recipients	Antigen	Average $\log_2$ of hemagglutination titers
BM C3H.SW+Factor$_{(T,G)-A--L}$	(T,G)-A--L	6.5
BM C3H.SW+Factor$_{(T,G)-A--L}$	(Phe,G)-A--L	6.2
BM C3H/DiSn+Factor$_{(T,G)-A--L}$	(H,G)-A--L	5.1
BM C3H.SW+Factor$_{(T,G)-A--L}$	(T,G)-Pro--L	1.1
BM C3H.SW+Factor$_{(Phe,G)-A--L}$	(Phe,G)-A--L	6.1
BM C3H.SW+Factor$_{(Phe,G)-A--L}$	(T,G)-A--L	6.0
BM C3H/DiSn+Factor$_{(H,G)-A--L}$	(H,G)-A--L	5.4
BM C3H.SW+Factor$_{(H,G)-A--L}$	(T,G)-A--L	5.4
BM C3H.SW+Factor$_{(H,G)-A--L}$	(Phe,G)-A--L	4.5
BM SJL+Factor$_{(T,G)-Pro--L}$	(T,G)-Pro--L	6.9
BM C3H.SW+Factor$_{(T,G)-Pro--L}$	(T,G)-A--L	0.8

a) Factors to (T,G)-A--L and (Phe,G)-A--L were prepared from C3H.SW "educated" T cells and factors to (H,G)-A--L and (T,G)-Pro--L were prepared from C3H/DiSn and SJL "educated" T cells, respectively.

the A--L alone. In contrast an immunoadsorbent of Sepharose-coupled to poly(LGlu)-poly(DLAla)--poly(LLys),G-A--L,removed the activity of the (T,G)-A--L factor.

Table 3 demonstrates that the cooperative activity of a factor to (T,G)-Pro--L is removed by an immunoadsorbent of the homologous antigen. However, no reduction was observed in the activity of a factor to (T,G)-Pro--L following passage on a (T,G)-A--L immunoadsorbent confirming the results shown in Table 1 that there is no "cross-cooperative" effect between factors to (T,G)-Pro--L and (T,G)-A--L.

From the above described data it can be concluded that

Table 2

SPECIFICITY OF A (T,G)-A--L T CELL FACTOR

Cells and factors transferred into irradiated recipients	Antigen	Average log$_2$ of hemagglutination titers
BM C3H.SW+Factor	(T,G)-A--L	5.4
BM C3H.SW+Effluent from a (T,G)-A--L immuno-adsorbent[a]	(T,G)-A--L	1.8
BM C3H.SW+Effluent from a (Phe,G)-A--L immunoadsorbent	(T,G)-A--L	0.8
BM C3H.SW+Effluent from a (T,G)-Pro--L immunoadsorbent	(T,G)-A--L	5.5
BM C3H.SW+Effluent from an A--L immunoadsorbent	(T,G)-A--L	4.5
BM C3H.SW+Effluent from a G-A--L immunoadsorbent	(T,G)-A--L	1.0

a) Effluent of a T-cell factor produced with (T,G)-A--L after passing through antigen-Sepharose column. Equivalent to one spleen of "educated" T cells.

the specificity of the T cell factor is similar to that of antibodies although it appears not to be identical with antibody specificity.

ISOLATION AND PURIFICATION OF A T CELL FACTOR PRODUCED WITH (T,G)-A--L

The major objective of this part of the research, which was performed in collaboration with Dr. D. Givol and Miss D. Beitsch, was to try to isolate and characterize antigen specific T cell factors. The general properties (size and charge) of the (T,G)-A--L factor were analyzed by fractionation on a DEAE-cellulose ion exchange column and by gel filtration on Sephadex G-150.

Table 3

SPECIFICITY OF A (T,G)-Pro--L T CELL FACTOR

Cells and factors transferred into irradiated recipients	Antigen	Average $\log_2$ of hemagglutination titers
BM SJL + Factor	(T,G)-Pro--L	6.9
BM SJL + Effluent from a (T,G)-Pro--L immunoadsorbent[a]	(T,G)-Pro--L	0.8
BM SJL + Effluent from a (T,G)-A--L immunoadsorbent	(T,G)-Pro--L	6.3

a) Effluent of a T cell factor produced with (T,G)-Pro--L after passing through antigen-Sepharose column. Equivalent to one spleen of "educated" T cells.

The fractionation of the educated T cell supernatant specific for (T,G)-A--L on Sephadex G-150 column is shown in Fig. 1. Most of the activity emerges from the column in fraction B which corresponds to molecular weights smaller than 150,000. Each fraction eluted from the Sephadex column was also analyzed by sodium dodecyl sulphate (SDS) polyacrylamide gel electrophoresis. However, from this last analysis it appeared that the fractionation by gel filtration is a crude one and the number of bands in each of the fractions was not significantly smaller than in the whole supernatant.

Figure 2 demonstrates the fractionation pattern of a T cell factor from an anion exchange column of DEAE-cellulose using a step gradient of increasing NaCl concentrations for eluting the absorbed fractions of the factor. Results shown in Fig. 2 reveal that most of the cooperative activity of the factor was found in the fraction eluted with a 0.25 M salt concentration. Reports on fractionation of immunoglobulin by a similar procedure indicated that IgG is eluted with 0.02 M salt IgA with salt concentrations between 0.1 M and 0.15 M, IgD with 0.1 M salt and IgM with 0.2 M salt (19). Thus, this T cell factor does not seem to be related to immunoglobulins on the basis of a crude comparison of the data given above. This is in agreement with previous reports which failed to

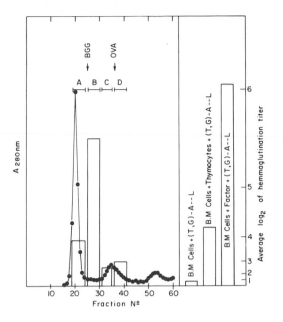

Figure 1. G-150 Sephadex gel filtration of a (T,G)-A--L
specific factor. The factor was concentrated and applied on
a Sephadex G-150 column (2.5 x 80 cm) equilibrated with 0.1 M
NH₄HCO₃. The protein content was determined by absorbance at
280 nm. Fractions containing discrete peaks of absorbance
were pooled and designated A, B, C, and D. The eluted
fractions were dialyzed against PBS and portions equivalent
to one spleen from the G-150 fractions and the intact supernatant containing the factor were transferred into syngeneic
irradiated recipients with 10^7 bone marrow cells and 10 μg
(T,G)-A--L to test the activity of the fractions. Antibody
titers were assayed in the sera of recipients, 12 days after
transfer, using the passive microhemagglutination method.

---

show a relationship of this factor with any of the known
immunoglobulin classes (12,13). SDS polyacrylamide gel
electrophoresis of the active fraction eluted with 0.25 M
salt showed the presence of a number of protein bands. Thus,
ion exchange chromatography achieves only a crude purification step.

In this study effort was also made to recover the factor
from the antigen-immunoadsorbents and to analyze its activity

492

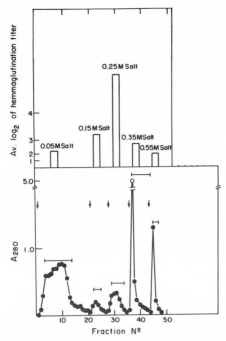

Figure 2. Chromatography on DEAE-cellulose of a T cell factor. The supernatant of 60 spleens containing educated T cells was applied on a DEAE-cellulose column (1 x 10 cm) previously equilibrated with 0.05 M NH_4HCO_3. Elution was carried out by a step gradient by means of increasing salt concentration with NaCl. The elution products were dialyzed against PBS and one spleen equivalents were transferred into irradiated recipients together with 10^7 bone marrow cells and 10 µg antigen. Antibody titers were assayed in the sera of recipient mice 12 days after transfer using the passive microhemagglutination method.

in helping B cells to mount an immune response. 25 ml of (T,G)-A--L educated T cells supernatant, derived from 50 spleens (15) were passed through a 2 ml column of (T,G)-A--L-Sepharose. The column was washed with PBS and eluted with 0.1 M NH_4OH. The eluate, containing about 50 µg of protein was neutralized with NH_4HCO_3 and acetic acid and dialyzed against PBS. Portions of this eluate equivalent to a volume of 0.5 ml of the original T cell supernatant were injected to irradiated recipients together with B cells and antigen. Antibody response was determined 12 days after transfer by measuring direct hemolytic plaque forming cells (PFC) in the

493

spleens of the recipients and by checking the antibody titers
in the sera of the recipients using the passive microhemagglutination technique. As is shown in Table 4 the eluate of
a (T,G)-A--L immunoadsorbent was as active as the T cell
supernatant in cooperating with B cells to mount an immune
response to (T,G)-A--L.

Table 4

ACTIVITY OF A PURIFIED T CELL FACTOR SPECIFIC FOR (T,G)-A--L

Cells and factors transferred into irradiated recipients	Mean PFC/ spleen	Average $\log_2$ of hemagglutination titers
10^7 C3H.SW BM cells	1096 $(1.10)^b$	0.8
10^7 C3H.SW BM cells+10^8 C3H.SW thymocytes	28457 (1.11)	4.4
10^7 C3H.SW BM cells+C3H.SW T cell factor[a]	32558 (1.16)	5.7
10^7 C3H.SW BM cells+T cell factor eluted from a (T,G)-A--L Sepharose column	32774 (1.22)	5.4
10^7 C3H.SW BM cells+Effluent from a (T,G)-A--L Sepharose column	1345 (1.15)	1.6

a) Produced by 1 spleen equivalent of "educated" T cells.
b) Geometric means of hemolytic direct PFC. Standard errors
   are given in parentheses.

It is also shown in the Table that the antigen immunoadsorbent eliminated the helping activity from the effluent which
passed through the column.

The eluate possessing the activity of the (T,G)-A--L
specific factor was injected into rabbits. The activity of
the rabbit antiserum was assessed by mixing the T cell factor
with 0.75 ml antiserum before the addition of B cells and
antigen, and the transfer into irradiated recipients. The
results given in Table 5 demonstrate that over 90% of the
cooperative activity of the T cell factor was inhibited by
the antiserum, whereas the normal rabbit serum used as a

Table 5

INHIBITION OF THE ACTIVITY OF A SPECIFIC T CELL FACTOR BY ANTISERUM

Cells, factors and sera transferred into irradiated recipients	Mean PFC/ spleen	Average $\log_2$ of hemagglutination titers
10^7 C3H.SW BM cells	1020 (1.04)[a]	1
10^7 C3H.SW BM cells+10^8 C3H.SW thymocytes	31666 (1.12)	4.8
10^7 C3H.SW BM cells+C3H.SW T cell factor	32713 (1.14)	6.3
10^7 C3H.SW BM cells+C3H.SW T cell factor+antiserum	1794 (1.19)	0.8
10^7 C3H.SW BM cells+C3H.SW T cell factor+normal rabbit serum	32863 (1.09)	6.2

a) Geometric means of hemolytic PFC. Standard errors are given in parentheses.

control did not interfere with the factor's helper activity.

The purified (T,G)-A--L factor by mean of affinity-chromatography on a (T,G)-A--L-Sepharose column was analyzed in 10% SDS-polyacrylamide gels. As can be seen in Fig. 3 a major purification step of this factor was achieved by the affinity chromatography. Two major peptide chains were revealed on the gel of molecular weights of 45,000 and 70,000. We do not know at present which of these bands represents the active factor.

THE T CELL FACTOR SPECIFIC FOR (T,G)-Pro--L IS A PRODUCT OF THE H-2 COMPLEX

The antibody response of mice to (T,G)-Pro--L is genetically controlled. SJL mice are high responders to this immunogen, whereas DBA/1 and SWR mice are low responders. The gene(s) controlling antibody response to this immunogen has been designated Ir-3 (20). Genetic analysis of the immune response to (T,G)-Pro--L performed in SJL and DBA/1

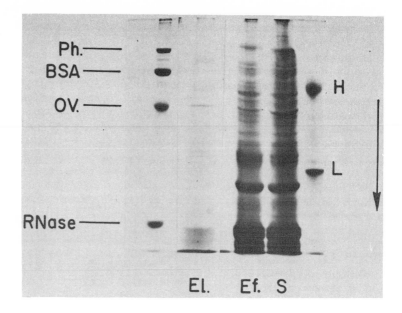

Figure 3. 10% SDS polyacrylamide gel electrophoresis of a
(T,G)-A--L factor purified by affinity chromatography.
S - The whole supernatant. Ef - (T,G)-A--L column effluent.
El - (T,G)-A--L column eluate.

mice, their F_1 hybrids as well as in the backcross progeny,
showed no linkage between the immune response potential to
(T,G)-Pro--L and the major histocompatibility (H-2) locus of
the mice (20).

The cellular basis of the immune response to (T,G)-Pro--
L has been studied using the antigen specific T cell factor.
T cells of SJL (high responder) mice were compared with T
cells of DBA/1 and SWR mice for their ability to produce cooperative factors. In parallel B cells of these strains were
tested for their response to the T cell product. It was
found that T cells of both SJL high and DBA/1 low responder
strains produced active cooperative factors to (T,G)-Pro--L,
whereas supernatants of cultures from educated T cells of SWR
low responder mice were not effective. The factors of SJL
and DBA/1 origin cooperated efficiently in eliciting antibodies to (T,G)-Pro--L only with B cells of SJL and SWR mice
and hardly at all with marrow cells of DBA/1 low responders

(17). Thus, the cellular genetic defect is on the level of the B cell population in DBA/1 mice and on the level of the T cells in SWR mice (21,22).

Since studies on the molecular nature of the T-cell factor produced to (T,G)-A--L to which the response is H-2 linked, suggested that it is a product of a gene in the I region of the H-2 complex (14) it was of interest, to establish the nature of the T cell factor specific for (T,G)-Pro--L to which the immune response was found not to be linked to H-2. The activity of a factor produced to (T,G)-Pro--L was removed by an antigen coated column (Table 3) whereas no reduction in the cooperative activity of the (T,G)-Pro--L T cell factor was observed after passage through an anti-immunoglobulin immunoadsorbent. The activity of a factor prepared with (T,G)-Pro--L in SJL mice was also removed by an anti-H-2^S column suggesting that the (T,G)-Pro--L specific factor is a product of the H-2 complex. Further mapping of the factor has been achieved with alloantisera produced against sub-regions of the H-2 complex which were kindly provided by Drs. B. Benacerraf and M.E. Dorf.

As shown in Table 6 the factor to (T,G)-Pro--L produced by DBA/1 (H-2^q) mice was removed completely by anti H-2^q sera, and not at all by anti-H-2^b immunoadsorbent. These results indicate that the factor carries alloantigens of the strains in which it is produced. The activity of the factor produced in DBA/1 mice was removed by an immunoadsorbent prepared with antiserum directed against the K and I region antigens of H-2^q (DBA/2 x B10.Br)F$_1$ anti-6R, whereas antiserum directed against the D end of H-2^q (C3H x B10.D$_2$)F$_1$ anti-B10.AKM did not interfere with the cooperative activity of the factor with B cells to elicit anti-(T,G)-Pro--L antibodies. On the basis of these results, we can assume that the (T,G)-Pro--L specific factor is a product of the left-hand (K) side of H-2, either of the K or I region. The results of further experiments in which anti Ia sera were used are given in Table 7. A (T,G)-Pro--L specific factor produced in SJL mice was removed by an anti-H-2^S ((B10 x A.CA)F$_1$ anti B10.S) immuno-adsorbent. The activity of the same factor was removed by an immunoadsorbent prepared with an antiserum specific for I-A^S + I-B^S + I-C^S ((B10 x A.TL)F$_1$ anti 7R) but not with an immunoadsorbent coated with antiserum directed against I-A^k + I-B^k + I-C^k ((B10 x A.TH)F$_1$ anti A.TL). The activity of this factor was reduced with an anti I-A^S + I-B^S (B10.D$_2$ x A.TL)F$_1$ anti 9R immunoadsorbent as well as with an immunoadsorbent coated with anti H-2^r serum ((C3H x B10)F$_1$ anti B10.RIII)

Table 6

IDENTIFICATION OF THE T CELL FACTOR SPECIFIC FOR (T,G)-Pro--L
AS A PRODUCT OF THE K+I END OF THE H-2 COMPLEX[a]

Cells and factors transferred into irradiated recipients	Antigen	Average $\log_2$ of hemagglutination titers
BM SJL + Factor	(T,G)-Pro--L	4.6
BM SJL + Effluent from an anti H-2^q immunoadsorbent	(T,G)-Pro--L	0.7
BM SJL + Effluent from an anti H-2^b immunoadsorbent	(T,G)-Pro--L	4.3
BM SJL + Effluent from an anti K+I end of H-2^q immunoadsorbent	(T,G)-Pro--L	0.5
BM SJL + Effluent from an anti D end of H-2^q immunoadsorbent	(T,G)-Pro--L	5.4

a) Factor was obtained from DBA/1 (H-2^q) "educated" T cells.

which cross reacts with H-2^s. These results indicate that the T
cell factor specific for (T,G)-Pro--L is a product of I-
region genes and probably of genes in the I-A sub-region of
the H-2 complex. It should be noted that the involvement of
K region genes in the production of the factor has not been
excluded yet.

The results described above demonstrate that the (T,G)-
Pro--L specific factor is a product of I region genes as was
previously found for the (T,G)-A--L specific T cell factor
(14). It is noteworthy that other T cell products have been
described which regulate B cell activity and which are coded
by the H-2 complex. Armerding and Katz (8) have described a
non-specific T cell product which can trigger B cells in the
presence of antigen. This allogeneic effect factor (AEF) has
been characterized as an I-region product (23). Tada and
colleagues have found an H-2 derived suppressor molecule

Table 7

REMOVAL OF THE ACTIVITY OF THE T CELL FACTOR SPECIFIC FOR
(T,G)-Pro--L WITH ANTI Ia ANTISERA[a]

Cells and factors transferred into irradiated recipients	Antigen	Average $\log_2$ of hemagglutination titers
BM SJL + Factor	(T,G)-Pro--L	4.8
BM SJL + Effluent from an anti H-2^S immunoadsorbent	(T,G)-Pro--L	1.6
BM SJL + Effluent from an anti I-A^S + I-B^S + I-C^S immunoadsorbent	(T,G)-Pro--L	2.2
BM SJL + Effluent from an anti I-A^k + I-B^k + I-C^k immunoadsorbent	(T,G)-Pro--L	4.3
BM SJL + Effluent from an anti I-A^S + I-B^S immunoadsorbent	(T,G)-Pro--L	2.4
BM SJL + Effluent from an anti H-2^r immunoadsorbent	(T,G)-Pro--L	2.8

a) Factor was obtained from SJL (H-2^S) "educated" T cells.

produced by T cells which is specific for the antigen in the presence of which it is prepared (24,25). It is very likely that all these factors are closely related.

The apparent contradiction between results showing that the (T,G)-Pro--L specific T cell factor is a product of the H-2 complex and results of genetic analysis which show no linkage of the response to H-2, could be explained if the existence of two genes regulating this immune response is taken into consideration. In this case one of the genes is linked to H-2 and is involved in the production of the T cell factor, and the second gene is not H-2 linked and is expressed in the B cell population. Table 8 demonstrates that the existence of two genes controlling the response to (T,G)-

Table 8

ANTIBODY RESPONSE TO (T,G)-Pro--L IN F_1 HYBRIDS OF LOW RESPONDER STRAINS[1]

Strain	Average $\log_2$ of hemagglutination titers[b]
SJL[a]	6.0
DBA/1	0.4
SWR	0.2
(DBA/1 x SWR)F_1	5.3

a) Control high responder.
b) Secondary antibody responses measured in sera of mice 10 days after second injection of 10 µg (T,G)-Pro--L.

Pro--L has been confirmed. Thus, the F_1 hybrids between two low responder mouse strains to (T,G)-Pro--L (DBA/1 and SWR) were found to be good responders. The defect in the response of DBA/1 mice to (T,G)-Pro--L was found to be expressed in their B cell population whereas the genetic defect in SWR mice was found in the inability of their T cells to produce an active T cell factor. The responsiveness of the F_1 hybrids between these two low responders of complementary types provides strong evidence that two distinct genes control the immune response to (T,G)-Pro--L. Evidence for two Ir genes controlling the response to T-dependent antigens has been reported recently (26-28). Dorf et al. (26) demonstrated that the immune response to the linear synthetic terpolymer of L-glutamic acid, L-lysine, and L-phenylalanine (GLΦ) is controlled by at least two genes which are localized in different regions of the H-2 complex. Munro and Taussig (27) reported about the presence of two genes which regulate immune responsiveness to (T,G)-A--L. These authors found that the F_1 hybrids between B10.M mice, which do not produce a cooperative factor to (T,G)-A--L, and B10.Br mice in which the defect in response to (T,G)-A--L is expressed exclusively in B cells, are high responders. Similar findings have been made by Rüde and Günther (28) in rats for the response potential to (H,G)-A--L. Thus, F_1 hybrids between intermediate and low responder rats to (H,G)-A--L, responded with high titers to this immunogen.

EFFECT OF T CELL FACTORS ON THE SPLENIC LEVELS OF CYCLIC AMP IN MICE

During the past decade, cyclic AMP (cAMP) has been identified as a key intermediate in the response of cells to exogenous stimuli. The possible role of cyclic nucleotides in the induction and regulation of immune responses has been the subject of investigations in numerous laboratories (29). A large number of intracellular processes is now known to be affected by cAMP such as differentiation, replication, lymphocyte transformation, B cell proliferation, etc. Therefore, it was of interest to find out whether the T cell factor will affect the levels of cAMP in mouse spleen cells.

In collaboration with Dr. Amir Shneyour, we have performed the following experiments: High responder mice to (T,G)-A--L were injected with 10 µg of the immunogen in complete Freund's adjuvant. Six to 8 weeks following immunization the mice were sacrificed and their spleen cell suspensions were exposed for 30 minutes at 37°C to different doses of the (T,G)-A--L specific T cell factor. After this incubation period, the reaction was stopped and the levels of cyclic AMP in the cells were assayed. As can be seen in Table 9, which represents two of the experiments performed, a significant increase was observed in the levels of cAMP in spleen cells of primed high responder mice of two strains. The levels of cAMP increased when instead of a supernatant containing the T cell factor of an equivalent of half a spleen, a factor equivalent to one spleen was incubated with 10^7 spleen cells. No further enhancement in cAMP levels was detected when higher doses of the factor (2 spleens equivalent) were added to the incubation mixture (Table 9). No significant change in cAMP levels was observed following incubation of cells with supernatants of spleen cells of irradiated mice which were injected with 10^8 thymocytes and phosphate buffered-saline (PBS) instead of (T,G)-A--L. Furthermore, when spleen cells of mice primed with an unrelated antigen (dinitrophenyl-ated bovine serum albumin) were incubated with the T cell factor specific for (T,G)-A--L only a small increase was detected in the levels of cAMP, similar to that observed with unprimed spleen cells which were incubated with the (T,G)-A--L specific T cell factor. The same enhancing effect on the cAMP levels was observed with a factor specific for (T,G)-Pro--L when incubated with spleen cells of SJL mice (high responders) which were immunized with the homologous antigen.

The above described results, although preliminary,

501

Table 9

EFFECT OF A T CELL FACTOR SPECIFIC FOR (T,G)-A--L ON THE LEVELS
OF cAMP IN SPLEENS OF PRIMED HIGH RESPONDER MICE

	pmoles cAMP/10^7 primed spleen cells	
	C57BL/6	CWB
10^7 cells alone	2.7 $\pm$ 0.3[a]	12 $\pm$ 0.24
10^7 cells + 10μg (T,G)-A--L	2.5 $\pm$ 0.2	9.8 $\pm$ 0.49
10^7 cells + Factor (0.5 spleen equivalent of "educated" T cells)	4.7 $\pm$ 0.5	16.3 $\pm$ 0.97
10^7 cells + factor (1 spleen equivalent of "educated" T cells)	6.1 $\pm$ 0.2	19.8 $\pm$ 1.78
10^7 cells + factor (2 spleens equivalent of "educated" T cells)	N.D.	18 $\pm$ 0.9

a) Mean values of triplicates $\pm$ standard errors.

suggest that the specific T cell factor has an enhancing
effect on the levels of splenic cAMP in high responder mice.
Many questions are still unsolved, e.g., which cell population
in the spleen is affected by the factor, what is the effect
of the factor on the cAMP levels in low responder cells, how
far this effect is specific, etc. Further establishment of
this phenomenon will hopefully provide a convenient system
for assaying the biological activity of the specific T cell
factor and help in understanding the mechanism by which it
triggers B cells to elicit an antibody response.

CONCLUDING REMARKS

In this paper I have presented data on the properties
of antigen specific T cell factors which are able to replace
T cells in cooperation with B cells for antibody production.
The specificity of these factors appears to resemble although
not to be identical to that of antibodies. The antigen
specific factors produced with (T,G)-A--L and (T,G)-Pro--L,

as well as the nonspecific helper factor (AEF, 8, 23) and an antigen specific suppressor factor (24,25), appear to be products of the I region of the H-2 complex. Therefore, it is logical to assume that, as in the case of antibodies, we are dealing with a population of molecules similar in their properties but, in the case of antigen specific factors, different in their specificities. They are also expected to have a variable and constant region. If one assumes that the constant region is the I region gene(s) product, the nature of the variable part should now be established taking into consideration recent reports (30,31) which provide evidence that the same idiotypic determinants can be found on both T and B lymphocytes.

Although the identification of the molecule(s) composing the antigen specific T cell factor is still incomplete, the isolation of the factor in an active form from antigen Sepharose columns represents a major purification step. Further characterization of the molecular properties of the isolated specific T cell factors will shed light on the nature of T cell receptors and their function in triggering B cells for antibody production or in cell mediated immunity.

ACKNOWLEDGMENTS

The studies reported here were supported in part by a grant 1R01 AI 11405-03 from the National Institutes of Health, U.S. Public Health Service.

Substantial parts of this study were performed together with my Ph.D. student, Miss Ronit Isac.

REFERENCES

(1) H.N. Claman, E.A. Chaperon and R.F. Triplett. J. Immunol. 97 (1966) 828.

(2) G.F. Mitchell and J.F.A.P. Miller. J. Exp. Med. 128 (1968) 821.

(3) N.A. Mitchison. Eur. J. Immunol. 1 (1971) 10.

(4) G.E. Roelants and A. Ryden. Nature 247 (1974) 104.

(5) G.E. Roelants, A. Ryden, L.B. Hagg and F. Loor. Nature 247 (1974) 106.

(6) K. Rajewsky and R. Nohr. Eur. J. Immunol. 4 (1974) 111.

(7) A. Schimpl and E. Wecker. Nature (New Biology) 237 (1972) 15.

(8) D. Armerding and D.H. Katz. J. Exp. Med. 140 (1974) 19.

(9) M. Feldmann and A. Basten. Nature (New Biology) 237 (1972) 13.

(10) M.J. Taussig. Nature 248 (1974) 234.

(11) M. Feldmann. J. Exp. Med. 136 (1972) 737.

(12) M.J. Taussig and A.J. Munro. Nature 251 (1974) 63.

(13) A.J. Munro, M.J. Taussig, R. Campbell, H. Williams and Y. Lawson. J. Exp. Med. 140 (1974) 1579.

(14) M.J. Taussig and A.J. Munro. Feder. Proc. (1975) In press.

(15) M.J. Taussig, E. Mozes and R. Isac. J. Exp. Med. 140 (1974) 301.

(16) E. Mozes, R. Isac and M.J. Taussig. J. Exp. Med. 141 (1975) 703.

(17) E. Mozes, in Progr. Immunol. II Vol. 2. eds. L. Brent and J. Holborow. (North-Holland Publishing Co., 1974) p. 191.

(18) E. Mozes, H.O. McDevitt, J.-C. Jaton and M. Sela. J. Exp. Med. 130 (1969) 493.

(19) J.L. Fahey and E.W. Terry, in Handbook of Experimental Immunology. second edition. ed. D.W. Weir (Blackwell Scientific Publication, London, 1973) Chapter 7.

(20) E. Mozes, H.O. McDevitt, J.-C. Jaton and M. Sela. J. Exp. Med. 130 (1969) 1263.

(21) G.M. Shearer, E. Mozes and M. Sela. J. Exp. Med. 135 (1972) 1009.

(22) E. Mozes and M. Sela. Proc. Nat. Acad. Sci. 71 (1974) 1574.

(23) D. Armerding, D.H. Sachs and D.H. Katz. J. Exp. Med. 140 (1974) 1717.

(24) T. Tada, K. Okumura and M. Taniguichi. J. Immunol. 111 (1973) 952.

(25) T. Tada, in Immune Recognition. Proc. 9th Leuk. Cult. Conf. ed. A.S. Rosenthal. (Academic Press, New York). In Press.

(26) M.E. Dorf, J.H. Stimpfling and B. Benacerraf. J. Exp. Med. (1975) In press.

(27) A.J. Munro and M.J. Taussig. Nature 256 (1975) 103.

(28) E. Rüde and E. Günther. in Progr. Immunol. II Vol. 2. eds. L. Brent and J. Holborow. (North-Holland Publishing Co., 1974) p. 223.

(29) C.W. Parker, T.J. Sullivan and H.J. Wedner, in Advances in Cyclic Nucleotide Research. Vol. 4. eds. P. Greengard and G.A. Robson. (Raven Press, New York, 1974) p. 1.

(30) H. Binz and H. Wigzell. J. Exp. Med. 142 (1975) 197.

(31) K. Eichmann and K. Rajewsky. Eur. J. Immunol. In press.

DISCUSSION FOLLOWING EDNA MOZES

MILLER: I understand that (T,G)-A--L must be added to
    release T cell factor; yet the antigen cannot be bound
    to it since the factor is retained on a (T,G)-A--L
    immunoabsorbent. Further, is (T,G)-A--L bound to the
    petri dish?

MOZES: We have performed experiments in which we added
    ^{125}I-(T,G)-A--L to the *in vitro* cultures of the spleens
    containing the educated T cells. The antigen was not
    bound to the petri dish (99% of the radioactivity was
    retained). All of the radioactivity was found in the
    effluent from a (T,G)-A--L column, whereas no radio-
    activity could be detected in the eluate containing the
    active T cell factor. We think that this indicates
    that the factor has a low affinity to the antigen and,
    therefore, that the release of the factor which is
    probably bound to the antigen in the *in vitro* cultures
    occurs easily.

MILLER: What is the viability of (T,G)-A--L-activated
    thymus cells after 6 hours *in vitro?* Also, if the
    cultured cells are washed after culture and injected
    in vivo, are they active in triggering bone marrow
    cells?

MOZES: After 6 hours of incubation *in vitro,* the viability
    of the cells is still quite high; I do not remember the
    precise percentage of viable cells. We have not tried
    to wash the activated thymocytes after culture or to
    inject them into mice. However, Michael Taussig has
    done it in one of his first experiments and found that
    cells possess a suppressive activity rather than a
    cooperative activity.

    [*EDITOR'S NOTE:* See Taussig, M.J. Nature 248:236,
    1974 - DHK.]

MILLER: Your data show only direct plaque-forming cells.
    From the work of Dr. McDevitt and his colleagues, it
    seems that the IgM response to (T,G)-A--L is the least
    T cell dependent. By contrast, the IgG response is
    highly T cell dependent. Have you looked for the pro-
    duction of indirect plaque-forming cells?

MOZES: In 1968, Dr. McDevitt published a paper showing that after priming mice in CFA with (T,G)-A--L and boosting them in aqueous solution, differences between low and high responder mice were observed in the IgM antibody response which we measure as highly T dependent. However, we have looked for production of indirect plaque-forming cells in these experiments and found that we get a low number of these plaques (about 25% of the total response measured); we have also measured mercaptoethanol-resistant antibodies in the serum of recipient mice and there we found that between 30-40% of the total antibodies produced were of the IgG class.

MILLER: I notice that the work you described with this type of factor has been performed with synthetic polypeptides. Has any one attempted to produce similar factors using classical carrier-hapten systems? In other words, can thymus cells activated to protein antigens release a factor which will enable hapten-primed B cells (from anti-θ serum-treated lymphoid cells) to respond to the hapten-protein conjugate?

MOZES: We have not performed exactly the experiment you suggest. We have generated successfully a factor with DNP-BSA and showed that it cooperated with bone marrow cells and antigen to elicit anti-DNP antibodies. I should add that the helper effect obtained in these experiments was less impressive than that observed with the synthetic polypeptides. (We have observed only about three or four-fold increase in the number of PFC above background when the DNP-BSA factor was used).

UNANUE: The polyacrylamide gel electrophoresis disclosed many bands. Was there serum in the incubation medium?

MOZES: The answer is no. We incubate the spleen cells containing the educated T cells with antigen in a serum-free medium.

UNANUE: Was protein synthesis required to generate the factor?

MOZES: I do not think so since when we added ^{3}H-leucine to the *in vitro* incubation medium, the factor generated was not labelled. We assume, therefore, that the factor was either shed or secreted from the cells and not newly synthesized during the incubation period.

UNANUE: Can you generate the factor in cultures of thymocytes depleted of macrophages?

MOZES: I have not done these experiments yet.

HÄMMERLING: Does the rabbit anti-factor serum exhibit
specificity for the particular factor against which it
was raised or does it cross-react with factors produced with other antigens?   Secondly, did you try to
find reaction of this rabbit antiserum with T and/or B
cells?

MOZES: We have used the rabbit anti-factor serum only in
the (T,G)-A--L system and therefore, I cannot tell you
yet whether the antiserum will inhibit factors produced with other antigens.   As to the second question,
we have not tried to react this antiserum with cells.

NOSSAL: Have you tried peripheral B cell sources, eg. anti-
θ serum-treated spleen cells, as a target for the factor?   The reason I ask is that we find marrow a difficult organ to analyze in adoptive immunity.   It contains, as well as a few mature B cells, many pre-B
cells and stem cells which can confuse interpretation.

MOZES: We have performed a few experiments in which we
used anti-θ serum-treated spleen cells, and the results
obtained were similar to those with bone marrow cells.
The reason we use bone marrow cells is to avoid as much
as possible T cell contamination in our B cell preparation.

NOSSAL: Can you tell us a little about the cell dose, PFC
response characteristics of the adoptive assay and also
of the kinetics, i.e. influence of the day of killing
of the adoptive hosts?

MOZES: We have performed our experiments with 10^7 bone
marrow cells and have done also a few experiments using
2×10^6 bone marrow cells, but the differences in the
results were not significant.   We have analyzed the
optimal kinetics and found that the peak of the response occurs on day 12 after transfer of the bone
marrow cells plus factor plus antigen.

E. MÖLLER: Have those strains which have a genetic restriction in their acceptor site for the factors been studied

or characterized as to their response to B cell mitogens? It would be extremely interesting to know, since this acceptor site might be the triggering receptor on B cells, and in view of recent findings of genetic restrictions with regard to the response to other B cell triggering substances which also appear to be determined by a gene not linked to *H-2*.

MOZES: These kinds of experiments were performed only with the synthetic polypeptides built on A--L and with (T,G)-Pro--L, and all of them are T dependent immunogens.

PAUL: Edna, I have a question concerning the cAMP assay of factor. Am I correct in concluding that the (T,G)-A--L factor can stimulate primed spleens without the addition of fresh (T,G)-A--L.

MOZES: This is correct. When antigen was added to the incubation mixtures of cells and factor, no additional effect on the cAMP levels was observed.

MUNRO: Is the failure to produce active T cell factor to (T,G)-Pro--L in SWR mice linked to *H-2?*

MOZES: The experiments in which we absorbed the factor to (T,G)-Pro--L by anti-Ia sera immunoadsorbents suggest that it is linked to *H-2*. In addition, we have performed genetic analysis experiments in which the response to (T,G)-Pro--L of F_1 hybrid mice and their backcrosses was studied and their ability to respond to (T,G)-Pro--L appeared to be *H-2*-linked. This was only one experiment in which 30 backcrossed mice were used. We are repeating this experiment now with more mice, and I hope to soon be able to confirm this observation.

J. KLEIN: I am confused about the genetics of the (T,G)-Pro--L factor. What was the original backcross which provided evidence for the genetic control of response to (T,G)-Pro--L? Shouldn't it have shown a two-gene segregation ratio?

MOZES: The original strains used for analysis of the genetic control of the immune responses to (T,G)-Pro--L were SJL high responder mice, DBA/1 low responders, their F_1 hybrids and backcross mice. The DBA/1 mice produce an active cooperative factor to (T,G)-Pro--L which can trigger high responder B cells to produce antibodies. On the other hand, their B cells cannot accept the T cell signal and therefore, they bear a B cell defect. Since the defect in DBA/1 is expressed only by one gene, there was no way to detect two-gene segregation ratios using the above strain combination.

SHEARER: Will the A--L backbone or loop-A--L generate a T cell factor that will stimulate bone marrow cells in the presence of (T,G)-A--L?

MOZES: I do not think so since the activity of a factor produced with (T,G)-A--L is not removed by an A--L-Sepharose column. Since the G-A--L-coated columns removes the activity of the (T,G)-A--L-specific T cell factor, it might be possible to generate a T cell factor with G-A--L which will stimulate bone marrow cells in the presence of the synthetic polypeptides derived from A--L [(T,G)-A--L, (H,G)-A--L and (Phe,G)-A--L)].

E. MÖLLER: I would like you to clarify the specificities of the factor. As I could read your slides, the (T,G)-A--L factor was neither specific for the (T,G)-Pro--L nor for the A--L backbone. And yet you stated that the factor was similar to antibody in its specificity.

MOZES: The (T,G)-A--L factor cooperated with bone marrow and (T,G)-A--L, (Phe,G)-A--L and (H,G)-A--L to elicit antibody responses; it is here that we observe cross-reactivity between antibody and the factor. However, this factor did not cooperate with bone marrow cells in eliciting an anti-(T,G)-Pro--L response, despite the fact that anti-(T,G)-A--L antibodies cross-react with (T,G)-Pro--L. The fact that the factor to (T,G)-A--L was not removed by an A--L immunoadsorbant indicates, in my opinion, that the cross-reactivity between (T,G)-A--L and the other polypeptides derived from A--L is not due to the A--L region alone.

McDEVITT: How do you deal with the fact that the factor has a specificity similar to that of antibody, and quite dissimilar to that of the *H-2*-linked *Ir* gene control, where a responder to (Phe,G)-A--L (*H-2q*) will not respond to (T,G)-A--L or (H,G)-A--L?

MOZES: The data I have presented show that the factor specificity is similar to that of antibodies but it is not identical with it. We have not performed experiments with H-2^q bone marrow cells and factors to either (T,G)-A--L or (H,G)-A--L. In my slides I showed that a factor to (T,G)-A--L will help in eliciting a response to either (Phe,G)-A--L or (H,G)-A--L only when mixed with high responder bone marrow cells, and only in the presence of the immunogen to which the response is generated.

BENACERRAF: Could you give more information on the comparative specificity of the antibody to (T,G)-A--L and specific factor to this antigen. What percentage of the antibody is directed to (T,G) and what percentage to G-A--L (which is the specificity of the factor). I feel that your data is very strong evidence for difference in determinant specificity between antibody and helper factor to (T,G)-A--L.

MOZES: I would say that about 70% of the antibody to (T,G)-A--L is directed to (T,G), and I agree with you that my data show differences in the specificity of the antibody and the helper factor to (T,G)-A--L.

CHARACTERIZATION OF THE ANTIGEN-SPECIFIC SUPPRESSIVE T CELL FACTOR WITH SPECIAL REFERENCE TO THE EXPRESSION OF *I* REGION GENES

TOMIO TADA AND MASARU TANIGUCHI

Laboratories for Immunology
School of Medicine, Chiba University

Abstract: This paper deals with the partial characterization
of the antigen-specific suppressive T cell factor with
special reference to its genetic nature. The suppressive T cell factor was extractable from thymocytes and
spleen cells of mice that had been primed with a relatively high dose of protein antigen, and exerted a
strong suppressive effect on the T cell dependent antibody response against a hapten coupled to the same
carrier proteins both in *in vivo* and *in vitro* experimental systems. The factor had specificity and affinity
for the immunizing antigen, but possessed no Ig determinants as revealed by absorption studies. The activity
was associated with a protein having a molecular weight
between 35,000 and 55,000, probably composed of small
molecular weight subunits. The factor was not easily
released from the primed T cell by a short-term culture
with antigen. The target of the suppressive T cell
factor was found to be the helper T cell with specificity
for the same antigen.

Absorption experiments using alloantisera against
restricted subregions of the $H-2$ complex firmly established that the T cell factor is a product of I region
genes in $H-2^d$, $H-2^k$ and $H-2^s$ mice. Although exact location of the gene(s) codes for the T cell factor is still
unknown, available evidence indicates that the factor is
probably encoded by genes in the $I-B$ (plus $I-E$) subregion.
However, there was no correlation between the absorbing
capacity and Ia specificities of alloantisera, suggesting that the factor is not an Ia molecule of known specificity. It was further found that the T cell factor can

513

only suppress the response of *H-2* histocompatible spleen cells. Studies using various combinations of strains and their F$_1$ hybrids indicated that the acceptor site of the helper T cell for the suppressor molecule is also determined by genes on the left side half of the *H-2* complex. It was postulated that paired genes in the *I* region code for both the suppressor molecule and acceptor site being complementary to each other.

INTRODUCTION

It is becoming increasingly clear that suppressor T cells play essential regulatory roles over a wide variety of immune responses (reviewed in 1). The possible importance of suppressor T cells has been pointed out in the maintenance of self-tolerance (2) and genetically determined unresponsiveness against certain antigens (3,4), and the relaxation of such a regulatory function of T cells is now being suspected as a cause of various immunological disorders including autoimmune phenomena. Thus, the function of the suppressor T cell appears to be concerned with the determination of the immune responsiveness of animals against given antigens, and to participate in actual self-not self discrimination. This postulate naturally focuses attention on the possible genetic background of the suppressor function, even though not all antibody responses encountered are known to be under genetic control.

Our previous studies (5,6) have demonstrated an antigen-specific suppression of IgG antibody response by passively transferred thymic and splenic suppressor T cells. It has been shown that T cells obtained from donors primed with a relatively high dose of carrier antigen greatly suppressed the antibody response of normal syngeneic recipients against a hapten coupled to the homologous carrier. Neither normal T cells nor those obtained from mice primed with unrelated antigens had such a suppressive activity, and thus the suppression was shown to be clearly antigen-specific. A similar type of antigen-specific T cell-mediated suppression has also been demonstrated in a number of other experimental systems (7-12), and now provides a clue to study the mechanism of the homeostatic regulation in the immune system.

In order to dissect the mechanism of the above suppressive cell interactions, we have attempted to separate a subcellular component of T cells that can mediate the antigen-

514

specific suppression of the immune response. This communication will review our recent studies on the nature and activity of the suppressive T cell factor which has turned out to be an *I* region gene product.

GENERAL FEATURES OF THE ANTIGEN-SPECIFIC SUPPRESSIVE T CELL FACTOR

The method employed to obtain the suppressive T cell factor has been described in detail previously (13). In brief, mice were immunized with two injections of 100 μg of keyhole limpet hemocyanin (KLH) 2 weeks apart, and thymocytes and spleen cells were taken 2 weeks after the second immunization. These cells had shown to possess strong suppressive activity in the syngeneic host that was immunized with di-nitrophenylated KLH (DNP-KLH) (3,4). The cells were disrupted by sonication, and cell-free extract was obtained by ultra-centrifugation at 40,000 G for 1 hr. These extracts will be referred to as T (thymus) and S (spleen cell) extracts.

To test the *in vivo* activity of these extracts, they were injected intravenously into syngeneic (or allogeneic in some cases) mice at a dose corresponding to 1×10^8 original cells concomitantly with the immunization with DNP-KLH plus 10^9 *Bordetella pertussis* vaccine. The animals were killed 6 days after the immunization, and the number of DNP-specific direct and indirect plaque forming cells in their spleen was enumerated using sheep erythrocytes coated with DNP_{34}-bovine serum albumin (DNP-BSA) by chromium chloride.

For detailed analysis of the immunosuppressive T cell factor with respect to its genetic nature, an *in vitro* antibody response was utilized. 10^7 of spleen cells from mice primed 4 weeks prior with DNP-KLH were cultured in the Marbrook system (14) with 0.1 μg/ml of DNP-KLH to induce an *in vitro* secondary antibody response. The suppressive T extract at a dose comparable to 10^7 original thymocytes was added at the beginning of the culture. The DNP-specific IgG antibody forming cells were assayed after a 5 day culture.

In both *in vivo* and *in vitro* experimental systems the administration of KLH-primed T and S extract caused strong suppression of DNP-specific antibody response against DNP-KLH (13,15). In general, indirect (IgG) PFC response was more profoundly suppressed than direct (IgM) PFC response, perhaps reflecting the difference in their T cell-dependency. The immunochemical and physicochemical properties of the suppressive T cell factor as revealed by both *in vivo* and *in vitro* systems were in good agreement. The activity was found to be clearly antigen-specific: KLH-primed T extract could suppress the DNP-specific IgG antibody response induced by DNP-KLH but not those induced by the hapten coupled to bovine gamma globulin (BGG) or egg albumin (EA). In reverse experiments where suppressor T cells were primed with BGG or EA, the T extract was incapable of suppressing antibody response against DNP-KLH, while being able to inhibit the response against DNP-BGG or DNP-EA, and thus the suppression was specific for the carrier by which suppressor T cells had been primed. This suppressive effect is obviously not due to the excessive amount of enhancing T cell factor (too much help) in the extract, because a reduction of the dose of T cell extract resulted in the decrease of suppression but not in the augmentation of the antibody response. The factor did not enhance the response of T cell-depleted spleen cells, indicating that it is not a T cell-replacing factor.

Furthermore, this carrier-specific suppressive effect of the T cell factor was found to be based on its specific binding to the corresponding carrier antigen. As shown in the result of an *in vitro* experiment, absorption of KLH-primed T cell extract with an immunoadsorbent composed of KLH completely removed the suppressive activity, while that with unrelated antigens (in this case, Ascaris extract, Asc) failed to do so (Table I). However, every effort to remove this antigen-specific suppressive activity of T extract by absorption with insolubilized antibodies against mouse Ig was unsuccessful, indicating that the suppressive T cell factor is not Ig in nature.

The molecular weight of the suppressive T cell factor was calculated to be between 35,000 and 55,000 daltons based on the elution from a Sephadex G-200 column. In our more recent studies, the extract was obtained from radioiodinated thymocytes, and the antigen-specific component was coprecipitated with KLH and rabbit anti-KLH. The precipitate was dissolved in sodium dodecyl sulfate (SDS) and subjected to SDS polyacrylamide gel electrophoresis. The major radioactive material migrated to the position with a molecular weight around 27,000, indicating that the T cell factor is composed of smaller subunits. The Ia molecule in the same cell lysate migrated to approximately the same position when electrophoresed under the same condition. Other studies indicated that the activity of the suppressive factor is resistant to RNase but is easily destroyed by pronase, as well as by heating it at 56°C for 2 hr and storage at 4°C for 1 week (13).

TABLE I

Absorption of KLH-primed thymocyte extract with
antigens and anti-immunoglobulin antibodies

Absorbed with	Anti-DNP PFC/culture	
	Direct	Indirect
Control	970 ± 281	2,654 ± 104
Unabsorbed	650 ± 76	328 ± 145
KLH	712 ± 188	2,577 ± 157
Asc	766 ± 205	500 ± 219
Anti-Igs	982 ± 398	507 ± 210
Anti-Fab	626 ± 26	314 ± 81
Anti-μ	325 ± 53	206 ± 79
Anti-γ	322 ± 38	241 ± 85
No antigen	40 ± 15	24 ± 5

The target of this immunosuppressive T cell factor was
found to be the helper T cell having an identical carrier-
specificity (15). This was shown by the following experiment:
DNP-EA-primed spleen cells were stimulated *in vitro* with a
mixture of DNP-EA and DNP-KLH. In this particular situation
of the secondary anti-DNP antibody response, one can predict
that DNP-specific B cells would equally bind DNP-EA and DNP-
KLH molecules, while the helper T cells present in this reaction mixture are only capable of reacting with the EA molecule.
Under this experimental condition, the addition of EA-specific
T extract resulted in a strong suppression of anti-DNP-antibody
response, whereas a comparable dose of the KLH-specific T cell
factor produced no suppressive effect. The result excludes
the possibility that the antigen-specific T cell factor directly acts on B cells, because the factor cannot express the suppressive activity unless the helper T cell with the identical

517

specificity to that of the factor coexists. Thus, the target of the suppressor T cell is obviously the helper T cell having the specificity for the same carrier molecule.

Another interesting point of this suppressor molecule distinguishable from other antigen-specific and non-specific T cell factors is the mode of release of the factor from primed T cells. It has been shown by a number of investigators that cooperative and suppressive T cell factors can be released from T cells into supernatant by a short-term culture with appropriate stimuli. We have tried to obtain the suppressive factor by culturing KLH-primed thymus and spleen cells in Petri dishes with DNP-KLH for 6 to 12 hr. The supernatant was collected by centrifugation. The residual cultured cells were washed, and then subjected to sonication and ultracentrifugation to obtain the cell-free extract. Both the culture supernatant and residual cell-extract were added to the culture of DNP-KLH primed spleen cells in order to determine which of them contains the suppressive activity.

It was found that the suppressive activity was definitely present in the extract of cultured cells, while the supernatant contained only a little suppressive activity. No enhancing activity was observed in either fraction at varying doses in the present experimental system. It was further confirmed that the suppressive activity of the extract from residual cultured cells was completely removed by a single passage through a column of immunoadsorbent of KLH, but not of Asc. Hence, the antigen-specific suppressive T cell factor seems to remain more firmly bound to the membrane of primed T cells than other known T cell factors.

THE ANTIGEN-SPECIFIC SUPPRESSIVE T CELL FACTOR AS AN *I* REGION GENE PRODUCT

In the course of heretofore mentioned studies, we were aware of the fact that the suppressive T cell factor could not act across the major histocompatibility barrier of mouse strains. It was found in an *in vivo* study that the KLH-specific T cell factor of BALB/c mice could not suppress the antibody response of C57BL mice against DNP-KLH. Similarly, the T cell extract derived from C57BL mice primed with KLH could not alter the response of BALB/c mice, while being able to suppress the response of syngeneic C57BL mice. However, the factor obtained from BALB/c mice could significantly suppress the response of DBA/2 mice that have the same $H-2^d$ haplotype as BALB/c strain. These results prompted us to explore the genetic nature of the suppressive T cell factor with respect to (1) the genes code for the T cell factor, and (2) the structure of the acceptor site of the helper T cell for the suppressor molecule.

The availability of alloantisera against restricted subregions of the $H-2$ complex enabled us to analyse genetic characteristics of the suppressive T cell factor. The strains mostly used in the present experiments were BALB/c ($H-2^d$) and C3H ($H-2^k$) mice. The T extracts of these mice primed with KLH were absorbed with immunoadsorbents composed of gamma globulin fractions of alloantisera with known specificities for $H-2$ subregions, and the absorbed materials were added to the culture of DNP-KLH-primed spleen cells of syngeneic mice together with an appropriate amount of DNP-KLH.

Table II shows the result of an absorption experiment using the BALB/c T cell factor. Two alloantisera against whole $H-2^d$, i.e., (B10 x A.CA)F_1 anti-B10.D2 and B10 anti-B10.D2, could consistently absorb the suppressive activity of the KLH-primed T extract, indicating that the suppressive factor is a product(s) of the major histocompatibility gene complex. Two other antisera reactive with the products of the K-end (K, $I-A$ and $I-B$ subregions) of $H-2^d$ were also capable of removing the suppressor molecule, while an antisera raised against methylcholanthrene-induced $H-2^d$ tumor, i.e., (B6 x A)F_1 anti-$H-2^d$ tumor, which can only react with the K region gene product of $H-2^d$ (H-2.31), was unable to remove the suppressive activity. An antiserum reactive with the products of the right hand side of $H-2^d$ ($I-C$, S and D), i.e., (B10 x LP.RIII)F_1 anti-B10.A(5R) was incapable of absorbing the suppressive activity. Thus by simple subtraction and logical deduction, the absorbing capacity of alloantisera is associated with the specificity for $I-A$ and/or $I-B$ subregions. However, two alloantisera raised against $I-C$ subregions, i.e., B10.A(18R) anti-B10.A(5R) and (B10 x LP.RIII)F_1 anti-B10.A(2R), showed a marginal absorbing capacity in repeated experiments, and therefore the participation of the $I-C$ subregion was not completely excluded by the present experiments. As will be discussed later, these antisera are reactive with Ia. 15 which is encoded by a gene present in the $I-E$ subregion detected in only $H-2^d$ and $H-2^k$ strains.

A similar result was also obtained in SJL ($H-2^S$) mice. The KLH-specific suppressive T cell factor was completely absorbed with A.TL anti-A.TH (anti-I^S) but not with (A.AL x B10)F_1 anti-A.TL (anti-K^S), as shown in Table III. As will

519

be discussed later, the same was true for the $H-2^k$ factor. Therefore, it is obvious that the suppressive T cell factor is, in fact, an I region gene product in various strains of mice.

TABLE II

Absorption of the suppressive T cell factor

with alloantibodies directed toward $H-2^d$ subregions

Absorbed with	Specificity	Indirect PFC/culture
Control	——	$1,450 \pm 141$
Unabsorbed	——	175 ± 135
$(B10xA.CA)F_1$ anti-B10.D2	$H-2^d$	$1,593 \pm 251$
B10 anti-B10.D2	$H-2^d$	$1,353 \pm 156$
$(B10xA)F_1$ anti-B10.D2	$K^d, I-A^d, I-B^d$	$1,519 \pm 330$
B10.A anti-B10.D2	$K^d, I-A^d, I-B^d$	$1,507 \pm 216$
$(B6xA)F_1$ anti-$H-2^d$ tumor	K^d	281 ± 68
$(B10xLP.RIII)F_1$ anti-B10.A(5R)	$I-C^d, S^d, D^d$	341 ± 117
B10.A(18R) anti-B10.A(5R)	$I-C^d$	572 ± 92
$(B10xLP.RIII)F_1$ anti-B10.A(2R)	$I-C^d$	661 ± 198

TABLE III

Absorption of the suppressive T cell

factor of $H-2^s$(SJL) mice with alloantisera

T extract absorbed with	Specificity	Indirect PFC/culture
Control	——	$4,624 \pm 288$
Unabsorbed	——	517 ± 241
$(A.ALxB10)F_1$ anti-A.TL	K^s	496 ± 158
A.TL anti-A.TH	I^s	$3,796 \pm 723$

We have further attempted to learn whether or not the suppressive T cell factor is associated with known Ia molecules. Since $H-2^d$ mice possess Ia. 11 and 8 encoded by genes in $I-A$, Ia. 15 in $I-E$ and Ia. 6 and 7 in $I-C$ subregions, the absorption was carried out using antisera reactive with these Ia determinants. Some antisera have been raised against different strains which share one or two Ia specificities with $H-2^d$ mice. The BALB/c factor was absorbed with these alloantisera, and the residual activity was assessed by adding the absorbed material to the culture of BALB/c spleen cells.

As shown in Table IV, two alloantisera raised against $H-2^d$ containing anti-Ia. 11 were capable of absorbing the suppressive activity, whereas antisera raised against different haplotypes, i.e., anti-$H-2^b$ (anti-Ia. 8) and anti-$H-2^k$ (anti-Ia. 7) were ineffective in removal of the suppressor molecule. Here again some antisera reactive with Ia. 15 produced incomplete but appreciable absorbing capacity.

TABLE IV

Failure to absorb the suppressive T cell factor
with alloantisera raised against different haplotypes

Absorption with	Specificity		Indirect PFC/culture
	$H-2$ subregions	Ia	
Control	———	——	1,356±208
Unabsorbed	———	——	264± 32
B10xA anti-B10.D2	$K^d, I-A^d, I-B$	11	1,384±118
B6xA anti-B10.D2 absorbed with $H-2^d$ tumor	$I-A^d, I-B^d$	11	1,205±393
C3H.QxHTH anti-C3H.B10	K^b, I^b	8	317± 81
AxB10.A(15R) anti-B10	K^b, I^b	8	334± 95
B10.A(4R)xHTI anti-B10.A	$I-B^k, I-E, I-C^d$	6,7,15	449±413
B10.A(4R)x129 anti-B10.A(2R)	$I-B^k, I-E, I-C^d$	6,7,15	288± 70
A.TH anti-A.TL	I^k	7,15	486±248
A.THxB10.HTT anti-A.TL	$I-A^k, I-B^k, I-E$	15	275± 30
B10.A(18R) anti-B10.A(5R)	$I-E, I-C^d$	6,7,15	579± 92

The results at first glance seem to indicate that the suppressor molecule is associated with Ia. 11, but this conclusion will not be verified unless we can exclude the possibility that these antisera do not react with other unknown molecules which are coded for by genes in the $H-2$ complex, inasmuch as no defined Ia specificity associated with the $I-B$ subregion has been recognized in $H-2^d$ mice.

Therefore, we have attempted to analyse this problem by using $H-2^k$ mice, in which Ia. 1 and 2 are encoded by genes in $I-A$, Ia. 3 in $I-B$, Ia. 15 in $I-E$ and Ia. 7 in the $I-C$ subregions. C3H mice were immunized with KLH to obtain the KLH-specific suppressive T cell factor. The T extract was absorbed with various alloantisera directed to different subregions of the $H-2$ complex with different anti-Ia specificities as depicted in Table V. It is evident that all of the alloantisera reactive to I region gene products were capable of removing the suppressive activity, while there was apparently no meaningful association between Ia specificities and absorbing capacity. However, it is at least clear that an antiserum lacking antibodies reactive with $I-A$ subregion gene products, i.e., (B10.A 4R x 129)F_1 anti-B10.A 2R, *does* absorb the suppressor molecule, indicating that the suppressive T cell factor is *not* the product of genes present in $I-A$ subregion. Similarly, three antisera which are *not* reactive with $I-C$ subregion products *could* absorb the activity, inferring that the $I-C$ subregion is not involved in coding for the T cell factor. On the other hand, an antiserum which is only reactive to the product of $I-E$ subregion of $H-2^k$, i.e., B10.A(18R) anti-B10.A(5R), was capable of absorbing the suppressor activity, and thus the molecule in C3H appeared to be encoded by genes in the $I-E$ subregion or its vicinity. However, it is not the Ia. 15 molecule *per se*, as the antisera lacking anti-Ia. 15 activity could absorb the suppressor molecule. Since the $I-E$ subregion has been recognized in only $H-2^k$ and $H-2^d$ mice by the presence of Ia. 15, and is considered to comprize a part of the $I-B$ subregion at the left side of the $I-C$ subregion, it is probable that the suppressor molecule in the present studies is coded for by gene(s) in the $I-B$ subregion including $I-E$. As the absorption of the $H-2^d$ factor with this same antiserum was always incomplete, it appears that the gene composition of the $I-E$ subregion of $H-2^d$ is different from $H-2^k$ despite sharing a same gene coding for Ia. 15. Alternatively, the suppressor molecule may be a heterogeneous population, and multiple I region genes could be involved. If this is the case, various alloantisera may be capable of absorbing a part of the population resulting in a sufficiently

TABLE V

Lack of association of absorbing capacity and Ia specificity of alloantisera

Absorbed with	Specificity		Indirect PFC/culture
	H-2 subregions	Ia	
Control	—	—	1,616 ± 231
Unabsorbed	—	—	150 ± 39
A.QR anti-B10.A	*K*	—	118 ± 18
(C3H.H-2°x129) anti-C3H	*K,I-A,I-B,I-E,I-C*	1,2	1,455 ± 115
A.TH anti-A.TL	*I-A,I-B,I-E,I-C*	1,2,3,15,7	1,458 ± 141
(B10.D2xA.TH) anti-A.TL	*I-A,I-B,I-E,I-C*	1,2,3	1,675 ± 157
(A.THxB10.HTT) anti-A.TL	*I-A,I-B,I-E*	1,2,3,15	1,540 ± 101
[B10.A(4R)x129] anti-B10.A(2R)	*I-B,I-E*	15,7	1,475 ± 84
B10.A(18R) anti-B10.A(5R)	*I-E*	15,7	1,588 ± 75

overt reduction of the suppressive activity. Therefore, more definite mapping of the genes for the suppressor molecule should await further detailed analysis using recombinant strains.

REQUIREMENT FOR HISTOCOMPATIBILITY IN THE EFFECTIVE SUPPRESSION BY THE T CELL FACTOR IN DIFFERENT MOUSE STRAINS

As already mentioned in the previous section, the suppressive T cell factor under present investigation could not act across the major histocompatibility barrier in the *in vivo* transfer experiment. This apparent lack of suppression in histoincompatible recipients is not due to the non-specific stimulation by allogeneic factor that overcame the suppressive effect, since we have confirmed that the T cell extracts from unprimed allogeneic mice had no such a stimulatory activity in both *in vivo* and *in vitro* experiments. Therefore, it is apparent that identities among genes in major histocompatibility complex is definitely required for the effective suppression. The simplest explanation for this histocompatibility requirement is that the acceptor site on the helper T cell for the suppressive T cell factor has a complementary structure to the suppressor molecule, with which the most effective and efficient suppression is made possible. If this is the case, one can predict that both the suppressor and acceptor molecules on T cells are coded for by paired genes both present in the same *I* region, and one of which is selectively expressed on the suppressor or helper T cell. To study this possibility, we have examined the effect of the suppressive T cell factor from one strain of mice on the antibody response of syngeneic, semisyngeneic and allogeneic spleen cells, some of which differ from the donor strain in certain loci in the *H-2* complex.

The strains used in this study are BALB/c, A/J, (BALB/c x A/J)F_1, C3H, CBA, (BALB/c x CBA)F_1, SJL and B10.S. These mice were used as donors of the KLH-specific T cell factor as well as the sources of primed spleen cells to induce *in vitro* secondary antibody response against DNP-KLH. Several possible combinations of donors and recipients were made, and the degree of suppression of indirect PFC response was calculated by comparing with the response without the suppressive T cell factor. The essential results selected from such experiments using various combinations are summarized in Table VI to VIII.

As is expected, the suppressive effect of the KLH-specific T cell factor is, in general, clearly related to the iden-

TABLE VI

Suppression of *in vitro* antibody response by the T cell
factor from histocompatible strains

Donor strain	Recipient strain	Identities[*]	% suppression of indirect PFC
BALB/c	BALB/c	K,I,S,D	86
	A/J	S,D	0
	(BALB/cxA/J)F$_1$	$\underline{K},\underline{I},S,D$	75
	(BALB/cxCBA)F$_1$	$\underline{K},\underline{I},\underline{S},\underline{D}$	92
	CBA	none	0
CBA	CBA	K,I,S,D	93
	C3H	K,I,S,D	81
	(BALB/cxA/J)F$_1$	$\underline{K},\underline{I}$	94
	A/J	K,I	74
	BALB/c	none	0
(BALB/cxCBA)F$_1$	(BALB/cxCBA)F$_1$	K,I,S,D	91
	BALB/c	$\underline{K},\underline{I},\underline{S},\underline{D}$	88
	CBA	$\underline{K},\underline{I},\underline{S},\underline{D}$	75
	A/J	$\underline{K},\underline{I}$	76
	SJL	none	0

[*] Semisyngeneic regions are underlined.

tities in genes in the *H-2* complex between donor and recipient strains with two exceptional cases (see below). The general rule will be found in Table VI, which indicates that all syngeneic and semisyngeneic (parents and F_1) combinations are effective in inducing the suppression. Thus, the BALB/c factor could suppress the responses of BALB/c, (BALB/c x CBA)F_1 and (BALB/c x A/J)F_1, and the CBA factor could suppress the responses of CBA, C3H and (BALB/c x CBA)F_1. However, the BALB/c factor was incapable of suppressing the CBA response, and the CBA factor did not suppress the BALB/c response, indicating that identities of genes in the *H-2* complex is definitely required for effective suppression. One important point to be stressed is that the CBA factor could suppress the responses of A/J and (BALB/c x A/J)F_1 which share the *K, I-A* and *I-B* subregions with CBA. On the other hand, the BALB/c factor was incapable of suppressing the response of A/J, which shares the *I-C, S* and *D* regions with BALB/c. Hence, it is concluded that the gene(s) which codes for the acceptor site is located in the left side half of the *H-2* complex. It is also apparent from the experiments using (BALB/c x CBA)F_1 that the acceptor for $H-2^d$ and $H-2^k$ factors are codominantly expressed on T cells of the F_1 mice, and that the F_1 mice could produce perhaps separate molecules which suppress either the $H-2^d$ or $H-2^k$ response.

However, there were so far two exceptional strains which do not fit the above general rule. One is A/J strain which did not produce the suppressive T cell factor under the identical condition. As shown in Table VII, the T extract from A/J mice could not suppress the responses of both A/J and C3H mice. We have repeated several experiments using different immunization regimens with the constant failure to produce the KLH-specific suppressive T cell factor in A/J strain. If (BALB/c x A/J)F_1 mice were used as donors, they could produce a factor which can only suppress the responses of BALB/c and (BALB/c x A/J)F_1, indicating that the factor is only reactive with the acceptor molecule coded for by gene(s) of $H-2^d$. The same T extract of (BALB/c x A/J)F_1 consistently failed to suppress the responses of A/J and C3H, indicating that the suppressive T cell factor reactive with $H-2^a$ and $H-2^k$ acceptors is not present in the extract of F_1 thymocytes. From these results we are compelled to conclude that A/J mice cannot produce the KLH-specific suppressor molecule, although the acceptor site for $H-2^k$ factor is clearly expressed on their responding spleen cells (see Table VI). This finding is probably consistent with the observation made several years ago by Cerottini and Unanue (16), who showed that A/J strain is

TABLE VII

Failure to produce suppressive T cell factor in
A/J and (BALB/c x A/J)F$_1$ strains

Donor strain	Recipient strain	Identities*	% suppression of indirect PFC
A/J	A/J	K^k, I^k, S^d, D^d	0
	C3H	K^k, I^k	0
	BALB/c	S^d, D^d	0
(BALB/cxA/J)F$_1$	A/J	$\underline{K^k, I^k}$	0
	C3H	$\underline{K^k, I^k}$	0
	BALB/c	$\underline{K^d, I^d}, S^d, D^d$	70
	(BALB/cxA/J)F$_1$	$K^{d/k}, I^{d/k}, S^d, D^d$	70

* Semisyngeneic regions are underlined.

a high respondor to KLH, while CBA and BALB/c were rather poor respondors, and that the responsiveness to KLH is not under H-linked Ir gene control. It may also imply that A/J mice lack the expression of one of the paired genes to produce suppressor molecule, while the experssion of the other gene for the acceptor site is intact. Alternatively, the expression of the suppressor molecule is determined by unknown other regulator genes not linked to H-2 complex. Such possibilities should be examined in the future using combinations of congeneic recombinant mice.

Another exceptional case is the response of B10.S mice. As presented in Table VIII, there are striking differences in the sensitivity to the suppression by H-2^S factor in SJL and B10.S spleen cells. The response of SJL spleen cells was markedly suppressed by the T extract derived from either SJL or B10.S, indicating that both strains could produce the suppressive T cell factor. As already mentioned in the previous section, the suppressive T cell factor of SJL mice was completely removed by A.TL anti-A.TH (anti-I^S), and thus the T cell factor in H-2^S mice is also an I region gene product. However, the response of B10.S spleen cells was *not* suppressed by the

527

T extract either from B10.S or SJL, which had been shown to suppress the response of SJL under the identical condition. Furthermore, the B10.S factor consistently enhanced the response of B10.S spleen cells, while suppressing the response of SJL spleen cells. This difference is most likely to be due to the difference in the sensitivity of responding cells to the suppressor factor rather than in the amount of the suppressive T cell factor produced by these strains. The results again suggest that the suppressor and acceptor molecules on T cells are coded for by separate genes, and the expression of acceptor gene is lacking in B10.S mice. Our more recent studies indicated that all of the congeneic mice with B10 background produced the suppressor molecule which was reactive with $H-2$ histocompatible spleen cells, but the acceptor for the syngeneic suppressor molecule was not detectable in all cases examined. Thus, it seems possible that the expression of I region genes is influenced by other gene(s) not linked to the $H-2$ complex.

The above data thus far suggest that the possible acceptor site of the helper T cell for the suppressor molecule is also encoded by genes in the left side half of the $H-2$ complex,

TABLE VIII

Failure to accept the suppressive effect of

the $H-2^S$ factor in B10.S mice

Donor strain	Recipient strain	Identities	% suppression of indirect PFC
SJL	SJL	K,I,S,D	72
	B10.S	K,I,S,D	0
	CBA	none	0
B10.S	SJL	K,I,S,D	63
	B10.S	K,I,S,D	0[*]
	CBA	none	0

[*] Definite enhancement.

and that these genes for suppressor and acceptor molecules
are paired with each other. It is probable that one of the
paired genes is expressed selectively on the surface of different T cell subsets, with which effective and efficient
interactions between different subpopulations are made possible. In certain exceptional cases one of the expressions is
lacking, and this may attribute to the different responsiveness of strains to certain antigens such as KLH, which is not
under *Ir* 1 gene control. Thus, it is likely that although
both suppressor and acceptor molecules are coded for by paired genes in the *H-2* complex, the expression of which is independent of each other. However, it is not concluded at the
present time whether one of the paired genes is lacking in
some strains or its expression is depressed by other unknown
genes not linked to the *H-2* complex in majority of such exceptional cases.

DISCUSSION

The studies presented here indicate not only that the
antigen-specific factor from the suppressor T cell is an *I*
region gene product, but also that the acceptor site for it
on the helper T cell is determined by genes in the left side
half of the *H-2* complex. Thus, it appears that the products
of the major histocompatibility complex are, in fact, mediating the network of T-B and T-T cell interactions. The results
lead to a postulate that there should exist paired genes which
code for two or more functionally complementary structures on
different lymphoid cell populations with which they could
effectively and efficiently interact. A hypothetical schema
is presented in Figure 1. T cells when activated with antigen
would differentiate into suppressor or helper T cells, depending on the immunization regimens and properties of the antigen.
Suppressor and helper T cells may express complementary structure encoded by one of the paired genes in the *H-2* complex
with which the suppressor T cell can interact with the helper
T cell to induce suppression of the antibody response. It is
probable that the interaction between the helper T cell and B
cell is also made possible via *I* region gene products as has
been pointed out by Katz and Benacerraf (17). Such soluble
mediators with the nature of the *I* region gene product have
been reported by Taussig and his associates (18-21) and Katz
and his associates (22-24). More recently, Kapp et al (25)
have succeeded in obtaining a similar antigen-specific T cell
factor to ours in genetically non-respondor mice to a synthetic polypeptide GAT.

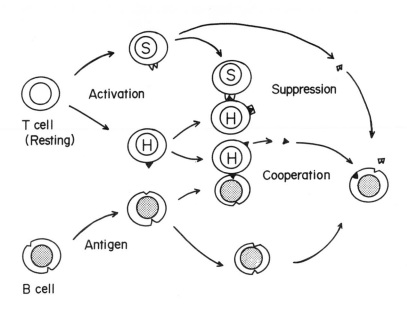

Figure 1. A hypothetical schema of interactions
between different lymphoid cells via *I* region gene
products. Helper T cell (H) and suppressor T cell (S)
are supposed to express one of the paired genes in the
I region as indicated ▼ and ◪. A complementary
interaction between these molecules could lead to the
inhibition of helper activity resulting in the suppression of T cell-dependent antibody response by the B cell.
A similar interaction between the helper T cell and B
cell can be postulated. The antigen binding capacity
of some of these molecules facilitates cell interactions.

The chemical and physicochemical properties of the suppressor molecule are very similar to those reported by the
above investigators (18-25). It is a protein with a molecular
weight between 35,000 and 55,000, and perhaps composed of
small molecular weight subunits, one of which seems to be
close to the Ia molecule. Despite its specific binding to
the immunizing antigen, it is not immunoglobulin in nature.
The immunochemical and physicochemical properties of the suppressive T cell factor is summarized in Table IX. It is
obvious only a few differences are found from those of cooperative factors. Thus, the most important questions are

TABLE IX

Properties of the suppressive T cell factor

Specificity for	Carrier
Sensitivity to DNase	–
RNase	–
Pronase	+
Ig determinants	–
Molecular weight	35,000 ∼ 55,000
H-2 barrier	+
I region gene expression	+
T cell surface antigens	+
Target	Mostly helper T cell
Release by antigen	Weak
Activity	Suppression
Possible nature	T cell receptor

1) what are the interrelationships between these different T cell factors with the nature of the I region gene product ?, and 2) what ascribes for the antigen-specificity of the T cell factors ?

There are no clear answers for these questions at the present moment. However, it is apparent that both the antigen-specific cooperative factor of Taussig and coworkers and the allogeneic effect factor of Katz and his associates directly act on B cells to augment their response, whereas the suppressive T cell factor acts on helper T cells resulting in the suppression of the T cell-dependent antibody response. Both augmenting factors are released from T cells by a short-term culture with antigen or allogeneic cells, while the suppressor molecule is not released under a similar condition. Furthermore, the antigen-specific cooperative factor appeared to be coded for by genes in the I-A subregion and even acts on histoincompatible B cells (18-21). Although we were unable to locate exactly the gene(s) codes for the suppressive T cell factor, the available evidence indicates that it is perhaps the product of gene(s) in the *I-B* (+ *I-E*) subregion at least in $H-2^k$ mice. However, the factor is not likely to be the Ia molecule *per se* with a known numbered specificity. Therefore, we currently favour the hypothesis that there exists a set of specialized genes which codes for functionally different but structurally complementary cell surface molecules. Although it is not known how the antigen-binding site is incorporated to the molecule, it is tempting to assume that the antigen-specificity of some of these molecules would focus on each other for the effective cell interactions.

Finally, the production of the suppressor molecule seems to be regulated by an unknown gene(s) not linked to the *H-2* complex, which would attribute to the responsiveness of animals to certain antigens such as KLH which are not controlled by *H*-linked *Ir-1* genes. Even in animals which do not produce the suppressor factor, the acceptor for it is normally expressed, and *vice versa*. The results again suggest that the suppressor and its acceptor are coded for by paired genes, the expressions of which are independent of each other, and thus the suppression is determined by at least two genes. The other possibility is that the genes code for the suppressor and acceptor molecules are identical, but the expression on the cell surface is modified by other cell membrane moieties to construct different activity sites. These possibilities should be carefully examined in the future studies. On the bases of above findings, it is now of crutial importance to clarify the nature of these multiple *I* region gene products and their interrelationships for more precise understanding of the whole picture of the immunoregulatory system.

ACKNOWLEDGEMENTS

We wish to express our sincerest thanks to Drs. B. Benacerraf and C.S. David for their generous supply of allo-antisera specific for restricted regions of the *H-2* complex together with a lot of valuable advice. We are grateful to our colleagues, Drs. T. Takemori, Kyoko Hayakawa and A. Yano, in the Laboratories for Immunology, Chiba University, who participated in the studies described herein. We also wish to thank Ms. Yoko Yamaguchi for her excellent secretarial assistance in preparation of the manuscript.

The studies reported here were supported by a Grant-in-Aid for Scientific Research from the Ministry of Education, Science and Culture, Japan.

REFERENCES

(1)   R.K. Gershon, in: Contemporary Topics in Immunology.
        vol. 3, eds. M.D. Cooper and N.L. Warner. (Plenum
        Press, New York, 1974) p. 1.

(2)   A.C. Allison, in: Immunological Tolerance: Mechanisms
        and potential therapeutic applications. eds. D.H. Katz
        and B. Benacerraf. (Academic Press, New York, 1974)
        p. 25.

(3)   J.A. Kapp, C.W. Pierce, S. Schlossman and B. Benacerraf.
        J. Exp. Med. 140 (1974) 648.

(4)   B. Benacerraf, J.A. Kapp, P. Debré, C.W. Pierce and
        F. De La Croix. Transplant. Rev. 26 in press.

(5)   T. Tada and T. Takemori. J. Exp. Med. 140 (1974) 239.

(6)   T. Takemori and T. Tada. J. Exp. Med. 140 (1974) 253.

(7)   R.K. Gershon and K. Kondo. Immunology 21 (1971) 903.

(8)   A. Basten, J.F.A.P. Miller, J. Sprent and C. Cheers.
        J. Exp. Med. 140 (1974) 199.

(9)   P.J. Baker, P.W. Stashak, D.F. Amsbaugh and B. Prescott.
        J. Immunol. 112 (1974) 2020.

(10)   M. Zembala and G.L. Asherson. Nature 244 (1973) 227.

(11)   T. Tada, M. Taniguchi and T. Takemori. Transplant. Rev.
        26 in press.

(12)   D.C. Benjamin. J. Exp. Med. 141 (1975) 635.

(13)   T. Takemori and T. Tada. J. Exp. Med. in press.

(14)   J. Marbrook. Lancet ii (1967) 1279.

(15)   M. Taniguchi, K. Hayakawa and T. Tada. J. Immunol.
        in press.

(16)   J.C. Cerottini and E.R. Unanue. J. Immunol. 106 (1971)
        732.

(17) D.H. Katz and B. Benacerraf. Transplant. Rev. 22 (1975) 175.

(18) M.J. Taussig and A.J. Munro. Nature 251 (1974) 63.

(19) M.J. Taussig, E. Mozes and R. Isac. J. Exp. Med. 140 (1974) 301.

(20) A.J. Munro, M.J. Taussig, R. Campbell, H. Williams and Y. Lawson. J. Exp. Med. 140 (1974) 1579.

(21) M.J. Taussig, A.J. Munro, R. Campbell, C.S. David and N.A. Staines. J. Exp. Med. 142 (1975) 694.

(22) D. Armerding and D.H. Katz. J. Exp. Med. 140 (1974) 19.

(23) D. Armerding, D.H. Sachs and D.H. Katz. J. Exp. Med. 140 (1974) 1717.

(24) D.H. Katz and B. Benacerraf, in: The Immune System: Genes, Receptors, Signals. eds. E.E. Sercarz, A.R. Williamson and C.F. Fox. (Academic Press, New York, 1974) p. 569.

(25) J.A. Kapp, C.W. Pierce, F. De La Croix and B. Benacerraf. J. Immunol. in press.

DISCUSSION FOLLOWING TOMIO TADA

KATZ: Does the concept of two immune suppression genes fit your data on the failure of (BALB/c x A/J)F_1 factor to suppress the A/J haplotype and if so, how do you view this?

TADA: From the two exceptional cases which I just presented, we are compelled to conclude that the suppression is achieved only if both suppressor and its acceptor are present. Since these molecules are expressed independently of each other, it is obvious that there are two genes which code for suppressor and acceptor sites, and therefore, the two-gene theory ideally fits our data.

BENACERRAF: You have found that A/J mice do not produce suppressor factor. What was the antigen used? Is it a general defect of the $H\text{-}2^a$ mice or is it related to the antigen involved? I ask this question because in the GT system, A/J mice are also not suppressors, and at the present time we have relatively limited information with respect to the range of specificity of specific immune suppression genes. I would like also to add that Patrice Debré has investigated the GT-specific factor of BALB/c mice in our laboratory and has demonstrated that such a factor is also suppressive for A/J mice. On the other hand, A/J mice do not produce factors active in their strain or in BALB/c or B10.BR mice.

TADA: We have mostly used KLH in this series of experiments. It has been confirmed by repeated experiments that A/J mice cannot produce the suppressor factor to KLH. However, I do not think this is a general defect of A/J mice, since in other experimental systems, eg. suppression of tumor immunity and idiotype suppression, A/J mice do produce suppressor T cells perfectly well. We cannot draw any conclusion at the present time, unless we test more antigens in different mouse strains. I think the results obtained by Dr. Debré are in complete agreement with ours.

MILLER: Was KLH the only antigen used to generate "primed suppressor T cells"? From the data you presented, I notice that no other protein antigen seemed to have been tried. If you have used others, were they able to prime suppressor T cells to produce suppressor factors?

TADA: We have used several protein antigens to generate suppressor T cells, eg. EA, BGG, Ascaris extract, etc. All of them could produce suppressor T cells specific for these antigens, but KLH was superb among those antigens tested.

MILLER: In some of the data you presented, you used "primed T cells" as a source of suppressive factors. I presume these are thymocytes from mice primed to KLH. In other experiments, the factor used was produced from "thymocytes and spleen cells". Have you or any one else attempted to identify the cell type responsible for producing the factor? For example, do these cells disappear some months after adult thymectomy? Are the T cells involved bearing Ly-1,2,3, Ly-1 or Ly-2,3 antigens? Is the factor produced from purified T cells uncontaminated by B cells and macrophages?

TADA: We can obtain suppressor cells from both the thymus and spleen. Also, suppressor activity is observed in nylon fiber column-purified splenic T cells. Adult thymectomy resulted in a diminution of suppressor activity. As far as I know, the suppressor T cell in our system is X-ray sensitive and relatively cortisone-resistant. I wish to study the Ly antigens of our suppressor T cell since in other systems it has been shown that suppressor T cells possess Ly-2,3.

GERSHON: Since, as we have discussed, splenic T cells from mice immunized with KLH induce suppressor T cells in normal mice and contain in themselves helper cells, it is possible your factor is not a suppressor but rather an inducer of suppressor; perhaps because it contains idiotype. Have you injected your factor into normal mice and seen if you can get either suppressor cells or factors from the normal mice? The possibility that some of the pecularities in acceptance you noted could be explained by differences in idiotype recognition.

TADA: No, we have not studied whether or not the suppressor factor can induce suppressor T cells in the recipient. I only know that KLH is not a good antigen to produce a particular idiotype.

GERSHON: This is more a suggestion than a question. It would be a worthwhile exercise for you, or for some of the other people working with T cell factors, to see if their factors could be absorbed with the chicken anti-mouse immunoglobulin made by Ulrich Hämmerling and Francis Loor which are able to identify T cell membrane extracts and which may be related to some of the factors being discussed. Some conventional anti-immunoglobulin sera don't identify these T membrane products, whereas the chicken serum does.

TADA: I would try that, if the antiserum becomes available to me.

NOSSAL: To clarify Gershon's comment, he is not stating that the chicken anti-mouse Ig antibodies, which unequivocally stain T cell surfaces by immunofluorescence, have any effect on T cell factors; he is suggesting that the factor people should try to establish this.

SHREFFLER: I just want to comment on the results concerning removal of the factor by anti-Ia sera. The results are not as inconsistent as they may have appeared because of the recent changes in mapping of some Ia specificities. The removal of C3H factor by antisera against Ia.7 would indicate reactivity with a product of the I-C region, irrespective of the existence of I-B and I-E regions. The antisera containing cross-reactive anti-Ia.8, which should react with I-A region products of BALB/c, usually have rather weak anti-Ia.8 activity, so failure to remove the factor may not be unexpected.

TADA: I was aware of the fact that some anti-I-C antisera could absorb both the H-2^d and H-2^k factors marginally. Therefore, the participation of I-C subregion genes is not completely excluded. The crucial question I have now is whether or not the suppressor molecule is, in fact, identical to a known Ia molecule itself. I appreciate your comment.

TAUSSIG: What is the evidence that the KLH-suppressor factors is a product of Ir genes, apart from mapping to the I region? Are there differences in response, at the whole animal level between strains which can or cannot produce the suppressors?

537

TADA: As has been reported by Cerottini and Unanue, the
responsiveness of mice to KLH is not under H-linked *Ir-1*
gene control, but definitely differs between mouse
strains.* A/J is a high responder, while CBA is a low
responder. Such a difference may be related to the
genetically determined ability to produce the suppressor
or to accept the suppressor molecule.

*[*EDITOR'S NOTE:*   See Cerottini, J-C and Unanue, E.R.
J. Immunol. 106:732, 1971 - DHK.]

E. MÖLLER: Would you explain how you conclude that factors
act on T cells from the results of the experiment where
you mixed the antigens DNP-EA and DNP-KLH with extracts
from cells primed to EA or KLH. To my mind, this conclusion is complicated by the fact that KLH is a B cell
mitogen, whereas EA is not, and thus, KLH but not EA
could synergize with another factor, helper or suppressor to increase the degree of suppression as evident in
the B cell population.

TADA: I do not understand your question very well. My
conclusion was made upon the assumption that both DNP-EA
and DNP-KLH are T cell dependent antigens in equal
degree, and it is actually true in this experimental
system. Both EA and KLH are good producers of the
suppressive T cell factor. My point is that EA-specific
factor can only suppress the anti-DNP antibody response
if EA-specific helper T cells co-exist and vice versa.
I know this is an indirect evidence, but still gives an
idea on the target of the suppressive T cell factor.

PAUL: Tomio, can you tell me how intact cells and extracted
factors compare in their relative activity?

TADA: In order to induce a comparable degree of suppression
to that induced by live suppressor T cells, we have to
inject the factor extracted from as twice as many T
cells.

PAUL: Tomio, have you tested the capacity of anti-Ia
immunoabsorbents to actually bind internally labelled
Ia antigens of appropriate specificity.

TADA: Yes, we have obtained extracts from thymocytes which
had been surface-labelled with ^{125}I by the lactoperoxidase method. A small, but significant, radioactivity

was retained to the appropriate immunoadsorbent of anti-Ia. We can also co-precipitate some radioactive materials with anti-Ia and anti-mouse Ig.

BENACERRAF: I would like to make a plea that we refer to genes controlling specific immune suppression as Is genes rather than Ir genes until we know more about these systems.

Also, as more Is-genetically-controlled suppression are identified for different antigens, it is reasonable to expect that they may map in different regions of I and that different anti-I antisera neutralize different factors with different specificities.

TADA: I completely agree with you.

HISTOCOMPATIBILITY GENE PRODUCTS AS MEDIATORS OF LYMPHOCYTE INTERACTIONS

DAVID H. KATZ, DIETER ARMERDING AND ZELIG ESHHAR

Department of Pathology
Harvard Medical School

INTRODUCTION

Amid extensive speculation on the probable importance and involvement of soluble T cell factors in T-B cell interactions (1-3), considerable attention has been focused on the identification and characterization of such factors. In previous reports from our own laboratory, we have described the biological and biochemical properties of such a factor which appears to induce and regulate triggering and differentiation of other lymphocytes (4-8). The factor is obtained from culture supernatants of short-term *in vitro* mixed lymphocyte reactions between alloantigen-activated T cells and the appropriate target cell population; we have termed the active moiety of such supernatants allogeneic effect factor (AEF) (4). In this paper we shall briefly review the biological, biochemical and immunological properties of AEF.

The AEF preparations that will be discussed here have been prepared in the manner illustrated in Fig. 1 (4). Mouse thymocytes (strain A) are injected intravenously into sublethally irradiated syngeneic recipients together with heavily irradiated semi-syngeneic (A x B)F1 hybrid spleen cells. After 6-7 days, the recipient spleen cells consisting of alloantigen-activated T cells are harvested and co-cultured with equal numbers of irradiated (A x B)F1 target spleen cells. This can be done in serum-supplemented (4), or, more recently, in serum-free medium (9). Twenty-four hours later, the culture supernatant is obtained by centrifugation and then tested for biological activity as described below.

PREPARATION OF ALLOANTIGEN-ACTIVATED T CELLS
AND *IN VITRO* INDUCTION OF ALLOGENEIC EFFECT FACTOR (AEF)

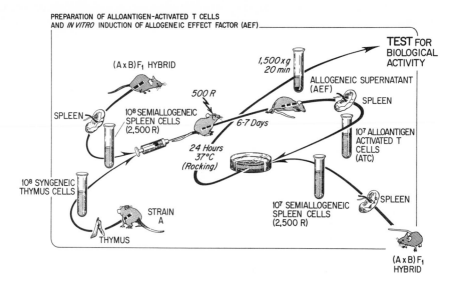

Figure 1. See text for explanation (Ref. 4)

GENETIC AND CELLULAR REQUIREMENTS FOR AEF PRODUCTION

Analysis of the conditions required for induction and production of AEF have demonstrated the following:

1) The effector and target cells must differ at the *H-2* complex for both *in vivo* sensitization and *in vitro* mixed lymphocyte culture (MLC); disparity at the M-locus or minor histocompatibility differences are not sufficient for optimal AEF production in the conditions described in Fig. 1 (10). However, these findings may not be discordant with those of Kettman (11) and Röllinghoff and Wagner (12) who have found M-locus differences to be sufficient for production of active allogeneic supernatants in primary MLC; thus, the production of AEF across M-locus differences may occur with somewhat different kinetics than that across *H-2* differences in the activated T cell system employed in our own studies.

2) Metabolically active T cells are necessary for AEF production; thus inhibitors of protein synthesis and secretion, oxidative phosphorylation and divalent cation-dependent processes prevent production of AEF *in vitro*; in contrast, inhibitors of DNA and messenger RNA synthesis have little or no effects on AEF production (13).

3) AEF is produced only in the presence of the appropriate allogeneic or semi-allogeneic target cells in the MLC; in other words, there is no detectable spontaneous release of active molecules into supernatants of cultures containing alloantigen-activated T cells alone (10).

4) Macrophages do not produce AEF and are not required for the *in vitro* production of AEF (10). However, we have not, as yet, conlusively eliminated the possibility that some (or all) of the biologically active molecules may be released from the irradiated target cell population; experiments currently in progress should answer this question.

BIOLOGICAL PROPERTIES OF AEF

The principal biological activity of AEF that has been studied in depth is the capacity of this material to functionally replace the requirement for helper T cells in *in vitro* antibody responses. The earlier work of Dutton *et al* (2) and Schimpl and Wecker (14, 15) made it clear that such factors were active in this regard insofar as *in vitro* responses to particulate erythrocyte antigens or haptenated erythrocytes were concerned. Our own studies extended these observations to soluble DNP-protein conjugates in which case AEF can reconstitute helper cell function in responses of T cell-depleted primed spleen cells under the appropriate conditions (4). Recent studies by Dr. Colleen Hayes in our laboratory have also shown that AEF can exert biologically enhancing effects on T cell functions as well (16).

PHYSICOCHEMICAL AND BIOCHEMICAL PROPERTIES OF AEF

The experiments performed thus far on the physicochemical features of AEF indicate that the active component(s) consists of protein and/or glycoprotein which is heat-labile ($56^{\circ}C$, 1 hour), thereby indicating the importance of tertiary structure to activity, is uniformly charged and is in the molecular range of 30,000 to 45,000 using Sephadex gel chromatography for estimation of the molecular weight (4, 17). Moreover, the active moiety appears to consist of two components associated either covalently or non-covalently (6, 7, 17). The latter conclusion stems from observations made by dissociative chromatography of AEF in guanidinium-HCl on Sepharose 6B. Under such conditions AEF dissociated into sub-fractions which could be tested for biological activity after removal of guanidinium-HCl by dialysis. Analysis of the various sub-fractions showed that neither a heavy subunit (*ca.* 40,000 daltons) nor a light subunit (10,000 - 12,000 daltons) alone was capable of exerting a full reconstituting activity on the response of anti-θ serum-treated spleen cells. In contrast, a mixture of the two fractions exerted an activity on the response of such cells which was almost 50% greater than that obtained with the unfractionated AEF (6, 7, 17). This finding strongly indicates, therefore, that the active moiety of AEF consists of two subunits -- one heavy and one light -- which may be associated either covalently or non-covalently. It has not, however, been formally proven that such linkage is a necessity for exertion of biological activity. That AEF consists of glycoprotein has been recently shown by studies demonstrating the adsorption of AEF on a lectin matrix (Con A-Sepharose). The adsorbed material can be eluted in biologically active form by competing sugars (17).

IMMUNOLOGICAL AND IMMUNOCHEMICAL PROPERTIES OF AEF

Thus far, we have analyzed the immunological properties of AEF by various immunochemical and functional techniques. Immunochemical analysis has shown that AEF does not react or cross-react with any heterologous anti-sera directed against immunoglobulin determinants (17). The biological activity of AEF is not antigen-specific (4). Moreover,. the active components of AEF are not adsorbed by SRBC (17). In our initial studies on the activity of AEF, we found that although it did not manifest any specificity for antigens against which the *in vitro* antibody responses were directed, AEF did exhibit some strain-specific properties suggesting a relationship to antigens or gene products coded in the major histocompatibility gene complex (4). Subsequent detailed analysis of this point has shown that strain specificity is not very strict in terms of the target cells on which AEF can exert its biological effects in primary *in vitro* antibody responses (10); studies are currently underway to determine whether or not greater restrictions may exist for responses of previously primed B lymphocytes. Nevertheless, the earlier observations on apparent strain specificity of AEF activity together with observations from our laboratory on genetic restrictions of T-B interactions demonstrating the involvement of *I* region genes in the control of such interactions (see Katz and Benacerraf, this volume) prompted us to determine whether antisera directed against *I* region-associated (Ia) antigens would react with AEF. Indeed, in studies performed in collaboration with Dr. David Sachs demonstrated that, as shown in Fig. 2, AEF subjected to an appropriate

ANTI-θ-SERUM TREATED
DBA/2 SPLEEN CELLS

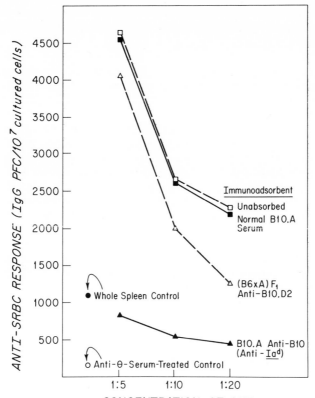

Figure 2. Removal of biological activity of AEF derived from DBA/2 (H-2^d) T cells by an anti-Ia^d immunoadsorbent. Three different concentrations of AEF were subjected to immunoadsorbents prepared from either normal B10.A serum or from (B6A)F$_1$ anti-B10.D2 or B10.A anti-B10 (anti-Ia^d) ascites. These AEF were then tested and compared to unabsorbed AEF for activity on the *in vitro* response to SRBC of anti-θ serum-treated DBA/2 spleen cells. Control responses of whole spleen cells and anti-θ-treated cells in the absence of AEF are shown to the left. The IgG antibody responses are presented and paralleled the IgM response pattern of the same cultures (not shown). (Taken from reference 5.)

anti-Ia immunoadsorbent exhibited markedly diminished (80% or more) biological activity on responses of B lymphocytes indicating substantial reactivity of this antiserum with the biologically active component(s) of AEF (5). Consistent with these findings is the observation that AEF binds to isogeneic lymphoid cells (10).

In view of the interesting association demonstrated in recent years between the ubiquitous small protein β_2-microglobulin (β_2m), and various gene products of the MHC in several species (see 18-21 for reviews), and the clear evidence for the presence of histocompatibility antigen determinants and a smaller molecular weight subunit of AEF, we sought to ascertain whether or not an association existed between β_2m and the biological and/or structural properties of AEF. Recent studies performed with Drs. Ralph Kubo and Howard Grey have demonstrated conclusively the association between an entity antigenically related to β_2-microglobulin and the biologically active moiety of AEF, since the latter can be completely and specifically absorbed by antisera directed against β_2m determinants (22). Thus, in the experiment shown in Fig. 3, unprimed DBA/2 spleen cells depleted of T lymphocytes failed to develop an appreciable anti-SRBC plaque-forming cell (PFC) response; untreated control spleen cells developed around 400 PFC of the IgG class in response to SRBC (data not shown). The addition of unabsorbed AEF to the T cell-depleted spleen cells reconstituted and facilitated the response in magnitude proportional to the concentration of AEF used. Three immunoadsorbents prepared from either normal rabbit serum or two anti-human β_2m antisera, one of which had been previously absorbed with purified human β_2m, served as negative controls in this experiment; the latter two sera were deliberately chosen for their incapability to cross-react with mouse β_2m. As shown in Fig. 3, absorption of AEF with these adsorbents did not result in a significant loss of biological activity when compared to unabsorbed AEF. However, quite in contrast is the binding capacity of two other cross-linked antisera, one of which was raised in rabbits against the presumed mouse β_2m and the other obtained by priming with human β_2m and boosting with mouse β_2m. Both of these immunoadsorbents substantially removed the activity of AEF (22).

The results of the preceding experiment demonstrate the capacity of antisera directed against a mouse β_2m-like protein to specifically absorb the biological activity of AEF. Since there is as yet no conclusive proof that these antisera are indeed specific for the mouse β_2m analogue, an

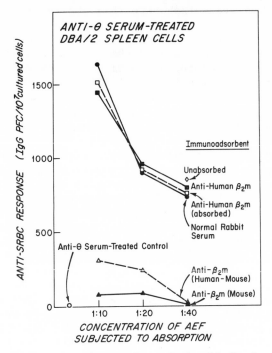

Figure 3. Absorption of the biological activity of AEF by anti-$\beta_2 m$ antisera. Three different concentrations of AEF were subjected to immunoadsorbents prepared from either: 1) normal rabbit serum; 2) rabbit anti-human $\beta_2 m$ antiserum (Unabsorbed); 3) rabbit anti-human $\beta_2 m$ antiserum (previously absorbed with purified human $\beta_2 m$); 4) rabbit antiserum raised initially against human and then boosted with mouse $\beta_2 m$; and 5) rabbit anti-mouse $\beta_2 m$ antiserum. These AEF were then tested and compared to unabsorbed AEF for activity on the *in vitro* response to SRBC of anti-θ serum-treated spleen cells. The control response of anti-θ-treated cells in the absence of AEF is shown at the lower left. The activity of unabsorbed AEF is shown at only one dilution (1:40) for purposes of clarity of the figure but paralleled the normal rabbit serum-absorbed AEF at the higher concentrations. The IgG antibody responses are presented and paralleled the IgM response pattern of these same cultures (not shown). (Ref. 22).

attempt was made to corroborate this observation with anti-serum prepared against human $\beta_2 m$ and which was known to be cross-reactive with the mouse $\beta_2 m$-like protein. These experiments (not shown) demonstrated that an immunoadsorbent consisting of cross-reacting anti-human $\beta_2 m$ removed more than 80% of the biological activity of AEF. Most importantly, however, was the observation that addition of purified human $\beta_2 m$ (100 µg/ml) to the cross-reacting anti-human $\beta_2 m$ immunoadsorbent prior to absorption of AEF substantially, and specifically, blocked the capacity of this adsorbent to remove AEF activity (22). This finding corroborates the observations shown in Fig. 3 and, moreover, demonstrates that the anti-$\beta_2 m$ binding sites in the cross-reacting anti-human $\beta_2 m$ serum are those responsible for its absorptive capacity for AEF. Finally, the possibility that the absorption of AEF by anti-$\beta_2 m$ antisera reflects reactivity or cross-reactivity of such antisera with Ig or Ig-like determinants on AEF has been ruled out by the failure of polyvalent anti-Ig antisera to manifest any absorptive capacity for AEF under identical conditions (22). Taken collectively, therefore, these results strongly indicate that $\beta_2 m$ or an antigenically-related entity is associated with the biologically active component of AEF.

The demonstration of $\beta_2 m$-like determinants associated with Ia determinants on AEF is contradictory to earlier biochemical studies indicating little or no $\beta_2 m$ in association with Ia molecules obtained from solubilized cell surface membranes (23, 24). Possible explanations for this apparent contradiction are discussed in detail elsewhere (22).

The association of $\beta_2 m$ with histocompatibility antigens and the remarkable sequence homologies of the molecule to constant region domains of Ig has been shown in several species (18-21, 25). Hitherto, no apparent biological function could be assigned to this small molecule. However, recent observations have demonstratrated that antisera against $\beta_2 m$ may have either enhancing or suppressive effects on certain lymphocyte functions indicating the possible involvement of $\beta_2 m$ in various immune processes (26-29). Recently, Schimpl *et al* (30) reported that incorporation of anti-human $\beta_2 m$ antiserum into cultures containing a comparable T cell factor appeared to block the capacity of their factor to stimulate antibody production. Such observations and the results of our studies indicating an association of $\beta_2 m$ with the biological activity of AEF strongly suggest that $\beta_2 m$ is involved in cell-cell interactions and the consequences of such interactions on lymphocyte triggering and differentiation.

RELATIONSHIP OF AEF TO OTHER BIOLOGICALLY ACTIVE FACTORS POSSESSING HISTOCOMPATIBILITY ANTIGEN DETERMINANTS

Concurrent studies conducted in other laboratories have recently demonstrated the existence of antigen-specific T cell factors which exhibit remarkable similarities to each other and to AEF in terms of molecular size, their lack of identifiable immunoglobulin determinants and the presence on them of determinants coded for by genes in the major histocompatibility complex, specifically in the *I* regions of *H-2*. The elegant work of Mozes and of Taussig and Munro on antigen-specific enhancing factors and of Tada and colleagues and, more recently Kapp et al, on antigen-specific suppressive factors are all reviewed in detail within this volume and need not be reiterated here.

The point to emphasize is that these studies have demonstrated the existence of a class of molecules, produced by antigen-activated T cells, which exert biological activity in the regulation of immune responses and which bear determinants coded for by *I* region genes. The functional effects of these molecules are either enhancing or suppressive and either non-specific or antigen-specific depending on the manner in which they are induced, and they appear to be capable of acting on T lymphocytes and on B lymphocytes. Although much has been learned about these soluble T cell factors in a relatively short time, there are still many unanswered questions to be addressed, such as:

1) Are there distinct molecules for each type of target cell and for different biological functions?
2) What are the relationships, in biological and structural terms, of the antigen-specific factors and the non-specific AEF-type factors?
3) How do these murine T cell factors, which appear to possess determinants coded by genes in the *I* region of *H-2*, relate to the idiotype-positive molecules, apparently reflecting T cell receptor activity, described by Binz and Wigzell (this volume) which, in the rat at least, may not bear MHC determinants (although no conclusive evidence exists in this regard as yet)?

Finally, and perhaps most important, are we exercising sufficient caution in interpreting and extrapolating what our

phenomena show us to the biological meaning they may reflect?
While it is true that we have been rapidly progressing to a
point at which biochemical analysis of these intriguing biologically active molecules is possible, we should continue to
probe the aforementioned question and bear in mind that the
properties of such molecules may be quite different once removed from the cell cytoplasm and/or surface membrane. And
if, as we suspect, their main physiological activity is exerted while they are integral components of the surface membrane and during membrane-membrane contact in the course of
cell interactions, then we could all find ourselves making
potential misinterpretations based on what we observe with
the molecules in cell-free soluble form.

CONCLUSIONS

The observations presented here provide strong evidence that the molecules involved in regulatory cell interactions in immune responses and lymphocyte differentiation
are gene products of the major histocompatibility complex
and, more specifically, of the *I* region of the *H-2* complex
in the mouse. Evidence at the present time indicates that
biologically active molecules possessing Ia determinants can
be obtained in soluble form from T lymphocytes and shown to
exert their functional effects in either non-specific or
antigen-specific ways under various conditions. Much additional investigation is necessary, however, in order to establish the biological relationships between such molecules
as we study them in the experimental systems utilized in our
laboratories and the natural events transpiring in the immune system.

ACKNOWLEDGMENTS

We are most appreciative to all of the colleagues who
participated in the performance of these experiments and con-
tributed to others not directly reported herein, including
Dr. Martin Dorf, Dr. Howard Grey, Dr. Colleen Hayes, Dr.
Ralph Kubo and Dr. David Sachs. We also thank Henry Dimuzio,
Mary Graves, and Mercy Koshy for skilled technical assistance
and Charlene Small for secretarial assistance. The studies
reported here were supported by Grant AI-10630 from the
National Institutes of Health. Dr. Armerding is a Research
Fellow of the Damon Runyon Memorial Fund for Cancer Research,
Inc.

REFERENCES

(1)   D.H. Katz and B. Benacerraf. Adv. Immunol. 15 (1972) 1.

(2)   R.W. Dutton, R. Falkoff, J.A. Hirst, M. Hoffman, J.W. Kappler, J.R. Kettman, J.F. Lesley and D. Vann. Prog. Immunol. 1 (1971) 355.

(3)   D.H. Katz. Transplant. Rev. 12 (1972) 141.

(4)   D. Armerding and D.H. Katz. J. Exp. Med. 140 (1974) 19.

(5)   D. Armerding, D.H. Sachs and D.H. Katz. J. Exp. Med. 140 (1974) 1717.

(6)   D.H. Katz and D. Armerding. in: Immune Recognition - Proceedings of the Ninth Leukocyte Culture Conference. ed. A.S. Rosenthal. (Academic Press, New York, 1975) p. 727.

(7)   D.H. Katz, M.E. Dorf, D. Armerding and B. Benacerraf. in: Molecular Approaches to Immunology - Miami Winter Symposia, Vol 9. eds. E.E. Smith and D.W. Ribbons. (Academic Press, New York, 1975). p.211.

(8)   D.H. Katz and D. Armerding. in: Cellular and Soluble Factors in the Regulation of Lymphocyte Activation - FASEB Symposium, April, 1975. Fed. Proc., in press.

(9)   D. Armerding, Z. Eshhar and D.H. Katz. Manuscript submitted for publication. 1975.

(10) D. Armerding, Z. Eshhar and D.H. Katz. Manuscript in preparation. 1975.

(11) J. Kettman. Unpublished observations.

(12) M. Röllinghoff and H. Wagner. J. Immunol. 114 (1975) 1329.

(13) Z. Eshhar, D. Armerding and D.H. Katz. Manuscript in preparation. 1975.

(14) A. Schimpl and E. Wecker. Nature New Biol. 237 (1972) 15.

(15) A. Schimpl and E. Wecker. J. Exp. Med. 137 (1972) 547.

(16) C.E. Hayes, D. Armerding and D.H. Katz. Unpublished observations.

(17) D. Armerding and D.H. Katz. Manuscript in preparation. 1975.

(18) B.A. Cunningham and I. Berggard. Transplant. Rev. 21 (1974) 3.

(19) J.L. Strominger, P. Cresswell, H. Grey, R.H. Humphreys, D. Mann, J. McCune, P. Parham, R. Robb, A.R. Sanderson, T.A. Springer, C. Terhost and M.J. Turner. Transplant. Rev. 21 (1974) 126.

(20) N. Tanigaki and D. Pressman. Transplant. Rev. 21 (1974) 15.

(21) L. Rask, L. Östberg, B. Lindblom, Y. Fernstedt and P.A. Peterson. Transplant. Rev. 21 (1974) 85.

(22) D. Armerding, R.T. Kubo, H.M. Grey and D.H. Katz. Proc. Nat. Acad. Sci. U.S.A. 72 (1975) 4577.

(23) S.E. Cullen, C.S. David, D.C. Shreffler and S.G. Nathenson. Proc. Nat. Acad. Sci. 71 (1974) 648.

(24) E.S. Vitetta, J. Klein and J.W. Uhr. Immunogenetics 1 (1974) 82.

(25) J. Silver and L. Hood. Nature 249 (1974) 764.

(26) E. Möller and U. Persson. Scand. J. Immunol 3 (1974) 445.

(27) J.J. Lightbody, L. Urbani and M.D. Poulik. Nature 250 (1974) 227.

(28) B.G. Solheim. Transplant. Rev. 21 (1974) 35.

(29) R.T. McCalmon, R.T. Kubo and H.M. Grey. J. Immunol. 114 (1975) 1766.

(30) A. Schimpl, T.H. Hunig and E. Wecker. Prog. Immunol. II 2 (1974) 135.

I-REGION GENE PRODUCTS IN CELL COOPERATION

MICHAEL J. TAUSSIG, ALAN J. MUNRO AND ALMA L. LUZZATI

Basel Institute for Immunology
and
Department of Pathology
University of Cambridge

Our work has centered around the properties of
two functionally distinct types of molecule and their
role in immunological cell interactions (1-5). These
molecules are the antigen-specific T cell 'factors'
and the cell-bound 'acceptors' with which the factors
interact. The T cell factors, which may be the soluble
expression of the T cell antigen receptors, are able
to transmit a stimulatory or cooperative signal to
other cells, in particular B cells; the acceptors
carry the sites at which the T cell signal is received.
Our work has led us to conclude that the T factor/
receptor and the B cell acceptor are coded for, at least
in part, by distinct genes in the I-region of the
mouse H-2 complex, and are in fact the structural
products of H-2 linked Ir genes.

Since the 'factor/acceptor' model has recently
been described in some detail (5), we will only
summarise here our previous data, and mention in more
detail some recent work and some present problems.
The main properties of the specific T cell factor
are shown in Table I. Most important among these are
specificity for the antigen against which the factor
was prepared, and origin as a product of genes in the
I-region of the H-2 complex. For the antigens
(T-G)-A--L and (Phe,G)-A--L, the genes coding for the
specific factors have been shown to map in the I-A
subregion, which is known to contain the immune response
genes for these antigens.

Recently, in collaboration with Dr M Julius,
the cellular origin of the factors has been more

TABLE I

PROPERTIES OF THE ANTIGEN-SPECIFIC T CELL FACTOR

1. Produced in vitro by educated T cells incubated with antigen. Tested with antigen and B cells in irradiated recipients.

2. Antigen-specific cooperative activity; binds to specific antigen immunoadsorbent.

3. Non-immunoglobulin - not affected by anti-Ig reagents.

4. Molecular weight approximately 50,000 on G100 Sephadex.

5. Product of genes in the mouse H-2 complex. Genes coding for factors for (T,G)-A--L and (Phe,G)-A--L mapped to the I-A sub-region of H-2, by absorption of the factor with anti-Ia sera. Factor is not removed by the cross-reactive anti-Ia sera.

6. Not produced by some strains which are low responders to the antigen under test.

---

closely examined. There has been some suggestion that the factors are in reality macrophage or even B cell products, since it is difficult to provide formal proof that the cell releasing the factor is really the T cell (6). We have attempted to remove B cells and macrophages from specifically primed T cells by passage through nylon wool columns (7). Although the cells obtained were more than 95% theta-positive, with only about 0.1% B cells and probably fewer macrophages, there was no diminution in their ability to produce T cell factor in vitro. This confirms the original finding that anti-theta treatment of educated T cells prevented the production of factor (1) and makes it very likely, therefore, that the factors described are true T cell products.

The vital quality of antigen specificity has

recently been studied using synthetic polypeptide
antigens. We have previously found that a factor
specific for (T,G)-A--L was removed only by a
(T,G)-A--L immunoadsorbent, and not by (Phe,G)-A--L,
(T,G)-Pro--L or A--L, although cross-reactivity
between (T,G)-A--L and (Phe,G)-A--L factors can be
demonstrated in vivo (8).

Factors to (T,G)-A--L and (T,G)-Pro--L do not
appear to cross-react in any assay, despite the common
(T,G) determinant. This is surprising since anti-
(T,G)-A--L antibody cross-reacts completely with
(T,G)-Pro--L, and indicates that the factors and
antibodies for (T,G)-A--L recognise different
d eterminants.(T,G)-A--L and (T,G)-Pro--L factors have
been used in a 'reciprocal' experiment to test factor
specificity, by mixing together the factors for these
antigens and passing the mixture over either a
(T,G)-A--L-sepharose adsorbent or (T,G)-Pro--L-
sepharose. The unadsorbed fraction was then tested in
each case for its remaining specificity. The result
of this experiment is shown in Table II, where it will
be seen that the (T,G)-A--L adsorbent only removed the
(T,G)-A--L cooperative activity from the mixture, and,
vice versa, (T,G)-Pro-L only removed the (T,G)-Pro--L
specific activity. This result suggests a high degree
of specificity in the T cell factor, and infers the
presence of a specific antigen-binding site.

As already mentioned, the genes coding for the
(T,G)-A--L-specific factor have been mapped to the
I-A subregion of H-2, by absorbing the factor with
region-specific alloantisera (generously provided in
part by Drs. C.S. David and N.A. Staines) (2,3,4).
This suggests an Ir gene origin for the factor, and
this is supported by the inability of certain low
responder strains to produce the (T,G)-A--L factor.
These are the B10.M(H-2^f) and SJL (H-2^s) strains.
B10.M are high responders to (Phe,G)-A--L and can be
shown to produce the factor specific for (Phe,G)-A--L;
SJL are low responders to both (T,G)-A--L and
(Phe,G)-A--L and cannot produce either factor (5,9).
Thus in these cases, factor production reflects
responder status, which is detemined by H-2 linked
Ir genes. However, not all low responders are 'T cell
low responders', as are these two; strains of
haplotypes H-2^k (B10.BR), and H-2^j (I/St) are able to

TABLE II

SPECIFICITY OF T CELL FACTORS FOR (T,G)-A--L AND (T,G)-PRO--L

Factors	Immunoadsorbent	PFC response to:	
		(T,G)-A--L	(T,G)-Pro--L
-	-	- (100)	- (200)
(T,G)-A--L and (T,G)-Pro--L (mixed)	-	+ (1,100)	+ (1,500)
"	(T,G)-A--L	- (150)	+ (1,150)
"	(T,G)-Pro--L	+ (1,050)	- (100)

Factors for (T,G)-A--L and (T,G)-Pro--L were prepared separately and mixed. The activity of the mixture was tested before and after passage over antigen immunoadsorbents. (Results are mean plaque forming cell responses to (T,G)-A--L or (T,G)-Pro--L - tested separately - with 5 animals per group).

556

produce the factor, but carry instead acceptor defects (below), and may be termed 'B cell low responders'.

We assume that, by analogy with immunoglobulin, the factor carries a variable (V) region forming the binding site, linked to a 'constant' (C) region, which is responsible for biological activities, and that the C region, at least, is coded by genes in the I-A subregion. The origin of the V-region genes for the T cell factors has yet to be established, though the sharing of idiotypes between T and B cells suggests that the V genes may in fact be those which code for the antibody binding sites (10,11). A mechanism for linking Ig V-genes to I-region C-genes would then have to exist. Alternatively, V genes may be present in the H-2 complex itself, coding for a 'second' (i.e. immunoglobulin independent) antigen recognition system. A search for antibody idiotypes on T cell factors may help to resolve this important point.

The acceptor is the molecular site on the B cell (and perhaps T cell) surface with which the specific T cell factors interact (5,12). The properties of the B cell acceptor are summarised in Table III.

TABLE III

PROPERTIES OF THE B-CELL ACCEPTOR

1. Detectable on B cells (bone marrow cells, purified peripheral B cells), but not on thymocytes. Responsible for absorption of T cell factors by B cells.

2. Expressed non-clonally and probably specific for a class of T cell factor rather than antigen-specific.

3. Blocked by anti-H-2 sera, in the mouse. Acceptor for (T,G)-A--L and (Phe,G)-A--L factors is blocked by antisera to the I-A subregion (anti-Ia), including cross-reactive anti-Ia sera. Acceptor is probably either identical with, or closely linked to, Ia-bearing molecules.

4. Acceptor site for the (T,G)-A--L factor is not expressed on the B cells of some low responder strains.

5. Acceptor sites preserved throughout species, indicated by absorption of mouse factor by human lymphocytes.

The ability of B cells to absorb the T cell factors for (T,G)-A--L and (Phe,G)-A--L can be blocked by pretreatment of the cells with anti-Ia sera, in particular alloantisera against the I-A subregion (kindly provided by Dr. C. David) (Table IV). This is of course similar to the T cell factor itself; there are, however, alloantisera which react with the acceptor but not with the factor, suggesting that these are products of different genes in the I-A subregion. The specificity of the antisera which block the B cell acceptor suggests that the latter is present on, or very closely linked to, the molecules which carry the serologically detectable B cell Ia specificities. This is illustrated in Table V. Strains of haplotypes H-2^b and H-2^d, and H-2^b and H-2^s, carry certain common Ia determinants coded by the I-A subregion (indicated in Table V) (13). As a result appropriate alloantisera show cross-reaction when tested for cytotoxicity on the B cells of these strains (14). Table V shows that such alloantisera will also block the acceptor site, provided there is a shared Ia determinant in the I-A subregion. However, cross-reactive antisera do not remove the T cell factor of the cross-reactive strain - the factor has only been found to be removed by antisera raised against the haplotype of the strain in which it is produced. Thus the (T,G)-A--L factor prepared in H-2^b mice is removed by anti-H-2^b sera, but not by anti-H-2^d sera, despite the shared Ia8 determinant. The inference is that the factor and acceptor are different molecules and carry different Ia determinants.

The cellular distribution of the acceptor is in agreement with the known occurrence of the serologically detected Ia determinants, e.g. it is easily demonstrated on B cells, but apparently absent from thymocytes. Educated or activated T cells, peripheral T cells and

TABLE IV

BLOCKING THE B CELL ACCEPTOR WITH ALLOANTISERA

Antiserum Pretreatment of B cells	Response	(PFC/spleen)
None	+	(10,200)
Anti-H-2	-	(20)
Anti-K	+	(6,500)
Anti-I	-	(18)
Anti-I-A	-	(15)
Anti-(I-B,I-C)D	+	(6,700)
Anti-D	+	(10,400)

B10.A bone marrow cells were treated with various alloantisera before reaction with a T cell factor specific for (Phe,G)-A--L (raised in B10 mice) and (Phe,G)-A--L. The cells were subsequently transferred into irradiated recipients and the PFC response to (Phe,G)-A--L measured 12 d. later. Negative response is a result of blocking of the B cell acceptor site (unabsorbed factor can be recovered in these groups).

Antisera:
anti-H-2 = B10 anti-A/J
anti-K = AQR anti-B10.A
anti-I = A.TH anti-A.TL
anti-I-A = (B10.HTTx A.BY) anti A.TL
anti-(I-B,I-C)D = B10 anti-A/J absorbed with B10.A(4R) spleen cells
anti-D = B10.BR anti B10.D2

macrophages have yet to be tested.

TABLE V

BLOCKING THE ACCEPTOR WITH ANTISERA TO CROSS-REACTIVE Ia DETERMINANTS

Bone marrow cells	Blocking antiserum	Response (PFC/spleen)
B10.D2 (H-2^d) Ia 8,11	-	+ (22,000)
	Anti-H-2^d (Ia 8,11)	- (25)
	Anti-H-2^b (Ia 8,9)	- (10)
	Anti-I^s (Ia 4,9)	+ (38,000)
B10 (H-2^b) Ia 8,9	-	+ (11,400)
	Anti-H-2^b (Ia 8,9)	- (10)
	Anti-H-2^d (Ia 8,11)	- (50)
	Anti-I^s (Ia 4,9)	- (15)

B10.D2 or B10 bone marrow cells were pretreated with
alloantisera as indicated prior to absorption of T cell factor
for (T,G)-A--L (prepared in B10.A, H-2^a, mice) and (T,G,)-A--L.
The cells were subsequently transferred into irradiated
recipients and the 12 d. PFC response to (T,G)-A--L measured.
A negative response is a result of blocking the acceptor site.
Antisera: anti-H-2^d = B10.A anti B10.D2
           anti-H-2^b = B10.A anti C3H.WB
           anti-I^s = A.TL anti-A.TH

The acceptor molecule is another contender for
an Ir gene product. In addition to being coded for by
I-region genes, the acceptor for the (T,G)-A--L factor
is absent from some low responders· As in the case of
the factor, this phenomenon shows the specificity
expected of Ir genes from the responses of whole
animals. Thus, B cells of mice of haplotype H-2^k are
unable to absorb or react to the factor specific for
(T,G)-A--L, an antigen to which the animals are low
responders; the same cells, however, do absorb and
respond to the factor for (Phe,G)-A--L, to which the
mice are high responders (5,15). This implies the
existence of at least two separate "classes" of
acceptor site and corresponding classes of factor, with
the responses to (T,G)-A--L and (Phe,G)-A--L utilising
different classes (5).

In summary, there is good evidence from these
functional studies to indicate the existence of (at
least) two types of Ir gene in the I-region
controlling the antibody response, one of which codes
for the antigen-specific T cell factors (C and/or V
genes), while the other codes for the corresponding
B cell acceptor. Defects in either type of gene can
arise, leading to T-cell and B-cell low responders.
That this two gene hypothesis is substantially correct
has been shown by complementation of the genes. The
F1 hybrid of a 'T cell low responder', B10.M, and a
'B cell low responder', B10.BR was found to be a high
responder as predicted (5). Since these strains are
congenic and share the same background (non H-2) genes,
both the complementing genes must lie in the H-2
complex. Almost certainly they are the Ir genes
coding for the factor and acceptor. Several other
instances of Ir gene complementation have been
discovered (16-19), and in some cases recombinational
events have mapped the genes involved to different I
subregions, including I-C, though functional studies
are lacking in these cases (18,19). The characterisa-
tion of the (T,G)-A--L factor and acceptor suggest that
both the (T,G)-A--L genes will be in the I-A region,
and a search will be made for recombinants, e.g.
derived from the (B10.M x B10.BR) F$_1$ hybrids, to
substantiate this prediction. A detailed model to
account for the apparent antigen-specificity of Ir
gene control has been proposed by us elsewhere (5).

An interesting feature of the factor-acceptor
interaction is that it does not exhibit the restrictions with respect to allogeneic combinations, that
have been found for viable T and B cells (12,20,21).
The factor produced in one strain is quite capable
of activating the B cells of any other strain,
provided the latter is genetically capable of receiving the signal (e.g. is a high responder) (4). This
suggests that the inability of histoincompatible T and
B cells to collaborate is due either to some other
requirement of cell-cell contact, or the result of
suppresive allogeneic reactions (22-24), rather than
any restriction on the delivery of a T cell signal to
a B cell. This is underlined by the xenogeneic
reactivity of the mouse T cell factor. We have
recently found that human peripheral blood lymphocytes
can be triggered in vitro to proliferation and
antibody formation by antigen (heterologous erythrocytes) and the appropriate specific mouse factor.
Some of the characteristics of this phenomenon are
shown in Table VI. Human lymphocytes can be induced
to make a small primary response to SRBC in the
absence of factor, although in the experiment shown
the background response was very low. In the
presence of the mouse factor, a very sizeable antibody
response occurs, which reaches a peak at about 8 days.
This is accompanied by a large cell proliferation,
which is certainly in excess of that which could be
produced by the proliferation of the antigen-specific
clones alone. At the end of 8 days, for example, the
cell number may have risen 2-3 fold over the starting
number, while control cultures generally fall by a
similar extent. However, despite this non-specific
proliferation, the factor is not acting as a general
B cell mitogen - the proportion of cells which
contain Ig is relatively small (ca. 1%), and about
the same as the number of specific plaque forming
cells. Moreover, reciprocal experiments show that the
factor is acting specifically (Table VII). A mouse
factor raised to SRBC did not help HRBC; and vice versa,
a factor to HRBC allows human cells to respond to
HRBC but not to SRBC. This specificity is overcome,
however, if both antigens are present with the factor
to one of them. As Table VII shows, the presence of
HRBC and SRBC, with a factor specific for HRBC, causes
a tremendous response to both HRBC and SRBC. Indeed
the response is synergistic being far higher than that

TABLE VI

THE ANTIBODY RESPONSE IN VITRO OF HUMAN LYMPHOCYTES ACTIVATED BY A MOUSE T CELL FACTOR

Factor (SRBC)	Antigen	Day 5		Day 8	
		Cells ($\times10^5$)	PFC	Cells ($\times10^5$)	PFC
-	SRBC	0.7	0	0.9	0
-	HRBC	0.7	0	0.9	0
Yes	-	0.8	0	0.8	0
Yes	SRBC	13.0	750	20.5	13,000
Yes	HRBC	0.2	0	1.1	0
Absorbed by anti-H-2*	SRBC	1.0	0	0.6	0
Absorbed by packed SRBC*	SRBC	0.8	0	1.2	0

Human peripheral blood lymphocytes were pretreated with mouse factor specific for SRBC and incubated with SRBC or HRBC as shown. The cell input per well was 6 x 10^5. Results are given as cell yield and PFC per well.

* Treatment of the T cell factor by passage over anti-H-2 immunoadsorbent or absorption with packed SRBC prior to test.

Table VII

The specificity of activation of human lymphocytes by mouse T cell factors

Factor	Antigen	Day 6			Day 8		
		Cells ($\times 10^5$)	PFC to SRBC	PFC to HRBC	Cells ($\times 10^5$)	PFC to SRBC	PFC to HRBC
-	SRBC	1.5	0	0	3.4	82	0
SRBC	SRBC	5.5	307	5	9.9	545	0
SRBC	HRBC	1.0	0	0	2.0	0	0
HRBC	HRBC	3.0	18	122	2.8	10	75
HRBC	SRBC	2.2	0	0	2.5	65	0
HRBC	HRBC and SRBC	2.5	332	72	3.7	5056	2425

Human peripheral blood lymphocytes were treated with mouse factors produced against either SRBC or HRBC, together with either SRBC or HRBC or both as antigen. Results are given as cell yield and PFC per well after 6 or 8 days in culture. The initial cell input was 6 x 10^5 cells per well.

observed to either antigen alone. Our interpretation of this result, and of the high degree of cell proliferation, is that as a consequence of the specific response to one antigen in vitro, non-specific mitogenic factors are released which cause T and B cell proliferation, and can result in the generation of a response to particulate 'bystander' antigens (25).

As well as responding to mouse factor and antigen in vitro, human lymphocytes also absorb the mouse factor, if incubated with it for 30 minutes in vitro (in the absence of antigen). Thus interaction probably occurs between a mouse factor and a human lymphocyte acceptor site. The mouse factor can be shown to be the same as the one which successfully activates mouse cells in vivo (i.e. it is an H-2 pro-duct and absorbed by specific antigen, Table VI). In short, the reaction between mouse factor and human cells has the characteristics of that which occurs between the mouse factor and mouse cells. This in turn indicates that the sites on the acceptor molecules with which the factor combines are closely preserved throughout species, despite the fact that within the species individual members (low responders) may lose the function of certain acceptor sites. Of course, it remains to be proven that the acceptor site on human cells is on molecules which are analogous in genetic origin to those in the mouse. If the acceptor is associated with an HL-A-linked gene product, it may give us a functional approach to the immune response genes of man.

REFERENCES

(1) M. Taussig. Nature 248 (1974) 234.

(2) M.J. Taussig and A.J. Munro. Nature 251 (1974) 63.

(3) A.J. Munro, M.J. Taussig, R. Campbell, H. Williams and Y. Lawson. J. Exp. Med. 141 (1974) 703.

(4) M.J. Taussig, A.J. Munro, R. Campbell, C.S. David and N. Staines. J. Exp. Med. 142 (1975) 694.

(5) A.J. Munro and M.J. Taussig. Nature 256 (1975) 103.

(6) P. Erb and M. Feldmann. J. Exp. Med. 142 (1975)
     460.

(7) M.H. Julius, E. Simpson and L.A. Herzenberg.
     Eur. J. Immunol. 3 (1973) 645.

(8) E. Mozes, R. Isac, D. Givol, D. Beitsch and R. Zakut.
     Proceedings of the Fifth International Conference on
     Lymphatic Tissue and Germinal Centers in Immune
     Reactions. In press (1975).

(9) E. Mozes, R. Isac and M.J. Taussig. J. Exp. Med.
     141 (1975) 703.

(10) H. Binz and H. Wigzell. J. Exp. Med. 142 (1975)
     197.

(11) K. Eichmann and K. Rajewsky. Eur. J. Immunol.
     In press.

(12) D.H. Katz, T. Hamaoka, M.E. Dorf and B. Benacerraf.
     Proc. Nat. Acad. Sci. (U.S.) 70 (1973) 2624.

(13) D.C. Shreffler and C.S. David. Adv. Immunol. 20
     (1975) 125.

(14) D.H. Sachs and J.L. Cone. J. Exp. Med. 138 (1973)
     1289.

(15) M.J. Taussig, E. Mozes and R. Isac. J. Exp. Med.
     140 (1974) 301.

(16) E. Rüde and E. Günther. Prog. Immunol. II (1974)
     223.

(16a) J.H. Stimpfling and T. Durham. J. Immunol. 108
     (1972) 943.

(17) M. Zaleski, H. Fuji and F. Milgrom. Transplant. Proc.
     5 (1973) 201.

(18) M.E. Dorf, J.H. Stimpfling and B. Benacerraf. J.
     Exp. Med. 141 (1975) 1459.

(19) I. Melchers and K. Rajewsky. Eur. J. Immunol. In press.

(20) D.H. Katz, M. Graves, M.E. Dorf, H. Dimuzio and

B. Benacerraf. J. Exp. Med. 141 (1975) 263.

(21) D.H. Katz, in: Proceedings of the 10th Leukocyte Culture Conference. ed. V. Eijsvoogel. (Academic Press). In press.

(22) E. Heber-Katz and D.B. Wilson. J. Exp. Med. 142 (1975) 928.

(23) H. Von Boehmer, L. Hudson and J. Sprent. J. Exp. Med. 142 (1975) 989.

(24) H. Waldmann, H. Pope and A.J. Munro. Nature. In press.

(25) H. Waldmann. Immunology 28 (1975) 497.

SUPPRESSIVE ACTIVITY OF LYMPHOID CELL EXTRACTS FROM NON-RESPONDER MICE INJECTED WITH THE TERPOLYMER L-GLUTAMIC ACID^{60}- L-ALANINE^{30}-L-TYROSINE^{10} (GAT)

JUDITH A. KAPP, CARL W. PIERCE, AND BARUJ BENACERRAF

Department of Pathology
Harvard Medical School

Abstract: The immune response by inbred strains of mice to the terpolymer L-glutamic acid^{60}-L-alanine^{30}-L-tyrosine^{10} (GAT) is under H-2 linked genetic control. In non-responder mice, GAT does not elicit a GAT-specific antibody response but does stimulate development of a population of GAT-specific suppressor T cells. Furthermore, extracts prepared from lymphoid cells of GAT-primed non-responder mice inhibit the development of GAT-specific antibody responses to GAT coupled methylated bovine serum albumin (GAT-MBSA) by normal non-responder syngeneic mice. This suppression is specific and dose-dependent. The activity can be removed from these extracts by passage over GAT-Sepharose, but not BSA-Sepharose. The molecular weight of the active component(s) is between 10,000-50,000.

INTRODUCTION

Our interest in antigen-induced suppressor T cells grew from studies of the mechanism by which an H-2 linked immune response (Ir) gene(s) controls the antibody response to the synthetic terpolymer GAT in inbred strains of mice. Both responder (H-2 ^{a,b,d,k}) and non-responder (H-2 ^{p,q,s}) mice develop primary GAT-specific IgG plaque-forming cell (PFC) responses to GAT-MBSA *in vivo* and *in vitro*. Responder, but not non-responder, mice develop GAT-specific IgG PFC responses to GAT (1). In addition, GAT specifically decreases the ability of non-responder mice to develop a GAT-specific response to a subsequent challenge with GAT-MBSA (2). This unresponsiveness is attributed to the stimulation of GAT-specific suppressor T cells (3).

GAT-induced suppressor T cells have the following characteristics:

1. They are induced by 1-100 µg GAT in Maalox, doses of GAT that are immunogenic for responder mice (2).

2. Suppressor T cells are demonstrable for three weeks after injection of 10 µg GAT in Maalox (Kapp , unpublished observation).

3. At all times that have been tested after induction, suppressor activity is abrogated by 800 R X-irradiation (3).

4. GAT-induced suppressor T cells are specific. They do not inhibit a response to sheep erythrocytes (SRBC) even in the presence of GAT-MBSA. Furthermore, they suppress the response to GAT in cultures stimulated with GAT coupled to pigeon erythrocytes (GAT-PRBC) without affecting the response to the carrier PRBC (4).

5. There was no demonstrable suppressor cell memory (4).

One mechanism by which some suppressor T cells can inhibit the response by normal lymphocytes is by the elaboration of mediators (5,6,7). Thus far, we have been unable to detect suppressive activity in the supernatant fluid of cultured spleen cells containing suppressor T cells. However, using the technique described by Tada (8) a suppressive extract has been prepared from sonicated lymphoid cells of non-responder mice primed with GAT in Maalox 3-7 days previously. In this communication we shall describe some of the characteristics of these extracts.

COMPARISON OF LYMPHOID CELL EXTRACTS FROM CONTROL AND GAT-PRIMED MICE

Since suppressive activity has been demonstrated in extracts of lymph node, spleen or thymus from GAT-primed non-responder mice (9), spleen cells and thymocytes were pooled and adjusted to 6×10^8 cells/ml before sonication. The activity of extracts equivalent to 1.5×10^8 lymphoid cells from control (Maalox primed) and GAT-primed mice on the response to GAT-MBSA by two non-responder strains and one responder strain of mice is shown in Table I.

TABLE I

EFFECT OF LYMPHOID CELL EXTRACTS ON PRIMARY RESPONSES
TO GAT-MBSA *IN VIVO*

STRAIN[a]	EXTRACT= 15 X 10^7 CELLS	GAT-SPECIFIC IgG PFC/SPLEEN[b] (ARITH. MEAN)	INHIBITION	P=
A.SW	None	13,200	-	-
A.SW	Control	12,500	5%	.860
A.SW	GAT	2,200	83%	<.001
DBA/1	None	10,200	-	-
DBA/1	Control	11,800	0%	.209
DBA/1	GAT	1,900	82%	<.001
DBA/1	GAT-MBSA	13,400	0%	.088
C57BL/6	None	7,300	-	-
C57BL/6	Control	5,100	30%	.315
C57BL/6	GAT	5,100	30%	.373

a. All mice received 10 μg of GAT as GAT-MBSA in Maalox-
pertussis I.P. one hour before extracts were injected I.V.
(8-12 mice/group).

b. Day seven PFC response.

These data demonstrate that: a) extracts from control
lymphoid cells do not significantly suppress the GAT-specific
PFC response to GAT-MBSA; b) extracts from GAT-primed
non-responder ($H-2^s$ and $H-2^q$) mice suppress the GAT-specific
response to GAT-MBSA by syngeneic mice; and, c) extracts from
GAT-primed responder ($H-2^b$) mice do not suppress the
GAT-specific response to GAT-MBSA by responder mice. Furthermore, the correlation between suppression by GAT, suppressor
T cells and their extracts is strengthened by the observation
that no suppressive activity is demonstrable in extracts of
lymphoid cells from non-responder mice immunized with
GAT-MBSA.

We have also observed (data not shown) that extracts,
like suppressor cells, from GAT-primed non-responder mice
suppress the GAT-specific response to GAT-PRBC without

inhibiting the response to the carrier, PRBC.

The effect of lymphoid cell extracts from the two non-responder haplotypes, $H-2^q$ and $H-2^s$ on the immune response to GAT-MBSA by syngeneic and allogeneic mice was assessed (Table II).

TABLE II

EFFECT OF EXTRACTS FROM GAT-PRIMED MICE ON
RESPONSE TO GAT-MBSA BY ALLOGENEIC MICE *IN VIVO*

TEST STRAIN[a]	N=	EXTRACT= 15 X 10[7]	GAT-SPECIFIC IgG PFC/SPLEEN[b] (ARITH. MEAN)	INHIBITION	P=
DBA/1	11	None	11,500	–	–
DBA/1	3	Control-DBA/1	11,900	0%	.862
DBA/1	12	GAT-DBA/1	3,700	67%	<.001
DBA/1	3	Control-A.SW	12,700	0%	.554
DBA/1	11	GAT-A.SW	10,400	9%	.642
A.SW	13	None	11,400	–	–
A.SW	6	Control-A.SW	11,700	0%	.884
A.SW	11	GAT-A.SW	1,700	85%	<.001
A.SW	3	Control DBA/1	16,000	0%	.218
A.SW	9	GAT-DBA/1	5,000	56%	.003

a. All mice received 10 μg GAT as GAT-MBSA in Maalox-pertussis I.P. one hr before injection of extracts I.V.
N= number of mice tested.
b. Day seven PFC response.

The immune response by DBA/1 $(H-2^q)$ mice was suppressed only by the extracts from GAT-primed DBA/1 mice. On the other hand, the immune response by A.SW $(H-2^s)$ mice was suppressed by the extracts from GAT-primed DBA/1 mice as well as GAT-primed A.SW mice.

The activity of extracts from GAT-primed DBA/1 mice on the development of immune responses by normal DBA/1 spleen cells *in vitro* has also been evaluated (Fig. 1).

This extract was not cytotoxic at dilutions of 1/100 or greater. At a 1/100 or lower dilution, nonspecific suppression of the response to SRBC is occasionally observed. However, at higher dilutions this extract routinely enhanced the response to SRBC. The control extract (data not shown) not only failed to inhibit responses to GAT-MBSA and SRBC, but also enhanced these responses at dilutions of 1/200 to 1/10,000. The extract from GAT-primed DBA/1 mice specifically suppressed the GAT-specific response to GAT-MBSA at dilutions of 1/200 to 1/1000. These dilutions are equivalent to 15 X 10^5 and 3 X 10^5 cells, respectively.

ANTIGENIC SPECIFICITY OF THE EXTRACT

Since the suppression mediated by extracts from GAT-primed mice is specific for GAT regardless of the carrier, we examined the possibility that the active component had affinity for GAT. An extract from GAT-primed DBA/1 mice was passed over GAT-Sepharose or BSA-Sepharose columns (9). The untreated extract and the effluent from each of these immuno-adsorbents were titrated for specific suppressive activity *in vitro*. The titration curve of the untreated extract was similar to that shown in Fig. 1 and inhibition was specific for the response to GAT-MBSA at dilutions of 1/100 to 1/800. In Fig. 2 data for the 1/800 dilutions demonstrate that the GAT-specific activity was removed by passage over GAT-Sepharose, but not BSA-Sepharose. Similar data (not shown) was obtained for 1/200 and 1/400 dilutions of these extracts. Similar results were obtained when the column absorbed extracts were assayed for suppression of the GAT-MBSA response *in vivo* (9).

ESTIMATE OF MOLECULAR WEIGHT

An extract from GAT-primed DBA/1 lymphoid cells was passed through successively smaller Amicon ultrafiltration membranes. The data in Table III demonstrate that *in vivo* suppressive activity of the unfractionated extract is significant at 1:2 and 1:4 dilutions. When tested undiluted, the only fraction of the extract that showed significant suppressive activity (77% inhibition) was material with a molecular weight range of 10,000 to 50,000. Similarly, fractionation of the extract by passage over a G-100 Sephadex column indicated that the peak activity eluted in the same volume as an ovalbumin marker (MW 45,000).

TABLE III

TITRATION AND SIZING OF GAT-INDUCED SUPPRESSOR EXTRACT FROM DBA/1 MICE *IN VIVO*[a]

DILUTION	AMICON FRACTION	GAT-SPECIFIC IgG PFC/SPLEEN[b] (ARITH. MEAN)	INHIBITION	P=
-	-	21,900	-	-
1:2	-	8,100	63%	.006
1:4	-	5,500	75%	.004
1:8	-	17,500	20%	.145
NEAT	>100,000	14,300	35%	.165
NEAT	50,000 - 100,000	16,100	26%	.146
NEAT	10,000 - 50,000	4,900	77%	.003
NEAT	<10,000	17,300	21%	.465
1:2	Pool of All	7,300	66%	.005

a. All mice received 10 μg GAT as GAT-MBSA in Maalox-pertussis I.P. one hour before injection of extract I.V.
b. Day seven PFC response.

In conclusion, we have identified mediator from activated T cells which is induced by a specific antigen, GAT. This mediator suppresses GAT-specific antibody responses in an antigen-specific manner, has antigen binding properties and has a molecular weight of 10,000 to 50,000 which is too small to be classical immunoglobulin antibody.

ACKNOWLEDGEMENTS

This investigation was supported by U.S.P.H.S. Research Grants AI09920 and AI09897 from the National Institute of Allergy and Infectious Diseases. CWP is the recipient of U.S.P.H.S. Research Career Development Award 5-K04-AI-70173 from the National Institute of Allergy and Infectious Diseases

REFERENCES

1. J.A. Kapp, C.W. Pierce and B. Benacerraf. J. Exp. Med 138:1107, 1973.

2. J.A. Kapp, C.W. Pierce and B. Benacerraf. J. Exp. Med. 140:172, 1974.

3. J.A. Kapp, C.W. Pierce and B. Benacerraf. J. Exp. Med. 140:648, 1974.

4. J.A. Kapp, C.W. Pierce and B. Benacerraf. In: *Suppressor Cells in Immunity*. Ed. S.E. Singhal and N.R.St.C. Sinclair. University of Western Ontario Press, London, Ontario 1975. pp. 84.

5. R.R. Rich and C.W. Pierce. J. Immunol. 112:1360, 1974.

6. D.W. Thomas, W.R. Roberts and D.W. Talmadge. J. Immunol. 114:1616, 1975.

7. M. Zembala and G.L. Asherson. Eur. J. Immunol. 4:779, 1974.

8. T. Tada, M. Taniguchi and T. Takemori. Transplant. Rev. 26: In press.

9. J.A. Kapp, C.W. Pierce, F. DeLaCroix and B. Benacerraf. J. Immunol.: In press.

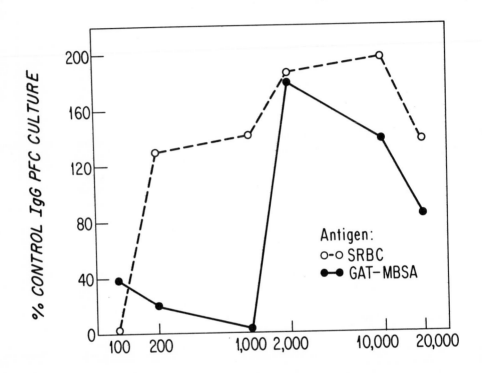

FIGURE 1.

Effect of a lymphoid cell extract on the IgG PFC
response to SRBC and GAT-MBSA by normal DBA/1 spleen
cells *in vitro*. Extracts were prepared from 6 X 10⁸
spleen cells and thymocytes from DBA/1 mice primed
three days earlier with 10 µg GAT in Maalox. PFC
responses were assayed on day 5 and the results are
expressed as a percent of the response in spleen cell
cultures with antigen but no extract.

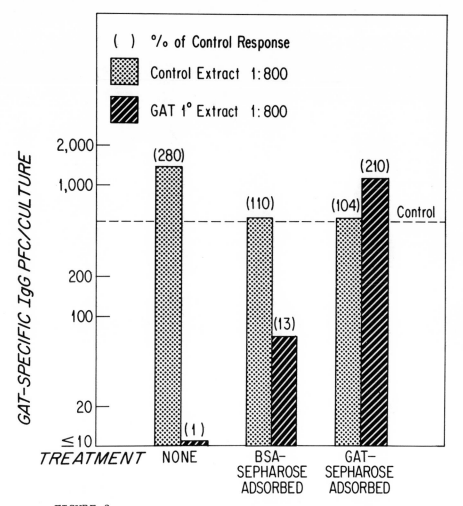

FIGURE 2.

Adsorption of GAT-specific suppressive extract with
GAT- or BSA-Sepharose. Extracts were prepared from
6 X 10[8] spleen cells and thymocytes from DBA/1 mice
immunized three days earlier with Maalox (Control) of
10 µg GAT in Maalox. The effects of untreated extracts
(1:800 final dilution) and extracts which had been
passed over BSA-Sepharose or GAT-Sepharose on the
immune response by normal DBA/1 spleen cells incubated
with GAT-MBSA are compared.

ANTI-β_2MICROGLOBULIN - A SELECTIVE PBA FOR HUMAN AND MOUSE B LYMPHOCYTES

ERNA MÖLLER, ULLA PERSSON, LARS RASK AND OLLE RINGDEN
Division of Immunobiology
Karolinska Institutet
and
Transplantation Immunology Laboratory
Huddinge Hospital
and
Department of Medical Chemistry
Uppsala University

Abstract: Rabbit anti-human $\beta_2$microglobulin directly activates a selective subpopulation of human and mouse B
lymphocytes. Activation results in DNA and polyclonal
antibody synthesis, and occurs through a mitogen receptor not identical to any of the hitherto identified B
cell receptors. Mitogenic material can be absorbed onto
and eluted from $\beta_2$microglobulin coated Sepharose particles. Since anti-$\beta_2$microglobulin is the first described PBA capable of activating human blood lymphocytes,
it is likely to be of clinical importance.

INTRODUCTION

$\beta_2$microglobulin is a protein with a molecular weight of
11.800, which was first described by Berggård and Bearn (1).
It has since been shown to have a structure exhibiting great
homology with constant regions of the immunoglobulin molecules (2,3). $\beta_2$microglobulin is one of the two non-covalently
linked chains that constitute the H-2 molecule in mice and
the HLA-A and -B molecules in man (4). It remains to be
established whether all surface bound $\beta_2$microglobulin is part
of MHS structures or not.

Antibodies against human $\beta_2$microglobulin was found to be
mitogenic for both mouse (5) and human (6,7) B lymphocytes.
No effect was observed in suspensions of thymocytes or purified T cell suspensions from spleen cells. Immunofluorescence
tests demonstrated that rabbit anti-human β microglobulin
bound to both T and B lymphocytes. Anti-$\beta_2$microglobulin has
also been found to inhibit the activation of T lymphocytes
by non-specific mitogens and antigens and in mixed lympho-

cyte cultures with human cells (9,10,11,12). Recently, it has been claimed that the AEF (allogeneic effect factor) of Amerding and Katz (13) contains $\beta_2$microglobulin, since AEF contains a fragment of 11.500 m.w. which is absorbed on anti-$\beta_2$microglobulin-Sepharose columns.

THE ACTIVE MITOGENIC PRINCIPLE IN ANTISERA AGAINST β_2MICROGLOBULIN

The mitogenic activity of anti-β_2m sera produced in rabbits against mouse splenic lymphocytes was removed by prior absorption with soluble $\beta_2$microglobulin. Absorption removed not only the mitogenic activity, but also the capacity of the serum to induce polyclonal antibody synthesis in vitro (5). Recently, we have performed absorptions of rabbit anti-human $\beta_2$microglobulin sera on columns prepared with $\beta_2$microglobulin coupled to Sepharose. As can be seen from Table 1, the mitogenic activity for human blood lymphocytes is removed in the absorbed material. Some mitogenic activity can, however, be recovered from the columns by treatment at low pH. Similar results are obtained with mouse spleen cells. These results strongly support the notion that the specific antibodies against $\beta_2$microglobulin were responsible for mitogenicity of such sera. This is further supported by the findings that normal rabbit sera, or antisera against immunoglobulins or light and heavy chains, or rabbit antiserum against mouse B lymphocytes (anti-MBLA serum) were devoid of mitogenic material (5).

Table I
Mitogenic activity of anti-$\beta_2$microglobulin, before and after absorption on $\beta_2$microglobulin-coupled Sepharose and after elution at low pH (cpm $\pm$ s.e. x 10^{-3}).

Preparation	Dilution of tested material			
	1/4	1/10	1/40	1/100
Unabs. anti-β_2m	48.3 ± 1.9	33.8 ± 2.3	24.7 ± 1.7	5.9 ± 0.7
abs. anti-β_2m	3.2 ± 0.3	1.5 ± 0	1.1 ± 0.1	1.0 ± 0.1
eluted anti-β_2m	8.5 ± 0.7	2.3 ± 0.3	1.0 ± 0	1.2 ± 0

unabsorbed, absorbed or eluted NRS, all $0.6 - 1.2 \pm 0.2$

Not only the IgG portion of anti-β_2m sera contains mitogenic activity, but also F(ab)$_2$ fragments of such sera. Thus, equally strong stimulation by F(ab)$_2$ as by IgG molecules for human blood lymphocytes were recently reported by Östberg et al. (14). Fab´ fragments in their experiments were non-mitogenic. However, we have recently found some, but weak, stimulatory effect of Fab´ anti-β_2m for human splenic lymphocytes. But, it should be noted, these data need further documentation. Therefore, we believe that it has been established that the mitogenic principle in rabbit anti-human $\beta_2$microglobulin sera is in fact the antibody to β_2m.

OPTIMAL CONDITIONS FOR MITOGENICITY OF ANTIBODIES TO β_2MICROGLOBULIN

Peak responses in suspensions of human blood lymphocytes are obtained in microcultures containing between $1.5-4 \times 10^5$ cells/0.2 ml of Mishell-Dutton tissue culture medium (15) supplemented with 10% heat-inactivated human AB serum. Deletion of serum from the cultures does not decrease mitogenicity (7). Maximum increase in DNA synthesis is observed after 2-3 days of incubation. Optimal cell concentrations for mitogenicity of cells from other human organs vary - for spleen cells usually 4×10^5 cells/microculture is optimal (15). Similar cell concentrations are needed for optimal DNA synthetic response of mouse spleen lymphocytes. However, in mouse cultures, serum should be omitted as discussed below. Different anti-β_2m antisera have divergent mitogenic activity, the reason for which will be further evaluated. Optimal conditions for the induction of antibody synthesis by anti-β_2m in mouse spleen cell cultures is obtained using conditions as for specific induction of primary antibody synthesis in vitro. Peak responses are usually reached after 2-3 days in culture. Polyclonal antibody secretion is revealed either as increased numbers of PFC reacting with haptenated red blood cells or as the formation of blast cells, containing large amounts of intracellular immunoglobulin, as determined by staining of fixed cells with fluorescein-labelled antisera. We would like to stress that only a proportion of those blasts that appear in treated cultures contain intracellular immunoglobulin - in cultures of human spleen cells approximately 30% are Ig positive (15). Similar findings are obtained also with the B cell mitogen, LPS, which possibly implies that only a fraction of all B cells which are activated by LPS or anti-β_2m have the capacity to synthesize immunoglobulin (16). This difference might reflect the maturation stage of the B

lymphocyte, as discussed by Gronowicz and Coutinho (17).
Human blood lymphocytes activated by anti-β_2m develop into
blast cells, but the proportion of Ig positive blasts in
blood is very low (~1%). Again, this is probably a
reflection of the maturation stage of B cells that are to be
found in blood compared to those present in tonsils, adenoids
or spleen. This particular point can be further emphasized by
the experiments shown in Fig. 1. LPS, which is known to be a
polyclonal B cell activator (PBA) of mouse spleen cells, very
rarely gives increased DNA synthesis in cultures of human
blood lymphocytes. Therefore, we studied whether LPS would
activate mouse blood lymphocytes, but found that it did not.
Therefore, we compared the mitogenic activity of LPS, anti-
β_2m, Con A and PHA on human cells from blood and spleen (7).

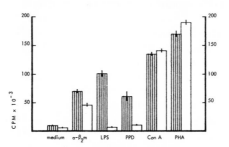

Fig. 1
Mitogenic activity of optimal concentrations of
different mitogens for human splenic lymphocytes
(hatched bars) and human blood lymphocytes (open bars).

The results showed that human spleen, like mouse spleen
contains B lymphocytes which are sensitive to LPS, whereas
such cells are absent among the B cells in the blood. As can
be seen, however, anti-β_2m, is a potent activator also of
blood lymphocytes. Thus, anti-β_2m could be a helpful substance
for the study of functional properties of human B
lymphocytes.

Finally, cells from different individuals differ
somewhat in their sensitivity to activation by anti-β_2m. This
is reflected, only in part, by the proportion of B
lymphocytes found in the blood. Therefore, we reinvestigated
whether there was a difference in the response to anti-β_2m
between different mouse strains, in order to elucidate the
genetics of responsiveness to anti-β_2m. We found that

cells from mouse strains $\underline{A(H-2^a)}$ and CBA and C3H $\underline{(H-2^k)}$ as
well as the LPS-low responder strain C3H/HeJ $\underline{(H-2^k)}$ responded
well to anti-β_2m, whereas cells from C57BL and $\underline{B10.5M (H-2^b)}$
usually gave lower responses. In preliminary experiments,
cells from (AxBL)F$_1$ gave an intermediate response. This point
needs further investigation.

B CELLS ARE DIRECTLY ACTIVATED BY ANTI-β_2MICROGLOBULIN

Our earlier findings have indicated that only B
lymphocytes, and not T lymphocytes are sensitive to the
mitogenic effect of anti-β_2m. Removal of T cells from mixed
mouse lymphoid cell suspensions, as well as removal of
adherent cells neither interfere with mitogenicity nor with
induction of polyclonal antibody synthesis (5). Recently, it
has been claimed that a cooperation between T and B cells was
needed for an optimal effect of anti-β_2m on human blood
lymphocytes (14). Therefore, we reinvestigated this, in the
mouse system, using graded doses of T and B cells obtained
from the same spleen, or alternatively by mixing thymus and
bone-marrow cells in distinct proportions. One experiment is
shown in Fig. 2, where it can be seen that we did not observe
any effect on DNA synthesis by the admixed T cells - the only
variable that determined mitogenicity seemed to be the
content of B cells. However, we have not yet performed
similar studies for induction of antibody production. Our
results were thus in accordance with our earlier findings
that removal of Thy-1 positive cells from cell suspensions
usually give a higher response than the mixed suspensions at
equal cell concentrations.

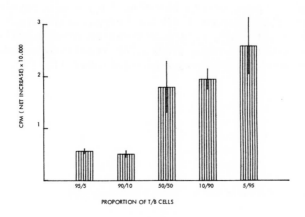

Fig. 2.
Spleen cells were divided into the T and B compartments
with the aid of anti-MBLA and anti-Thy 1 sera respectively. Thereafter graded mixtures of these cell suspensions were tested for susceptibility to activation to
DNA synthesis by anti-β_2m. The anti-Thy 1 treated
suppression is believed to contain 5% T and 95% B, the
MBLA treated cell 95% T and 5% B. Backgrounds were
subtracted.

DOES ANTI-β_2MICROGLOBULIN ACTIVATE A SPECIFIC SUBSET OF LYMPHOCYTES?

There is good reason to believe that T cells which
respond to PHA and Con A are partly distinct. Similar
evidence has been obtained for B cells sensitive to the
different PBA´s, dextransulphate (DxS), LPS and PPD (17). As
was shown by G. Möller in 1970 (18) a quantitative principle
applies to the activation of cells by antigen and mitogens,
in so far as two different mitogens or an antigen and a
mitogen in optimal doses resulted in inhibition of activation, whereas two suboptimal concentrations could give a
synergistic response. Completely additive effects between
mitogens is only observed when the substances activate
distinct cell subpopulations.

In order to investigate the target cell subpopulation
sensitive to the mitogenic and polyclonal activating
properties of anti-β_2m, we investigated whether the anti-β_2m
would interfere with activation of cells by PBA´s and PTA´s.
It is expected that optimal concentrations of two mitogens
would result in less than optimal responses if they activate
partly similar subpopulations but that they would result in
completely additive responses if the target cells are
distinct and no influence of the activation of one cell
population is exerted on the other. The results of studies on
activation of DNA synthesis is shown in Table II.

Table II.
Effect on DNA synthesis of mouse lymphocytes by mixtures
of B cell mitogens.

Target cells	Mitogen	Observed response (cpm)	Expected response (net increase)	% difference
CBA spleen	-	10.883		
	a-β_2m	19.538		
	DxS	56.021		
	both	63.255	53.793	-3
A spleen anti-θ treated	-	5.290		
	a-β_2m	22.888		
	LPS	59.740		
	both	80.739	72.048	+5

Thus, we did not observe any inhibitory effects by
mixing anti-β_2m with either DxS or LPS, two substances known
to be B cell activating substances with a high capacity to
give rise to a DNA synthetic response (17). We studied
possible synergy between anti-β_2m and LPS also in the human
system. As for the mouse situation additive effects were
obtained for splenic lymphocytes (Fig. 3a). LPS does not
activate human blood lymphocytes whereas anti-β_2m does. The
results with blood lymphocytes are shown in Fig. 3b, where we
found that addition of 100 ug LPS to cultures with varying

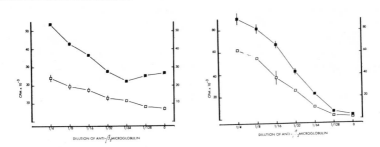

Figs. 3a and 3b.
Mitogenic effect of varying dilutions of anti-β_2-
microglobulin in the presence of 100 ug/ml of LPS for
human splenic lymphocytes (a) and for human blood
lymphocytes (b).
□——□ anti-β_2m, ■——■ anti-β_2m + LPS.

585

concentrations of antibody caused an increase of the response at all dilutions. This could be interpreted to indicate that LPS does react with B blood lymphocytes, some of which are anti-β_2m sensitive,so that a subliminal LPS concentration aids the activation by anti-β_2m. Alternatively, anti-β_2m activity could be enhanced by absorption on LPS molecules. Further studies on this point are in progress.

We also studied, but do not show here, that additive responses were regularly found in mixed suspensions of both human and mouse T and B cells when T cell mitogens, such as Con A or PHA, were mixed with optimal concentrations of anti-β_2m. We conclude that the splenic B cell subsets which respond with DNA synthesis and are sensitive to the mitogenic properties of LPS, DxS and anti-β_2m are distinct.

Secondly, we investigated the interaction between different PBA's for the induction of polyclonal antibody synthesis. Results presented in Table III show that slight inhibitory effects were regularly found, albeit small, when optimal concentrations of anti-β_2m were mixed with optimal concentration of either LPS or PPD, both known to be excellent inducers of antibody synthesis in vitro. PFC are measured against NNP- or FITC-labelled SRBC with a high epitope density.

Table III.
Interaction between different PBA's for induction of poly-clonal antibody synthesis measured against NNP-SRBC.

Experiment 1.   Experiment 2.

Mitogen	Response	% diff.	Mitogen	Response	% diff.
-	320		-	360	
anti-β_2m	1380		anti-β_2m	1280	
LPS	4040		LPS	4120	
both	3620	-31	both	3910	-24
PPD	3860		PPD	5170	
both	3100	-28	both	4240	-27

Thus, slight inhibition of responses were obtained with optimal concentrations of two different PBA´s. If inhibition were due to the fact that optimal concentrations of two mitogens caused superoptimal activation and hence decreased responses, one would expect that suboptimal concentrations of the two mitogens would have synergistic effects (18). This was further evaluated and one experiment is shown in Table IV where both synergy at low concentrations and inhibition at high is shown for LPS and anti-β_2m for induction of polyclonal antibody synthesis.

Table IV.
Influence of mixing various concentrations of two different PBA´s on the induction of polyclonal antibodies against heavily coupled NNP-SRBC.

Treatment	PFC/culture in the presence of various concentrations of LPS/ug/ml			
	0	1	10	100
-	40	290	360	400
anti-β_2m 1/10	310	453	336	273(-)
anti-β_2m 1/100	130	660(+)	430	380(-)
anti-β_2m 1/1000	83	516(+)	386	437

+ denotes synergistic responses, - denotes inhibition.

Not presented here are experiments where the effects of mixing fetal calf serum, also a PBA (19) on the PFC inducing capacity of anti-β_2m on mouse splenic lymphocytes. We have earlier reported that no activation occurs in the presence of 10% FCS in the tissue culture medium. Similar effects can be reproduced in synergy experiments. As a rule the admixture of 0.1% FCS (of a mitogenic batch, such as Rehatuin) increases back-ground DNA synthesis in cultures 2-3 times. Such a concentration decreases the response to anti-β_2m to less than 50%, higher concentrations are not as inhibitory. No effect of FCS on the response to LPS is observed. Therefore, it is possible that FCS in part activates the same population of B cells as anti-β_2m, but further experiments are needed to clarify this point. Thus, our results have implicated that slight synergy occurs between anti-β_2m on the one hand, and PPD or LPS on the other hand for induction of PFC.

In summary, the cells which respond with increased DNA synthesis to anti-β_2m are distinct to those that respond to DxS and to PPD. The B cell subset that responds to anti-β_2m by increased DNA synthesis is distinct from that which responds with increased DNA synthesis to LPS, but partly overlapping with that which responds to LPS with antibody secretion. The experiments reported above, which indicate that anti-β_2m, but not LPS can activate human peripheral blood lymphocytes also argues in this direction.

WHICH CELL RECEPTOR IS RESPONSIBLE FOR THE MITOGENIC ACTION OF ANTI-β_2MICROGLOBULIN?

It is unfortunate that there are many different cell surface structures, with presumed receptor activity whose function is completely unknown, and definite receptor sites for various functions, whose structure is unknown. Since anti-β_2m is a mitogen acting directly on B cells, it is plausible that the surface sites on the B cells which transmit the mitogenic signal to the interior of the cell contains β_2m. The cell surface structures with known content of β_2m include H-2 and HLA antigens, TL antigens on thymocytes and possibly other products of the MHS (4). However, in no instance have we found that antibodies against H-2 or HLA antigens can specifically inhibit anti-$\beta_2$mitogenicity. Neither does anti-β_2m pretreatment of mouse cells inhibit H-2 cytotoxicity. Experiments where human blood lymphocytes were either pretreated with monospecific highly cytotoxic anti-HLA-A or -B sera never resulted in inhibited mitogenicity. However, in the human experiments, unlike the mouse situation, it is possible that antibodies were not present against all specificities, which could explain lack of inhibition. Therefore, we performed experiments where mixtures of highly cytotoxic multispecific sera (reacting with more than 80% of random panel donors) were added to the cultures. In final serum dilutions of 1/2 we observed a slight inhibitory effect, but in serum dilutions of 1/10 or lower no inhibition ensued. Thus, we conclude that the mitogenic receptor either is not the HLA carrying cell surface structure, or, the mitogenic signal is not transmitted through anti-β_2m reacting with this molecule in a similar way as anti-HLA antibodies. It should be noted, that anti-HLA antibodies do not have any mitogenic effect. Anti-Ig pretreatment of cells does not inhibit anti-β_2m mitogenicity of either mouse or human lymphocytes. Thus, we do not believe that the Ig receptor on B cells is involved in anti-β_2m activation. This is further supported by the findings that anti-β_2m pretreatment of pure T or B cell suspensions at any concentration fails to interfere with specific antigen binding to cells from mice immunized against SRBC or hapten-protein conjugates as measured by the rosette assay.

Furthermore, neither in the human system, nor in the mouse system did we find any inhibition of formation of C´3-RFC by anti-β_2m, or other sera such as anti-Ig, anti-Thy1, anti-MBLA, anti-H-2 or HLA-A,B,C or anti-HLA-D. Recently, the Fc receptor on B cells has been implicated as a receptor for the triggerring signal to B cells (20). Fc binding can be inhibited by antibodies against Ia-antigens present on the cells - the inhibition, however, is mediated also on F_1 cells by antibodies against only one of the parental strain Ia specificities, and thus could be steric. The purified Fc receptor when studied chemically seems to lack both β_2m and Ia specificities (21). Furthermore, antibodies against β_2m do not interfere with cytotoxicity against Ia specificities in the mouse or HLA-D products in the human. Therefore the Fc receptor probably does not contain β_2m. This conclusion was also reached from our own experiments. Thus, pretreatment of cells with anti-H-2 sera, or of H-2 sera absorbed with thymocytes and red cells so as to only be cytotoxic for B cells, and not for T cells, clearly inhibit Fc-RFC formation even in low concentrations of antibody. Antibodies against Thy1, MBLA, light chains of Ig, and β_2m also inhibit Fc-RFC, but only in high concentrations of antibody. We initially believed that this "non-specific" inhibition could be caused by the presence in the sera of immune complexes. Thus, all sera were ultracentrifuged extensively, and thereafter again

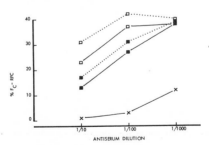

Fig. 4.
Inhibition of Fc-RFC by preincubation of lymphocytes with varying dilutions of anti-Thy 1 (■······■), deaggregated anti-Thy 1 (□······□), deaggregated anti-β_2m (■——■), deaggregated normal rabbit serum (□——□) and deaggregated anti-H-2 sera (x——— x).

tested for inhibition. Results of one such experiment is shown in Fig. 4. It can be seen that high concentrations of uncentrifuged anti-θ serum did inhibit slightly, but not the centrifuged serum. Deaggregated anti-β_2m caused only slight inhibition, not more than NRS at a high concentration, whereas the anti-H-2 serum was strongly inhibitory even at a final dilution of 1/1000. Thus, we have not found any evidence that the receptor with which anti-β_2m reacts on B cells is identical to the receptor for Fc.

In conclusion, the surface receptor with which anti-β_2m reacts to exert its mitogenic effect is not identical to any of the hitherto identified B cell receptors, and remains to be elucidated.

ACKNOWLEDGEMENTS

The authors thank Ms. Märit Larsson and Elsie Ekelund for excellent technical assistance.
This work was supported by grants from the Swedish Medical Research Council.

REFERENCES

(1) I. Berggård and A.G. Bearn. J. Biol. Chem. 243 (1968) 4095.

(2) O. Smithies and M.D.Poulik. Science 175 (1972) 187.

(3) P.A. Peterson, B.A. Cunningham, I. Berggård and G.M. Edelman. Proc. Nat. Acad. Sci. (Wash.) 69 (1972) 1697.

(4) G. Möller (editor) Transpl. Rev. 21 (1974).

(5) E. Möller and U. Persson. Scand. J. Immunol. 3 (1974) 445.

(6) B. Solheim and B. Rankin. (Personal communication).

(7) O. Ringdén and E. Möller. Scand. J. Immunol. 4 (1975) 171.

(8) B. Solheim. Transpl. Rev. 21 (1974) 35.

(9) M.L. Bach, S.W. Huang, R. Hong and M.D. Poulik. Science 182 (1973) 186.

(10) B. Lindblom, L. Östberg and P.A. Peterson. Tissue Antigens 4 (1974) 186.

(11) B. Solheim and E. Thorsby. Tissue Antigens 4 (1974) 83.

(12) C. Vincent, M. Robert and J.P. Revillard. Cell. Immunol. 18 (1975) 152.

(13) D. Amerding and D. Katz. Transpl. Rev. 22 (1975) 175.

(14) L. Östberg, B. Lindblom and P.A. Peterson. Eur. J. Immunol. In Press.

(15) O. Ringdén and E. Möller. Scand. J. Immunol. suppl. In Press.

(16) J. Forman and G. Möller. Transpl. Rev. 17 (1973) 108.

(17) E. Gronowicz and A. Coutinho. Transpl. Rev. 24 (1975) 3.

(18) G. Möller. Immunology 19 (1970) 583.

(19) A. Coutinho, G. Möller, J. Andersson and W.W. Bullock.
Eur. J. Immunol. 3 (1973) 299.

(20) D. Sachs and H. Dickler. Transpl. Rev. 23 (1975) 159.

(21) L. Rask, L. Klareskog, L. Östberg and P.A. Peterson.
Nature 257 (1975) 231.

GENERAL DISCUSSION - SESSION VI

PROPERTIES OF HISTOCOMPATIBILITY GENE PRODUCTS INVOLVED IN REGULATION OF IMMUNE RESPONSES

G.J.V. Nossal, Chairman

NOSSAL: As the data we have heard has been rather heterogeneous, I want to give our discussion some focus to
initiate it. This is to ask what may be the <u>target</u> for
the action of the various soluble factors that have
been described. We now know that the genesis of a
"helper" effect involves an interaction between macrophages, T_1 cells, T_2 cells and B cells, already giving
3 potential sites for factor action. It is not unlikely that suppressor cells may require T_1-T_2 interactions,
and, as suppressor cells could easily act on either
helper T cells or B cells, this gives us 3 further potential sites of action. Then we must consider macrophage-B cell interactions-- a seventh possible site--
not to speak of T cell-macrophage interactions, B cell→
T cell interactions, etc. Finally, at each of these
target sites we have to worry about antigen-specific
effects as well as antigen non-specific effects. Who
wants to begin to indicate where in this network the
best-defined factors may act?

BENACERRAF: I would like to make a correction on your
scheme, i.e. the generation of suppressor cells requires the bypassing of macrophage presentation. This
statement is based upon the fact that Tada, with conventional antigen, might inject the antigen in a state
and concentration which bypasses the macrophages to
generate suppressor cells. In our own laboratory we
fail to stimulate the suppressor cells if we use macro-
phage-bound GAT in non-responder mice.

NOSSAL: I am glad you reminded me of Basten and Miller's
finding that thoroughly good deaggregation of HGG (presumably by-passing the macrophage) selectively activates the suppressor mechanism in their B-cell tolerance model

MILLER: Recent work performed with my colleague A. Basten
(*Transplantation Reviews* 26:130,1975) strongly suggests
that the target cell for suppression is not the helper T cell but the B cell. In these experiments
HGG-tolerant spleen cells were transferred to irradi-

ated recipients with DNP-primed B cells and other
spleen cells primed to two carriers, HGG and KLH. The
recipients were then challenged with either DNP-HGG and
KLH, DNP-KLH and HGG, or with both DNP conjugates.
Marked suppression of anti-DNP antibody production was
observed on challenge with DNP-HGG, but not with DNP-
KLH, as expected. However, when challenge was performed with both DNP-HGG and DNP-KLH, inhibition of the
anti-DNP response was observed. The site of suppression must, therefore, be the hapten sensitive B cell,
not the carrier-reactive T cell. If the latter had
been the target, one would have expected a normal response in the presence of both DNP-KLH and DNP-HGG.
Absorption of anti-DNP antibody to DNP coupled to two
non-cross-reacting carriers implies non-specificity at
the effector phase. In other words suppression, although specific in induction, is non-specific in expression. This non-specificity may be explained in
terms of a role for an accessory cell, such as the macrophage, and we have demonstrated a requirement for adherent cells in the mediation of suppression.

GERSHON: It is important to add another pathway to Gus
Nossal's diagram. Both Tony Basten and I have shown
that Ig$^+$ B cells are importantly involved in generating
suppressor T cells. We also have similar, but less hard,
evidence that Ly-1$^+$ cells are important in inducing
specific suppressor activity in the Ly-2$^+$ population.

NOSSAL: Before you become too excited about B cell surface factors, should we not remember that one very well
known B cell factor can exert surprisingly strong suppressor effects on both B and T cells? I am referring,
of course, to antibody. The further we go with *in
vitro* systems, the more amazed we become at the strong
effects which antigen-antibody complexes in the zone of
antigen excess can have in blockading B and T cells.
There may, therefore, be systems in which anti-carrier
antibody made by B cells as a result of a helper effect
may "masquerade" and be read out as specific T cell
suppression.

RAJEWSKY: Tomio Tada thinks that the target of his suppressive factor is the T helper cell. In the experiments of Basten and Miller, which Jacques Miller just
mentioned the target of carrier-specific suppressor
cells appears to be the B cell. It seems to me that

594

these two conflicting views would be compatible in a
hypothesis which attributes to the suppressor cell the
function to arm helper cells with antigen-specific suppressive factors, thereby converting helper cells in
turn into suppressors:

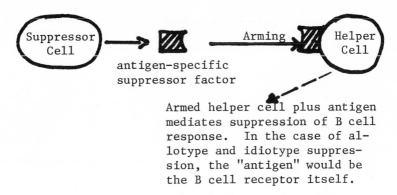

antigen-specific
suppressor factor

Armed helper cell plus antigen
mediates suppression of B cell
response. In the case of allotype and idiotype suppression, the "antigen" would be
the B cell receptor itself.

This scheme seems to be compatible with most systems of
suppression so far reported, in particular also at
least with part of the allotype suppression phenomenon,
where the Herzenberg group has surprisingly found the
helper cell to be the target. Idiotype suppression may
have the same mechanism. One may note that the scheme
would not require the assumption of allotype-specific
helpers, and that one can easily map onto it classical
inhibition of immune response by 7s antibody.

MILLER: Dr. Rajewsky's scheme is elegant, and there may
     be cases in which suppression is mediated through the
     intermediary of helper cells which become armed by an-
     tigen-specific factors produced by suppressor cells.
     However, in the HGG-tolerant system that Dr. Basten and
     I have been investigating, the fact that suppression is
     non-specific in expression is difficult to reconcile
     with an antigen-specific factor. In recent experiments
     (Miller, Vadas and Gamble, unpublished) it was shown
     that helper cells were inhibited by anti-Ly-1 sera,
     whereas suppressor cells were not. Unfortunately,
     these findings do not allow us to decide whether the
     helper cell (Ly-1) may become suppressive *in vivo* as a
     result of the arming mechanism postulated by Dr.
     Rajewsky.

SIMONSEN: Is Klaus Rajewsky in fact suggesting that the

suppressor T cell is passing on a passively acquired antibody to the helper T cell, which is thus suppressive in its helper function?

RAJEWSKY: Yes, that is what I am suggesting.

GERSHON: In response to Klaus - since purified Ly-2$^+$ cells produced suppression it would rule out that they must work by putting a factor on a Ly-1$^+$ cell which causes the helper cell to become a suppressor.

RAJEWSKY: I think you misunderstood my point. I was saying that the cell producing the suppressive factor (which may well be Ly-2 positive) arms the Ly-1 positive helper cell with suppressor factors, and that as a result the previously helping cell becomes suppressive.

GERSHON: I think I misunderstood Klaus's suggestion. The point is, that in order to get a response to suppress, helper cells from some source must be present. Therefore the Ly-2$^+$ cell could always work by putting something on the Ly-1$^+$ cell.

Also, I would like to say that I am not totally convinced that the data of Tony Basten and Jacques Miller show the target of suppression to be the B cell. While at a first (and even second or third) glance the data are highly indicative of that conclusion, because of the highly complex nature of the experiment (look who's talking!) one could think of several alternative suggestions to this conclusion.

KAPP: The evidence presented to determine the target of suppressor T cells and their products is indirect. In the GAT system, we also have indirect evidence and this data suggests that B cells are the target of suppression. GAT-induced suppressor T cells as well as extracts from these cells suppress the GAT-specific response in non-responder mice immunized with GAT-MBSA and GAT coupled to pigeon erythrocytes (PRBC), but no suppression of the anti-PRBC response is demonstrable. I think until direct evidence is obtained we should not conclude that the target of suppressor T cells has been established.

GERSHON: In response to Judy Kapp's comment, there is some direct evidence on the target of suppression.

Herzenberg, McCullough and myself have all been able to
show in different systems that the T cell becomes suppressed and cannot work when suppressor cells are removed and that B cells function normally when the suppressors are removed.

UHR: I want to make 2 points that bear on the proposed
role of soluble factors in the immune response. I ob-
ject to the terms secretion or shedding to describe the
appearance of a T cell factor in the incubation medium
of cell cultures and the serum of animals. There are
many mechanisms by which cell-associated molecules can
be transposed into the media. These include secretion,
spontaneous shedding, ligand-induced shedding, cell
lysis and, most important of all, proteolytic release.
Proteolytic enzymes could not only be supplied by serum
or lysed cells, but also could be supplied by the T cell
itself. It is an extremely difficult task to determine
which mechanism(s) is operative in a given situation
even when dealing with well-characterized *in vitro*
models. For example, Dr. Mge Grundke spent several
months in my laboratory attempting to determine whether
release of cell surface Ig from an established Burkitt
cell lymphoma line was caused by shedding or cell
lysis. Cell lysis was determined to be the mechanism
involved only after double labelling with ^{51}Cr and ^{125}I,
and elucidation of the kinetics of release of both
labels under a wide variety of culture conditions.
From these considerations, I would make a plea for the
use of mechanistically - noncommital terms to describe
the presence of a T cell factor in the medium or serum.

My second point is more controversial. I have heard no
"hard" data to indicate that T cell factors, in particular, antigen-specific ones, exert their physiological effects as soluble molecules apart from the cell
that synthesized the factor. I think the simplest
working hypothesis, therefore, is that the T cell with
its antigen-specific factor on the surface is directly
interacting with the target cell whether a B cell,
another T cell, macrophage, etc. In this regard, one
should not be misled by a pseudoanalogy with immunoglobulin antibody. This molecule is, of course, secreted by plasma cells as well as functioning as antigen-specific receptors on the surface of small lymphocytes. In this instance, it is clear that the secreted
molecules, present in large concentrations in the

serum, have important biological functions that do not depend directly on additional cells (e.g. antibody can neutralize toxins). There is no evidence at this time that T cell antigen-specific factors play such roles, and therefore, there is no raison d'etre from this point of view to postulate their presence in the serum.

KATZ: Jon has just reiterated, albeit much more elegantly, the point I was trying to make to Michael Taussig in yesterday afternoon's session (Session IV) regarding Michael's view of the apparent paradox between the lesser degree of genetic restrictions manifested by the soluble factors as compared to the viable, functioning cell. This is, indeed, a very crucial matter to bear in mind as we analyze and interpret data in these systems; otherwise we can all become unwittingly led down the wrong path.

NOSSAL: The cell interaction scheme was in no way meant to imply that the normal, physiological cell interactions depend on solubilized molecules. For example, our own work on antigen tracing has convinced us of the importance of spatial proximities of cells in immune induction. However, the investigator quite legitimately strives to isolate the factor in order to uncover the chemistry, while realizing it could well act physiologically as a membrane-associated entity. So there is no disagreement between us.

MUNRO: You suggest that antigen-specific factor reacts on the cells which make it. With the (T,G)-A--L helper factor this seems unlikely as the factor appears to be made by T-cells and will activate B-cells from H-2^f non-responder strains when transferred to irradiated H-2^f recipients. This strain fails to make factor for T,G-A--L, consequently factor-T cell interaction would be of no advantage.

KATZ: Perhaps you are viewing it just the reverse of the way it actually happens; in other words, it is possible that the factor, had it remained on the surface of the T cell from which it was derived, would not have activated the histoincompatible H-2^f non-responder B cells.

UHR: The issue is whether the physiological function of this factor is brought about by the molecule in solution. I do not argue about the mechanism of action in these model systems.

Let me remind you that Dr. Mozes showed the results of electrophoresis on sodium-dodecyl sulfate gels of serum-free incubation medium in which the antigen-spesific helper factor had been released from primed T cells by antigen. There were innumerable peaks, so these all represent secreted molecules, or is it more likely that these molecules have been released from the cells by lysis or proteolysis.

UNANUE: I would like to make a few points on the macrophage factors: Biologically, the macrophage factors 1) induce B cell differentiation, 2) increase helper T cell activity, and 3) increase proliferation of thymocytes with differentiation to mature T cells. The materials are triggered by a) phagocytosis including immuno-adjuvants, and b) an activated T cell. The factor(s) are approximately 20-25,000 daltons and do not contain H-2 determinants.

KATZ: Emil, could you give us a point of clarification here with respect to the comparative activities, in biological terms, of the factors produced by macrophages such as the one(s) you and Calderon have been studying (Calderon, J. and Unanue, E.R. *Nature* 253:359, 1975), the lymphocyte-activating factors (LAF) described by Gery, Waksman and Gershon derived in Con A and PHA stimulated culture supernates of macrophage-enriched populations (Gery, I., Gershon, R.K. and Waksman, B.H. *J. Exp. Med.* 136:128, 1972) and the T cell factors, such as allogeneic effect factor (AEF). I bring this up because the macrophage factors are distinguishable physicochemically (smaller molecular weight) and immunologically (absence of H-2 determinats) than the AEF molecules.

UNANUE: The macrophage factors biologically resemble, or are identical to the activities of AEF generated from MLC supernatants.

NOSSAL: With respect to adjuvants activating macrophages to produce factors which stimulate B cells, we should not forget Metcalf's work showing the macrophage as an important source of bone marrow colony growth stimulating factor (CSF). This is particularly the case after activation by agents such as bacterial endotoxin or flagellin.* I can thus agree with you that the macrophage may well be a very central target for the mode of action of adjuvants.

*[EDITOR'S NOTE: For references to these points, see:
1) Metcalf, D. Immunology 21:427, 1971.
2) Metcalf, D. J. Immunol. 113:235, 1974 – DHK.]

ARMERDING: There are a lot of different factors from probably different cell sources exhibiting identical effects, for example on the antibody responses of B cells, which also differ in their physicochemical properties. It remains open to discussion which of these factors have physiological meaning.

SESSION VII

Biochemistry and Immunocytology of Cell Surface Products of the Major Histocompatibility Complex

HENRY KUNKEL, CHAIRMAN

CYTOLOGICAL ANALYSIS OF HISTOCOMPATIBILITY MOLECULES

EMIL R. UNANUE

Department of Pathology
Harvard Medical School

Abstract: This paper reviews immunocytological studies of
histocompatibility antigens. Mapping studies have
disclosed that histocompatibility antigens are found
diffusely throughout the cell surface. In the case
of Ia antigens, there is a tendency to form small microclusters. The redistribution of histocompatibility antigens is different from other ligands. Finally, co-
capping studies have indicated that Ia antigens are
not associated with Fc receptors. Anti-Ig-Ig complexes, however, associate with Fc receptors on the
cell surface.

INTRODUCTION

This paper reviews some of the immunocytochemical
approaches for studying surface macromolecules associated
with the major histocompatibility complex (MHC). These
studies have involved three laboratories from our department: that of Morris J. Karnovsky who, with Abul Abbas, was
responsible for all the ultrastructural work; that of Baruj
Benacerraf and Martin Dorf, responsible for the genetic analysis; and our own. Most of these studies have been published (1 - 3).

One fundamental question which we and others have
asked concerns the way in which surface macromolecules are
organized on the plasma membrane. Are macromolecules distributed totally at random on the cell surface or are they
organized in some particular way? Do they have a fixed relationship with other surface molecules? Is this relationship
at any given time totally random? What controls the distribution of surface molecules prior to or after interaction
with ligands? What is the fate of ligand-receptor complexes,

how does a lymphocyte handle these complexes and what determines the reexpression of new antigens? Inasmuch as molecules of the MHC appear to be involved in a number of important interactions with antigens and/or other cell surfaces, these questions become critical in trying to outline their mode of action. Three kinds of approaches have been followed for answering some of these questions: one is to map surface molecules by immunoelectron microscopy; second is to determine whether surface molecules are mobile by studying their redistribution, *i.e.*, patching and capping; lastly is to determine whether redistribution of one molecule influences the anatomical disposition of a second molecule, *i.e.*, the co-capping kind of experiments.

MAPPING STUDIES

The fluid mosaic model of membrane structure proposed by Singer and Nicolson (4) envisions protein molecules embedded to a variable extent within a fluid phospholipid bilayer. The extent to which proteins are embedded depends, in part, on their amphipathic structures, the hydrophobic domains of the proteins interacting with the hydrophobic regions of the membrane. Membrane proteins are viewed as capable of freely diffusing within the plane of the fluid membrane, a point firmly confirmed by the many observations that most surface molecules patch and cap. The fluid mosaic model, therefore, envisions a non-random distribution of proteins on the cell surface. However, as Singer has also analyzed, several restrictions can be placed on this non-random pattern (5). Short-range organization of surface proteins with other protein molecules can be envisioned to take place.

We believe that the distribution of surface macromolecules on lymphocytes prior to their interaction with ligands can be studied adequately only using scanning electron microscopy or by freeze-etching analysis. Regular thin-section transmission electron microscopy is, as expected, inadequate inasmuch as molecules are seen only in one plane, the plane of sectioning. However, using scanning or freeze-etching, one obtains a two-dimensional analysis of the distribution of molecules. Scanning electron microscopy is limited, however, at present because of its low resolution. In our laboratory we have used extensively the freeze-etch analysis (3, 6).

There are several critical technical aspects when doing mapping which should be analyzed: 1) in many studies, the markers that have been used have been very large

molecules—viruses (7), protein-like hemocyanins (8)—which
are inadequate for precise distribution analysis. These
large markers serve only to give rough indications inasmuch
as they produce extensive degrees of steric hindrance. In
our experience, the most suitable marker is the molecule
ferritin of about 120 Å in diameter and easily visualized;
2) many mapping studies have been done in situations leading
to patching, distorting and altering the original distribution of the molecules on the membrane. Clearly, the best
way to avoid redistribution is either by using only monovalent antibodies or by studying prefixed cells, points which
have been highlighted in papers by Davies (9, 10), de Petris
and Raff (11), and us (6). The first studies mapping H-2
antigens on murine cells, including some of ours, gave the
false impression that these antigens were in large, gross
clusters. Subsequent and more careful studies have disclosed
that this gross clustering was the result of patching resulting from the use of bivalent antibodies. In thymocytes,
using prefixed cells or monovalent antibodies, H-2 antigens
are distributed diffusely, forming an irregular network
without any gross patching (12). In the case of Ia antigens,
the network contains a few microclusters—by this we mean
small, irregular groups of five to ten molecules (3). Our
most extensive studies on mapping have been done on Ia
antigens on murine spleen cells. The procedure used was a
double-antibody method, the first being an appropriate mouse
anti-Ia antibody tagged with fluorescein; the second antibody
was a monovalent rabbit anti-fluorescein tagged with ferritin
(6).

When we mapped the Ia antigens of the "entire" I
region using an A.TH anti-A.TL antibody and testing it on
B10.BR spleen cells, we found two distinct patterns: 94 percent of the cells had a high density of Ia antigens (about
112 ferritin grains per 0.25 μ^2 of cell surface), while the
remaining 6 percent had a low density of about one-half that
shown for the other cells. In contrast, when using the same
A.TH anti-A.TL serum to observe the topographical distribution of the Ia determinants coded for by a particular
subregion, e.g., I-A by testing the antibody on spleen cells
from 4R mice or the Ia determinants of the I-C subregion by
testing on spleen cells from B10.HTT mice, the proportion of
cells bearing high and low density Ia was about two-thirds
and one-third, respectively. The pattern of distribution
was diffuse but with a definite tendency to form small aggregates, leaving large spans of bare membrane (3) (Table I).

Table I: Distribution Pattern of Ia Antigens in
Freeze-Etched Replicas of Labeled Cells

I Region Antigens Labeled	Number of Ferritin Grains[a] on:		Proportions of Cells[b] with:	
	Densely Labeled Cells (in 0.25 μ^2 area)	Sparsely Labeled Cells	Dense Micro-clusters	Sparse Micro-Clusters
I-A + I-B + I-C	131 ± 5	71 ± 9	95	5
I-A + I-B + I-C[c]	112 ± 12	49 ± 3	94	6
I-A	119 ± 13	61 ± 11	72	28
I-C	123 ± 6	58 ± 6	67	33

This table summarizes the kind of distribution pattern of Ia antigens (3).

[a]Values shown as arithmetic means ± standard errors, based on counts of at least ten areas from six to eight cells in each experiment.

[b]Based on examining one hundred consecutive ferritin-labeled (*i.e.*, Ia-positive) etched surfaces in replicas.

[c]In this experiment, cells were fixed in 1% paraformaldehyde prior to labeling.

This kind of pattern is definitely not that of molecules distributed totally at random but implies a certain degree of organization. When patterns similar to these were subjected to mathematical analysis, it became clear that the distribution was non-random, although the kind of organization, if indeed present, has not been defined. Several possible technical points have been considered as producing artifacts leading to small degree of aggregation. For example, the patterns were identical when studied in prefixed cells or in cells handled at low temperature, to a great extent ruling out cross-linking effects. The *average* ratio of markers to antibody was about 1 to 2. However, our antibody preparations are heterogeneous insofar as marker-to-antibody ratio; this heterogeneity to some extent could lead to one site having more labeled antibody than a second, producing a false impression of microclustering. However, previous analysis of surface Ig carried out in a more extensive way disclosed a similar distribution with small microclustering

(6). These last studies with Ig explored a number of technical variables, all of which lead to the conclusion that the pattern was most likely a true one.

The nature of the association of molecule to molecule, if indeed true, has not been ascertained. It could result from protein-to-protein associations on the cell surface or could represent the manner in which the molecules are inserted on the membrane as they are being generated. Perhaps the molecules to be inserted come in small packets from the cytoplasm, and these remain as such on the surface. Functionally, one could envision an advantage for the cell of having receptors in microclusters if these have to interact with antigens or other cells because of summation of single interacting sites. What surrounds these microclusters? Attempts to identify the relationship on the membrane of two membrane molecules using two visual markers have been totally unsatisfactory in our hands; and thus, we cannot give any clear answer at the present time.

Other conclusions to derive from the electron microscopy study on Ia antigens were: 1) Ia antigens were mostly found on cells having surface Ig, *i.e.*, B cells (Table II); 2) the bulk of Ig-negative cells had no detectable Ia. We have estimated that the amounts of Ia antigens on normal (non-activated) peripheral T cells must be in the order of less than one hundred molecules per cell; finally, 3) there was no relationship between the morphology of the B cells and the density of Ia antigens.

Table II: Proportion of B10.BR Spleen Lymphocytes with Surface Ig and Ia Antigens by Double Label

Exp.	% Ig+ Cells	% Ia+ Cells	% Ig+ Ia+ Cells	% Ig- Ia+ Cells	% Ig+ Ia- Cells
1	51.4	53.7	48.6	5.1	2.8
2	46.6	48.5	45.1	3.4	1.5
3	49.8	50.7	46.2	4.5	3.6

Surface Ig was labeled by anti-Ig conjugated to hemocyanin and Ia antigens by the hapten sandwich method employing ferritin as the visual marker. All percentages are expressed as proportions of the total spleen lymphocyte populuation based on

examining at least two hundred viable, small
lymphocytes in thin sections (3).

REDISTRIBUTION

The second point which we would like to analyze concerns the redistribution of MHC molecules on the cell surface
upon ligand binding. Unquestionably, MHC molecules redistribute—that is to say, can form aggregates and cap—indicating
that, like other surface molecules, they can move and diffuse
within the plane of the membrane. However, the pattern of
redistribution of these is quite different from surface molecules.

Table III: Characteristics of Surface Redistribution
of Molecules from the MHC

1. Redistribution is slow: capping takes place
    after long incubation (fifteen minutes to
    two hours). Capping is usally found in no
    more than one-third to one-half of the cells.

2. Redistribution is disorganized: multiple
    aggregates are found—bipolar caps are
    frequently seen.

3. Redistribution is not associated with cell
    motility nor does it produce gross contrac-
    tion of the cells.

4. Redistribution is favored by a double-antibody
    method and by treatment of cells with col-
    chicine.

5. Endocytosis is not extensive: complexes
    remain for long periods on the cell surface.

Table III summarizes some of the characteristics of
the redistribution of MHC antigens. Patching and capping of
MHC cell surface antigens is slow in contrast to the time
taken for other molecules. While Ig, for example, caps in
five minutes or less at 37°C, H-2 or HL-A antigens take
thirty to sixty minutes to do the same. Usually, the number
of cells capping tends to be small—at the most, one-half of
the total again in contrast to Ig where mostly all cells cap.
The pattern of redistribution is also particular in that in

many instances multiple large aggregates are formed on the cell surface. Bipolar caps, a phenomenon first reported by Stackpole and associates when studying TL antigens (13), are occasionally seen. Ig redistribution, in contrast, is a well-integrated phenomenon where *all* the complexes coalesce into one point on the cell surface. Redistribution of the MHC complexes is not accompanied by gross changes in cell shapes. It is interesting to note that the microtubular-disrupting drugs favor capping of MHC. Finally, one important difference between MHC molecules and Ig concerns the fate of the complexes. While the bulk of Ig complexes— 90 percent or so—are interiorized by pinocytosis and digested, the MHC molecules tend to remain for long periods on the cell surface, slowly disappearing, most likely by shedding with small degree of endocytosis.

It is interesting to note that TL antigens in studies done by the Sloan-Kettering group (13) behave in about the same way; TL antigens are also associated with the murine MHC. The phenomenon of modulation reported by Boyse, Stockert, and Old (14) several years ago and thought to be explained by disappearance of complexes from the cell surface is now known to result from large aggregates which remain on the membrane and which are in a form that does not fix complement adequately (15). Redistribution of HL-A molecules (16) or, for that matter, of Beta-2 microglobulin (17) also follows the same pattern. A comparison of the redistribution patterns for Ig, concanavalin A, and MHC antigens are shown in Table IV.

Table IV

	Two Ligands	Time	Energy	Need For Motility	Colchicine	Endocytosis
Ig	Not necessary	Immediate	+	Not required	May enhance	< 90%
Con A	Not necessary	Immediate	+	Required	Enhancement (++++)	Extensive

Table IV, Continued

Two Ligands	Time	En-ergy	Need For Mo-tility	Colchicine	Endo-cytosis
H2 TL β2M } Usually re-quired	Long	+	Not re-quired	Enhance-ment (++)	Very little

This table summarizes previously published work done by several laboratories. See References 1, 15, 16, 17, 18, 19, and 20.

The basis for these contrasting results is not clear. It is our feeling that active redistribution involves a close interaction between surface complexes and cytoplasmic structures such as the contractile elements and the micro-tubular system of the cell. In some way or another, the cells have learned how to coordinate surface complexes and drive them to a single area. This interaction is poorly coordinated with determinants of the MHC either because structurally the molecules of the MHC are perhaps more deeply embedded on the cell surface and, therefore, are more diffi-cult to drive; or, alternatively, because the relationship with cytoplasmic structures is disorganized, leading to un-coordinated caps. This, together with the lack of endocytosis, certainly implies different surface structural relationships, the nature of which remain to be elucidated.

CO-CAPPING

The relationship on the cell surface molecules coded for by the MHC among themselves or with other membrane proteins has been studied most effectively by co-redistribu-tion or co-capping experiments. Redistribution of one molecule will not alter the topography of a second molecule unless this second molecule is physically linked to the first one. This approach has been used successfully by Kourilsky and coworkers (16, 21) to show that the major serologically defined antigens are independent of each other as well as independent of surface Ig. Likewise, it was the approach first used by Poulik and associates (22) to determine that some Beta-2 microglobulin molecules were associated with molecules of the MHC.

Our own studies have focused on the relationship between Ia molecules and molecules coded by the H-2D and H-2K
loci, surface Ig, and the Fc receptor (1). The interest in
the Fc receptor came as the result of Dickler and Sachs' observation of a possible relationship between Ia molecules
and Fc receptors. The main conclusions to emerge were: 1)
redistribution of anti-Ig did not lead to changes of Ia antigens. This was done by either co-capping Ig or by simply
allowing the Ig-anti-Ig complexes to be eliminated from the
membrane at which time the cells were studied for the distribution of Ia antigens. 2) Similar results were found
regarding molecules coded by H-2K or H-2D—redistribution of
one or the other did not change the distribution of Ia antigens.

The Ig-Fc receptor interrelationship was studied by incubating cells with fluorescein-labeled keyhole limpet
hemocyanin (F.KLH) and appropriate dose of rabbit anti-KLH
(2). These complexes were found to bind mostly to B cells
via an Fc receptor-like molecule. The KLH-anti-KLH could be
capped and eliminated from the cell surface, new receptors
being generated in a few hours of culture. Following elimination of the Fc receptor, we found that Ig molecules were
not altered in their distribution or amount. That is to say,
that the Fc receptors were separated on the cell membrane
from the Ig molecules. In contrast, redistribution. of the
Ig led to co-redistribution of the Fc receptor. Exposure of
murine spleen cells with anti-Ig produced caps of anti-Ig-Ig
complexes. If the capped cells were then exposed under non-
capping conditions to F.KLH-anti-KLH, the complexes became
bound to the capped area and not diffuse, as it happened when
the cells were not treated first with anti-Ig (Table V).
Under these conditions, Ia molecules were found diffuse
throughout the cell surface. The co-redistribution of Fc
receptors by anti-Ig was also produced, albeit somewhat less
effectively by pepsin-digested anti-Ig, implying that the Fc
fragment of the anti-Ig antibody was not entirely responsible
for the co-capping of the Fc receptor.

Table V: Effect of Preincubation with Anti-Ig on the Distribution of Fc Receptors

	First Incubation		Second Incubation	Fc Receptors		Ig	
Exp.	Ligand	Temp., Duration	Ligand (4°, 30 Minutes)	%	% Caps	%	% Caps
1	F.KLH + anti-KLH	4°, 30 min.	—	37.6	0	—	—
	RAMG	4°, 30 min.	F.KLH + anti-KLH	40.8	0	—	—
	RAMG	37°, 15 min.	F.KLH + anti-KLH	22.3	76.0	—	—
	RAMG	20°, 30 min.	F.KLH + anti-KLH	29.7	61.3	—	—
2	F.KLH + anti-KLH	4°, 30 min.	—	37.2	0	—	—
	RAMG	37°, 15 min.	F.KLH + anti-KLH	21.8	70.2	—	—
	RAMG	37°, 15 min.	F.GARG	—	—	30.0	85.2
	RAMG	37°, 60 min.	F.KLH + anti-KLH	3.9	N.D.[a]	—	—
	RAMG	37°, 60 min.	F.RAMG	—	—	1.4	N.D.[a]

[a]N.D. = Caps not counted because of low percentage of postive cells.
RAMG = Rabbit anti-mouse Ig. Two representative experiments are shown;
similar results were obtained in five other experiments. Not shown is
further control in which cells were incubated at 37° for one hour without any ligands. These bound KLH-antibody complexes diffusely.

Table VI: Effect of Modulating Fc Receptors on Surface Ig

Exp.	First Incubation Ligand	Temp., Duration	Second Incubation Ligand (4°, 30 minutes)	Fc Receptor %	Fc Receptor % Caps	Ig %	Ig % Caps
1	F.KLH + anti-KLH	4°, 30 min.		42.0	0	—	—
	F.KLH + anti-KLH	37°, 15 min.	RB.F(ab')$_2$ anti-Ig	46.0	69.0	44.4	3.6
2	KLH + anti-KLH	37°, 15 min.	F.RAMG	—	—	45.7	1.0
	KLH + anti-KLH	37°, 15 min.	F.GARG	41.4	64.8	—	—
3	F.RAMG	4°, 30 min.		—	—	42.4	0
	F.KLH + anti-KLH	4°, 30 min.		39.9	0	—	—
	KLH + anti-KLH	37°, 60 min.	F.RAMG	—	—	41.3	0
	KLH + anti-KLH	37°, 60 min.	F.KLH + anti-KLH	3.4	N.D.[a]	—	—

[a] N.D. = Caps not counted because of low percentage of positive cells. RAMG = Rabbit anti-mouse Ig. Representative experiments are shown. Similar results were obtained in three other experiments.

Thus, one is able by these kinds of experimentation to clearly separate Ig from Ia from Fc receptors. In other words, co-capping of the Fc receptor by anti-Ig will not alter the topography of Ia molecules.

The interrelationships between Ig and Fc is quite a unique phenomenon; it implies that the Ig on the membrane can bind in some way to the Fc receptor provided it is complexed by a ligand. Insofar as the explanation of blocking Fc receptor by anti-Ia reported by Dickler and Sachs (23), some points are worth emphasizing. The interaction of one ligand with the cell may produce a series of topographical, conformational, or metabolic changes in the cell which could easily reflect in the subsequent interaction with second ligand (5). Precedence for this statement are abundant: 1) for example, we have observed in scanning electron microscopy studies that the interaction of anti-Ig with the cell clears its surfaces of the small, microvillous projections (24); 2) interaction of certain ligands—Con A, anti-lymphocyte globulin—inhibits capping of anti-Ig (19) or the contractile events produced by anti-Ig (25), *i.e.*, one ligand exerts effects on the cell which oppose those produced by a second one. 3) Elevation of cyclic nucleotides is known to induce important conformational changes in lymphocytes (26)—indeed, it is interesting to note that cholera toxin inhibits opsonized red cells to lymphocytes (27)—or that increased levels of cyclic AMP are reflected in decreased binding of sheep red cells to human T cells (28). It is our impression, therefore, that anti-Ia in some as yet unknown way is inducing some kind of topographical or conformational changes which in some way reflect in the Fc receptor.

ACKNOWLEDGEMENTS

The author's studies were supported by grants AI 10091, AI 10677, and NCI 14723 from the National Institutes of Health.

REFERENCES

1. Unanue, E. R., Dorf, M. E., David, C. S., and Benacerraf, B., Proc. Nat. Acad. Sci. USA, *71*:5015, 1974.

2. Abbas, A. K. and Unanue, E. R., J. Immunol., *115*:in press, 1975.

3. Abbas, A. K., Dorf, M. E., Karnovsky, M. J., and Unanue, E. R., J. Immunol., *116*:in press, 1976.

4. Singer, S. J. and Nicolson, G. L., Science, *175*:720, 1972.

5. Singer, S. J., Adv. Immunol., *19*:1, 1974.

6. Abbas, A. K., Ault, K. A., Karnovsky, M. J., and Unanue, E. R., J. Immunol., *114*:1197, 1975.

7. Hämmerling, U., Poliack, A., Lampen, N., Sabety, M., and de Harven, E., J. Exp. Med., *141*:518, 1975.

8. Unanue, E. R., Perkins, W. D., and Karnovsky, M. J., J. Exp. Med., *136*:885, 1972.

9. Davis, W. C., Science, *175*:1006, 1972.

10. Davis, W. C., Alspaugh, M. A., Stimpfling, J. H., and Walford, R. L., Tissue Antigens, *1*:89, 1971.

11. de Petris, S., and Raff, M. C., Eur. J. Immunol., *4*:130, 1974.

12. Abbas, A. K., Karnovsky, M. J., and Unanue, E. R., unpublished observations.

13. Stackpole, C. W., Jacobson, J. B., and Lardis, M. P., Nature, *248*:232, 1974.

14. Boyse, E. A., Stockert, E., and Old, L. J., Proc. Nat. Acad. Sci. USA, *58*:954, 1967.

15. Stackpole, C. W., Jacobson, J. B., and Lardis, M. P., J. Exp. Med., *140*:939, 1974.

16. Kourilsky, F. M., Silvestre, D., Neauport-Sautes, C., Loosfelt, Y., and Dausset, J., Eur. J. Immunol., *2*:249, 1972.

17. Neauport-Sautes, C., Bismuth, A., Kourilsky, F. M., and Manuel, Y., J. Exp. Med., *139*:957, 1974.

18. de Petris, S., J. Cell Biol., *65*:123, 1975.

19. Yahara, I. and Edelman, G. S., Proc. Nat. Acad. Sci. USA, *69*:608, 1972.

20. Unanue, E. R. and Karnovsky, M. J., J. Exp. Med., *140*:1207, 1974.

21. Neauport-Sautes, C., Lilly, F., Silvestre, D., and Kourilsky, F. M., J. Exp. Med., *137*:54, 1973.

22. Poulik, M. D., Bernoco, M., Bernoco, D., and Cepellini, R., Science, *182*:1352, 1973.

23. Dickler, H. B. and Sachs, D. H., J. Exp. Med., *140*: 779, 1974.

24. Karnovsky, M. J. and Unanue, E. R., experiments to be published.

25. Schreiner, G. F. and Unanue, E. R., J. Immunol., *114*: 809, 1975.

26. Schreiner, G. F. and Unanue, E. R., J. Immunol., *114*: 802, 1975.

27. Zuckerman, S. H. and Douglas, S. D., Nature, *255*:410, 1975.

28. Chisari, F. V. and Edgington, T. S., J. Exp. Med., *140*:1122, 1974.

DISCUSSION FOLLOWING EMIL UNANUE

NOSSAL: I wish to be reassured that you feel the fixation
method of your cells <u>absolutely</u> restricts receptor
movement. When we take B lymphocytes that have been
purified by the method of Haas and Layton for NIP-
binding cells, fix with 1% or even 4% paraformaldehyde
and stain with NIP-polymerized flagellin-rhodamine
(Nossal, G.J.V. and Layton, J.E., manuscript submitted),
the stainings look linear in the "profile" plane of the
cell. However, if one focuses up and down very carefully under 1000-fold magnification, very fine patches
are seen. While this <u>could</u> indicate inhomogeneous
distribution, we feel a more likely explanation is
fixation which is not absolutely complete. As regards
Fab-reagents as markers, it is, of course, difficult to
exclude a small amount, eg. 1% of $F(ab)_2$ or undigested
antibody. The reason for my concern is that we were
fooled once in our attempts at this kind of mapping,
as you have said, and we had better be certain of our
ground the second time around!

UNANUE: The kind of experiments that you mention must be
done by electron microscopy. Immunofluorescence will
not give a correct appraisal of the distribution of
surface molecules.

We have no indication that macromolecules on <u>prefixed</u>
cells redistribute upon ligand binding. The patterns
that we obtain on prefixed cells using divalent antibodies are identical to those obtained in cells examined
in the cold with monovalent antibodies.

CUNNINGHAM: Ichiro Yahara has shown that capping with
Con A co-caps *H-2* antigens. This suggests that the
differences in the capping with anti-*H-2* and Con A is
more a property of the capping agent than a property of
the receptor.

MILLER: My colleagues and I (Basten, Miller, Abraham,
Gamble and Chia, <u>Intern. Arch. Allergy</u>, in press) have
obtained similar results with reference to the distribution of Fc receptors, Ig determinants and Ia antigens.
If Fc receptors were first capped, anti-Ia serum applied
under non-capping conditions was still found to bind
diffusely to the great majority of B cells, implying
that at least <u>some</u> Ia antigens are distinct from Fc

receptors. This conclusion is valid only if complete removal of Fc receptors occurred as a result of the capping procedure. We were, however, able to demonstrate some residual Fc receptors following capping with aggregates but only about half the cells displayed this, whereas almost all still labelled diffusely with anti-Ia. Have you looked for residual Fc receptor following initial capping of the receptor?

UNANUE: Under our conditions, all the Fc receptors capped with KLH anti-KLH and the membrane was left bare of Fc receptors which regenerated after a few hours.

AMOS: Killer (K) lymphocytes bind to allogeneic target cells if the targets are viable. In general, K cells will not bind to dead cells. Henney, using glutaraldehyde and Todd and Stulting, using formaldehyde, can obtain fixed cells that still permit good binding. The conditions for fixation are very restrictive, in our case, 0.2% formaldehyde in the cold. Can you predict what is happening on the surface with this restricted cross-linking?

UNANUE: We have not examined cells under these conditions. I would predict that at a certain concentration of fixative, one would produce only certain degrees of cross-linking without much denaturation of the proteins and without affecting cell viability.

DUPONT: In the study of spleen cells for *H-2* antigens, you found approximately 5% cells without Ig but with Ia. Are these T cells? Do they have Ly-antigens?

UNANUE: We assume that they are T cells but have no definitive proof inasmuch as we have not tested these cells with other markers.

SACHS: Dr. Dickler and I have tried similar co-capping studies to those you have described. We likewise find that capping of the Fc receptor leaves Ia antigens readily detectable on most of the B cells. However, when Dr. Dickler has used a very sensitive assay for the Fc receptor, involving an indirect staining technique, he has found that Fc receptors are still detectable distributed on the surface of the majority of these B cells. Most of the Fc receptors are indeed in the cap, but there are clearly others which are not capped

While we think it is likely that these studies indicate a separability of the two entities, we would hesitate to rule out the possibility that the sensitivity of detection of Ia antigens is such that the remaining uncapped Fc receptors could account for this apparent separability.

UNANUE: This is not the explanation for our results which clearly indicated that after capping anti-Ig: 1) Fc receptors were formed only on the cap area; 2) there was no loss of Ia from the cell surface; and 3) there was no concentration of Ia on the cap area.

KUNKEL: There is some other suggestive evidence that the Ia determinants on the B cell and the Fc receptor are distinct. Drs. Winchester and Wernet in our laboratory have found several lymphoid lines that express the human Ia determinants very thoroughly but yet are completely devoid of Fc receptors. The latter have been searched for both by a sensitive radiolabelling technique and by fluorescence.

DAUSSET: In the absence of Francois Kourilsky, I would like to give a summary of his last work done with F. Lemonnier, C. Neauport-Sautes and Peter Démant. Using non-specific anti-*H-2* antisera, redistribution of private *H-2.4* and public *H-2.28* was done on T lymphocytes from $H-2^{\alpha}$ and $H-2^{d}$ mice. Redistribution of *H-2.4* into patches and caps did not induce concomitant redistribution of specificity *H-2.28* which remained diffuse. Redistribution of *H-2.28* induced redistribution of *H-2.4*. These data suggest that at least some of the *H-2.28* sites are expressed on polypeptide chains independent from those carrying *H-2.4* and that other *H-2.28* sites may be linked to molecules carrying *H-2.4* Since on $H-2^{\alpha}$ cells both specificities are products of the *D* region of the *H-2* complex, these results suggest that there are at least two genes in the *D* region. Thus, *H-2.28* is a determinant shared for *K*, *D* and a third product. Working with a mono-specific serum labelled anti-*W4* (*4^{\alpha}*), we observed that it reacts with *HLA-A^{q}* at the *HLA-A* locus but also with several *HLA-B* alleles (*W27* as well as *B5* , *B12* , *W17* and *W21* cells).

Redistribution experiments show that the specificities detected in both *HLA-A* and *B* locus is present on molecules *A9* and on molecules *W27*. This specificity shared

619

by the products of both loci could be called interlocus specificity and is probably the equivalent of the long-public *H-2* specificities (Lepraud and Dausset, <u>Transplantation</u> <u>19</u>:177, 1974).

AMOS: I should like to issue a warning to those who regard co-capping as proof of identity. Linda Gooding and Peter Cresswell at Duke have been studying an antigen on the L cell. In capping studies, the molecule co-caps with *H-2*. In DEAE chromatography two peaks can readily be separated.

[*EDITOR'S NOTE:* This comment was actually made at the end of the General Discussion of Session I, but was translocated to the present discussion since it was actually out of context in the earlier session but directly pertinent to the discussion of Unanue's paper — DHK.]

ISOLATION AND STRUCTURE OF PRODUCTS OF THE HUMAN
HISTOCOMPATIBILITY GENE COMPLEX

J. L. STROMINGER, L. CHESS, R. E. HUMPHREYS,
D. MANN, P. PARHAM, R. ROBB, S. SCHLOSSMAN, T. SPRINGER, AND
C. TERHORST

The Biological Laboratories
Harvard University

The Sidney Farber Cancer Center
Harvard Medical School

National Cancer Institute

INTRODUCTION

The first part of this paper will describe the
purification of HL-A antigens from several human
lymphoblast lines (B cells transformed by Epstein-
Barr virus [EBV]), their analysis and preliminary
sequence data. The second part will deal with
several other polypeptides from human lymphocyte
membranes which were first detected as impurities
in the HL-A antigen preparations. The latter are
extremely interesting and some of them appear to
be B cell specific determinants of the human lymphocyte. The most thoroughly studied of these is
probably the analogue of the mouse Ia antigen.

HL-A ANTIGENS FROM HUMAN LYMPHOCYTES

A number of attempts had been made to purify
HL-A antigens from human lymphocytes, notably by
Sanderson and Batchelor (1) who used splenic
lymphocytes. Very small amounts were obtained
from this source. Cultured lymphoblasts appeared
to be a preferable source, both because they were
available in potentially larger amounts than human
spleens and because an experiment with a single

human spleen cannot be repeated. However, cultured lymphoblasts are available in reproducible supply and do not seem to have any altered HL-A specificities. Remarkably, these lymphoblasts also
contained far more HL-A antigens than splenic or
peripheral blood lymphocytes. This was shown by
absorption experiments with HL-A antisera using
three types of cells, all from the same individual
(2). Peripheral blood lymphocytes from RH had a
very low absorptive capacity for these antisera.
PHA-stimulated lymphocytes had a greatly enhanced
capacity and RH lymphocytes transformed by EBV and
growing continuously in cultures had an enormously
enhanced absorptive capacity for HL-A antisera,
i.e., the representation of HL-A antigens on the
surface of the cultured lymphocyte transformed by
EBV was in the range of 20-50 fold greater than
peripheral blood lymphocytes; all four of the
HL-A specificities of RH cells were similarly
affected. This enhanced representation was specific in that other membrane markers, such as 5'-
nucleotidase or radioiodinatable surface protein,
were increased in the transformed cell only 2-3
fold, the same as the increase in surface area.
One interpretation is that the virus itself induced or enhanced expression of the antigen in some
way. Alternatively, the virus may have selected
for transformation a subpopulation of B lymphocytes
which already had an enhanced representation. The
explanation is not known but the fact that the
HL-A antigens are so much more densely represented
on the cultured lymphoblasts has made possible
their isolation in relatively large amounts.

a. Preparation of HL-A antigens after papain solubilization. Two principle methods have been used
for solubilization of HL-A antigens. They are:
1. treatment with papain, and 2. solubilization
with detergent. Preparation of HL-A from the cell
line RPMI 4265 after papain solubilization (3) is
shown in Table I. The procedure for isolation is
not difficult, requiring only four steps. The
most interesting feature is that only about 70-
fold purification was needed to obtain pure HL-A
antigen from cell membranes, i.e. something in the
order of 1-2% of the total membrane protein in
the cultured lymphoblast is HL-A antigen. That is

TABLE I.

Purification of Papain-Solubilized HL-A
Antigens from 4265 Cells.

Purification Step	Protein (mg)	% Recovery of Inhibitory Units		Specific Activity (Inhibitory Units per mg)		Purification
		HL-A2	HL-A7	HL-A2	HL-A7	
1. Cell membrane	225	100%	100%	3,150	320	(1)
2. Papain Digest	45	32	41	5,000	660	1.5-2
3. CM-52 Chromatography	-	22	28	-	-	-
4. Sephadex G-150 Chromotography	6	22	28	25,800	3,330	8-10
5. DE-52 Chromatography	0.5 (HL-A2) 0.5 (HL-A7,12)	16	14	253,000	20,000	60-80

a very large representation of a single protein on the lymphocyte membrane surface. The yield of HL-A antigens
was about 4 mg per 50 gm of cells, i.e. about 80 mg/
kg. The cells used were homozygous for HL-A2 at the
first histocompatibility locus and had HL-A7 and 12
at the second. HL-A2 has a charge difference which
distinguishes it from most of the other specificities. It is readily separated on DEAE-cellulose
chromatography from a mixture of HL-A7 and HL-A12 as
the last step of purification. Separating the allelic specificities from each other is one of the
biggest problems in this field. It is relatively
easy to obtain pure HL-A antigens, i.e. a mixture
of the four specificities. Of course, the most interesting part of the chemistry requires that they
be separated. Starting with doubly homozygous cell
lines greatly reduces the problem. Several such
lines have been started from homozygous individuals
in the Indiana Amish community, an inbred religious
sect. From one such cell line (JY, HL-A 2,7/2,7)

the HL-A2 and HL-A7 antigen have been obtained in a
pure form.

Our first interesting finding was that these
antigens contain two subunits (4,5): a heavy chain
which is glycoprotein and a light chain which is
now known to be β_2-microglobulin(a protein first
isolated from human urine). SDS gels of the HL-A2
antigen preparation showed the heavy chain to have
a molecular weight of 34,000 and the light chain to
have a molecular weight of 12,000 (β_2-microglobulin).
SDS gels of the HL-A7,12 mixture showed a doublet
of 37,000 molecular weight in addition to β_2-micro-
globulin. One of the doublet glycoproteins may be
HL-A7 and the other HL-A12. However, since these
gels are denaturing gels, the glycoproteins could
not be recovered to prove that point.

Despite the apparent purity of the HL-A antigen preparations, isoelectric focusing revealed
considerable heterogeneity (3). For example, in
the HL-A2 preparation at least four bands with HL-
A2 antigenic activity were seen. The most interesting possible interpretation of this heterogeneity was that there was heterogeneity in the amino
acid sequence and, therefore, that some kind of V
region might exist in the HL-A antigens. However,
the heterogeneity turned out to be due to variability in the number of sialic acid residues on the
molecule (6). The HL-A2 preparation was treated
with neuraminidase as a function of time. The initial preparation contained a species with two sialic acid residues as the major component but there
were also species with three and species with one
sialic acid residue. As the result of treatment,
a preparation which was sialic acid free was obtained and all the heterogeneity disappeared. The same
result was obtained for the HL-A7,12 preparation.

Are these antigen preparations really pure? To
approach that question, the HL-A antigen preparations were labelled by reductive methylation with
formaldehyde and sodium borohydride (7). About two
methyl groups/mole were introduced on the ε-amino
groups of lysine of the molecule. This treatment
did not alter immunological activity at all. Essen-

tially 100% of these labelled preparations of HL-A2 antigens formed a specific complex with HL-A2 antisera. No significant complexation was observed with normal serum or with specificity controls (HL-A antisera with specificities other than HL-A2).

However, when the HL-A7,12 preparation or another HL-A antigen preparation containing HL-A3, W25, 12 and 27 were used, only about 70% of the total antigen could be complexed (7). With the HL-A7,12 preparation, about 40% complexation was obtained with HL-A7 antiserum, 30% with HL-A12 antiserum and a total of 70% with a mixture of antisera. What does that mean? The residual 30% of material could be third locus or other unidentified HL-A antigens, denatured antigens, or some other unrelated material co-purifying with HL-A.

Another evidence of purity is the single common amino terminal group found in the HL-A antigen preparations (7). The five preparations available all had glycine as the N-terminal amino acid of the heavy chain. An isoleucine residue was also found; it is the N-terminal residue of β_2-microglobulin.

With confidence that these preparation were pure, the heavy and light chains were reduced and alkylated by treatment with iodoacetic acid and then separated by gel filtration. Amino acid analysis of the heavy chain has been carried out and sequence studies initiated. The analyses of four preparations of the heavy chains of HL-A antigens obtained from RPMI 4265 cells and JY cells are shown in Table II. First of all, there were no significant differences between the heavy chain of HL-A2 from JY and HL-A2 from RPMI 4265 cells. Very small differences between HL-A7 and the HL-A7,12 mixture were found. However, on the order of 20 to 30 amino acid differences between HL-A2 and HL-A7 may be estimated. The degree of relatedness of these proteins can be examined from their amino acid analyses by the method of Marchalonis and Weltman (8). In this method an SΔQ value of less than 50 indicates significant relatedness between the proteins. By this method, HL-A2 from JY was identical to HL-A2 from 4265 (Table III). HL-A2 was very closely related to HL-A7 or to HL-A7,12. However, the heavy chains of

TABLE II

AMINO ACID COMPOSITION OF PAPAIN SOLUBILIZED HLA2
AND HLA7+12 FROM CELL LINE RPMI 4265 AND PAPAIN SOLUBILIZED
HLA2 and HLA7 FROM CELL LINE JY IN mol/100 mol.

Each analysis was done in duplicate for 24, 48 and 72 h.

Amino Acid	HLA2$_{JY}$	HLA2$_{4265}$	HLA7$_{JY}$	HLA7+12$_{4265}$
Asp[a]	7.9	7.9	9.7	9.4
Thr[b]	7.6	7.5	6.2	6.9
Ser[b]	5.2	5.2	5.2	5.0
Glu[a]	13.9	13.9	14.8	14.4
Pro	4.3	4.5	5.4	5.4
Gly	7.9	7.6	8.0	6.9
Ala	8.8	8.5	8.0	7.8
Val[c]	6.3	6.4	5.0	5.0
Met	1.3	1.5	1.1	1.0
Ile[c]	1.6	1.8	2.6	2.9
Leu	6.2	6.3	6.4	6.7
Tyr[b]	4.8	4.7	4.5	5.3
Phe	2.9	2.9	2.3	2.4
Lys	4.2	4.3	3.7	3.6
His	4.8	4.5	3.5	3.3
Arg	7.6	7.8	8.8	9.3
CMCys	1.5	1.6	1.6	1.7
Trp[d]	3.2	3.2	3.1	3.2

[a] Ammonia not determined.

[b] Extrapolated zero-time values.

[c] 72 h value only.

[d] Determined spectrophotmetrically.

TABLE III

RELATEDNESS AMONG HLA ANTIGENS AND β_2-MICROGLOBULIN
AS DETERMINED FROM THE AMINO ACID COMPOSITIONS
BY THE SΔQ METHOD.

Protein	HLA2 (4265)	HLA2 (JY)	HLA7 (JY)	HLA7+12 (4265)	β_2-M (human)	β_2-M (mouse)
HLA2$_{4265}$	0					
HLA2$_{JY}$	1	0				
HLA7$_{JY}$	13	16	0			
HLA7+12$_{4265}$	14	18	4	0		
β_2-M$_{human}$	172	183	183	173	0	
β_2-M$_{mouse}$	138	147	153	141	70	0

TABLE IV

AUTOMATED NH$_2$-TERMINAL SEQUENCE ANALYSIS OF
PAPAIN SOLUBILIZED HLA2 AND HLA7+12 FROM
LYMPHOBLASTOID CELL LINE RPMI 4265

Cycle Number	PTH amino acid HLA2	HLA7 12	Cycle Number	PTH amino acid HLA2	HLA7 12
1	Gly	Gly	11	Ser	Ala
2	Ser	Ser	12	Val	Val
3	-	-	13	Ser	Ser
4	Ser	Ser	14	-	Arg
5	Met	Met	15	(Pro)	(Pro)
6	Arg	Arg/Val	16	Gly	Gly
7	Tyr	Tyr	17	-	(Pro)
8	Phe	Phe	18	Gly	Gly
9	Phe	Tyr	19	Glu	Glu
10	Thr	Thr	20	-	-

the various HL-A antigen preparations and β_2-micro-globulin were not related $(S\Delta Q \sim 170)$. This calculation, carried out with various classes of immunoglobulin heavy chain (IgG, IgA, IgD and IgM) also resulted in relatively larger $S\Delta Q$ values. The lowest $S\Delta Q$ was obtained in comparison with IgD heavy chain but it was in the order of 70 (the same value as was obtained in comparison of human β_2-microglobulin with either mouse β_2-microglobulin or with the Fc fragment of Eu myeloma protein (an IgG).) There is homology between the heavy chain of the HL-A antigens and the heavy chain of the IgD, but it is not very extensive.

N-terminal sequence data (Table IV) showed no differences between the two HL-A2 antigen preparations. HL-A7 and the HL-A7,12 mixture were very similar and the latter showed heterogeneity at only a few positions. However, there were three differences in the first 13 amino acids between HL-A2 and HL-A7, although there may be only in the order of 20-30 amino acid differences in the whole molecule. There are four half cystine residues per heavy chain in the papain derived product (see below). The heavy chain has a polypeptide molecular weight of about 29,000. If the heavy chain of HL-A is homologous to the heavy chain of immunoglobulin then one would expect four half cystine residues in a molecule of 29,000 molecular weight. Using [^{3}H] carboxymethyl cysteine labelled HL-A antigens in sequence studies up to 40 residues, well past where one would expect the first cysteine residue, no significant counts were found. That is beyond the place that one might expect to find the first cysteine residue if there was strong homology to immunoglobulins. The homology between the sequences of HL-A antigens and those of H-2 antigens reported at this meeting is striking. Further information will greatly clarify our knowledge of the structure and evolution of these interesting proteins.

b. Preparation of HL-A antigens after detergent solubilization. Most membrane proteins are solubilized by detergents which have HLB (hydrophilic lipophilic balance) numbers in the range of 12-14. The HLB number is an empirical measure of a detergents tendency to make oil-in-water or water-in-oil emulsions. The solubilization of HL-A antigens appeared similar to the solubilization of bacterial membrane proteins except for the fact that a group of relatively hydrophilic Brij detergents appeared to be relatively selective in solubilizing HL-A antigens (9).

The purification of detergent-soluble material using an anti-β_2-microglobulin immunoabsorbent column is summarized in Table V . An earlier procedure (9) yielded partially purified material. After membrane preparation and solubilization in detergent, the next steps are passage through a lectin affinity column, absorption on an anti-β_2-microglobulin affinity column and subsequent elution with purified soluble β_2-microglobulin, and removal of the excess β_2-microglobulin on a Bio-Gel A-5m column. The purification required to get pure antigen was only about 50-fold over the detergent-solubilized membranes and the yields were on the order of 50%. About 7 mg of HL-A antigen were prepared from 150 g of cells. The anti-β_2-microglobulin column has also been used successfully on a small scale without the lectin column step (R.Robb, unpublished). Alternatively, repeated agarose gel filtration after passage through the lectin column also yielded pure antigen and may be more applicable to large scale work (T.Springer, unpublished). The detergent solubilized HL-A antigens also contained two polypeptides, a heavy chain of 44,000 daltons, and a light chain of 12,000 daltons, thus showing that the previously observed structure was not the result of proteolysis by papain.

Treatment with papain showed that there is an intermediate in the degradation of the heavy chain (MW 44,000) which has MW 39,000 (9). The cleavage by papain proceeds in two steps, removing a maximum of 5,000 daltons at each step to yield finally the 34,000 MW heavy chain of the papain solubilized HL-A antigens. β_2-microglobulin is resistant to papain under these conditions.

c. Homology between HL-A antigens and immunoglobulins. A number of laboratories including our own have demonstrated that the light chain of HL-A is identical to β_2-microglobulin (5,10,11,12). More-

629

over, β_2-microglobulin was sequenced and was shown
to have sequence homology to the immunoglobulin domains, especially to the C_3H domain of IgG (13).
Several other points of homology between the HL-A
antigens and the immunoglobulins included the two-
chain structure and limited proteolysis by papain,
and the possibility of sequence homology of the
heavy chain of HL-A antigens and immunoglobulin has
been discussed above. It seemed logical therefore
to look further. Did the HL-A antigens have a four
chain structure as does IgG, for example, i.e. two
heavy chains and two light chains? Reducing agents
had always been used in purification. Preparations
were then made of the detergent solubilized HL-A
antigens without reducing agents present (15). On
agarose gel filtration the peak of HL-A activity
was considerably broader and tailed towards the
high molecular weight end. The column effluent was
divided into four pools, each of which was subjected to radioiodination and double-antibody precipitation. Pool 4, the lowest molecular weight pool,
contained a 44,000 mol. wt. polypeptide, plus the
12,000 molecular weight polypeptide but little material of higher molecular weight; on reduction
with mercaptoethanol exactly the same pattern was
obtained. However, using the highest molecular
weight pool, there was no HL-A antigen at 44,000
daltons, a small amount of material at about 85,000
daltons and a very large amount of material with
considerably higher molecular weight. When this
material was reduced, a 44,000 daltons polypeptide
was obtained plus the 12,000 daltons polypeptide.

Another way of looking at these pools (15) is
by two-dimensional SDS gel electrophoresis using
no reducing agent in the first dimension and adding
mercaptoethanol in the second dimension. In the
low molecular weight pool only the 44,000 and 12,000
daltons polypeptides were seen (in addition to impurities of 29,000 and 34,000 daltons). All of
these polypeptides were on a diagonal line. Any
protein which is disulfide-linked (and is therefore
reduced in the second dimension of the gel) will
lie below this diagonal. In the higher molecular
weight pool from the agarose column the 44,000
daltons polypeptide was reduced in amount. Another

TABLE V

PURIFICATION OF DETERGENT SOLUBILIZED HL-A
FROM 150g OF J. YODER CELLS

Purification Step	mg	% Recovery of Inhibitory Units		Specific Activity (Inhibitory Units/mg)		Fold Purification
		HL-A2	HL-A7	HL-A2	HL-A7	
Detergent-solubilized Membrane	750	100	100	330	140	(1)
Lectin Column Chromatography	111	85	83	1890	760	5.6x
Anti-β_2-micro-globulin Column	–	63	59	–	–	
Bio-Gel A-5m Column	7	54	50	19000	7300	55x

TABLE VI

INHIBITION BY p23,30 OF CYTOLYSIS OF
AMISH CELL LINES BY AMISH ANTISERA

Amish Cell Line	Cell Source of p23,30 added	Amish Antisera					
		35	76	192	289	590	RMB
KL	IM-1	+	–	–	+	–	+
	RPMI 4265	–	+	–	–	–	+
	JY	+	+	+	+	–	+
SL	IM-1	+	–	–	–	–	+
	RPMI 4265	–	+	–	–	–	+
	JY	+	+	+	+	–	+
PY	IM-1	+	–	–	+	–	+
	RPMI 4265	+	+	–	–	–	+
	JY	+	+	+	+	+	+
JY	IM-1	+	–	–	+	–	+
	RMPI 4265	–	+	–	–	–	+
	JY	+	+	+	+	+	+

polypeptide appeared below the diagonal at about
85,000 daltons in the first dimension but at 44,000
in the second. In the highest molecular weight
pool almost no monomer at 44,000 daltons was present
and virtually everything was an oligomer which was
excluded from the gel in the first dimension. In
the second dimension it was reduced and had a molecular weight of 44,000. It seems clear that the
HL-A antigen preparation contained a heavy chain in
the oligomeric form. Observations which led to the
same conclusion had also been made by two other
laboratories (16,17). What is the significance of
these observations? Is the polymerization an artifact which occurs after isolation of the HL-A antigen --i.e. did heavy chains in the preparation become crosslinked to each other during isolation?
Two kinds of experiments to examine that possibility
have been carried out (T. Springer, unpublished).
If, indeed, the antigens are present in a tetramic
structure in the membrane before solubilization,
then a chemical crosslinking reagent should cross-
link the chains in various ways forming at least
heavy chain dimers and light-heavy dimers. The only product obtained with crosslinking reagents was
a dimer containing a light chain and a heavy chain.
A dimer containing two heavy chains was not formed.
In another set of experiments cells were treated
with iodocetamide to block all the free SH groups
before isolating the antigens. Under these conditions little or no oligomer was present in the isolated HL-A antigens (R. Robb, unpublished). Both
of these experiments seem to suggest that HL-A antigens do not exist in the membrane as oligomeric
forms.

Despite this there is other evidence of homology to immunoglobulins (15). The heavy chain of
34,000 consists of a carbohydrate of about 3-4,000
daltons and a polypeptide of about 29,000 daltons,
i.e the polypeptide is two "immunoglobulin domains"
in size. If it is homologous to immunoglobulin, it
should contain two intrachain S-S bridges. In all
three preparations of solubilized antigens there
were four half cystines involved in intrachain
bridges, i.e. two bridges for each 29,000 daltons
or one intrachain bridge for each "immunoglobulin
domain"(14). That result is consistent with an

homology of the heavy chain of HL-A antigens to
immunoglobulins. It remains to be shown wet-
her the intrachain bridges are distributed one in
each half of the heavy chain polypeptide.

In the detergent solubilized molecule, there
are two additional easily reduced SH groups, not
present in the papain solubilized molecule (14).
These additional SHs must be located in the hydrophobic region of the molecule which is presumably
buried in the membrane. They provide the potential
for intrachain bridges leading to the formation of
oligomers, but, as indicated above, presently it
is uncertain whether or not those oligomers have
any biological significance.

B CELL SPECIFIC ANTIGENS FROM HUMAN LYMPHOCYTES

At an early stage of purification the HL-A antigen preparations (obtained after papain solubilization) all contain impurities in varying amounts
with molecular weights of 70,000; 30,000; 23,000
and 13,500. The latter is distinguishable from
β_2-microglobulin.

These materials were separated by careful gel
filtration. In addition to the peak of HL-A antigen, three additional peaks of protein were obtained which calibrated on the gel column at molecular
weights of 75,000; 135,000 and in the excluded
volume. The 75,000 molecular weight material was
composed of two polypeptides with molecular weights
of 23,000 and 30,000. The material which calibrated at a molecular weight of 135,000 on the Sephadex column was composed of apparently identical
polypeptides of molecular weight 70,000 each. The
material of very high molecular weight in the excluded volume of the column contained a single
polypeptide of molecular weight 13,500, apparently
highly aggregated. The purity of some of these
preparations is illustrated by SDS gels (Fig. 1)
(R. Humphreys, unpublished).

Rabbits were immunized with all these preparations. The properties of the antisera which were
obtained are extremely interesting.

633

a. Rabbit anti-p23,30 serum.

1. Lysis of peripheral blood lymphocytes andlymphoblast lines. Only a fraction of peripheral blood lymphocytes were lysed by the antiserum in complement-mediated cytotoxicity assays (Figure 2). However, two B cell lymphocyte lines, RH-1 and IM-1, were totally lysed at antiserum dilutions of 1:2000. When peripheral blood lymphocytes were separated into B, T and null cells, the T cells were not lysed at all; the B cells were completely lysed and a fraction of the null cells were lysed. In separate experiments with the null cell population the population lysed by anti-p23, 30 serum was found to bear the EAC rosette receptor and to cause the ADCC reaction. The null cell population which was not lysed by the anti-p23,30 serum did not bear the EAC rosette receptor and did not participate in the ADCC reaction. An anti p23,30 serum blocked the ADCC reaction (but not MLC reactions). By contrast, anti-β_2-microglobulin serum lysed all of these populations of cells.

Peripheral blood lymphocytes of 40 individuals were separated into T cells and B cells. All of these individuals' B cells were lysed by the sera and, at the low dilution used (1:10), some of the T cells were also lysed. However, at 1:500 or 1:1000 the antiserum was absolutely specific for B cells of the separated populations. T cell lines and B cell lines established from the same individuals were also examined. Three such pairs of lines were available. Again, in each case only the B cell line was lysed at high dilution (1:500). At low dilution some partial lysis of one of the T cell lines was observed.

2. Separation of cells in the fluorescence activated cell sorter. In the Herzenberg fluorescence activated cell sorter the difference between T, B and null cells was dramatically observed. Cells were treated with anti-p23,30 serum and then with FITC conjugated goat anti-rabbit IgG. The fluorescence activated cell sorter yields data regarding both the number of cells and their relative fluorescence. A very high fluorescence was

obtained with B cells, but no reaction was observed
with T cells. A population of null cells was
shown to react with the p23,30 antiserum (Figure 3).

3. Precipitation of polypeptides from [^{35}S]
methionine internally labelled and detergent solubilized membranes. Another way of examining the
specificity of these antisera is to radiolabel membranes and ask what polypeptides are precipitated.
This question was of special interest with the
p23,30 antiserum because it had been obtained by
immunization with p23,30 polypeptides prepared after papain solubilization. The native form of the
p23,30 complex might be different in the membrane.
When radiolabeled membranes were solubilized in
detergent and their extract treated with p23,30 antiserum, three polypeptides were observed in the
precipitate with molecular weights of 39,000,
34,000 and 29,000. Apparently the p23,30 polypeptides originated from these. The precursor product
relationship among these has not yet been elucidated.

Many HL-A antisera contain additional antibodies specific for polypeptides other than HL-A
(obtained by double antibody precipitation from
radiolabeled membranes). DAL (an HL-A27 antiserum)
MWS (a W28 antiserum) and BC (an HL-A3 antiserum)
all brought down a small amount of the 30,000 daltons polypeptide. BEL (an HL-A27 antiserum) is
very interesting because it contains an antibody
directed against a 70,000 daltons component as
well as an antibody directed against the 30,000
daltons component.

Using a rabbit anti-β_2-microglobulin serum
only the 44,000 daltons heavy chain of the HL-A antigens and the 12,000 daltons β_2-microglobulin were
precipitated. No polypeptides corresponding to
p39,34,29 were observed. At least as defined by
this type of experiment, no polypeptide other than
that of 44,000 daltons is associated with β_2-mic-
roglobulin in the human lymphocyte membrane.

4. Lysis of various Amish cell lines by
Amish antisera and its inhibition by p23,30 antigens. The p23,30 antigen has been obtained from

635

three different cell lines: IM-1 (presently available as the purest of the preparations), RPMI 4265 and JY. JY is a member of the Indiana Amish community, a highly inbred human population. A number of cytolytic anti-sera from the multiparous women of this community do contain HL-A antibodies but apparently have antibodies directed against other lymphocyte membrane components (18). These sera were used in cytotoxicity assays against four cell lines, also derived from the Amish population (Table VI). The antisera used lysed all four of the cell lines. Several patterns are evident. First of all, JY p23,30 antigen inhibited lysis of the JY cell line by all of the antisera; the same was true of JY p23,30 antigen as an inhibitor of lysis of cells of his relative, PY. An interesting pair of antisera are 35 and 76. Antiserum 35 which lysed all four cell lines was blocked by the IM-1 p23,30 antigen in each case. Antiserum 76, however, was not inhibited by the IM-1 p23,30 antigen; by contrast, it was blocked by the p23,30 antigen from RPMI 4265 cells in every case. All of the data suggest that the p23,30 antigens from IM-1, 4265, and JY cells are alloantigens; some of them inhibit some of the Amish alloantisera and others inhibit other Amish alloantisera. Antiserum RMB is interesting because it was inhibited by all three of the p23,30 antigens. Possibly it recognized a determinant common to all of them.

5. Use of p23,30 rabbit antisera in purification of P23,30 antigens. An interesting use of this antiserum is in following the p23,30 complex in a crude mixture, e.g., the spearation of solubilized membrane proteins on a gel filtration column. The p23,30 complex, detected by inhibition of cytolysis, immediately preceded the HL-A antigens.

b. Rabbit anti-p70 serum and anti-p13.5 serum.

Only a fraction of peripheral blood lymphocytes were lysed by anti-p70 serum but the RH-1 B cell lymphoblast line was lysed totally (Figure 4). B cells in separated populations of peripheral blood lymphocytes were lysed completely at a titer of 1:125. Null cells and T cells were lysed only at lower dilutions of antiserum. Similar data were obtained for rabbit anti-p13.5 serum (Figure 5).

These preliminary experiments need to be extended but the data presently available suggest that several of the different antigens in the cultured human lymphoblast may be B cell specific. Like the HL-A antigens, one or more of these may be representatives of a genetic polymorphism. Certainly there is evidence that this is the case for the p23,30 proteins.

ACKNOWLEDGMENTS

The studies reported here were supported by Grants AI-10736, AI-09576, NCI-CB-74-13, and N01-CB-53881 from the National Institutes of Health.

FIGURES

Figure 1.   SDS-polyacrylamide gels of lymphocyte
    membrane proteins. A: HL-A antigen prepared
    with DTT-preactivated papain containing "con-
    taminants" of 70,000, 30,000 and 23,000 dal-
    tons. B: Purified 70,000 daltons component.
    C: Purified complex of 23,000 and 30,000 dal-
    tons components. D: Purified HL-A antigen
    containing 35,000 and 12,000 daltons components.

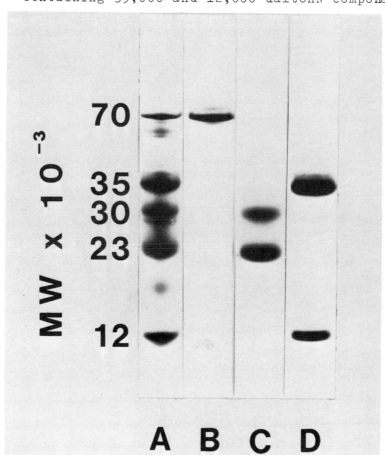

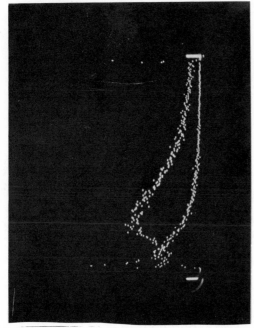
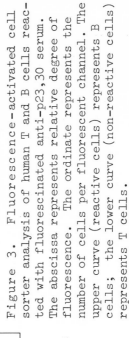

Figure 3. Fluorescence-activated cell sorter analysis of human T and B cells reacted with fluorescinated anti-p23,30 serum. The abscissa represents relative degree of fluorescence. The ordinate represents the number of cells per fluorescent channel. The upper curve (reactive cells) represents B cells; the lower curve (non-reactive cells) represents T cells.

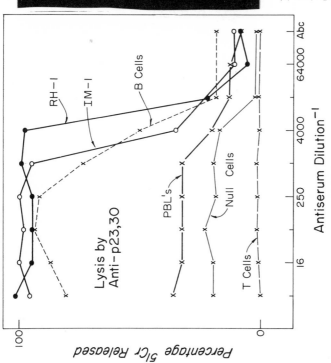

Figure 2. Lysis of several purified populations of lymphocytes by anti-p23,30 rabbit sera. The IM-1 and RH-1 are lymphoblasts. Peripheral blood lymphocytes (PBL's) from one individual (RH) were separated into B, T, and Null lymphocyte populations.

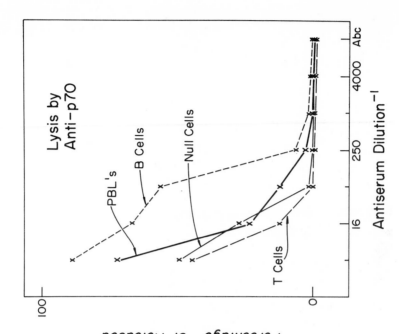

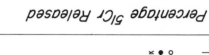

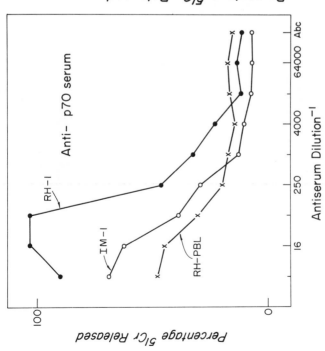

Figure 4. Lysis of various lymphocytes with anti-p70 serum. The cells used are descri-bed in Figure 1. Ordinate is percentage 51Cr released.

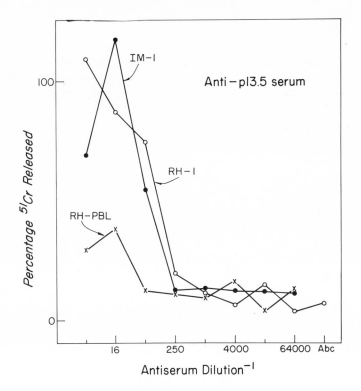

Figure 5. Lysis of lymphoblast lines and peripheral blood lymphocytes by anti-pl3.5 serum. A fraction of PBL's is lysed. In separate experiments the sole reactivity of anti-pl3.5 against subpopulations of PBL's was recorded against B lymphocytes.

REFERENCES

(1) A.R. Sanderson and J.R. Batchelor. Nature 219(1968)184.

(2) J.M. McCune, R.E. Humphreys, R.R. Yocum and J.L. Strominger. Proc. Nat. Acad. Sci. 72 (1975) 3206.

(3) M.J. Turner, P. Cresswell, P. Parham, and J.L. Strominger. J. Biol. Chem. 250 (1975) 4512.

(4) P. Cresswell, M.J. Turner and J.L. Strominger. Proc. Nat. Acad. Sci. U.S.A. 70 (1973) 1603.

(5) P. Cresswell, T. Springer, J.L. Strominger, M.J. Turner,, J.M. Grey and R.T. Kubo. Proc. Nat. Acad. Sci. U.S.A. 71 (1974) 2123.

(6) P. Parham, R.E. Humphreys, M.J. Turner and J.L. Strominger. Proc. Nat. Acad. Sci. U.S.A. 71 (1974) 3998.

(7) P. Parham, C. Terhorst, H. Herrmann, R.E. Humphreys, M.D. Waterfield and J.L. Strominger. Proc. Nat. Acad. Sci. 72 (1975) 1594.

(8) J.J. Marchalonis and J.K. Weltman. Comp. Biochem. Physiol.38 (1971) 609.

(9) T.A. Springer, J.L. Strominger and D. Mann. Proc. Nat. Acad. Sci. U.S.A. 71 (1974) 1539.

(10) H.M. Grey, R.T. Kubo, S.M. Colon, M.D. Poulik, P. Cresswell, R. Springer, M. Turner and J.L. Strominger. J. Exper. Med. 138 (1973) 1608.

(11) K. Nakamuro, N. Tanigaki and D. Pressman. Proc. Nat. Acad. Sci. U.S.A. 70 (1973) 2863.

(12) P.A. Peterson, L. Rask and J.B. Lindblom. Proc. Nat. Acad. Sci. U.S.A. 71 (1974) 35.

(13) B.A. Cunningham and I. Berggard. Transplant. Rev. 21 (1974) 3.

(14) J.L. Strominger, P. Cresswell, H. Grey, R.E. Humphreys, D. Mann, J. McCune, P. Parham, R. Robb, A.R. Sanderson, T. Springer, C. Terhorst and M.J. Turner Transplant. Rev. 21 (1974) 126.

(15) J.L. Strominger, R.E. Humphreys, J.M. McCune, P. Parham, R. Robb, T. Springer and C. Terhorst. The immunoglobulin-like structure of human historcompatibility antigens. Fed. Proc. (in press).

(16) P. Cresswell and J.R. Dawson. J. Immun. 114 (1975)523.

(17) P.A. Peterson, L. Rask, K. Sege, L. Klareskog, H. Anundi and L. Ostberg. Proc. Nat. Acad. Sci. U.S.A. 72 (1975) 1612.

(18) D.L. Mann, L. Abelson, S.D. Harris and D.B. Amos. J. Exper. Med. 142 (1975) 84.

(Only a limited number of references have been provided, mainly those from the authors' laboratories. Complete documentation can be found in various articles in Transplantation Review, Vol. 21, 1975, in the articles cited above, and in other articles in this volume).

DISCUSSION FOLLOWING JACK STROMINGER

BACH: If you take the 23,30 peak and analyze it on a non-SDS gel such as by isoelectrofocusing or by urea or chloralhydrate gels to get a charge separation, do you find microheterogeneity?

STROMINGER: There is good evidence for microheterogeneity by several techniques.

BENACERRAF: Do you have any evidence for heterogeneity in the 23,30 polypeptide chains when they are extracted from the B cells of an individual rather than from a cell line?

STROMINGER: We have not prepared the p 23,30 antigen from normal human B cells.

CUNNINGHAM: How do you identify your PTH-amino acids?

STROMINGER: The identification of phenylhydantoin amino acids released from the automatic sequencer was performed by gas liquid chromatography, thin layer chromatography on polyamide plates, and if necessary, on the amino acid analyzer after back hydrolysis.

CUNNINGHAM: Do you ever see more than one amino acid at a given position?

STROMINGER: In the first 15 amino acids of *HLA 7 + 12*, so far we have seen two amino acids only in position 6: Val/Arg.

DAUSSET: You have shown some differences between two *HLA-A2* molecules.   It is established in man, as in mouse, that each molecule bears several determinants--one private and several public--these semi-public specificities being shared by several allelic products of the same locus (Lepraud and Dausset, Tissue Antigens 4:329, 1974). The same public specificities are frequently associated in the same population but a different set of public specifities would be found in another population.   Thus, two *HLA-A2* molecules could be sometimes in the same population and more frequently in two different populations.   The question is--are you confident on the minor difference that you observed?

STROMINGER: The differences in amino acid composition of
the two *HLA-A2* preparations are not significant.   They
are within the range of error of the methods.   No
sequence differences in the two molecules have been
found so far.

STUDIES ON THE CHEMICAL BASIS OF VARIABILITY AND THE COMPLEX CELLULAR EXPRESSION OF THE H-2K and H-2D PRODUCTS

S.G. NATHENSON[*][o], J.K. BROWN[*], B.M. EWENSTEIN[*][o], T.V. RAJAN[*][o]
J.H. FREED[*][o], D.W. SEARS[*], L.E. MOLE[+], M.D. SCHARFF[o]

[*]Department of Microbiology and Immunology and [o]Department of Cell Biology, Albert Einstein College of Medicine, [+]MRC Immunochemistry Unit, University of Oxford

Abstract: The H-2K and H-2D alloantigens are primary products of genes of the K and D regions which map at opposite ends of the mouse H-2 MHC (major histocompatibility complex). These membrane-located glycoproteins are approximately 45,000 daltons in molecular weight and in the membrane are associated with a 12,000 molecular weight polypeptide, the murine β_2-microglobulin. The H-2 products were analyzed by comparative tryptic peptide techniques. Comparison of products of the D and K genes, or of alleles within the D or K gene series showed that only from about 30 to 60% of the peptides were identical. This degree of variability is consistent with the high degree polymorphism shown by serological analysis of the H-2 products. Studies of mutants both at the H-2K and H-2D region showed small differences in peptide profiles, thus suggesting that minor alterations in primary protein structure may have remarkable biological effects. Preliminary N-terminal amino acid sequence analysis of the H-2 glycoproteins has supported the findings of their peptide variability. Comparison of the H-2 fragment released by papain digestion of the native glycoprotein also suggests that a region near the C-terminus is the site at which papain cleaves the native H-2 glycoprotein. Another approach to understanding the complexity of H-2 gene expression came from analysis of a regulatory variant selected for the lack of expression of H-2K^d. This variant clone also did not express the linked but separate H-2D^d product thus suggesting coordinate control of K and D gene expression. Altered homing properties of the variant suggested H-2 glycoproteins may play a role in cell sorting or recognition.

647

INTRODUCTION

The major histocompatibility complex (MHC) located on chromosome 17 of the mouse is a complex of genes involved in a diversity of immune and other functions (see reviews 1,2, 3). In its simplest representation it consists of four regions: K, I, S, and D (2,3,4). The H-2K gene (K region) and the H-2D gene (D region) are located at the extreme ends of the MHC and are separated by about 0.5 centimorgans (1,2, 3,4). The molecules determined by the H-2K and H-2D genes are glycoproteins of approximately 45,000 daltons (5) tightly integrated into the hydrophobic matrix of the plasma cell membrane. The antigenic specificity resides in the protein structure (6). In situ, the glycoproteins are non-covalently associated with an 11,600 dalton protein, the β_2-microglobulin. The association is probably in a 1:1 ratio and is thought to be specific (7,8).

While the linear order of the genetic regions in the MHC has been determined from past experiments (1,2,3,4), we do not know for certain the number of genes present in each region, nor do we understand their interrelationships. In addition, while we are aware of the polymorphism in the H-2 system, we know little of the extent of the genetic variability of the MHC genes, or about the complex expression of these genes in cells of different tissues and in cells at different periods in growth and development. These questions, and those of the biological role and functional interrelationships of the products of the different H-2 regions are difficult ones; but, equally challenging are the problems of formulating precise descriptions of the chemistry and structure of the MHC gene products, and of the relationship between that structure and gene function.

The purpose of this communication is to describe some of our recent studies directed at understanding of polymorphism or genetic variability of the genes of the H-2K and H-2D regions. First we will review some results of studies on the biochemical properties of the H-2K and H-2D antigens. Specifically, we will discuss the basis for the polymorphism expressed by the H-2K and H-2D genes by an analysis of the overall peptide structure of these glycoproteins isolated from both normal and mutant mouse strains.

A different approach to the study of H-2 complexity is analysis of regulation and expression of the H-2 products in cloned cell lines. We will also describe the isolation of a regulatory variant which shows coordinate control of both H-2K and H-2D products, and which, during a period of H-2 non-expression, shows altered cell-cell interaction as judged by a different homing pattern.

STUDIES ON THE PEPTIDE ANALYSIS OF SELECTED H-2K AND H-2D GENE PRODUCTS

Analysis of the peptides produced by trypsin digestion of proteins provides a qualitative approach to the investigation of their comparative primary structure. In earlier studies, we compared the peptide composition of two papain-solubilized, purified alloantigen fragments using 2-dimensional thin layer cellulose chromatography (9). With cyanogen-bromide and trypsin digested materials it was found that approximately 80 to 85% of the H-2^b and H-2^d peptides had similar chromatographic behavior. The 15 to 20% of the unique peptides from each strain was a minimum estimate due to the insensitivity of this method.

In our more recent studies, we have attempted to obtain information on two different questions. First, what are the similarities and differences in peptide composition among molecules determined by alleles of the same gene series? For example, the products of H-$2K^b$ vs H-$2K^d$? Secondly, what are the similarities and differences in peptide composition between products of the alleles of the H-2K and H-2D genes of the same haplotype (e.g., H-$2K^d$ vs H-$2D^d$)? For these studies we utilized ^{3}H- or ^{14}C-arginine or lysine labeled native NP-40-solubilized glycoproteins isolated by indirect immunoprecipitation and purified by SDS/BioGel chromatography or lentil lectin chromatography. Tryptic peptides of products were compared by double label techniques using ion exchange chromatography (9,10).

As an example of such a comparison, an ion exchange chromatogram of the mixture of ^{14}C-arginine labeled H-$2K^b$ peptides (private specificity H-2.33) and ^{3}H-arginine labeled H-$2K^d$ (private specificity H-2.31) is shown in Fig. 1. Approximately 11 peaks for H-$2K^b$ and 15 peaks from the H-$2K^d$ antigens are visualized, each peak presumably containing one or at the most, two peptides. Only four, or about 25 to 35%, of the peptides can be said to coincide on this map. Thus, approximately 65 to 75% of the peptides are unique. These profiles are in striking contrast to the control experiment comparing profiles between H-2 products from strains sharing the same H-2 haplotype, but differing

649

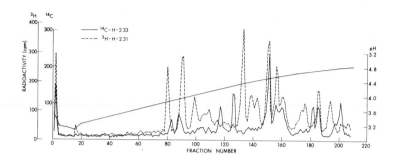

Figure 1. Comparison of the tryptic peptides of K gene products: ^{14}C-arginine-labeled H-2.33 and ^{3}H-arginine-labeled H-2.31. Preparation of the sample for the peptide column and its elution are described in reference 10 which should be consulted for further details. (----, [3]H —— H-2.31; ——, [14]C —— H-2.33) H-2.31 is the K gene product of B10.D2 (H-2[d]) and H-2.33 is the K gene product of B10 (H-2[b]).

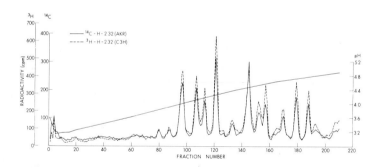

Figure 2. Comparison of tryptic peptides of ^{14}C-arginine-labeled H-2.32 and ^{3}H-arginine-labeled H-2.32 from two different mouse strains of the same genotype (H-2[k]). Preparation of the sample for the peptide column and its elution are described in reference 10 from which this figure is taken. (----, [3]H —— H-2.32 from C3H; ——, [14]C —— H-2.32 from AKR).

otherwise entirely in their genetic makeup (Fig. 2).

Studies of the products of different H-2 genes as shown in this example have been carried out on all H-2D and H-2K products from two haplotypes, H-2^d and H-2^b, for both lysine and arginine labeled peptides. A general summary is presented in Table I. Peptide comparisons of products from alleles of the same gene, for example, K^b vs K^d, or D^b vs D^d, showed about 30 to 35% similarities. Peptide comparisons of the products of the alleles of H-2K vs H-2D showed somewhat divergent results since K^b vs D^b showed between 50 to 55% similar peaks whereas K^d vs D^d showed between 30 to 33% similarities (10).

Table I

Summary of Peptide Comparisons for H-2^b and H-2^d Genotypes[*]

Gene Comparison	Serological Specificities	Total Coincident Arg and Lys Peaks
A) K vs K	33 (b) – 31 (d)	$\dfrac{8c}{24-27} = 33\text{-}30\%$
B) D vs D	2 (b) – 4 (d)	$\dfrac{9c}{26-24} = 35\text{-}38\%$
C) K vs D	4 – 31 (d)	$\dfrac{8c}{24-27} = 33\text{-}30\%$
	2 – 33 (b)	$\dfrac{13c}{26-24} = 50\text{-}54\%$

[*] Data taken from Brown, et al. (10).

These results were quite striking since they showed an extreme degree of diversity between the products of what are considered to be alleles of the same gene. In fact, differences between products of some $\underline{D}$ and $\underline{K}$ genes (e.g., $\underline{K}^b$ vs $\underline{D}^b$ were less than differences in alleles of the same genes $(\underline{K}^b$ vs $\underline{K}^d)$. These studies are still preliminary and pertain only to two of the 41 known haplotypes. However the results, if applicable to other haplotypes, point out the extraordinary uniqueness of the products. Nonetheless, these findings are not entirely unexpected since, as we noted previously, polymorphism has been a hallmark of the H-2 system. For example, there are at least eight serological differences between H-2K^b and H-2K^d including the private specificities H-2.33 and H-2.31 (3). These gene products differed in 70% of their peptides.

The heterogeneity described above could have arisen through a variety of genetic and selective procedures. In order to examine a more completely defined genetic situation we have carried out similar peptide analysis on two mouse haplotypes that arose through known mutations. One of these is the B6.C-$\underline{H-2}^{ba}$ strain of Bailey and co-workers (11) which carries a histocompatibility mutation in the $\underline{K}$ region of the $\underline{H-2}^b$ haplotype. The mutation arose spontaneously. The biological properties of this mutant are interesting since comparison of $\underline{H-2}^{ba}$ with $\underline{H-2}^b$ shows positive reciprocal MLR (mixed lymphocyte reactivity), as well as CML (cell mediated lympholysis), GVHR (graft versus host reactivity), and skin rejection (12). Since the genetic data suggest an alteration in the $\underline{K}^b$ region only, the findings imply that the differences in $\underline{K}$ region could give rise to the ability to stimulate an MLR, a biological activity thought to be mapped in the $\underline{I}$ region (see reference 2,3,4).

The second mutant strain is B10.D2.504 (M504); haplotype $\underline{H-2}^{da}$, a mutagenically induced histocompatibility mutation which was isolated by Egorov (13). It differs from the parental strain B10.D2 in the $\underline{H-2D}^d$ region, and also shows reciprocal reactivity in MLR and CML assays and by skin grafting in vivo (14).

By isolation of the internally radiolabeled products of the $\underline{K}$ and $\underline{D}$ regions by indirect immunoprecipitation with anti-H-2 alloantisera, we were able to examine the tryptic peptide profiles of the products of the mutants and their parents (15). An analysis of the H-2K^b and H-2K^{ba} products was carried out by using antisera directed against the H-2K^b

private specific cy H-2.33 which is carried by K products of both genotypes. The material isolated by immune precipitation and further purified by SDS-molecular seive chromatography was analyzed as shown in Fig. 3. A comparative chromatogram of arginine-labeled H-2K^b and H-2K^{ba} revealed almost identical profiles except for a broad peak (possibly containing more than a single peptide) around tube 195 to 200 which was contained in the H-2^b strain and was lacking in the H-2^{ba} strain. Examination of the lysine maps (data not shown) showed almost complete identity, except again for another peptide containing lysine (approximately tube 190) which was lacking in the product of H-2^{ba}. Thus the H-2 glycoprotein of the H-2^b parent revealed 2 or 3 peptides which were lacking in the mutant product.

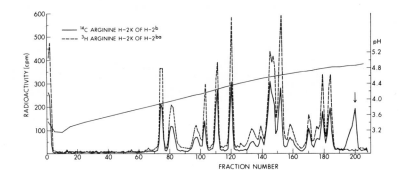

Figure 3. Comparison of tryptic peptides of the H-2K (H-2.33) gene products from H-2^b (———— ^{14}C-arginine and H-2^{ba} (---- ^{3}H-arginine). Arrow points to different peptides. Details are taken from reference 15 by Brown, et al.

Of course, these findings must be interpreted cautiously since the peptide comparison system detects only the 70% of the peptides which are water soluble at acidic pH. It is possible that some peptides containing altered amino acid residues are in the hydrophobic core, although chymotrypsin digestion of the core and subsequent chromatography showed no differences between strains.

Analysis of the H-2^d and H-2D^{da} glycoproteins of M504 has proved to be a more formidable task. While discontinuous sodium dodecyl sulfate polyacrylamide gel electrophoresis (SDS/PAGE) analysis of H-2K^b vs H-2K^{ba} products showed complete identity, analysis of H-2D^d vs H-2D^{da} from this mutant showed that the latter glycoprotein migrated more slowly. The carbohydrate sizes were identical and, therefore, were not the cause of this apparent size difference. Preliminary comparative peptide profiles document one or two peptide differences between H-2D^d and H-2D^{da} thus supporting the hypothesis of a structural alteration. However, more sophisticated isolation procedures presently in progress will be needed to substantiate these findings.

The peptide profiles are worthy of comment because they prove the sensitivity of the methodology to detect minor differences in structure. They confirm that there are small alterations in the H-2K and H-2D gene products of these variants as compared to their parental strains. Such results would be expected in true mutants and correlate with alteration of biological reactivities. Of course, for each case it is not clear yet what is the precise genetic change. For example, other linked genes whose products could not be examined by our immunoprecipitation technique could also have been altered during the mutagenic event, and could be responsible for the biological changes.

STUDIES ON THE POLYMORPHISM AND INTRAMOLECULAR ARRANGEMENT OF THE H-2 GLYCOPROTEINS

The comparative peptide profiles have allowed us to conclude that the gene products of alleles of genes of the same series, either $\underline{D}$ or $\underline{K}$, contain a considerable degree of uniqueness. Of course, peptide mapping studies tend to overestimate the number of differences in primary structure, since a few amino acid substitutions in very long peptides are reflected in an altered mobility, whereas in fact, many of the amino acid residues may be conserved. Thus, it is clear that the next step in understanding the basic molecular organization of the H-2 glycoproteins with reference to their genetic relationships, antigenic sites, membrane integration, and possible functional properties, is the description of their primary protein structure.

The studies to be described next are the first results of our approach to the determination of the sequence of the H-2 glycoproteins. These are extensions of our previous investigations on the comparative peptide analyses: they

are designed to describe further the genetic polymorphism,
and to characterize the molecular substructure of the H-2
glycoproteins.

We have previously shown that a soluble glycoprotein
fragment of approximately 37,000 daltons carrying the carbohydrate and the H-2 antigenic sites (16) can be generated
by papain cleavage of the native molecule (45,000 daltons)
(5). To gain an idea of the overall arrangement of the H-2
glycoprotein, we attempted to analyze the fragment produced
by papain proteolysis of intact molecules and determine its
relationship to the native moiety. Our primary approach
was analysis of the partial N-terminal sequence of selected
radiolabeled materials. In such an analysis only isotopic-
ally labeled residues are detected. Thus, only minute
quantities of antigens are required; however, only a few
residues are determined for each sequencer run. The method,
therefore, only provides a partial sequence or amino acid
profile.

In the present study the profiles for arginine and
leucine were determined for the 30 N-terminal residues of
both the NP-40 native glycoprotein and the major H-2 glycoprotein fragment produced by papain digestion. It was
reasoned that comparison of these preparations would establish whether the cleaved fragment was derived from the C-
or N-terminal part of the native molecule. Identification
of this fragment then allows one to position the site of
papain cleavage.

Antigenic material was prepared from genetically
characterized cells radiolabeled in culture with the ^{3}H-
leucine or ^{3}H-arginine. The H-2 material was isolated as
described previously but was purified before immunoprecipitation by lentil lectin chromatography rather than by
BioGel chromatography. The purified, NP-40-solubilized, and
papain-solubilized glycoproteins migrated as single peaks
a s judged by discontinuous polyacrylamide gel analysis.
The β_2-microglobulin also appeared as a single band.

Both the native and papain solubilized glycoproteins
were analyzed. First the native glycoprotein and murine β_2-
microglobulin as found together in an "immune" precipitate
were analyzed by automated sequencing techniques. This
analysis was performed as an internal control since it was
known (Smithies, personal communication) that the murine β_2-
microglobulin had a leucine at residue 23 and it has an

655

unblocked N-terminus. Major peaks of leucine radioactivity
in the thiazolanone derivatives were found at positions 5
and 17, as well as a smaller peak at position 23. The
assumption from this result that the leucine at 23 came from
β_2-microglobulin, and the leucine at 5 and 17 from the H-2
glycoprotein was tested by analysis of each component (Fig.
4). Clearly, the H-2.33 glycoprotein has leucine at
positions 5 and 17 (upper panel), and in agreement with
other data (Smithies, personal communication) the H-2 associated 12,000 dalton protein has a leucine at residue 23
(lower panel).

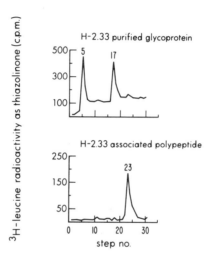

Figure 4.   Radioactive N-terminal sequence
patterns for ^{3}H-leucine labeled H-2.33 glycoprotein and
its associated polypeptide β_2-microglobulin.   Preparation of samples and sequencing techniques are discussed in the text and in reference 17.

Table II summarizes the data obtained from the sequencer runs for H-2.33 and H-2.2. The H-2.33 glycoprotein has
leucine at residue 5 and residue 17 and arginine at residue
6, 14 and 21. The H-2.2 glycoprotein has leucine at residue 17 and arginine at residue 6, 14 and 21. Thus, these
two glycoproteins show identity in four out of five residues
in the first thirty.

The papain cleaved H-2 fragment prepared from an indirect precipitate of NP-40-solubilized native antigen was

Table II

N-Terminal Amino Acid Profiles for Arginine- and Leucine-Labeled H-2 Alloantigens

POSITION

	5	10	15	20	25	30

Native (NP-40 solubilized)

H-2.33 (H-2K^b) - - - - L R - - - - - - - - R - - L - - - R - - - - - - - - - -

H-2.2 (H-2D^b) - - - - - R - - - - - - - - R - - L - - - R - - - - - - - - - -

Papain Cleaved

H-2.33 - - - - L R - - - - - - - - R - - L - - - R - - - - - - - - - -

Amino acid code: L = leucine; R = arginine; - = neither leucine or arginine are present at this residue. These data were obtained from B.M. Ewenstein, et al., in press.

analyzed next. The sequencer runs for the leucine labeled
and arginine labeled papain-solubilized H-2.33 glycoprotein
of 37,000 daltons showed an N-terminal sequence profile
identical to that found for the native molecule (Table II).
Thus we can conclude that the fragment derived by papain
cleavage of the NP-40 solubilized molecule is in fact the
N-terminal fragment of the native glycoprotein (16).

Our data allows us to conclude that the N-terminal segment of the proteolytically cleaved H-2 glycoprotein is
identical to the N-terminal segment of its native molecule.
Therefore, one site of cleavage by papain which generates
the 37,000 dalton fragment is located at a point quite close
to the C-terminal end. Previous studies with papain cleavage of cell membranes have shown that the H-2 antigenically
active 37,000 dalton glycoprotein fragment was water soluble. Extrapolating to the present studies we can tentatively conclude that since the loss of the small C-terminal
portion of the native molecule correlates with the loss of
water insolubility, the C-terminus probably is the region
which is responsible for hydrophobic interaction either with
the membrane or other membrane proteins.

With regard to our investigation of the H-2 diversity,
our preliminary data show that the H-2.2 and H-2.33 molecules share four out of five positions identified as containing arginine or leucine. While such a sample is clearly too
small to generalize to the entire molecule, the data support
our previous findings of consistent differences in tryptic
peptide profiles between these two gene products and support
the present concept that while the H-2 genes are quite
homologous, they are also strikingly unique.

STUDIES ON SOMATIC CELL VARIANTS IN H-2 EXPRESSION

Another approach to exploration of the biological
function, and the genetic and structural properties of the
H-2 system, is the use of MHC mutant somatic cell lines. If
mutants could be isolated, they would allow one to explore
biological questions such as the possible role of H-2
components in cell growth properties, propagation in vivo,
cell-cell recognition, etc. We have therefore attempted to
isolate somatic cell variants in the H-2 expression. Our
initial success in this approach led to the isolation of a
cell line which appears to be a variant in the regulation
of expression of H-2K and H-2D products (18).

To obtain this putative regulatory mutant in H-2
expression we chose as a source of cells, a hyperploid mouse
myeloma cell line (NP-2), a non-IgG producing clone from the
myeloma MPC-11 (19). This is an H-2K^d; H-2D^d positive cell
line. It was mutagenized by nitrosoguanidine and repeatedly
selected with anti-H-2K^d serum and complement. After twenty-
two selection cycles, only resistant cells remained. One
clone (clone 30) expressed less than 1% of H-2K^d of the
parent MPC-11 by absorption analysis.

The clone, however, was unstable, and over a period of
4-8 weeks, when grown without selection pressure, re-
expressed H-2K . Reselection produced cells again expressing essentially no H-2 on their surface. Fluctuation analysis of the reexpressing culture showed that the reverting
population was heterogeneous, with some individual cells
suddenly expressing H-2. Their progeny also, expressed H-2.
This ruled out chromosomal loss as the basis for non-
expression.

A significant property of the loss of H-2K^d expression
was the concomittant loss of the linked H-2D^d expression.
In addition, the kinetics of reexpression for H-2K^d, showed
coordinate reexpression of H-2D^d.

Proof that the clone 30 was not synthesizing antigenically active H-2 was provided from studies utilizing a
radioimmune assay with detergent lysates from test cells.
Within the sensitivity of the procedure, clone 30 extracts
lacked the ability to inhibit the antibody-target antigen
reaction whereas there was complete inhibition by the parent
NP-2 lysates.

The availability of a variant cell line which lacked
detectable surface and internal H-2K and H-2D products allowed us to explore the effect of no H-2 on a variety of biological parameters. Karyotype, doubling time, tumorgeneity
and cell size were not different between wild-type NP-2 and
its variant.

However, two physiological differences were noted:
First, the absence of H-2 antigens had an effect on cell
migration. Cr^{51}-labeled NP-2 cells or clone 30 cells were
injected I.P. into syngeneic (BALB/c) mice. There was a
reproducible delay in the appearance of clone 30 cells in

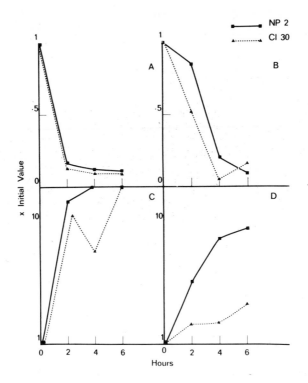

Figure 5. In vivo patterns of parent (NP-2) and variant (cl 30) cells. BALB/c syngeneic mice were injected through their tail veins with Cr^{51} labeled NP-2 or clone 30 cells, and at the time intervals indicated, radioactivity measured in blood (A), heart and lungs (B), liver (C), and spleen (D). For details see Rajan, et al (18).

the spleen (Fig. 5) while disappearance from circulation and appearance in the liver did not differ. This suggests that the surface membrane-located H-2 antigens may play a role in cell-cell recognition.

Second, an effect of the loss of H-2 on transplantation behavior was also noted. When the host differed from BALB/c only at the K locus, clone 30 grew out, even if the host had been preimmunized with BALB/c cells. The wild-type NP-2 cells were consistently rejected.

These studies, in summary, reveal an approach to the study of the expression of H-2 genes, and their biological properties. The variants are presumably regulatory. They are polyploid and hence probably have several H-2 structural genes. They reexpress H-2 without selective pressure. In addition, they reveal coordinate regulation of both H-2K and H-2D genes, though these loci are separated by an 0.5% crossover frequency.

The properties of these lines allow us to suggest strongly that H-2K and H-2D expression are not essential for cell structure or metabolism. H-2 expression, however, may be important for homing phenomena, thus suggesting a possible role in cell-cell interaction.

CONCLUDING THOUGHTS

In conclusion, we have addressed our work toward a description of the genetic and structural parameters of the H-2K and H-2D genes and their products. We have established that structural variation is quite extensive within the products of an alleleic series, with differences being possibly as great as one out of 10 amino acids. The H-2 proteins of mutants, however, showed almost complete identity with their parental counterparts, thus showing that small differences can have biological effects. Since such variants should be almost identical, these findings verify that the peptide profile methods seem to be measuring a real variability when considering "wild-type" genotypes.

In view of the extraordinary expression of polymorphism in the H-2 system, one should contemplate the possibility of unusual genetic mechanisms. One possible model is that the H-2K and H-2D regions contain clusters of duplicated genes — similar but not identical genes which are evolutionarily related. Expression of H-2 would then be under control of a regulator gene. Such a model might explain unusual peptide map profiles showing higher similarity between K and D genes (K^b vs D^b) than between alleles (K^b vs K^d). Such a thesis has been proposed by Bodmer (20).

Preliminary sequence analysis of H-2 glycoproteins has supported the findings of peptide variability, although our data are presently still quite limited in scope. The sequencing techniques have also permitted us to tentatively establish a region near the C-terminus as the site at which papain cleaves the native H-2 glycoprotein.

This treatment releases the N-terminal end as a water soluble, antigenically active, carbohydrate-containing 37,000 dalton fragment. We would postulate that the C-terminal fragment lost during this conversion contains the membrane binding property ot the native glycoprotein.

Another approach to the complexity of H-2 gene expression was explored by the use of somatic cell variants. A regulatory mutant selected for lack of expression of H-2K^d showed coordinate control of the linked, but separate, H-2D^d product. This finding suggests a common regulatory element for both D and K gene expression. Another intriguing property of the H-2 glycoproteins, which could be examined due to the availability of this mutant, was their role in determining homing properties for these cells in syngeneic mice. This suggests that H-2 may be important in cell sorting or recognition.

From our preliminary studies it appears that structural analysis of variants, both in intact animals and in somatic cells can provide some clues on the origin, genetic organization, and function of the MHC products. At present the results are only suggestive. Our hope is that further progress will establish the usefulness of the approach.

ACKNOWLEDGMENTS

We wish to thank Selma Hadjolian, Diane McGovern and Jane Addis for their expert technical assistance on parts of this work. Parts of the studies described here were supported by NIH grants AI-07289, AI-10702 and ACS grant IM-77 to SGN; NSF grant BMS-75-13609 and NIH grant AI-5231 to MDS. SGN was a faculty scholar of the Josiah Macy, Jr. Foundation during parts of these studies. JHF is a fellow of The Arthritis Foundation, JLB is supported by a fellowship from the Damon Runyon Memorial Fund and from the NIH. DWS is a fellow of the New York Heart Association and TVR is a fellow of the New York Cancer Research Institute, Inc. BME is supported by USPHS training grant 5T5-GM-1674.

REFERENCES

(1) G.D. Snell and J.H. Stimpfling, in: Biology of the
     Laboratory Mouse. ed. E. Green (McGraw-Hill, Inc.,
     New York, 1966) pp. 457-491.

(2) P. Demant. Transplant. Rev. 15 (1973) 162-200.

(3) J. Klein, in: Biology of the Mouse Histocompatibility
     H-2 Complex. (Springer Verlag, New York Heidelberg
     Berlin, 1975).

(4) D.C. Shreffler and C. S. David. Advan. Immunol. 20
     (1975) 125-195.

(5) B.D. Schwartz, K. Kato, S.E. Cullen and S.G. Nathenson.
     Biochemistry 12 (1973) 2157-2164.

(6) S.G. Nathenson and T. Muramatsu, in: Glycoproteins of
     Blood Cells and Plasma. eds. G.A. Jamieson and T.J.
     Greenwalt (Lippincott Co., Philadelphia, 1971) pp. 254-
     262.

(7) J. Silver and L. Hood. Nature 249 (1974) 764-765.

(8) L. Rask, J.B. Lindblom and P.A. Peterson. Nature 249
     (1974) 833-834.

(9) A. Shimada, K. Yamane and S.G. Nathenson. Proc. Nat.
     Acad. Sci. USA 65 (1970) 691-696.

(10) J.L. Brown, K. Kato, J. Silver and S.G. Nathenson.
     Biochemistry 13 (1974) 3174-3178.

(11) D.W. Bailey, G.D. Snell and M. Cherry, in: Proceedings
     of the Symposium on Immunogenetics of the H-2 System.
     eds. A. Lengerova and M. Vojtiskaya (Liblice, Prague,
     1970) pp. 155-162.

(12) J. Forman and J. Klein. Immunogenetics 1 (1975) 469-
     481.

(13) I.K. Egerov. Genetika (Moskva) 9 (1967) 136-143.

(14) J. Forman and J. Klein. J. Immunol. 115 (1975) 711-715.

(15) J.L. Brown and S.G. Nathenson.   Submitted for publication.

(16) A. Shimada and S.G. Nathenson.   Biochemistry 8 (1969) 4048–4062.

(17) B.M. Ewenstein, J.H. Freed, L.E. Mole and S.G. Nathenson.   Proc. Nat. Acad. Sci. USA.   In Press.

(18) T.V. Rajan, S.G. Nathenson and M.D. Scharff.   J. Natl. Cancer Inst.   In Press.

(19) P. Coffino and M.D. Scharff.   Proc. Nat. Acad. Sci. USA 68 (1971) 219–223.

(20) W.F. Bodmer.   Nature 237 (1972) 139–145.

DISCUSSION FOLLOWING STANLEY NATHENSON

BENACERRAF: In the derived line 30, which does not home in the spleen after losing $H-2$, is $H-2$ different when they re-express their $H-2$?

NATHENSON: We are presently extracting the $H-2$ and peptide mapping it.

BENACERRAF: Have you controlled the loss of homing pattern of your $H-2$ missing line with the behavior of another allogeneic or syngeneic myeloma line?

NATHENSON: We have checked the syngeneic parent clone NP-2 which does not home to the spleen. We have not checked with an allogeneic cell line.

MEO: Is the peptide mapping of $H-2^{ba}$ and $H-2^{da}$ gene products still compatible with a frame shift type of interactions involving more extensive alterations, probably affecting adjacent genes?

NATHENSON: Yes.

HOOD: Stan, can you be certain your $H-2$ mutants do not actually have multiple amino acid substitutions? This point is critical because if the mutants do differ from their "parental molecules" by multiple substitutions, this might suggest they are not simple mutations, rather they might be encoded by separate but closely-linked duplicated genes. One must be particularly cautious about peptides that come at the end of ion exchange gradients, as did your difference in the first mutant, since such peaks can contain multiple peptides because of the "washout effect" of the rapidly increasing salt gradient.

NATHENSON: The $H-2^{da}$ versus $H-2^d$ comparison shows two new peptides for the $H-2^{da}$ and one different one in the $H-2^d$. Such a mutation could be explained as a single amino acid exchange. Here the peptide differences are in the middle of the gradient. The $H-2^b$ versus $H-2^{ba}$ comparison is also a one or two peptide difference. This could be a single amino acid exchange or could be more since the mutant apparently has no new peptides and lacks the one or two of those in the parent. We are aware of the difficulties of peptides eluting at the

665

end of the gradient and are trying to further characterize these peptides.

BACH: Are the results you just presented on peptide mapping of the mutants consistent with a point mutation affecting a single amino acid, or can you state that the mutation is more complex than that? This is important because of the multiple biological reactions related to the mutation.

NATHENSON: The data for $H\text{-}2^{da}$ could be a point mutation; however, the $H\text{-}2^{ba}$ mutation could be a more extensive alteration as apparently more peptides are involved.

SACHS: Dr. Klein's original suggestion that the Hzl arose from an $H\text{-}2K$ region mutation was based on different absorptive capacities of B6 and Hzl for anti-$H\text{-}2.33$ antibodies. An alternative explanation might have been differences in levels of expression of the K region product rather than a sequence difference in the product. In this regard, did you find any difference in the yield of $H\text{-}2.33$ polypeptides obtained from the two strains.

NATHENSON: The yields of $H\text{-}2.33$ from $H\text{-}2^{ba}$ and from $H\text{-}2^{b}$ were identical within experimental error.

STRUCTURE AND BIOLOGICAL ACTIVITY OF H-2 ANTIGENS

BRUCE A. CUNNINGHAM, ROLAND HENNING, JOHN W. SCHRADER,
ROBERT J. MILNER, KONRAD RESKE AND GERALD M. EDELMAN

The Rockefeller University

Abstract: Physico-chemical studies and amino acid sequence
analysis of H-2 antigens have provided a working model
of these molecules that includes the size and arrangement of the subunits on the cell surface and in solution and the orientation of the molecules on the cell
surface. Comparisons of the partial amino acid sequences of $H-2K^b$, $H-2K^d$, $H-2K^k$, $H-2D^b$, and $H-2D^d$ gene
products support the hypothesis that the K and D loci
evolved by gene duplication. A variety of evidence
indicates that H-2 antigens can be physically associated with viral antigens on the cell and we have
found that H-2 and viral antigens can co-cap and co-
patch on the cell surface. We suggest that one function of H-2 antigens is to serve as adaptors that
combine with foreign antigens to form hybrid antigens,
which are recognized by cytotoxic T lymphocytes.

INTRODUCTION

Despite the detailed genetic information that has
helped define the major histocompatibility complex, little
is known about the structure and function of the products of
these genes. We have begun a detailed analysis of the structure and function of the major murine histocompatibility
(H-2) antigens, and we present here our studies on the physicochemical properties and partial chemical structure of these
cell surface glycoproteins (1). In addition, we discuss
data suggesting that these molecules may interact with foreign antigens such as viruses on the cell surface to form
hybrid antigens that can serve as the target of cytotoxic T
lymphocytes (2).

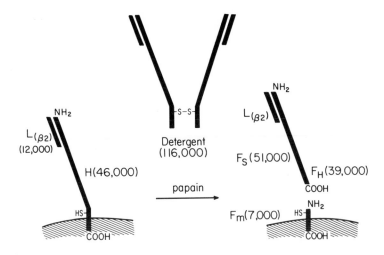

Figure 1. Working model (1) of H-2 antigens on the cell surface and in solutions containing ionic detergents. Papain treatment of detergent solubilized dimers also gives F_S monomers.

STRUCTURE OF H-2 ANTIGENS

H-2 antigens consist of two polypeptide chains, one heavy chain (M.W. 50,000) bearing the antigenic specificity and the carbohydrate (3), and a small polypeptide (M.W. 12,000), β_2-microglobulin (4), which has been shown to be homologous to the constant regions of immunoglobulin light and heavy chains (5). Treatment of cells with papain gives a water-soluble fragment that is smaller than the molecule solubilized by detergent but retains the antigenic specificity and carbohydrate.

The organization of H-2 molecules on the cell surface, the orientation of their peptide chains relative to the cell surface, and the nature and distribution of the polymorphism within the heavy chains are of significance in determining the biological function of H-2 antigens. We have, therefore, carried out an analysis of the molecular organization of H-2 antigens, the physico-chemical properties of the detergent solubilized molecule and its papain fragment, and the partial amino-terminal sequences of heavy chains of different haplotypes. On the basis of these and other studies, we have formulated a working model (Fig. 1) of the H-2 molecule to provide a framework for further experiments in relating structure to function.

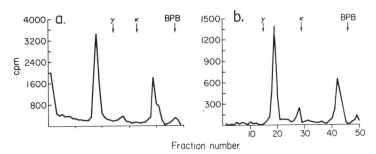

Figure 2. SDS polyacrylamide gel electrophoresis of (a) detergent solubilized H-2 antigens in the absence of reducing agents and (b) papain treated H-2 antigens in the presence or absence of reducing agents. Markers include IgG γ chain and $\varkappa$ chain, and bromphenol blue (BPB).

Detergent solubilized H-2 antigens. The present data indicate that the detergent solubilized H-2 molecule in solution is composed of two disulfide-linked heavy chains and two non-covalently associated light chains (β_2-microglobulin). The molecular weights of H-2 antigen subunits were determined under dissociating conditions after purification by immune precipitation from NP 40 extracts. SDS gel electrophoresis of immune precipitates in the absence of reducing agents showed two species with molecular weights of 92,000 and 12,000 (Fig. 2a). In addition, a 46,000 dalton species was occasionally observed. Elution of the 92,000 dalton component from gels followed by reduction and re-electrophoresis gave only one component with a molecular weight of 46,000, suggesting that the 92,000 dalton component is a disulfide-linked dimer of the H-2 antigen heavy chain. In accord with this result, reduction of immune precipitates with mercaptoethanol resulted in the disappearance of the heavy chain dimer (M.W. 92,000), the appearance of the monomer (M.W. 46,000) and no change in the β_2-microglobulin.

Molecular weight determinations were also made under other conditions. Gel exclusion chromatography in 0.5% deoxycholate (DOC) of NP 40 or DOC-solubilized spleen or lymphoma cell membrane material gave a major component with H-2 antigenic activity. Ultracentrifugation of detergent solubilized H-2 antigens on sucrose density gradients in 0.5% DOC gave a peak of antigenic activity at 5.9 S with some minor components at lower S values (Fig. 3). The diffusion coefficient was calculated using the partition co-

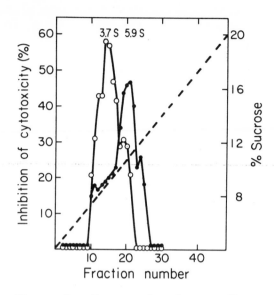

Figure 3. Sucrose density gradient centrifugation of (-•-) H-2 antigens solubilized in 0.5% deoxycholate and (-o-) papain treated H-2 antigens.

efficient obtained by gel exclusion chromatography on calibrated Sephadex G-200 columns. The molecular weight (6) calculated from the diffusion and the sedimentation coefficients was 116,000 daltons. This value is consistent with the hypothesis that intact H-2 antigens in detergent solution are composed of two heavy chains of 46,000 daltons each and two non-covalently associated β_2-microglobulin molecules (Fig. 1).

Recent data from other laboratories have suggested that H-2 and HL-A molecules consist of two disulfide-linked heavy chains and two non-covalently associated β_2-microglobulin chains (7,8). We and others (3), however, have observed the simultaneous presence of H-2 heavy chain dimers and monomers in the absence of reducing agents. This observation suggests that the H-2 heavy chain may not exist as a covalently bonded dimer on the cell surface. Treatment of cells or membrane fractions with iodoacetamide prior to detergent extraction greatly increased the amount of heavy chain monomer on SDS gels in the absence of reducing agents while oxidation of sulfhydryl groups on cells with o-phenanthroline/$CuSO_4$ prior to alkylation again increased the amount of heavy chain dimer. These findings suggest that

the H-2 molecule is predominantly a monomer on the cell surface, but that dimers or disulfide-linked dimers may exist,
at least transiently.

<u>Fragments obtained by papain cleavage</u>. SDS gel electrophore-
sis of H-2 antigens obtained by papain treatment of cells or
detergent extracts showed components of 39,000 and 12,000
molecular weight, both in the presence and in the absence
of reducing agents (Fig. 2b). Under nondissociating conditions and in the absence of detergent, gel chromatography of
papain solubilized H-2 antigenic material indicated a molecular weight of approximately 50,000 daltons. In sucrose
density gradient centrifugation experiments (Fig. 3),
papain treated detergent extracts showed a major peak of
activity at 3.7 S. Calculation of the molecular weight
using the diffusion coefficient from the column data and the
sedimentation constant gave a value of 49,000, indicating
that the main fragment obtained by papain hydrolysis is
monomeric and consists of a 39,000 dalton heavy chain fragment (F_H) and one non-covalently associated β_2-microglobulin
molecule (Fig. 1). We have designated this monomeric fragment F_s for water soluble fragment to contrast it with the
portion of the chain, F_m, that putatively extends into the
membrane. We have observed no F_s dimers after papain treatment regardless of the ionic strength, in agreement with the
results of Peterson <u>et al</u>. (8) but in contrast to observations of Strominger <u>et al</u>. (7) who found a non-covalently
associated HL-A dimer (M.W. 96,000) after papain treatment.

COMPARISON OF PARTIAL AMINO ACID SEQUENCES

For amino acid sequence studies, different cell preparations were incubated with individual ^{3}H-amino acids and
the specifically labeled H-2 heavy chains and their papain
fragments were isolated by preparative gel electrophoresis.
The location of the labeled residues were then determined
using the automatic sequencer (1). The amino-terminal sequence of the intact H-2K^b heavy chains was compared with
that of the papain fragment in order to define the relationship between the two polypeptides. For the three amino acids
tested, no difference was found in the first eight positions
(Fig. 4). These results suggest that the F_H fragment contains the amino-terminal part of the heavy chain and that
the F_m fragment is derived from the carboxyl-terminal part
of the polypeptide chain. Inasmuch as F_s can be obtained by
direct papain treatment of the cell membrane, the amino-
terminal end of the H-2 heavy chain probably extends away

671

		1	2	3	4	5	6	7	8
H–2K^b	H$_2$N ——	Pro	His	——	——	Arg	Tyr	——
H–2K^b F$_H$	H$_2$N ——	——	His	——	——	Arg	Tyr	——
H–2K^d	H$_2$N ——	——	His*	——	——	Arg*Tyr	——
H–2K^k	H$_2$N ——	——	His	——	——	Arg	Tyr	——
H–2D^b	H$_2$N ——	——	——	——	——	——	Tyr*	——
H–2D^d	H$_2$N ——	Pro*His	——	Leu	Arg	Tyr	——

Figure 4. Partial amino acid sequences of the heavy chains of H-2 antigens labeled with individual ^{3}H-amino acids as determined in the automatic sequencer. * denotes preliminary results; F$_H$=papain fragment.

from the cell surface (Fig. 1) with the carboxyl-terminal region (F$_m$) associated with the plasma membrane.

The location and the distribution of those residues that reflect the polymorphism of H-2 antigens probably bear an important relationship to the function of these molecules. Amino-terminal sequences from K and D gene products from different haplotypes were compared to determine whether this region of H-2 molecules contributes to the polymorphism of the H-2 system. The amino-terminal sequences of H-2K^b, H-2K^d, H-2K^k, H-2D^b, and H-2D^d heavy chains were identical at all the positions tested (Fig. 4). In addition to the data shown in Fig. 4, H-2K^b and H-2K^d heavy chains both had an arginyl residue at position 14, and tyrosine was detected at positions 22 and 27 in H-2K^b.

The fact that the amino acid sequences for the first eight positions of H-2 gene products from three independent haplotypes are constant for the amino acids tested does not preclude the possibility that other as yet unknown residues in this region express the antigenic polymorphism. Alternatively, those sites reflected in the polymorphism may reside in other regions or be distributed over the molecule. The similarity in the sequences of the K and D gene products is consistent with the hypothesis (9) that these genes evolved by duplication from a common ancestral gene. Our present data are too limited to allow any conclusion about the postulated common origin (5,10) of histocompatibility antigens and immunoglobulins. A more rigorous test of this relationship as well as the identification of sites recognized by cytotoxic T lymphocytes would provide an important basis for establishing the biological function of histocompatibility antigens.

FUNCTIONAL STUDIES

A number of previous studies have shown that H-2 antigens are involved in cell-mediated lysis of allogenic and xenogenic cells (11,12). Recently, however, it has become apparent that H-2 antigens also play a role in the lysis of chemically-modifed and virally-infected syngeneic cells (13, 14). These observations suggest that there is a special relationship between the major histocompatibility antigens and this subclass of T cells, but the basis of this relationship has not been established.

Recently, we have found (2) that H-2 antigens are also important in the lysis of syngeneic tumor cells. Cytotoxic lymphocytes capable of lysing EL4 tumor cells (H-2^b) were prepared using spleen cells from the parent C57BL/6 strain and cells capable of lysing P388 tumor cells (H-2^d) were prepared using lymphocytes from the parent strain DBA/2 or the H-2 compatible strain BALB/c. The lysis of target cells by syngeneic or H-2 compatible cytotoxic lymphocytes was inhibited by alloantisera against their shared H-2 antigens and the suppressive effect was correlated with the anti-H-2 activity of the alloantisera. Studies using systems in which antisera were directed against either the target cells or the cytotoxic lymphocytes indicated that it is the H-2 antigens on the target cell that are important in the cytotoxic interaction. Similar results have been recently reported (15).

If the H-2 antigens on the target cell are critical in the cytotoxic interaction, dual recognition may be required, i.e. cytotoxic lymphocytes might recognize H-2 antigens and foreign antigens separately via two different sets of receptors (Fig. 5a), or they may be part of an antigen complex that forms the actual target of cytotoxic lymphocytes (Fig. 5b). The most direct and appealing hypothesis is that the H-2 antigens and tumor associated antigens on the transformed cells are physically associated to form an antigenic complex. We selected viral antigens as an example of tumor-associated

673

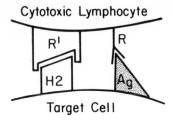

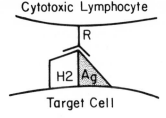

a. Dual Recognition

b. Adaptor-Antigen Complex

Figure 5. Possible roles for H-2 antigens in the interaction of cytotoxic lymphocytes and target cells. H2, H-2 antigen; Ag, other foreign antigens such as viruses; R', receptor for H-2 antigen; R, receptor for foreign or hybrid antigens.

antigens and examined the relationship on the cell surface between some viral antigens and H-2 molecules.

Both P388 and EL4 cells bear surface antigens that react with antisera against Rauscher leukemia virus. We found that capping of H-2 antigens on the tumor cells induced co-capping of these viral antigens (Fig. 6). Capping of viral determinants resulted in a partial redistribution of H-2 antigens. Experiments were carried out to establish the specificity of the reagents (2) and the results were confirmed using goat antiserum prepared against a purified component, gp69/71, of the virus. To exclude the possibility that receptors were co-capped because of trapping rather than because of a close physical association(16), tumor cells (EL4) were incubated with anti-H-2^b serum under conditions where capping could not take place. After this treatment, both the fluorescein-labeled H-2 antigens and the tetramethyl rhodamine labeled viral antigens appeared together in patches, indicating that co-patching had occurred.

These experiments suggest that there is a physical association between the major histocompatibility antigens and viral antigens on the tumor cell surface. Such an association would explain how the H-2 antigens could form part of an antigenic structure containing both "self" (H-2) and "non-self" (virus) components. The target of the cytotoxic lymphocytes developed against neoplastic or virally-infected syngeneic cells would then be the group of determinants formed by the juxtaposition of an H-2 molecule and a foreign antigen. We suggest that one of the functions of the major

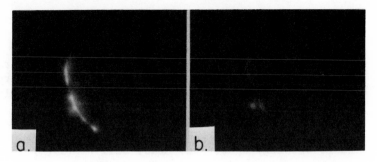

Figure 6. Co-capping of H-2 antigens and Rauscher leukemia virus antigens on an EL4 cell. a, distribution of fluorescein labeled antibodies showing capped H-2 antigens; b, distribution of tetramethyl rhodamine labeled antibodies showing co-capped viral antigens on the same cell.

histocompatibility antigens is to serve as adaptors that interact with foreign molecules to form adaptor-antigen complexes (Fig. 5b) that are recognized by cytotoxic T lymphocytes. Other products of the major histocompatibility complex may serve similar adaptor functions. The notion that T cell receptors interact with altered-self antigens could account both for the large number of T cells that recognize allogeneic products of the major histocompatibility complex (17) and for some of the known requirements (18,19) for the activation of T cells by soluble antigens.

REFERENCES

(1)   R. Henning, R.J. Milner, K. Reske, B.A. Cunningham and G.M. Edelman. Proc. Nat. Acad. Sci. In Press.

(2)   J.W. Schrader, B.A. Cunningham and G.M. Edelman. Proc. Nat. Acad. Sci. In Press.

(3)   B.D. Schwartz, K. Kato, S.E. Cullen and S.G. Nathenson. Biochemistry 12 (1973) 2157.

(4)   J. Silver and L. Hood. Nature 249 (1974) 764.

(5)   B.A. Cunningham and I. Berggard. Transplant. Rev. 21 (1974) 3.

(6)   G.A. Ackers. Adv. Protein Chem. 24 (1970) 343.

(7)   J.L. Strominger, P. Cresswell, H. Grey, R.E. Humphreys, D. Mann, J. McCune, P. Parham, R. Robb, A.R. Sanderson, T.A. Springer, C. Terhorst and M.J. Turner. Transplant. Rev. 21 (1974) 126.

(8)   P.A. Peterson, L. Rask, K.Sege, L. Klareskog, H. Anundi and L. Ostberg. Proc. Nat. Acad. Sci. 72 (1975) 1612.

(9)   J. Klein and D.C. Schreffler. Transplant. Rev. 6 (1971) 3.

(10)   J.A. Gally and G.M. Edelman. Ann. Rev. Genet. 6 (1972) 1.

(11)   B.J. Alter, D.J. Schendel, M.L. Bach, F.H. Bach, J. Klein and J.H. Stimpfling. J. Exp. Med. 137 (1973) 1303.

(12)   K.F. Lindahl and F.H. Bach. Nature 254 (1975) 607.

(13)   G.M. Shearer, T.G. Rehn and C.A. Garbarino. J. Exp. Med. 141 (1975) 1348.

(14)   R.F. Zinkernagel and P.C. Doherty. Nature 251 (1974) 547.

(15)   R.N. Germain, M.E. Dorf and B. Benacerraf. J. Exp. Med. 142 (1975) 1023.

(16)   G.M. Edelman, I. Yahara and J.L. Wang. Proc. Nat. Acad. Sci. 70 (1973) 1442.

(17)   D.B. Wilson, J.C. Howard and P.C. Nowell. Transplant. Rev. 12 (1972) 3.

(18)   P. Erb and M. Feldmann. J. Exp. Med. 142 (1975) 460.

(19)   A.S. Rosenthal and E.M. Shevach. J. Exp. Med. 138 (1973) 1194.

GENETIC AND EVOLUTIONARY IMPLICATIONS OF THE
PARTIAL AMINO ACID SEQUENCES OF H-2K AND H-2D ALLOANTIGENS

JACK SILVER AND LEROY HOOD

Division of Biology
California Institute of Technology

Abstract: Techniques have been developed for the amino acid
sequence analysis of picomole quantities of polypeptides.
These techniques have been applied to characterize β_2-
microglobulin and transplantation antigens of the mouse
isolated by indirect immunoprecipitation from spleen
cells. Eleven residues were identified throughout the
N-terminal 27 residues of the β_2-microglobulin. All
were consistent with residues seen at the corresponding
positions of β_2-microglobulins from other species. Two
K and two D transplantation antigens were examined and
the following generalizations emerged from the limited
partial amino acid sequence data: 1) the K and D molecules are homologous to one another; 2) they do not
show amino acid sequence homology with immunoglobulins;
3) the two K molecules differ from one another by multiple amino acid substitutions as do the two D molecules;
and 4) the K molecules as a class cannot be distinguished from the D molecules as a class. The genetic
and evolutionary implications of these observations are
discussed.

INTRODUCTION

The major histocompatibility complex (MHC) of mammals
is a genetic region which encodes a variety of cell surface
antigens, all of which seem interrelated with the immune system. Classically, this complex was defined in mice by rapid
graft rejection triggered by genetic differences at this
region. The existence of inbred and congenic mouse strains
(strains genetically identical but for a particular region)
has permitted a detailed genetic analysis of this region (1).
In the mouse, the major histocompatibility complex, or the

677

H-2 complex, can be divided by recombinational studies into four major regions--K, I, S and D (1). These regions code for three major classes of gene products: 1) the H-2K and H-2D gene products which represent the classical transplantation antigens (2); 2) the I region gene products which are coded by a region into which the immune response genes map (3); and 3) the S region gene products which appear to code for certain complement components found in the serum (4,5). By recombinational analysis, the H-2 complex has DNA sufficient to code for up to 2000 structural proteins about 20,000 daltons in molecular weight, depending on the amount of interspersed regulatory and nonfunctional DNA.

The H-2K and H-2D gene products exhibit extensive genetic polymorphism. Among the standard inbred mouse strains approximately nine alleles of the K and nine alleles of the D loci have been defined by serological techniques (1). When wild mice from different localities are examined, each new breeding unit (deme) appears to have new D and K alleles (6), suggesting a remarkable degree of polymorphism among the world-wide mouse population. The K and D gene products are found primarily on lymphoid tissue (2), suggesting that they function as "differentiation" antigens.

The H-2D and H-2K cell surface antigens are hydrophobic glycoproteins 45,000 daltons in molecular weight that can be isolated by indirect immunoprecipitation using specific alloantisera (7). These molecules are noncovalently associated with β_2-microglobulin (8), a polypeptide homologous to the constant region domains of immunoglobulin molecules (9). Numerous peptide map differences between the K and D gene products suggest that the multiple serological differences have their basis in multiple amino acid substitutions (10). The chemical studies as well as the presence of serological cross reactivities (11) are consistent with the supposition that the K and D genes (or clusters of genes) arose by a process of gene duplication from a single ancestral gene (12, 13). Others have suggested that the major histocompatibility complex may have given rise to gene families coding for other cell surface receptors such as the immunoglobulins (14-16).

We have developed microsequencing techniques to analyze picomole quantities of cell surface proteins so that some of these hypotheses may be tested directly by amino acid sequence analysis of the H-2 gene products (17-19). In this paper we present the partial N-terminal amino acid sequences of the mouse β_2-microglobulin as well as those of two K and two D

678

gene products. These data allow us to discuss 1) homology
relationships among the K and D molecules; 2) the lack of
homology among the transplantation antigens and immunoglobulins; and 3) the nature of the amino acid sequence diversity
seen among the K and D alleles.

MATERIALS AND METHODS

Antisera and Mice. Specific K and D region antisera
D-4, D-23, D-28b, and D-33 directed, respectively, against
the D^d, K^k, D^b, and K^b regions[*], were obtained from Jackson
Laboratories via the Transplantation and Immunology Branch,
NIAID, NIH. Mice of strains B10.A (4R) and B10.A (5R), which
are genotypically K^k D^b and K^b D^d, respectively, were obtained from our own mouse colony.

Strategy. Spleens were removed from mice and the cells
were cultured in vitro for 4 to 6 hr with groups of tritiated
amino acids (i.e., either alanine, lysine and valine or leucine, proline and tyrosine) (18). The radiolabeled H-2 gene
products were isolated by indirect immunoprecipiation with
specific alloantisera as previously described (7,8,20). The
radiolabeled K and D gene products from one mouse spleen
(about 10^8 cells) were purified by sodium dodecyl sulfate
polyacrylamide gel electrophoresis (SDS PAGE), eluted from
gels, concentrated, and sequenced in the presence of carrier
ovalbumin (which has a blocked α-amino group) in a Beckman
Model 890A sequencer as previously described (17-19). The
tritiated phenylthiohydantoin (PTH) amino acid residues were
resolved by thin layer chromatography in the presence of the
appropriate unlabeled PTH-amino acids and counted. Complete
details of these procedures will be published in a separate
communication (Silver and Hood, in preparation).

RESULTS

Isolation of Two Molecular Components with Alloantisera.
Because of the availability of inbred strains of mice that
differ solely at restricted portions of the H-2 complex, alloantisera can be prepared that are directed primarily
against the K or D gene products. These antisera can be
used to isolate K and D gene products by indirect immunoprecipitation (7,20). Sodium dodecyl sulfate polyacrylamide

---

[*] The capital letter K or D refers to the genetic region involved while the lower case superscript refers to the "allelic" form of that region.

gel electrophoresis of these immunoprecipitates reveals two
major molecular weight components, ∿45,000 and 12,000 daltons,
which are respectively the putative K or D gene products and
the putative β_2-microglobulin molecule (8).

   Amino Acid Sequence Analysis of the 12,000 Dalton Component. The sequence data obtained from the small polypeptide
are illustrated in Fig. 1A. For those residues that appear
two or more times (e.g., tyrosine, valine, proline) the repetitive yields ranged between 89-94% which is similar to the
repetitive yields obtained from conventional runs. Furthermore, these high repetitive yields suggest that a major component is being sequenced.

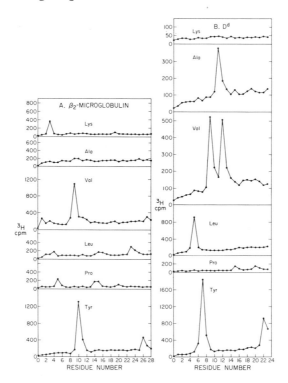

   Figure 1.A. Amino acid sequence data from the
H-2 associated polypeptide (β_2-microglobulin). B.
Amino acid sequence data from the D^d gene product.
The amount of radioactivity associated with each of
the six incorporated amino acids is plotted against
residue number (see text).

The partial sequence deduced from these data is compared to the known sequences of β_2-microglobulins isolated from the urine of other species in Fig. 2. A dash indicates that the corresponding residue is <u>not</u> one of the six labeled amino acids.

	1	2	3	4	5	6	7	8	9	10
Human	Ile	Gln	Arg	Thr	Pro	Lys	Ile	Gln	Val	Tyr
Dog	Val	Gln	His	Pro	Pro	Lys	Ile	Gln	Val	Tyr
Rabbit	Val	Gln	Arg	Ala	Pro	Asn	Val	Gln	Val	Tyr
H-2 associated polypeptide	-	-	Lys	-	Pro	-	-	-	Val	Tyr

	11	12	13	14	15	16	17	18	19	20
Human	Ser	Arg	His	Pro	Ala	Glu	Asn	Gly	Lys	Ser
Dog	Ser	Arg	His	Pro	Ala	Glu	Asn	Gly	Lys	Pro
Rabbit	Ser	Arg	His	Pro	Ala	Glu	Asn	Gly	Lys	Asp
H-2 associated polypeptide	-	-	-	Pro	Pro	-	-	-	Lys	Pro

	21	22	23	24	25	26	27
Human	Asn	Phe	Leu	Asn	Cys	Tyr	Val
Dog	Asn	Phe	Leu	Asn	Cys	Tyr	Val
Rabbit	Asn	Phe	Leu	Asn	Cys	Tyr	Val
H-2 associated polypeptide	-	-	Leu	-	-	Tyr	Val

Figure 2. Partial amino acid sequences of β_2-microglobulins from man, dog, and rabbit compared with the H-2 associated polypeptide of mouse. A dash indicates that no one of the six labeled amino acids (alanine, leucine, lysine, proline, tyrosine and valine) is present at that position. The rat β_2-microglobulin has lysine at position 3 and proline at position 15 (M. D. Poulik, C. Shinnick and O. Smithies, personal communication). The lysine at position 3 in the mouse β_2-microglobulin has been confirmed by other investigators (B. T. Ballou, D. McKean and O. Smithies, personal communication). Boxes indicate the corresponding residues are identical to their mouse counterparts. The β_2-microglobulin sequences were obtained from the following sources: human (31), dog (32), and rabbit (33).

Amino Acid Sequence Analysis of the 45,000 Molecular
Weight Components. The sequence data from one representative
45,000 molecular weight component is given in Fig. 1B. The
repetitive yields for all residues that could be examined
ranged between 89 and 94%. Once again this is consistent
with a single major component being present in each preparation. These sequences are presented in Fig. 3. In summary,
the two H-2K and two H-2D gene products that we have examined
appear to have unblocked N-termini and they appear to represent a single major molecular component.

DISCUSSION

The Small Polypeptide (12,000 daltons) is the Mouse β_2-
Microglobulin. All eleven residues that we were able to
identify are consistent with residues at homologous positions
in the known sequences of other β_2-microglobulin molecules
(Fig. 2). This extensive homology demonstrates unequivocally
that the small polypeptide associated with the 45,000 molecular weight components is the mouse β_2-microglobulin. More
importantly, the analysis of this partial amino acid sequence
at the level of a few hundred picomoles or less demonstrates
the feasibility and reliability of extending these micro-
sequence methods to the analysis of various cell surface
molecules available in limited quantities.

The Large Polypeptide (45,000 daltons) Represents an
H-2K or H-2D Gene Product. Control indirect immunoprecipitation experiments using specific alloantisera and radioactive-
ly labeled lymphocytes that lack the corresponding H-2K or
H-2D specificities revealed that very little ^{3}H protein is
isolated in the 45,000 molecular weight range (7,20). These
experiments suggest that very little radiolabeled protein in
the 45,000 molecular weight range is isolated by this procedure unless the specific antigen is present in the immunoprecipitation mixture. We feel that the serological controls
and the presence of amino acid sequence variability correlated with the differing alleles provide strong support for
the supposition that the 45,000 dalton polypeptides are the
H-2K or H-2D gene products.

The Four K and D Gene Products are Homologous to One
Another and Probably Have Descended from a Common Ancestral
Gene. Of the 8-9 residue positions that are identifiable in
each molecule, four are identical in all four proteins (residues 7, 11, 12, 15) (see Fig. 3). In addition, the K and D
molecules share residues at several positions (e.g. positions

2, 5, 9, 17, 22). The probability that any two randomly
chosen polypeptides would demonstrate this degree of identity
is less than 10^{-4}. Accordingly, the K and D molecules are
clearly related. These observations strongly support earlier
suppositions that the K and D loci descended from a common
ancestral gene (10-13).

	1	2	3	4	5	6	7	8	9	10	11
K^b	-	Pro	-	-	Leu	-	Tyr	-	Val	-	Ala
K^k	-	Pro	-	-	Leu	-	Tyr	-	-	-	Ala
D^b	-	Pro	-	-	-	-	Tyr	-	-	-	Ala
D^d	-	-	-	-	Leu	-	Tyr	-	Val	-	Ala

	12	13	14	15	16	17	18	19	20	21	22
K^b	Val	-	-	Pro	-	Leu	-	-	-	-	Tyr
K^k	Val	-	-	Pro	-	Leu	-	Lys	-	-	-
D^b	Val	-	-	Pro	-	Leu	-	-	Pro	-	Tyr
D^d	Val	-	-	Pro	-	-	-	-	Pro	-	Tyr

Figure 3. Partial amino acid sequences of
the K and D gene products. Dashes at a position
indicate a lack of any one of the six labeled amino
acids (alanine, leucine, lysine, proline, tyrosine
and valine) and are, accordingly, useful in homology
comparisons. For example, the D^b and D^d molecules
are identical at position 7 (both have tyrosine and
not identical at position 2 because the D^d molecule
does not have proline in this latter position. Boxes
indicate identical residues in two or more allelic
products.

The K and D Gene Products Do Not Appear to be Homologous to Immunoglobulins Based on Limited Sequence Comparisons.
It has been proposed that the immunoglobulin gene families
descended from the major transplantation locus. This

postulated evolutionary relationship is based on several
general features both systems share--their extreme polymorphism, their cell surface location, their role in regulating
the immune response, and a variety of general evolutionary
arguments (14,15). In addition, the K and D gene products
are noncovalently associated with β_2-microglobulin, a molecule homologous to the constant domains of immunoglobulins
(see 16) and preliminary structural studies have suggested
the presence of immunoglobulin-like domains in the K and D
molecules (21). The limited sequence data presented in Fig. 3
show no significant sequence homology with the various immunoglobulin domains or the β_2-microglobulins. There are a
number of possible explanations for this apparent lack of
homology. 1) The amino acid sequence data are insufficient
to determine sequence homology or lack thereof. This appears
unlikely, since comparing the same six residues from the N-
terminal 23 residues of β_2-microglobulin with those from the
four immunoglobulin domains of the myeloma protein Eu reveals
striking sequence homologies, even though only about 30% of
the residues are homologous (22). 2) The K and D genes are
not evolutionarily related to immunoglobulin genes. 3) The
N-terminal portions of the K and D molecules may be particularly variable, perhaps a reflection of some important
associated function. Other portions of these molecules may
show homologies with immunoglobulins. 4) The transplantation
antigens have sufficiently diverged from immunoglobulins to
mask any obvious sequence relationships. However, the association of the K and D products with an immunoglobulin-like
molecule suggests that conformational homology may exist.
Perhaps the contact residues between the two chains will be
structurally homologous to their immunoglobulin counterparts
from the V_L and V_H domains. Indeed, the six contact residues
for the V_L regions (positions 35, 37, 42, 43, 86, and 99) are
strikingly conserved in all light chains as are their seven
V_H region counterparts (positions 37, 39, 43, 45, 47, 95 and
108) (23). These postulated homologies can be tested by
additional sequence data. Whatever the case may be, the data
currently available do not reveal any homology relationship
between the transplantation antigens and immunoglobulins at
the level of primary amino acid sequences.

    The Two K Allelic Products Differ from One Another by
Multiple Amino Acid Residues as Do the Two D Allelic Products.
The K products differ by three out of ten residues and the D
products by four of ten residues (Fig. 3). These constitute
30-40% sequence differences over the limited regions examined.
This high degree of sequence diversity, if reflected in the

rest of the molecule, is unusual for alleles and requires that unusual evolutionary models be proposed to explain the rapid fixation of many substitutions. These models fall into two categories. 1) If we assume that the K and D genes have always existed as single gene copies and have evolved alleles since speciation, then intense selective pressures acting on small isolated populations are required to fix that many substitutions in such a relatively short evolutionary time span. 2) If the K and D genes existed in multiple copies prior to speciation, it would provide them with a sufficiently long evolutionary time span to fix many mutations. In addition, it would minimize selective pressures which might be exerted against them to prevent the accumulation of many mutations. At the time of speciation or subsequently, different individuals or groups of individuals would have inherited or fixed different copies of the K or D genes. Alternatively, a regulatory mechanism may have evolved which permitted different individuals to express different members of a closely linked multigene family (24,25). Various experimental approaches may allow one to distinguish among the various models. Whatever the genetic explanation for these complex alleles, the extensive serological polymorphism of the K and D loci of the mouse reflects extensive sequence differences among the corresponding "alleles" at the K and D regions.

The K Products as a Class Cannot be Distinguished from the D Products as a Class on the Basis of Limited Sequence Data. The D gene products do not appear to be significantly more closely related to one another than to the K gene products. For example, the D^d gene product shows 60% homology with K^b, 55% homology with K^k, and 55% homology with its allelic counterpart, the D^b gene product (Fig. 3). Likewise, apart from the proline residues at position 20, no amino acids are restricted to only the K or the D gene products (Fig. 3). This lack of "D-ness" or "K-ness" is perhaps the most surprising observation in these data. The existence of two subloci (LA and 4) in the major histocompatibility complex of man (see 26) that are analogous to the K and D regions of the mouse suggests that the gene duplication event(s) which created these regions occurred prior to the divergence of these species 75 million years ago. If the allelic forms of the K or D region arose subsequent to the divergence of the mammalian evolutionary lines, the alleles of one region should be more closely related to one another than to those of the second region. We can offer three types of explanations for our apparent inability to distinguish the K and D allelic products. 1) Perhaps our limited partial sequence data is insufficient to draw any conclusions concerning "D-ness" or "K-ness". 2) In the mammalian ancestor, the "allelic" forms arose as multiple closely linked genes. At speciation different individuals selected different pairs of genes, one of which became K and the other D. This assumes that speciation occurred with multiple individuals rather than a single breeding pair. 3) Gene duplication occurs at speciation and therefore there has been insufficient time for the K and D genes to diverge significantly. In addition, intense selection pressures acting on small isolated populations are required to create the high degree of sequence diversity between alleles. Additional amino acid sequence data may allow us to distinguish among these alternatives.

Chromosome 17 of the Mouse Codes for a Variety of Cell Surface Molecules that May Be Homologous to One Another. Chromosome 17 of the mouse codes for at least five different kinds of cell surface molecules: the T antigens, the K antigens, the I antigens, the D antigens, and the TL antigens (see 2). Recently it has been suggested that the T (27) and TL (28) antigens are homologous to the K and D gene products on the basis of similar molecular weights and their association with β_2-microglobulin. If confirmed by structural studies, this suggests that the corresponding genes may have diverged from a common ancestor. Furthermore, clusters or families of genes appear to be present which code for proteins with related structures and functions. These multigene families include the T, I and S regions that are respectively associated with embryological development (29), regulation of the immune response (3), and complement components (see 4, 5). It will be interesting to determine whether these multigene families share strategies for information storage, information expression and information evolution similar to those seen in the antibody gene families (see 30).

The approach we have taken to the analysis of the K and D gene products should lend itself to the study of other membrane proteins. In time these studies should provide insights into the fascinating organizational, regulatory, evolutionary, and functional mysteries of many complex eukaryotic systems.

ACKNOWLEDGMENTS

This work was supported by grants from the National Science Foundation and the National Institutes of Health. J.S. has an Established Investigatorship Award from the

American Heart Association. L.H. has an NIH Research Career Development Award. We thank Paul Morand for his outstanding technical assistance. This paper has been submitted in a more detailed form to the Proceedings of the National Academy of Sciences, U.S.A.

REFERENCES

(1) D. C. Shreffler and C. S. David. Adv. Immunol. 20 (1975) 125.

(2) J. Klein. Contemp. Topics in Immunobiol., in press (1975).

(3) H. O. McDevitt, K. B. Bechtol and G. J. Hammerling, in: Cellular Selection and Regulation in the Immune Response. ed. G. M. Edelman. (Raven Press, New York, 1974) p. 101.

(4) H. O. McDevitt. Fed. Proc., in press (1975).

(5) T. Meo, T. Krasteff and D. Shreffler. Proc. Nat. Acad. Sci. USA, in press (1975).

(6) J. Klein. Ann. Rev. Genetics 8 (1974) 63.

(7) S. G. Nathenson and S. E. Cullen. Biochim. Biophys. Acta 344 (1974) 1.

(8) J. Silver and L. Hood. Nature 249 (1974) 764.

(9) B. A. Cunningham and I. Berggard. Transplant Rev. 21 (1974) 3.

(10) J. L. Brown, K. Kato, J. Silver and S. G. Nathenson. Biochemistry 13 (1974) 3174.

(11) D. Murphy and D. C. Shreffler. J. Exp. Med. 141 (1975) 374.

(12) J. Klein and D. C. Shreffler. Transplant Rev. 6 (1971) 3.

(13) D. C. Shreffler, C. S. David, H. C. Passmore and J. Klein. Transp. Proc. 3 (1971) 176.

(14) W. Bodmer. Nature 237 (1972) 139.

(15) J. Gally and G. M. Edelman. Ann. Rev. Genetics 6 (1972) 1.

(16) J. L. Strominger, P. Cresswell, H. Grey, R.H. Humphreys, D. Mann, J. McCune, P. Parham, R. Robb, A.R. Sanderson, T. A. Springer, C. Terhorst and M. J. Turner. Transplant. Rev. 21 (1974) 126.

(17) J. Silver and L. Hood. Anal. Biochem. 60 (1974) 285.

(18) J. Silver and L. Hood. Nature 256 (1975) 63.

(19) J. Silver and L. Hood. Anal. Biochem. 67 (1975) 392.

(20) J. Silver, C. Sibley, P. Morand and L. Hood. Transp. Proc. 7 (1975) 201.

(21) P. A. Peterson, L. Rask, K. Sege, L. Klaresky, H. Anundi, and L. Östberg. Proc. Nat. Acad. Sci. USA 72 (1975) 1612.

(22) P. A. Peterson, B. A. Cunningham, I. Berggard and G. M. Edelman. Proc. Nat. Acad. Sci. USA 69 (1972) 1697.

(23) R. J. Poljak, L. M. Amzel, B. L. Chen, R.P. Phizackerley and F. Saul. Immunogenetics 2 (1975) 393.

(24) G. Gutman, E. Loh and L. Hood. Proc. Nat. Acad. Sci. USA, in press (1975).

(25) W. Bodmer. Transp. Proc. 5 (1973) 1471.

(26) H. O. McDevitt and W. F. Bodmer. Lancet I (1974) 1269.

(27) E. S. Vitetta, K. Artzt, D. Bennett, E. A. Boyse and F. Jacob. Proc. Nat. Acad. Sci. USA, in press (1975).

(28) E. S. Vitetta, J. W. Uhr and E. A. Boyse. J. Immunol. 114 (1975) 252.

(29) K. Artzt and D. Bennett. Nature 256 (1975) 545.

(30) L. Hood, J. H. Campbell and S.C.R. Elgin. Ann. Rev. Genetics 9 (1975), in press.

(31) B. A. Cunningham, J. L. Wang, I. Berggard and P. A.
      Peterson. Biochemistry 12 (1973) 4811.

(32) B. A. Cunningham and I. Berggard. Science 187 (1975)
      1079.

(33) O. Smithies and M. D. Poulik. Proc. Nat. Acad. Sci.
      USA 69 (1972) 2914.

THE CHEMISTRY OF MOUSE AND GUINEA PIG Ia ANTIGENS

BENJAMIN D. SCHWARTZ AND SUSAN E. CULLEN

Laboratory of Immunology
National Institute of Allergy and Infectious Diseases
and
Immunology Branch
National Cancer Institute

Abstract: Ia antigens of mice and guinea pigs are shown to be
molecules of ∿58,000 daltons comprised of two glycoprotein chains of 33,000 and 25,000 daltons which are
linked by disulfide bonds. One Ia antigen (murine Ia.7)
was shown to retain its antigenic activity after
digestion by glycosidases but not after pronase digestion, indicating the antigenic activity resides in
the protein portion of the molecule. Sequential
precipitation was utilized as a means of genetic mapping
of Ia specificities. Two Ia determinants encoded within one I subregion were found on one molecule, while
two Ia determinants encoded within different subregions
were found on different molecules. This technique was
employed to map Ia determinants to a subregion when no
recombinants informative for a given specificity were
available for analysis. Differences in Ia antigens
isolated from guinea pig B cells, T cells and macrophages were demonstrated and were shown to be related
to differences in carbohydrate structure or possibly
content. These differences may have implications for
cell interaction.

INTRODUCTION

The antigens encoded within the I region of the major
histocompatibility complex of the mouse and guinea pig have
been termed I region associated or Ia antigens. These Ia
antigens occupy a major role in the control of specific immune
responses and in the interaction of immunocompetent cells.
Alloantibodies to Ia antigens have been shown to block antigen
induced, genetically controlled immune responses in a haplotype specific manner, as measured by T cell proliferation

assays (1,2). They also block the induction of mixed lymphocyte reactions (3,4) and enhance graft survival (5). Ia antigenic determinants have been found on both helper and suppressor T cell factors (6,7), and identity of Ia antigens is
a prerequisite for optimal macrophage-T cell and T cell-B cell
collaboration (6,8). Because of the critical importance of Ia
antigens in so many aspects of the immune response, a chemical and structural analysis of these antigens was undertaken.

METHODS

Lymphoid cells were biosynthetically radiolabeled by
incubating cells at a density of 2-5 x 10^7/ml with ^{3}H-leucine,
^{3}H-fucose, ^{3}H-galactose, ^{3}H-glucosamine, or ^{3}H-mannose,
for 4-24 hours at 37°C in an atmosphere of 5% CO_2. The cells
were harvested, and the cell membranes dissociated in 0.5%
Nonidet P-40 (NP-40) in Tris buffered saline (TBS). After a
brief incubation at 4°C, nuclei and particulate matter were
removed by ultracentrifugation at 100,000 x g for 60 minutes
(9). The resulting supernatant was then chromatographed
through an affinity column of *Lens culinaris* lectin covalently
bound to Sepharose 4B in 0.3% NP-40 in TBS. Lentil lectin has
specificity for mannose and glucose, and therefore binds glycoproteins containing these sugars (10). After the effluent
fraction had been collected, the bound materials were eluted
with 0.1M α-methyl mannoside in 0.3% NP-40 in TBS, and the
eluted fraction collected. Since the eluted fraction contained only 5% of the ^{3}H-leucine labeled protein, but 70-100%
of the Ia activity from most cell types examined, passage
over the column yielded a 10-20 fold purification of the Ia
antigens. The binding of the antigens by the lentil lectin
provided evidence that these antigens were glycoproteins.
To further study both the material which bound to the lectin
and that which passed through, the effluent and eluted
fractions were concentrated approximately 10 fold. Radiolabeled IgG was removed by reacting the concentrated fractions with *Staphylococcus aureus* Cowan I strain (SaCI) bearing
protein A which binds to the F_c portion of most classes of
mouse and guinea pig IgG. In contrast to the results in
another report (11), we found that no murine or guinea pig
Ia, H-2 K or D, or GPLA-B antigens bound to protein A-
bearing SaCI. Following centrifugation, the IgG free supernatant was reacted with anti-Ia alloantisera. Any resulting
alloantigen-alloantibody complexes were precipitated by
SaCI (12). After thorough washing, antibody and Ia antigens
were dissociated from the SaCI by 2% SDS (non-reducing con-

ditions) or by 2% SDS and 2-5% 2-mercaptoethanol (reducing conditions). The SaCI was removed by centrifugation, and the supernatants analysed by electrophoresis through a discontinuous SDS-polyacrylamide gel. The radioactivity in each 2 mm gel slice was determined, and was plotted against migration distance in the gel.

CHEMISTRY AND STRUCTURE

Figure 1 shows the gel patterns of antigens derived from ^{3}H-leucine labeled guinea pig lymph node cells after electrophoresis on discontinuous 10% polyacrylamide-SDS gels. The same results have been obtained in the murine Ia system. Under non-reducing conditions (left half, top panel) the Ia antigens are seen to migrate predominantly as a single component of ∿58,000 daltons. Under reducing conditions (right half, top panel), Ia antigens electrophorese as two components of ∿33,000 and ∿25,000 daltons, respectively. The derivation of the two reduced smaller chains from the unreduced larger Ia bearing molecule was confirmed by isolating the 58,000 dalton molecule from the gel and re-electrophoresing it under non-reducing and reducing conditions (Figure 1, bottom panel). When disulfide bonds are kept intact, the mobility of the Ia antigen is that of a single 58,000 dalton molecule; when the disulfide bonds are reduced, the 33,000 and 25,000 dalton components appear. It thus appears that the Ia bearing molecules have two chains and that in NP-40 they exist as a unit consisting of one 33,000 and one 25,000 dalton component linked by disulfide bonds. Moreover, if iodoacetamide is added to labeled cells prior to their solubilization by NP-40 to prevent formation of new disulfide bonds, a 58,000 dalton component is still obtained, suggesting that this unit exists naturally on or within the cell, and is not an artifact introduced by the methods. The discrepancy between these results and those obtained using lactoperoxidase-catalysed cell surface radioiodination where only a single 25,000 dalton chain is obtained under both reducing and non-reducing conditions has previously been discussed (13).

If ^{3}H-fucose, ^{3}H-galactose, ^{3}H-glucosamine, or ^{3}H-mannose is used to internally radiolabel cells, and Ia antigens are isolated as above, both the 33,000 and 25,000 dalton components are labeled, indicating that each chain of the Ia molecule is a glycoprotein (13,14). After the digestion of the carbohydrate portion of one Ia antigen (murine Ia.7) with a mixture of glycosidases, the Ia.7 activity was readily detectable. However, pronase digested glycopeptides

693

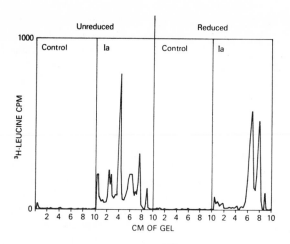

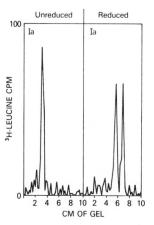

Figure 1. Discontinuous 10% polyacrylamide-SDS gel patterns of Ia antigens derived from ^{3}H-leucine labeled guinea pig lymph node cells. Under reduced conditions (left half, top panel), the Ia antigen migrates predominantly as a single component of 58,000 daltons. Under reduced conditions (right half, top panel) the Ia antigen migrates as two components of 33,000 and 25,000 daltons. The unreduced Ia antigen was isolated from the gel and re-electrophoresed under unreduced and reduced conditions (bottom panel) to show the derivation of the two smaller chains from the larger molecule (see text).

were not bound by anti-Ia.7 antibody (15). The retention of antigenic activity after loss of carbohydrate, but not after destruction of protein indicates that the antigenic site is most likely protein in nature, and that Ia antigens are primary gene products.

Figure 2 shows the electropherograms obtained when ^{3}H-leucine labeled mouse Ia and H-2 antigens are co-electrophoresed with their ^{14}C-leucine labeled guinea pig counterparts, the Ia and GPLA-B antigens. The chemical homology between the murine and guinea pig Ia antigens, and between the H-2 and B antigens is quite striking. When these antigens are labeled with ^{3}H-leucine for 24 hours, and analyzed on 15% polyacrylamide-SDS gels, a non-covalently associated β2-microglobulin like component is found with the H-2 D and K, and GPLA-B antigens, but not with the Ia antigens.

IMMUNOGENETIC STUDIES

Sequential precipitation has been employed to aid in the genetic mapping of new antigenic specificities, particularly when no recombinants informative for the specificity in question are available (16). The molecules bearing a given antigenic determinant are removed by immunoprecipitation, and the resulting supernatant is assayed for one or more other antigenic determinants. Figure 3 shows an example of this technique in the guinea pig system. A preparation of antigen containing determinants Ia.2 and Ia.4 was divided into three aliquots. The first was reacted with normal guinea pig serum (NGPS), the second with excess anti-Ia.4, and the third with excess anti-Ia.2. SaCI was added, and the precipitates removed. Each of the three resulting supernatants was in turn divided into three aliquots, so that each supernatant could be tested with NGPS, anti-Ia.4, and anti-Ia.2. The nine precipitates formed were then analysed on SDS polyacrylamide gels. When pretreated with NGPS (Figure 3, top row), both Ia.4 and Ia.2 remain in the supernatant. Pretreatment with anti-Ia.4 (middle row) substantially reduced the amount of Ia.4 seen on retesting, but did not affect the amount of Ia.2 at all. Pretreatment with anti-Ia.2 (bottom row) completely removed Ia.2 but left Ia.4 intact. This result proves that Ia.2 and Ia.4 are found on independent molecules, and thus would be the products of separate loci within the I region.

Figure 4 demonstrates the patterns obtained in an experiment which showed that two murine Ia determinants (Ia.8 and Ia.9) encoded in the same I subregion were co-precipitable. The experimental design is similar to that

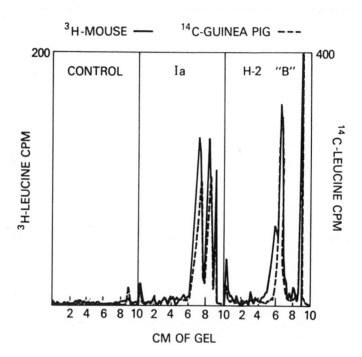

Figure 2. Discontinuous 10% polyacrylamide-SDS gel patterns of ^{3}H-leucine labeled murine Ia and H-2 antigens co-electrophoresed with their ^{14}C-leucine labeled guinea pig counterparts, the Ia and GPLA-B antigens. The homologies across species is striking.

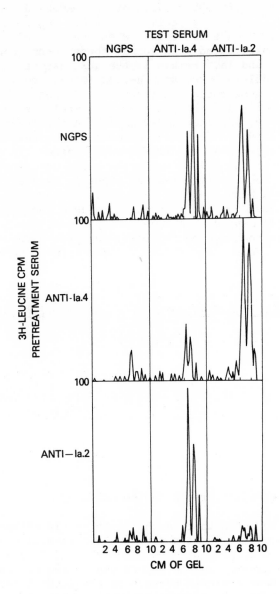

Figure 3. Discontinuous 10% polyacrylamide-SDS gel patterns of the final nine precipitates of a sequential precipitation experiment (see text for details). The molecules bearing guinea pig Ia.2 are separately precipitable from those bearing Ia.4.

already described. (B10.D2 x A)F$_1$ anti B10.A(5R) detects both H-2.33 and Ia.9 on *H-2*^{b} cells. (B10.A x A)F$_1$ anti B10.D2 detects Ia.8 on these cells. When the *H-2*^{b} antigen preparation was pretreated with normal mouse serum (top row), Ia.9 and H-2.33, and Ia.8 remain in the supernatant. Pretreatment with anti-Ia.9 and anti-H-2.33 (middle row) completely removes these specificities and Ia.8, while pretreatment with anti-Ia.8 (bottom row) completely removes both Ia.8 and Ia.9, but leaves H-2.33 in the supernatant. Thus, Ia.8 and Ia.9 are found on one molecule. Other experiments have shown that in all instances tested, Ia determinants mapping in the same I subregion are found on the same molecule. Ia specificities not mappable by analysis of recombinants have been assigned to a given I subregion because they are found on the same molecule as a specificity for which genetic mapping has been accomplished.

Using these techniques, the following maps have been obtained for the mouse, and strain 2 and strain 13 guinea pigs.

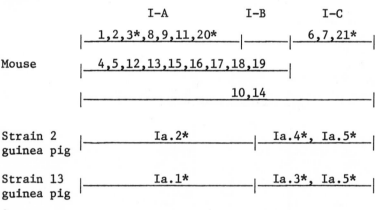

*Assigned by sequential precipitation only.

It should be noted that in the mouse, no Ia antigen is currently specifically mapped to the I-B subregion (in haplotype b, Ia.3 co-precipitates with Ia.8 and 9, and is thus in the I-A subregion). In the guinea pig no region designations have yet been assigned because of the lack of recombinants, and no order on the chromosome or allelic assignments is implied by the schematic.

TISSUE DISTRIBUTION

Since Ia antigens function as interaction structures

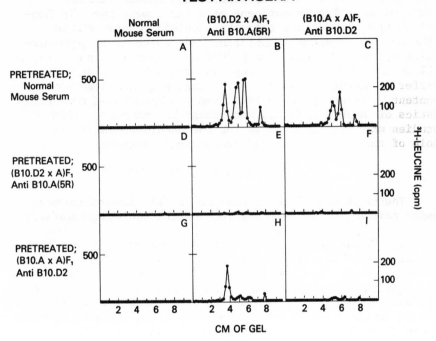

Figure 4. Discontinuous 10% polyacrylamide-SDS gel patterns of the final nine precipitates of a sequential precipitation experiment (see text for details). The results show that Ia.8 and Ia.9 are on the same molecule, but clearly separable from H-2.33

between cells (6,7,8), a chemical study of the Ia antigens found on various subpopulations of lymphoid cells was undertaken. Preliminary evidence in both the mouse and guinea pig indicates that Ia antigens are found on a two chain molecule on B cells, T cells, and macrophages. Moreover, in the guinea pig, though not in the mouse, Ia antigens derived from these subpopulations showed further differences. The Ia antigens of B cells were bound by lentil lectin, indicating that they contain mannose and/or glucose. Macrophage Ia antigens were shown to be glycoproteins by their labeling with ^{3}H-fucose, but were not bound at all by lentil lectin, showing that macrophage Ia antigens differ at least in carbohydrate structure, and possibly content. Ia antigens derived from T cells showed characteristics of both B cell and macrophage Ia antigens. These studies may provide a basis for the understanding of the role of the Ia antigens as interaction structures.

QUESTIONS TO BE ANSWERED

The presence of two chains in the Ia alloantigen molecules raises intriguing questions which require resolution:

1. Which chain bears the Ia determinant? 2. Are both chains encoded by loci within the I region, or does one chain possibly have its genetic origin in an independently segregating locus? 3. What is the role of each of the two chains? 4. Are the molecules bearing a single Ia determinant homogeneous or heterogeneous? 5. Do the cell surface bound Ia molecules have antigen recognition capabilities? 6. What is the relationship of Ia antigens to T cell factors? We are hopeful that chemical studies of the type described here will aid in answering many of these questions.

REFERENCES

(1) E.M. Shevach, W.E. Paul, and I. Green. J. Exp. Med. 136 (1972) 1207.

(2) R.H. Schwartz, C.S. David, D.H. Sachs, and W.E. Paul. Manuscript in preparation.

(3) D.H. Sachs, R.H. Schwartz, and C.G. Fathman. This volume.

(4) A.S. Rosenthal and E.M. Shevach. This volume.

(5) N.A. Staines, K. Guy, and D.A.L. Davies. Transplantation 18 (1974) 192.

(6) E. Mozes. This volume.

(7) T. Tada and M. Taniguchi. This volume.

(8) A.S. Rosenthal and E.M. Shevach. J. Exp. Med. 138 (1973) 1194.

(9) B.D. Schwartz and S.G. Nathenson. J. Immunol. 107 (1971) 1363.

(10) N. Sharon, and H. Lis. Science 177 (1972) 949.

(11) P.A. Peterson, L. Rask, K. Gege, L. Klareskog, H. Anundi, and L. Ostberg. Proc. Nat. Acad. Sci. 72 (1975) 1612.

(12) S.E. Cullen and B.D. Schwartz. Manuscript submitted.

(13) B.D. Schwartz, A.M. Kask, W.E. Paul, and E.M. Shevach J. Exp. Med. In press.

(14) S.E. Cullen, C.S. David, J.L. Cone, and D.H. Sachs. J. Immunol. In press.

(15) S.E. Cullen, J.H. Freed, P.J. Atkinson, and S.G. Nathenson. Transplantation Proc. 8 (1975) 237.

(16) S.E. Cullen, B.D. Schwartz, and S.G. Nathenson. J. Immunol. 108 (1972) 596.

BIOCHEMISTRY AND IMMUNOCYTOLOGY OF CELL SURFACE PRODUCTS
OF THE MAJOR HISTOCOMPATIBILITY COMPLEX

Henry Kunkel, Chairman

KUNKEL: The people here who are actively involved in sequence analyses of *H-2* and *HLA* molecules have already
met together before this session to compare their data.
I understand that Lee Hood is prepared to summarize all
of this for the rest of us, so I will now turn the floor
over to him.

HOOD: In Figure 1 is given a compilation of the available
amino acid sequence data on the transplantation antigens of man and mouse. A number of features are striking about these data. First, there is virtually complete agreement among four laboratories on the sequences of the mouse transplantation antigens where
overlapping data is available. This gives us some confidence that we are all analyzing the same molecules
and that the microsequencing techniques are working.
Second, the human transplantation antigens show 30-40%
amino acid sequence homology with their mouse counterparts. This establishes that the major histocompatibility complex of mouse and man are homologous complex
genetic loci which presumably code for homologous phenotypic functions.

Third, these data are consistent with two important observations made by Silver and Hood, namely 1) the *K*
gene products differ from one another by multiple amino
acid substitutions as do the *D* gene products, and 2)
the *D* gene products as a class cannot be distinguished
from the *K* gene products as a class (i.e., there is no
"*D*-ness" or "*K*-ness), a point also made by Cunningham,
et al (this volume). The genetic implications of the
former observation are intriguing. We have designated
"allotypes" that segregated in a Mendelian fashion and
differ by multiple amino acid residues as *complex allotypes*. Indeed, there are a number of examples of
complex allotypes in another complex and multigenic
system -- the immunoglobulins. Complex allotypes can
have three genetic explanations, the most interesting
of which is that they are coded by closely linked duplicated genes and the polymorphism arises as a result

Position

	1	2	3	4	5	6	7	8	9	10	11	12	13	14	15	16	17	18	19	20	21	22	23	24
																								(His)
$H\text{-}2K^k$	Met	Pro	His		Leu	Arg	Tyr	Phe	His		Ala	Val		Ile	Pro		Leu		Lys	–	Phe	Ala		
$H\text{-}2K^b$	–	Pro	His	–	Leu	Arg	Tyr	Val	–		Ala	Val		Arg	Pro	Leu	Leu		–	–	Arg	Tyr		
$H\text{-}2K^d$	–		His	–	–	Arg	Tyr		–															
$H\text{-}2D^d$		–*	His		Leu						Ala	Val		Arg	Pro		Leu				Pro		Tyr	
$H\text{-}2D^b$	Pro				–	Arg	Tyr		Val		Ala	Val		Arg	Pro	Leu			–		Pro	Arg	Tyr	
HLA-2	Gly	Ser		Ser	Met		Arg	Tyr	Phe	Thr	Ser	Val	Ser		Pro	Gly		Gly	Glu					
HLA-7,12	Gly	Ser		Ser	Met	Val	Arg	Tyr	Phe	Tyr	Thr	Ala	Val	Ser	Arg	Pro	Gly(Pro)Gly	Glu						

Figure 1. Transplantation antigens of mouse and man. The sequences in Fig. 1 are compiled from data presented at this meeting by Bruce Cunningham, Stan Nathenson, Lee Hood, Jack Strominger and Ellen Vitetta. These data in the first four cases are given in papers included in this volume. The data in the fifth case are to appear in a paper by Vitetta, et al. *Proc. Nat. Acad. Sci.*, in press. The boxes around mouse residues designate positions at which two or more chains are identical. The boxes around human residues designate positions that are identical to their mouse counterparts at one or more positions. A dash indicates that the residue found at that position in one or more of the mouse chains is missing in the designated chain. Blank positions indicate that no information is available on the residue present at that position. In the human, gene products for alleles 7 and 12 have been co-purified and sequenced as a mixture. *The Pro at position 2 in $H\text{-}2D^d$ as found by Cunningham, et al (this volume) was omitted from the figure as this data is still preliminary.

704

of a control mechanism (see Silver and Hood, this volume, for a discussion of the other possibilities). This hypothesis would contend that each mouse has structural genes that correspond to many of the transplantation antigens the species can express, and that they are regulated by a control mechanism. The group *a* and group *b* immunoglobulin allotypes of rabbit may be encoded by such a mechanism. This model raises a number of interesting possibilities (e.g., perhaps the high mutation rate at the *H-2* locus reflects the expression of a nearby *K* or *D* gene rather than an actual mutation). The lack of "*D*-ness" or "*K*-ness" is more difficult to explain in genetic terms (see Silver and Hood this volume).

Fourth, there are striking differences between the human and the mouse transplantation data. The human gene products from the *4* and *LA* subregions (i.e. 2, vs 7 or 12) differ far less than do their mouse counterparts at the *K* and *D* subregions (12.5% vs ∿50%). In addition, gene products at a subregion (e.g., *7* vs *12* and K^b vs K^k) appear to differ less in men than mice (∿5% vs ∿40%). This is nicely illustrated by the similarity of the human 7 and 12 gene products which were co-isolated from a single heterozygote individual. Finally, the question as to whether there is amino acid sequence homology between the transplantation antigens and immunoglobulins must be considered an open issue at this time. It will be extremely important to examine the more complete human sequences in this regard.

These data, coming from five different laboratories, constitute an important advance in our knowledge about gene products of the major histocompatibility complex. It is gratifying to see that major laboratories can pool their data in a cooperative venture of this type. It is comforting, indeed, to know that the *HLA* and *H-2* gene complexes are indeed homologous complex loci. I predict in another year we will have comparable amino acid sequence data on the Ia gene products of the mouse. Perhaps these data will begin to unravel in a similar fashion the complex functional and genetic mysteries of *Ir* genes and Ia gene products.

CUNNINGHAM: I think we should at least point out that the results obtained in all of these sequences are not quantitative and yields are generally poor. As a result, we could all be missing something such as a chain with a blocked N-terminus.

HOOD: I think that is an excellent caution. Microsequencing is in its infant stages. There are many aspects of these techniques that are not understood; hence great caution must be exercised in interpreting all these data. However, with adequate controls (e.g., the sequence of known polypeptides such as β_2-microglobulin) and repeated analysis on individual samples, one can begin to be confident of the data for homogeneous polypeptides. I suspect in the next few years our microsequencing techniques will increase in their reliability and certainty.

STROMINGER: We've separated the 23,000 and 30,000 dalton polypeptides of the human Ia and found that the N-terminal of the heavy (30,000) peptide was glycine and the N-terminal of the light (23,000) chain was isoleucine, as in β_2-microglobulin. We expected to find that the next 4 amino acid residues in each chain would show homology with the heavy and light chains of *HLA* sequence, but they did not. It is, nevertheless, striking that the N-terminals of the heavy and light chains of human Ia are identical with the N-terminals of the two *HLA* chains. The question is whether we will find homologies as we go further down the sequences of the Ia molecules -- I suspect we will.

BACH: Lee, during your talk you spoke of complex allotypes to explain the *H-2* and *HLA* SD locus polymorphism. I want to stress that it seems to me that we have to consider the simple model of a single locus for *K* and one for *D* with the polymorphism for each due to simple classical alleles of each locus. Would you agree there is no data to rule this out?

HOOD: There are three models to explain complex allotypes. 1) Complex allotypes may evolve by the divergence of alleles at a single genetic locus. If so, intense selective pressures are required to fix many substitutions in relatively short periods of evolutionary time. 2) Complex allotypes may evolve by gene duplication, mutational divergence and subsequent crossing-over events that contract the gene number to one. In different populations (e.g., inbred strains), different genes could remain. 3) Complex allotypes may evolve by gene

706

duplication with a control mechanism that permits them to be expressed so they mimic a Mendelian pattern of segregation. There is no data to distinguish among these alternatives at the present time. I would stress once again, however, that there is evidence in another complex and multigenic system, immunoglobulins, that the gene duplication model is used for complex allotypes. I merely want to raise the possibility that a another complex and multigenic system, the *H-2* complex, may employ a similar strategy.

J. KLEIN: Well, for those of us who have been working in *H-2* and *HLA* for some time, this is really an historic day -- because things that we have taken for granted for a while, namely the *K-D* homology and the homology between *H-2* and *HLA*, has been proven. I think that Don Shreffler, in particular, should feel a great satisfaction since he was the first one to propose the homology between *K* and *D*.

It is very striking to me, and I just don't understand that if the molecules are so homologous, and if the two genes are so homologous how the mouse can keep them separate. I would think that there has to be miss-pairing and a lot of exchanges and, therefore, we should be finding mice with 3 genes or 1 gene and so on. Moreover, why, in all species that have been studied, do we always find two genes, and not more? Perhaps this is why the mouse is different, but why have two genes always remained in all the different species? -- This is going to be very difficult to explain.

HOOD: Well, I think your question can be broken into two parts -- namely, why do you have the two loci, and how can you explain the lack of "*D*-ness" or "*K*-ness", if that holds up. One provocative hypothesis, for which there is absolutely no support, would be that perhaps, indeed, these molecules have a variable and a constant region, perhaps indeed they draw from the same set of variable region genes just as do human immunoglobulins. In fact, the mouse v_H locus now appears to have a recombination distance that is roughly comparable to the *H-2* locus. So, in a sense, you could say that this reflected diversity is a function of a pool of v genes which is shared and, hence, you would not expect to see differentiation into "*D*-ness" or "*K*-ness", whereas maybe the serologic specificities are associated with the constant portion of the molecule. Now, that is a wild speculation and I would hate to try to defend it.

The only other explanation that I could even begin to propose would be one in which you permit non-homologous recombination between multi-gene D-families and K-families that can continually scramble the information here. But then you get into difficulties where presumably you would have to say that anything that lost that middle information was a lethal, and you didn't see it. Beyond those two explanations, I don't know how to explain it. Again I would stress that perhaps with more data -- i.e. further sequencing into the molecules -- we will see D-ness and K-ness and we won't be left with this provocative difference.

KUNKEL: This might be the variable portion which is appearing now in the H-2 molecules, and the rest may be much more constant. In the human, the more constant part may be appearing first since there is considerably greater similarity between the two human chains compared to what you find in the mouse.

HOOD: I would agree with your statement concerning the possibility that we are now looking at the variable portion of the mouse H-2 molecules and that further along the sequence we will see more constancy.

NATHENSON: I think one point relevant to Henry Kunkel's comment about the N-terminal being the variable region is that the studies using tryptic peptide comparisons suggest that not only the N-terminal region is variable (to the extent of 10-30%, as shown by sequence analysis) but also the remainder of the molecule. We find, for example, a 70% difference in arginine and lysine peptides between K^b and K^d -- their differences are not all due to the N-terminal 30 residues, since there are over 350 residues in the whole protein, and these are being sampled by the peptide-mapping procedure.

HOOD: No, you have to make the model clear. The idea would be that within any one strain they only express one v-region for the D and one v-region for the K. The variability, or the pool, would be expressed in the species as a whole; otherwise, it obviously would not work. In other words, there would be a pool of v-

regions that would contain all of the diversity that could be seen by the mouse species as a whole. In a given strain, the regulatory mechanism would associate a particular v with a particular c and that would make K^k, for example.

NATHENSON: Are you talking about different molecules within each mouse?

HOOD: No, I'm saying that each mouse would have only two molecules -- one K and one D -- and that half of those molecules would be drawn from variable regions that would come from a common gene pool. Now, I don't want to press this model, because I don't really basically believe in it -- I'm just trying to show you how difficult it would be to explain the lack of "D-ness" or "K-ness" if it turns out to be true.

NATHENSON: Okay, well the "D-ness" or "K-ness" has also held up in the peptide maps which showed dissimilar comparisons, which is precisely what the sequence data show us.

MEO: I wish to make one comment and ask one question of Jan Klein. With regard to the multiple consecutive crossing-over hypothesis presented by Dr. Hood, and which I particularly favor, two possible evidences suggestive of a genetic instability of the MHC are: 1) the presence of a third HLA locus in man, which has no unequivocally demonstrated counterpart in the mouse, and might also not be present in all human populations; and 2) the murine Slp phenotype which lacks allelic allotypes. If its relationship to the Ss is that of a duplicated gene, as proposed by Shreffler (Shreffler, D.C. and Passmore, H.C. In *Immunogenetics of the H-2 System*. E. Lengerova and M. Vojtiskova, editors. Karger, Basel. 1971. p. 58), then it is possible that the duplication is carried out only by the Slp-positive strains and absent in populations of wild mice.

My question to Jan Klein is the following: Is there any difference in the mutation rate of the $H-2K$ or $H-2D$ genes in the homozygous versus heterozygous state to suggest iatrogenic cross-overs as a mechanism for the "high" mutation rate of these genes?

J. KLEIN: With regard to your comment, I'm not sure that

we know for sure that there is no third locus in H-2.

In answer to your question, the mutations that have been found have been derived from heterozygotes, so there is no comparison. But let's not overemphasize it -- the extremely high mutation rate has been found so far for only one allele, the K^b allele; there have been experiments done on others where the mutability does not seem to be extremely high. There is no indication yet that the mutation rate is as extreme in other H-2 alleles as we see with K^b.

MEO: Well, if the K^b haplotype is, indeed, an exception in terms of mutability, then we must consider possible explanations for this. One possibility may be, indeed, that the K^b allele is genetically assymetric as compared to the alleles at the K locus of other H-2 haplotypes, thereby favoring a higher degree of instability at this locus.

GERSHON: Lee, wouldn't a super polymorphism or all mice having all the required structural genes and the differences being due to regulatory genes, help explain David Katz's adaptive differentiation -- i.e. the placement of a B cell in the environment acts as an inductive signal and then changes regulatory gene activity, much in the way as taking a necessary substrate away from a bacteria alters regulatory gene control and causes a massive production of an enzyme which ordinarily is made in undetectable amounts.

HOOD: If this model is correct, then in theory lymphocytes in an organism could change their H-2 phenotype by shifting to the expression of another H-2 gene. How or under what conditions this shift might occur is not at all clear to me; however, adaptive differentiation could be explained by the shift in expression from one to a second member of the putative multi-gene family coding for the transplantation antigens.

BENACERRAF: I would ask Dr. Hood whether his model of multiple genes in the K or D region could be studied by investigating the expression of H-2 in somatic mutants or in viral transformed cells exhibiting the Zinkernagel-Doherty phenomenon.

HOOD: The examination of H-2 somatic mutants could have

important implications for the multi-gene model. If
these variants differed from the parental *H-2* gene
product by multiple amino acid residues, then the implication would be that these variants are not simple
mutants derived by single base substitutions, but
rather they represent the expression of a different
H-2 gene which is, presumably, a member of a multigene
family coding for the transplantation antigens. On the
other hand, if these variants turn out to be single
base substitutions, then nothing could be said about
the multigene model. This is why Dr. Nathenson's
studies on the *H-2* mutants are so very important.
Whether or not a similar explanation might hold for the
Zinkernagel-Doherty phenomenon is very difficult to say.

MAURER: One thing I would like to caution against is the
concern of no "*D*-ness" or no "*K*-ness". One cannot be
sure of the tertiary structure of the chain from the
amino acid sequence. Slight amino acid substitutions
in the primary amino acid sequences could cause great
changes in structures. It would be important to construct some models and see if the sequences of *D* and *K*
so far lead to similar tertiary structures.

HOOD: I quite agree that small changes in primary structure of a protein can lead to profound changes in its
three-diminsional structure. The point to be stressed
here in genetic terms is how can one explain the apparent lack of "*D*-ness" or "*K*-ness" in the *H-2* gene
products. If this observation is substantiated by additional amino acid sequence data, then very unusual
genetic mechanisms must be postulated to explain this
apparent paradox. (For a discussion see Silver and
Hood, this volume.)

UHR: I have a comment in reference to Lee Hood's remark
about possible hybridization studies. There may be a
problem in using nucleic acid probes to attempt to
definitively determine the number of genes coding for
the major histocompatibility antigens. Thus, studies
of other proteins coded for by chromosome 17, such as
the F-9 antigen, suggest the possibility of considerable structural homology among its products. Thus,
strong selective pressures for conservation may complicate gene counting of one particular set.

HOOD: I think you can set the stringency of criteria

to favor homologies that would only allow you to look
at things that are very, very closely related and
thereby get around the problem you are raising.

KUNKEL: As many of you know, Dr. Walter Bodmer has suggested for some years the possibility that the recognized genes in the *HLA* and *H-2* systems may be regulatory rather than structural genes. The marked differences in sequence between the different *H-2* types shown
today in a preliminary fashion raises again this possibility and I am sure Dr. Bodmer would consider these
as strong support for his theory. The same dilemma is
currently at the fore in the immunoglobulin system, and
the possibility that at least some of the allotype
markers are reflecting regulatory genes has strong support. Here too, the very great difference between allelic products is one type of supporting evidence for
such a concept.

HOOD: You are absolutely right, and I apologize for not
pointing out earlier that Bodmer has a beautiful paper
in 1973* in which he described some of the alternatives
that I have talked about and the implications of the
multi-gene model.

*[*EDITOR'S NOTE:* The reference mentioned above is W.F.
Bodmer *Transplantation Proc.* <u>5</u>: 1471, 1973 - DHK.]

Interrelationships Between Products of the Major Histocompatibility Complex and Their Relevance to Disease

BARUJ BENACERRAF, CHAIRMAN

GENERAL DISCUSSION - SESSION VIII

INTERRELATIONSHIPS BETWEEN PRODUCTS OF THE MAJOR
HISTOCOMPATIBILITY COMPLEX AND THEIR RELEVANCE TO DISEASE

Baruj Benacerraf, Chairman

CHAIRMAN'S INTRODUCTION

Much has been accomplished in this Conference which
brought together biochemists, geneticists, and biologists
concerned with traits controlled by the major histocompatibility complex (MHC), its genes, its functions and the molecules
responsible for immunological phenomena controlled by the
complex in animals. The record of this conference illustrates
the considerable advances which have been made since the MHC
was originally discovered in the mouse as a result of the
pioneering studies of Gorer and of Snell.

We are now able to identify various functions of the
MHC in addition to its original role in the rejection of allogeneic tissue. Among these functions are: 1) the activities of specific *Ir* genes and *Is* genes; 2) the regulation of
immune responses through the synthesis of helper and suppressor factors; 3) the coding for several complement components;
4) the role of K and D gene products of $H-2$ in T cell cytolysis of viral- or chemically-modified target cells. The MHC
may, therefore, be appropriately considered as the most important genetic region for immunological defenses. These
various functions of the MHC have been assigned to defined
loci and even to gene products which are becoming increasingly better understood. We are witnessing,with considerable ex-
citement, and on my part I must confess with some melancholy,
the inevitable evolution which important fields in biology
undergo when the biochemical approach becomes critical to the
definitive understanding of complex phenomena. Those of us
who are primarily biologists must concern ourselves now with
biochemical approaches to these problems or look for other
phenomena to satisfy our curiosity.

Our detailed understanding of the MHC will proceed very
rapidly in the next couple of years bringing solutions to
most of the problems which we have been discussing at this
conference. Moreover, such an understanding of the MHC, its
genes, its functions, the structure of its products and their
evolutionary relationships with immunoglobulins will serve as
models for the study of other differentiation phenomena which

depend upon cell interactions.

I propose to conduct this morning's general discussion along the following lines: First I shall list those points where there has been general agreement and which can be considered unquestionably established. Then I shall use the chairman's privilege to present our more recent views on the role of the MHC particularly as concerns the function of *H*-linked *Ir* genes, Ia molecules, and the helper-suppressor factors. We will then devote most of this morning to the discussion in depth of the many critical issues which have been raised by the data presented in the last three days. Among the areas of agreement I would like to list:

1. The definition at the molecular level of the gene products of the various regions of the murine MHC (*K*, *D*, *I*, *S*). The technology is now available to analyze the structure of the molecular products and to begin to obtain amino acid sequence data on some of these proteins.

2. The existence of antigen-specific factors produced by antigen-stimulated T cells. These specific factors appear to have similar molecular size in the range of 40,000 to 50,000 daltons, to bear determinants coded for by the *I* region and to be active in the regulation of B and T cell responses to antigen by providing specific helper or suppressor activity. Rapid progress in the molecular analysis of the factors will undoubtedly be forthcoming from the laboratories of Edna Mozes, Munro and Taussig, Tada, and our own laboratory, as the factors are purified from the antigen columns to which they bind specifically.

3. Another interesting phenomenon, well documented in this Conference, has been the gene complementation by distinct *H*-linked *Ir* genes required for specific immune responses in several systems. Examples of such gene complementation have been reported in the *trans*-position in the LDH system by Rajewsky and in both the *cis*- and *trans*-position in the GLΦ and GLT systems by Dorf, Maurer and ourselves, with the indication in the latter systems of more effective gene complementation in the *cis*-position.

4. Maybe the most intriguing new phenomenon controlled by the MHC has been the critical role of the K and D molecules as targets for cytotoxic T cells elicited specifically by syngeneic cells bearing viral coded, chemically modified antigens or tumor-specific transplantation antigens

(TSTA'S). This phenomenon, which has been discovered by Zinkernagel and Doherty for viral-coded antigens and by Shearer for chemically-modified antigens, may provide a basis for "immune surveillance". In addition this phenomenon may, as will be discussed later, also serve as a general model for the stimulation of specific T cells by thymus-dependent antigens presented in relation with critical sites on macrophages and B cells such as Ia.

The possible role of K and D products in immune surveillance deserves to be evaluated critically. I would like to digress a few minutes on this point. It would appear that the immunological system has evolved in higher organisms for two major tasks: 1) the defense against foreign organisms, viruses, bacteria and their toxic products; and 2) the destruction of autologous cells which have become potentially harmful for the host, because they have lost regulatory control through mutation or viral incorporation. The type of specific immune mechanism which evolved to meet these two distinct challenges optimally would be expected to differ substantially. The immunoglobulin systems with their enormous v region dictionaries (whether derived from germ line genes or somatic mutation) are ideally suited to provide specific defenses against foreign invaders and their products. Because these harmful agents are broadly represented in the biological realm, the antibody system had to be all encompassing in the specificities which it distinguishes. Because of the clonal expression of these immunoglobulin specificities on immuno-competent lymphocytes, as correctly postulated by Burnet, a limited number of B cell clones can be expected to be specific for a given antigen. In contrast, the recognition of alteration from self would best be achieved if 1) some special cell surface molecules would be assigned the role of self markers by the evolutionary process, and if 2) the populations of T lymphocytes concerned with the recognition of alterations in these target molecules, and thereby responsible for the destruction of the modified autologous cells, would be considerable. These populations of T lymphocytes would be restricted to the recognition of very slight changes in the target molecules either in sequence or more appropriately in tertiary structure. This process would be rendered more efficient if the target molecules could be readily modified by the expression, on the cell membrane in their vicinity, of new components (virally coded for instance) in close relationship with the target molecules. There is increasing evidence that these target molecules are products of the MHC, and in the case of specific cytolytic T

717

cells in the mouse, modified products of the K and D loci. It is not surprising, therefore, that a large population of T lymphocytes are specific for distinct MHC alloantigens as shown by Simonsen, Darcy Wilson, and Wigzell. Furthermore, one would also expect common idiotypes to be easily found on receptors against individual MHC alloantigens as demonstrated elegantly by Binz and Wigzell.

A major issue remains, however, to be clarified, since T cells are not only specific for alloantigens coded for by the MHC but also for a very large number of determinants on thymus-dependent antigens. These specific T cells are active in defenses against infectious agents. They are also concerned with the regulation of immune responses of B cells and T cells through the activity of specific helper and suppressor T cells and their antigen-specific factors. The question, therefore, must be asked whether the T cells specific for thymus-dependent antigens are distinct from those reactive with MHC alloantigens. There is as yet very little information on this critical issue.

Some relevant data on this point have been presented in this conference by Shevach and Rosenthal and by Pierce, Kapp and ourselves which indicate that the populations of T cells stimulated by thymus-dependent antigens are specific for the antigens in close relationship with a product on the macrophage cell membrane coded for by the MHC. Thus, different clones of T cells appear to be selectively stimulated by an antigen on syngeneic and allogeneic macrophages. These cells would be reactive with the complex of antigen and corresponding I region product. This interpretation implies also that the regulatory function of specific T cells has evolved as a consequence, and by making use of the reactivity of T cells with alloantigens of the MHC; it also provides a unifying framework for the development and relationship of these two immune defense systems, immunoglobulin antibodies and products of the MHC.

Let us now consider the function of histocompatibility-linked Ir genes and the genetic restriction in T - B cell cooperation in the light of the theory that a critical I region molecule acts as a carrier for antigen on macrophages and B cells for recognition by T cells, thereby contributing some specificity to their response.

It is generally accepted that H-linked Ir genes are ultimately concerned with the mechanism by which T cell regula-

tion of immune responses is effected. Initially, we, therefore, entertained the hypothesis that these genes code for
the antigen receptor on T cells, a molecule whose nature has
been controversial. The demonstration by several laboratories, including our own, that genetic non-responder animals
could have B cell defects as well as, or in addition to, T
cell defects led to a re-evaluation of the function of the Ir
gene product as the T cell receptor. Can all the functions
of H-linked Ir genes be explained by the new scheme proposed
above, whereby the Ir gene product interacts with the antigen
on macrophages, B cells and T cells to form antigenic complexes on the cell membrane capable of initiating primary responses and stimulating secondary responses to thymus-dependent antigens? Some, but not all, of the phenomena attributed to Ir gene function could be explained by this scheme.
For instance, this hypothesis would indeed explain the experiments of Shevach, et al in guinea pigs and their ability to
block selectively the specific responses in culture of
$(2 \times 13)F_1$ T cells immunized with GT and DNP-GL by the appropriate anti-2 or anti-13 alloantisera. This hypothesis
would also require a considerable degree of heterogeneity in
Ia molecules compatible with Ir gene function and specificity.
But this scheme would still leave several questions unanswered such as:

    1) The nature of the T cell receptor, and, more criti-
cally, 2) the nature of active helper and suppressor factors
which are antigen-specific, bear I region determinants and
are not neutralized by anti-immunoglobulin reagents. This
new class of antigen-specific molecules produced by T cells,
distinct from immunoglobulins, is also an excellent candidate
to be a product of H-linked Ir and Is genes.

    These considerations as well as the demonstration of
complementation of specific Ir genes for immune responses
raises the issue whether Ir genes may not have several functions; one of these could be the interaction with thymus-dependent antigen on macrophages and B cells to form complete
antigens, and the other, the generation of active factors by
T cells. Several important points must then be clarified
concerning these helper and suppressor factors: 1) What is
the nature of their receptor for antigen? Are they constituted by immunoglobulin v regions or are they coded for by the
I region of the MHC? 2) What is the relationship of the
factors to the Ia molecules on macrophages and B cells which
are proposed to be a site for antigen interaction for T cells
to be stimulated?

Let us now consider the genetic restriction to T - B cell cooperation for secondary responses to hapten conjugates of either conventional antigens, such as KLH, or of genetically restricted antigens, such as GLT and GLΦ, observed by Katz, Dorf and ourselves, and how they may be explained in the light of the hypothesis proposed earlier that the *I* region products may act as an antigen carrier contributing to specificity. These genetic restrictions to T - B cell cooperation which have been mapped in *I-A* were not observed in radiation chimeras by von Boehmer or in tetraparental mice by Bechtol, et al. I feel that the above mentioned hypothesis might reconcile some of these discrepant results.

The major conclusion that can be derived from the discovery of the allogeneic effect, which bypasses helper function in antibody responses, is that one of the essential signals which B cells need for antigen-specific differentiation is interaction at their Ia sites. Therefore, in the case of syngeneic cooperation between carrier-specific T cell and hapten-specific B cell, we had to postulate that the syngeneic T cells can cooperate physiologically by interacting with the Ia molecule on the B cell. An alternative explanation which could also fit the data on the genetics of macrophage-T cell interaction states that the primed T cells have been selected to interact with the antigen complexed with Ia or the Ir gene product. These T cells would thus be selected to recognize as "foreign" the syngeneic B cells bearing antigen in relation to their Ia molecules or Ir gene products and should be able to interact with the critical Ia sites on these cells to stimulate differentiation. This model would predict: 1) a considerable degree of heterogeneity in Ia molecules as in Ir gene products, and also 2) that T cells which have been stimulated and selected (or as Katz would prefer to say, adapted) to interact preferentially with allogeneic macrophages bearing antigen will now react preferentially with allogeneic B cells rather than with syngeneic B cells. According to this scheme, the T and B cell genetic restrictions observed would be acquired or better said, selected for, rather than constitutive, and would therefore not be observed in radiation chimeras. This scheme, however, does not explain the ability of nonresponder B cells in tetraparental mice to form antibodies of nonresponder allotype, nor does it deal with the interesting possibility proposed by Katz that B and T cells in chimeras adapt to express compatible cell interaction molecules, an issue which must be resolved experimentally.

Let us now consider the problems posed by the selective

generation of suppressor T cells in some non-responder
strains. In the absence of appropriate Ia or Ir gene products for the antigen on macrophage, direct interaction of the
antigen with T cells would be expected to stimulate suppressor cells preferentially. As a corollary, in the absence of
appropriate Ir gene products on B cells, these B cells could
not get their differentiating signal on their Ia molecules
and should be rendered tolerant by the antigen. This is precisely what we observed in the GAT system; non-responder B
cells are extremely susceptible to tolerance induction by free
GAT even in presence of F_1 T cells specific for GAT-MBSA, and
GAT-MBSA.

I would like to start now the general discussion. I
have selected 7 major topics which appear to have generated
interest and controversy in the past three days, and I propose that we consider them in the order listed.

1. a) Specificity of *H*-linked *Ir* gene function.
   b) Microheterogeneity of Ia molecules.

2. What is the evidence for a distinct *I-B* region?

3. a) What is the nature of the antigen receptor on
      helper and suppressor T cell factors? What is
      its relationship to v_H regions and to idiotypes of
      immunoglobulins?
   b) What is the range of specificity of active T cell
      factors in comparison with the range of specific-
      ity of antibodies?
   c) Is there a dual recognition system at the T cell
      level and at other levels?

4. Differences and similarities between helper and suppressor factors.

5. Why are allospecific T cells against MHC antigens
   very numerous?

6. What is the explanation for the *cis* - *trans*-prefer-
   ence in complementation of *H*-linked *Ir* genes? Does
   it explain the linkage desiquilibrium in the MHC?

7. Is the T and B cell cooperation observed between allogeneic cells in chimeras, due to T and/or B cell
   adaptation or to selection?

1. a) SPECIFICITY OF *H*-LINKED *Ir* GENE FUNCTION

BACH: Baruj, you bring up the point that Jan Klein thinks
that the *Ir* genes are not particularly specific. You,
on the other hand, believe they are more specific. I
think it would be most helpful if both of you would define this a little more precisely.

BENACERRAF: What I mean by the statement that the *Ir* genes
are specific is that: 1) There are distinct genes controlling different immune responses even with the paucity of recombinants available. 2) The amino acid sequences recognized or not recognized, as a consequence
of having the relevant gene are very precise, as shown
by the work of Sercarz and Hill with fowl lysozomes and
by the work done in Israel with the branched polymers
of known sequences. Furthermore, of all the 25 or 26
antigens which have been studied in inbred mouse
strains, only 2 clearly distinct antigens, ovomucoid
and (H,G)-A--L, have the same response pattern in
strains bearing different haplotypes. In all other
cases, the haplotype patterns of responsiveness seem to
relate very much to the structure of the antigen. A
similar situation has been observed with antibody idiotypes by Oudin. Thus, Oudin looking for idiotype finds
that they are specific for the antigen concerned in
practically every case. But when he looked the other
way, he finds the same idiotype on molecules as different from each other as anti-KLH and anti-ovalbumin antibodies.

BACH: I would like to ask Jan Klein to comment whether he
feels this is correct.

J. KLEIN: I think where we differ is that I would say that
the heterogeneity is much less or the specificity is
much less than that of an antibody.

BENACERRAF: I agree with Jan Klein on this point.

J. KLEIN: Okay then, there is a limited range of determinants that are recognized by the *Ir* gene system. The
specificity as we see it now is misleading on the basis
that the genes can recognize closely related determinants but may confuse the determinants which are totally
unrelated. So, I do not know, I cannot give you a number. It would be ridiculous...

BENACERRAF: Jan, when we speak of specificity I would like
    to make a distinction which immunologists always have
    to make, although others consider that we are fastidi-
    ous about it. Specificity refers usually to the abil-
    ity of a reagent to distinghish between two related or
    unrelated molecules. On this bases I think that we
    will find that *Ir* gene recognition systems are very
    specific. On the other hand, specificity refers also
    to the size of dictionary as compared to the antibody
    dictionary of specificity. On that point I would agree
    totally with Jan Klein that the *Ir* gene system's dic-
    tionary is very much smaller than the dictionary of im-
    munoglobulin v regions.

BACH: Then it is fair to say that there really is no basic
    disagreement?

BENACERRAF: I don't think there is as much disagreement as
    the verbal intensity of our discussions would imply.

HOOD: No, there is one issue to clarify here. A critical
    question concerns the molecular nature of the specific-
    ity about which the two of you are talking. If it is
    the recognition of antigen, I don't understand how you
    make molecules that, in a sense, are extremely broadly
    specific,because all proteins fold into an active site
    and they've got complementarity. If the specificity is
    based on some recognition phenomena, then maybe you
    could say that it can be much more broadly specific,
    but then I don't understand the molecular basis for
    that specificity.

BENACERRAF: Well, that is one of the reasons why I feel
    that specificity is very strict, but the dictionary is
    smaller. It will occasionally occur that two very dif-
    ferent molecules may have sequences in common at some
    point; and if the dictionary is small, you will find
    unexpected cross-reactivity. But you will also find
    clearly expected cross-reactivity at the *Ir* gene level;
    for instance, molecules which are as similar as the GLΦ
    and GLT molecules will be controlled by the same genes,
    whereas GA which is very different has a different
    genetic control.

HOOD: But let me stress the point that if you want to say
    the specificity is broadened, then I think you're
    forced into some kind of regulatory mechanism which I

don't really understand.

BENACERRAF: I never said it was broader. Jan said that.
I said it was less discriminatory in terms of numbers
of specificities recognized than the immune system.

HOOD: No, but I'm saying your two positions may force you
to different views of the mechanisms of specificity in
Ir gene systems.

BENACERRAF: Correct. That's right.

McDEVITT: Yes, but that's the whole point about *H-2*-linked
Ir genes. They have the same degree of specificity as
antibody; whether they have exactly the same molecular
basis in terms of exactly the same variable regions is
obviously going to be answered by biochemistry. But
the discrimination between sequences of G and T or between any of the specified sequence antigens that have
been studied are as great as any discrimination by antibody. The striking finding about *H-2*-linked *Ir* genes
is that the dictionary is genetically restricted and
there is not an unlimited range of variations, whereas
there is a near unlimited range of variations in antibody that is only limited in a very few cases by having
or not having the specific idiotypes. But the molecular basis of *Ir* gene recognition, I would predict, is
going to be based on microheterogeneity and I would expect that to be very similar to that of antibodies.

HOOD: Gee, I hear two different things here.

BENACERRAF: No, I do not think you do. Hugh McDevitt and
I are saying exactly the same thing, and this differs
to a slight extent from what Jan Klein said.

SACHS: It sounds like you are assuming that the Ir gene
product is the molecule doing the recognizing. We've
heard a lot of evidence at this conference, in fact,
that the molecule on T cells which recognize antigens
may be coded by genes linked to the heavy chain allotype.

BENACERRAF: Even if the Ir gene products are not the receptors of T cells, they could nevertheless have specificity, as we postulated earlier, in terms of their
ability to bind to an antigen and permit it to then be

recognized by a T cell, so it would still have specificity in that case. Now, you can have it one way or you can have it the other way; or possibly you can have it both ways. We're discussing the specificity of *Ir* genes in terms of the manner in which these genes permit responses to occur to specific antigens phenotypically without at the present time going deeply into the nature of the T cell receptor; that will be dealt with later in the discussion.

BACH: I would like to hear Lee Hood expand upon what he began to say a few moments ago because I get the same feeling that we are hearing two different things. Lee made the point, and it seems to me also that we are really hearing that, on the one hand, the Ir gene product has exactly the same specificity and yet the dictionary is smaller, and that seems to me to be an inherent contradiction. If you have more variable genes, you would have more chance of a higher fit in terms of affinity, and yet you would not have exactly the same degree of specificity; I would like to hear that discussed. I mean, it's been in the literature so long and this is an ideal place to discuss it.

BENACERRAF: I agree. Lee, is that what you meant?

HOOD: Yes, it seems to me that if you have a smaller repertoire, *a priori*, you have to have less discrimination because there is a greater chance for cross-reactivities that can be expressed and detected because of the limited number of molecular species.

McDEVITT: Okay, if you want to say that the *Ir* gene system has the same degree of specificity and degeneracy as antibody in terms of cross-reactivity, then the point I would make is that the actual number of sites that can be generated by the antibody system is larger, either because the antibody system has a larger number of *v* region genes (if we accept Hood's original position that there are multiple germ line genes), or because there's somatic mutation. The *Ir* gene system has the same precision of specificity, but the number of different sites it can generate is more limited. Moreover, the restriction is genetic, and has probably been acted upon in evolution and has been the result of selection. Now, that means that they are exactly the same, and if there are fewer genes, then you're right in stating

that you may pick up cross-reaction more readily. That
I will buy.

RAJEWSKY: Lee, I think the confusion really comes from the
fact that when one talks about antibody specificity,
one talks about the specificity generated by many different antibodies raised against an antigen, whereas
Hugh is talking about the specificity of the recognition site of any given Ir gene product or a given idiotype.

BENACERRAF: Yes, I think this is precisely the point I was
also making and from that point the specificity appears
to be exquisite. Now from the point of view of the
dictionary, it appears to be smaller. Now, how can we
actually explain the specificity of Ir genes? You have
a variety of choices. You can explain their specificity by saying that they code for a receptor which is involved either by itself or in conjunction with the v
heavy (v_H) chain. Alternatively, you can explain it by
saying that the Ir gene product puts certain restrictions on which heavy chains can actually function in
terms of those antigens that are recognized by putting
them together with an Ia molecule. Nevertheless, in
the phenotypic sense, the result of the Ir gene function is a recognition of high specificity, but of much
limited nature in terms of dictionary.

McDEVITT: Until Baruj's last comment, I felt really, up
until that moment, that we were in agreement. But if I
understood you correctly, what you said was that it
could be a system in which there was specificity in
receptors coded for the I region, or that the I region
products themselves with antigen could select out of a
series of v_H regions; those are two very different molecular mechanisms.

BENACERRAF: I was,in fairness,spelling out all the possibilities and not saying which one I prefer. I am still
of the opinion that we are dealing with some degree of
receptor recognition. However, you might very well
conceive that the Ir gene is simply putting restrictions on the system. It is a valid interpretation, and
it is also compatible with the hypothesis proposed
earlier that the Ia molecules are interacting with antigen to form complete antigens. So these various alternatives must be considered among the possibilities,

as well as the possibility that there is more than one way *Ir* genes function since we have now found that there is more than a single *Ir* gene involved in the responses to certain antigens.

McDEVITT: Well, the predictions of the two schemes are different, because the prediction of the *Ir* genes themselves coding for receptors would mean that they would have to be microheterogeneic, whereas the second scheme would predict a relatively limited degree of heterogeneity in *Ir* gene products which, when they combine with antigen, select out certain v_H regions.

PAUL: In a sense, this is a discussion beyond our capacity to resolve with the information we have at hand. We have no real idea of the molecular nature of the *Ir* gene product, and we have no idea of the combining energy. We often are confused by the relative specificity of the T lymphocyte and the specificity of the induction. A very nice example is one drawn from an old experiment carried out with Baruj in which an effort was made to explore the relative specificity of a gene and of the response that flowed from the gene, in the poly-lysine system. Responder guinea pigs to poly-L-Lysine (PLL) are able to discriminate clearly between PLL and hapten conjugates of PLL at the level of the response of their T cells following immunization. So, I would conclude that our information is extremely limited, and I think we often get very confused from the enormous sophisticated discriminatory possibilities of the T lymphocyte itself and from the results of immunizing animals with a group of antigens; and I share Fritz's view that it is beyond our ability to resolve until we know much more about the molecular nature of the recognizing molecule.

BENACERRAF: I agree with Bill.

SIMONSEN: Of course, Bill Paul is right that we have no idea yet about the chemistry of the Ia products, but I am not sure he is right that we have no idea about the affinity, because it seems to me that one very important lesson from the work of Edna Mozes and Taussig and Munro was that the affinity of the specific T cell factor was, in fact, very low; otherwise, it would not have been able to bind it to the (T,G)-A--L column. Moreover, the interesting difference between the

antigen specificity of the Taussig–Munro factor and the
lack of specificity of the allogeneic effect factor
which David Katz told us about, and one possibility I
would like us to consider is that, in fact, his AEF
factor is in molecular terms the same sort of thing as
the specific factor, but the affinity is much higher
for the alloantigens which provoked it; and, in fact,
the combining site of the AEF factor is blocked by the
allo-aggression determinants to which it is directed.
Therefore, we would have to suppose or postulate that
the effects it exerts, nevertheless, is due to another
part of the molecule than the antigen-combining sites.

1. b) MICROHETEROGENEITY OF Ia MOLECULES

E. MÖLLER: I have a comment with regards to heterogeneity.
It can be perfectly alright that the repertoire of the
T cell receptor is the same as that for B cells before
priming, but the fact that antigens are always presented on a particular molecular environment creates a
limited number of new antigenic determinants, and,
therefore, once activation has ensued, you may see that
it looks like a limited heterogeneity in the activated
B cell population. And if Baruj is correct in the
theory that he just put forward, and which has been
touched upon by others, this would explain the lack of
heterogeneity in this population, but would not at all
affect the dictionary of the T cell.

BENACERRAF: That is correct, except for the point that one
must then deal with the question of what is the nature
of the active T cell factors, and how they exhibit
specificities. The next critical issue concerns the
heterogeneity of the Ia molecules. If we are going to
have any type of recognition system controlled by the I
region, the molecules controlled by this region at the
present time are the Ia molecules. So we now must consider how heterogeneous they may be in terms of class
or subclass. Does somebody want to speak to that
issue?

J. KLEIN: I am impressed by two things. One is the genetic, and the other is more molecular. 1) The genetic
point is that there are a lot of recombinants in the I
region, and yet they seem to separate only 2 or 3
genes. It is a weak argument, but, nevertheless, one
would expect purely on a statistical basis that with

the large number of antigens that have been tested that
more separation of *Ir* genes would by now have been
achieved. This is not the case, which I consider sup-
portive evidence for the low number of *Ir* genes. 2)
The molecular point is that in my opinion I consider
that Ia molecules are the products of the *Ir* genes (although, I don't have any evidence for it). Some of the
data which I presented and which Bill Paul and David
Sachs presented on Ia molecules, indicate again that
there is a limited number of genes coding for Ia molecules.

BENACERRAF: I think you would agree that the number of recombinants that exist are not as large as you would put
it.

J. KLEIN: It is about half and half in the *K* and *D*
regions.

McDEVITT: Well, Jan, what about the picture in the immunoglobulin allotype situation . . . up until the last few
years? In other words, up until a very short time ago,
if you were just looking at mouse constant region heavy
chain allotypes, you would have said that there were a
very small number of genes involved. Even when you get
to idiotypes and begin to look at idiotype linkage
groups, there are a relatively small number of genes,
but you don't argue from that there are a relatively
small number of antibody molecules produced.

J. KLEIN: But, in the case of *Ir* genes, we have the recombinants, whereas we don't have the recombinants for
the allotypes. Secondly, the extent to which people
have looked for recombinants in allotypes is much less
than for recombinants in the *H-2* system.

PAUL: In fact, I think it is quite true now that serious
attention is being paid to the idiotype-allotype linkage, that it is not a difficult matter to document recombinants, and I think in almost every one of the
linkage situations that has been examined in any detail, at least one recombinant has been observed. I
think Jan has a rather good point. The only instance
that perhaps exists so far as a putative recombinant
between an *Ia* gene and an *Ir* gene deals with what used
to be called *I-B*.

BENACERRAF: We're going to come to the issue of the *I-B*
     subregion in a minute. But at the present time, I
     would like to have on the record with respect to the
     issue of Ia heterogeneity that with limited data avail-
     able at the present time, there are two sets of opin-
     ions. Some people believe that Ia molecules are going
     to turn out heterogeneous with some considerable level
     of microheterogeneity either because they act as anti-
     gen receptors or because they react as antigen carriers
     on macrophages and B cells. Others have more conserva-
     tive views, such as Jan Klein, that the Ia heterogeneity
     will be limited. Now everybody is on record; I'm on
     the side of Hugh McDevitt; you all can take sides if
     you wish, and now let's move on to the next point.

PAUL: Can I just ask a point of fact because it may be of
     practical advantage to those who are interested in this
     point. Yesterday, several of the speakers pointed out
     that there is good evidence that for the *D* and *K* anti-
     gens, it is the N-terminus of the major chain that
     sticks out of the membrane. Now, chemically this is
     very nice because you sequence from N to C, and this
     area sticking out is likely to have the variable func-
     tion; so one would know pretty quickly if there is
     variability. On the other hand, if all the variability
     was at the C end, it would be considerably more diffi-
     cult. The question is when you look at papain frag-
     ments of Ia, and Stan Nathenson implied that the papain
     fragments of Ia were smaller than they were for the NP-
     40 fragments, are the N termini also the same or are
     they different?

BENACERRAF: If somebody had information on Ia sequences
     they would have volunteered it. I think that a year
     from now we will have some information on that point.

GASSER: There is one type of observation that I think
     might be relevant to this argument. We now have sever-
     al systems in which there is an *Ir* gene-controlled re-
     sponse, but in these cases only the cell-mediated re-
     sponse is controlled genetically, but there is no dif-
     ficulty by the non-responder in making an antibody. I
     am referring in the first instance to the H-Y antigen;
     the non-responder to H-Y had no difficulty in making
     antibody. The second one that I am aware of is experi-
     mental allergic encephalomyelitis. The BN rat, which
     does not get the disease when injected with guinea pig

spinal cord, has no difficulty making antibody to encephalitogenic protein. The third example, which we
heard about at this conference, was presented by Dr.
Stimpfling. It seems significant to me that his
(B10.R3 x B10)F_1 is able to make an antibody response
but is not able to reject the skin graft.

BENACERRAF: Thank you, Dr. Gasser. It is becoming also increasingly apparent that when considering *Ir* gene function, we are also considering simultaneously regulation
systems, because that is what is controlled by the constant regions of the molecules, bearing *I* region determinants. Thus, in some cases help and in some cases
suppression results. We are dealing with a powerhouse
for the regulation of immune responses. Unless someone
else has data on Ia heterogeneity, then I suggest we
move to the next point. Would you, David Sachs, address yourself to the second point; namely, is there an
I-B region which bears unique serological specificities -- you told me yesterday that you wanted to address yourself to this issue.

2. EVIDENCE FOR EXISTENCE OF A DISTINCT *I-B* SUB-REGION

SACHS: As I mentioned to you and to Don Shreffler last
night, after Don presented the data on Tuesday on the
possible mistake in mapping, perhaps, of the *I-B* region
specificity, it seemed to me that there is one serum
which we have very recently been able to make which
might be able to pin this point down. I have the data,
but I think that there is a caveat in its interpretation. More specifically, this is the 4R anti-2R antiserum which has been produced in Don's lab as well as
in our lab several times, and if we just very quickly
review the previously accepted sub-regions of those two
strains (as shown below) you can see that if you make a
4R anti-2R, you'd predict that you might be able to
make antibodies against the *I-B*, the *I-C*, the *S* or the
G regions.

	K	I-A	I-B	I-C	S	G	D
2R	*k*	*k*	*k*	*d*	*d*	*d*	*b*
4R	*k*	*k*	*b*	*b*	*b*	*b*	*b*

In previous antisera, the only specificity that has
been picked up looked like it was an *I-C* specificity.
The trouble with these sera is that they only have
titers of 1:2 or 1:16 at the most. We then looked at

individual animals and found that 3 out of 18 B10.A(4R) animals hyperimmunized with 2R cells did give responses greater than 1:64. So by just pooling the sera of these animals, we got a reasonably high-titered serum. We absorbed this 4R anti-2R antiserum with B10.D2. Now, B10.D2 obviously should be *d* all the way across, and, therefore, should absorb any activity to *I-C* or to *S*. Now, the result is that the antiserum still reacts with 2R and with B10.A from which the 2R and 4R originated giving a percent lysis of 45%. This is exactly typical of the lysis obtained with the whole serum, which we showed to be reacting with B cells. According to what is known of the Ia antigen chart, this should be an *I-B* region specificity.

On the basis of this information, I think that we could resurrect the possibility that there are specificities in the *I-B* region. However, this assumes that the *I-C* region of the 2R and of the B10.A, from which the 2R was derived, is identical to the *d* allele in the *I-C* region of B10.D2. Since the B10.D2 derived that region from DBA/2 and the B10.A derived it from an unknown source, as it is a presumed recombinant, there is always the possibility that we are seeing residual antibodies which distinguish between two different *I-C* region products called *d*. There are ways to pin that down, but they have not been done as yet.

BENACERRAF: The best way -- the molecular way -- is by finding out if your antiserum co-precipitates molecules bearing *I-C* specificities.

SACHS: Yes, well, we will certainly look at that. However, even now the titer is down after the complete absorption against B10.D2, which took something like 16×10^8 cells/ml; the titer is still about 1:16 against the 2R and against the B10.A. I don't know if that will be enough for precipitation, but we will look at a few other recombinants as well.

BENACERRAF: Thank you, David. Now does anyone have any other thoughts about evidence for or against specificities in the *I-B* region this time?

SHREFFLER: I think maybe just a little clarification is necessary. What I said on Tuesday was that a specificity which had previously tentatively been mapped to

732

the *I-B* region no longer could be definitively mapped to that position. There are about 10 or 12 specificities that could be in the *I-A* or *I-B* subregions that have not yet been definitely mapped because appropriate recombinants are not yet available. So, I think the fact that specificity 3 is now either mapped in the *I-A* or *I-B* region should not be interpreted as evidence that the *I-B* subregion no longer exists. The *I-B* subregion was postulated on the basis of the immune response gene data. As I said, I've been unable to eliminate the *I-B* region on the basis of any kind of 2-gene interpretation. Klaus Rajewsky said the same thing, and I think Bill Paul has also looked at the data with the same conclusion. The other point made is that there seem to be only two molecules which can presently be mapped to the *I-A* and *I-C* regions respectively, but that may be elusory. Since we do not have antibodies that can detect a *I-B* region specificity, we obviously cannot detect those molecules. So I think we have to reserve judgment at this time as to whether the *I-B* region does or does not exist.

BENACERRAF: Thank you, Don. It does appear clearly that we have here a very important problem to resolve, both from the point of view of the serology and the *Ir* gene recombinants, and we hope that it will be resolved shortly. Now, we should discuss the third point which is even harder to resolve.

3. a,b,c) NATURE OF THE ANTIGEN RECEPTOR ON T CELL FACTORS AND RELATIONSHIP TO v_H REGIONS AND Ig IDIOTYPES; THEIR SPECIFICITY RANGE AS COMPARED TO IMMUNOGLOBULINS; AND POSSIBLE EXISTENCE OF DUAL RECOGNITION SYSTEMS AT THE T CELL LEVEL AND AT OTHER LEVELS

BENACERRAF: What is the nature of the antigen receptor on the Ia-bearing factors from T cells i.e., those factors which have helper activity of Munro, Taussig and Mozes and those that have suppressor activity of the type which has been described by Tada, by Asherson and which has been also studied in our laboratory by Judy Kapp and ourselves? First, is there any information on this issue, and then, in the absence of information, are there any preferences with respect to the nature of the Ia-bearing factors, and more importantly, does anybody wish to go on a limb with respect to the relationship of these factors with the v_H regions and idiotypes

733

considering the very convincing work presented the
other evening by Wigzell and Rajewsky on the nature of
the T cell receptor?

GERSHON: One of the points that I am unclear on, Edna, is
whether your factor and Michael's factor have the same
specificity.   Is there agreement or disagreement there?

MOZES: I think that we agree completely on the results
with the factor to (T,G)-A--L in that it will cooperate
well with   (Phe,G)-A--L and (H,G)-A--L.   In other
words, between cross-reacting antigens there is a
cross-reacting helper effect in the factor.   Now, about
the experiments concerning absorption of the factor on
the antigen column, we found that the (T,G)-A--L factor
is absorbed on a (Phe, G)-A--L column and on a G-A--L
column.   Now, I'm not sure whether Michael found that
the factor is absorbed by a (Phe,G)-A--L column.

TAUSSIG: In the experiments we've done passing factors
through specific immunoabsorbents, specificity of the
(T,G)-A--L factor looks rather complete.   In other
words, the (T,G)-A--L factor doesn't seem to be removed
very easily by anything other than (T,G)-A--L absorb-
ent.

BENACERRAF: Not by (T,G)-Pro--L?

TAUSSIG: Certainly not.   I think one point we agree completely on is that there is no evidence for any cross-
reactivity between (T,G)-A--L and (T,G)-Pro--L.   Regarding the question of cross-reactivity between
(T,G)-A--L and (Phe,G)-A--L, first of all, one would
expect the binding sites perhaps to be rather closely
related if they're really looking at the T,G or Phe,G
determinants.   Of course, there may be conformational
changes between those molecules, so that they may not
be as similar as they look on paper.   I don't think
we've done experiments in the same strains under exactly the same conditions, so I feel that this sort of
difference might really be less important than it
seems.   I do think the difference between the antibody
specificity to (T,G)-A--L versus (T,G)-Pro--L and the
factor specificity to (T,G)-A--L and (T,G)-Pro-L is a
very important point, and suggests that perhaps the
repertoire is different or perhaps that the T cell recognizes determinants basically different from those

seen by B cell.

MOZES: But you agree that the factor to (T,G)-A--L cooper-
ates well with bone marrow and (Phe,G)-A--L to produce
antibodies to (Phe,G)-A--L. Isn't that right?

TAUSSIG: Yes, I agree.

MILLER: I'd like a point of clarification, because if I
remember correctly from the studies of Dr. McDevitt,
there was no cross-reaction at the level of the T cells
between (T,G)-A--L and (Phe,G)-A--L, whereas there was
at the antibody level. Now why should the T cell factors cross-react?

McDEVITT: That was the question I raised in the discussion
yesterday, and I think it is very important. Michael
has a factor that won't cross-react with (T,G)-Pro--L
and won't cross-react with some of the cogeners --
(Phe,G)-A--L and (H,G)-A--L -- whereas Edna finds a
cross-reaction. In other words, Edna's result is that
a (T,G)-A--L factor is taken out by a (Phe,G)-A--L and
I assume an (H,G)-A--L column.

MOZES: We haven't tried an (H,G)-A--L column.

McDEVITT: Well, as Jacques very rightly points out, the
genetic control will discriminate very clearly between
(T,G)-A--L and (Phe,G)-A--L. Now there is a possibility either that this is a damaged factor or that there
is something wrong with it. Otherwise, it does not fit
with the genetic control of the immune response to
those three polymers.

NOSSAL: I wonder whether the time has come to introduce
what Gerry Edelman calls the P x Q argument. For example, supposing the whole game that Edna has played
would now be changed, and instead of comparing the
specificity and affinity considerations of immunoglobulin versus these defined proteins and T cell factors,
she did the comparison between the isolated heavy
chains of immunoglobulins. In other words, if one were
to use the assumption that the T cell receptor is a v
region stuck onto some kind of a constant region, but
for whatever reason there is no contribution to specificity by a light chain, might the presence of cross-
reactivity not be extremely different? Might this not

be something extremely relevant to our previous argument about the size of the repertoire? If nature designed the antibody system to be a single chain system, it might look very different from the way it now looks.

HOOD: I think the point Gus Nossal made is an excellent one which has an analogy in the immune system. If one examines the myeloma proteins that bind phosphorylcholine, there are a number that are identical and then there are a few that differ from one another. The heavy chains for all of these myelomas are very similar to one another and the fact that we have 3 sets of myeloma proteins that have 3 sets of cross-reacting specificities seems to correlate with their light chains. Accordingly, if you separate factors and only get one of the two chains, you may well, indeed, pick up a general heavy chain-like specificity that is no longer modulated by the other chain, so I think Gus' point is an extremely important one if you believe in multi-chain structures.

BACH: I just wonder whether we can compare a factor which is isolated from a cell, and which is shown to have antigen specificity, with the same factor sitting in the cell membrane. It is a different molecule in terms of what it can do. I would disagree with the concept that we are dealing with a damaged factor, because if we are talking about damaged factors, then we've got to be very careful of ascribing specificity to them.

MAURER: I think at this point, it is important to have some concern about whether or not all the people using the same polymer have been doing exactly the same thing with (T,G)-A--L in different laboratories or have studied different preparations. This possibility must be considered for (T,G)-A--L or (Phe,G)-A--L from the day you make it until you wind up using it in the laboratory. I don't want to get into the argument, but Baruj knows about the slight alterations which can occur in molecules on different kinds of storage which will alter immune response patterns, and which also alter cross-reactions. Michael Sela and I discussed the problem years ago; Edna knows how many preparations of (T,G)-A--L go down the drain because they don't behave the right way even though they're made the same way. The same situation exists here since it is quite possible that the (T,G)-A--L polymer in Stanford at one point changes; you do not get a cross-reaction there but you can get good pick up in the column in Israel. I think this is a serious point which those of us who work with polymers have to recognize.

WILSON: Maybe I am being overly naive about this, but isn't this the question of cross-reactivity of a product compared to cross-reactivity of stimulation? And isn't it, therefore, not surprising because this phenomenon has already been recognized for antibodies?

BENACERRAF: That is correct.

PAUL: I wonder whether there really is a controversy here because some strains or some haplotypes that respond to (T,G)-A--L also respond to (H,G)-A--L, and some do not. I think that we need to know whether Michael has used the strain that responds to (T,G)-A--L or not to (H,G)-A--L and Edna has used factor from a strain that responds to both. Moreover, we need to know whether T lymphocytes from animals immunized to (T,G)-A--L in a strain that can respond to both polymers are sensitive to (H,G)-A--L. I mean we are assuming there is a difference between the cell and the factor without really having demonstrated it at this point.

BENACERRAF: I want to caution you that the issue we are considering is broader than this very important point that we have been discussing. I think it would be more profitable if we could return to the larger issue; namely, what is the nature of the receptor on Ia-bearing factors? What is their range in specificity, and are there two distinct recognition systems as far as these factors are concerned? One involving the v_H region and the other one involving molecules coded for by the I region.

KATZ: Okay. I guess this is addressing this issue because I don't think one can be discussed without the other. I want to go back to the point that Fritz Bach made because it is a point that came up in the discussion that Mike Taussig and I had the other day, and I don't really think that the problem is going to ever be solved until we find out, in fact, what the truth is between these phenomena. I am referring again to the issue of where, on the one hand, you're talking about recognition which is presumably a cell membrane receptor bound phenomenon, and on the other hand, an interaction phenomenon, by whatever mechanism that may take place. This again is a large issue for which we have no evidence in terms of what happens *in situ*, because if it is largely a cell membrane-mediated phenomenon, then the phenomena that are studied by looking at soluble factors may be a nice reflection of only parts of the molecule(s) involved in these interactions; they may very well be far from the total picture. If this is the case, which I strongly suspect it to be, then the difference such as that which Hugh, in fact, was referring to, and indeed the whole question concerning the differences in specificities of the factors versus the specificities of the phenomena as they have been recognized to be controlled by *Ir* genes may not be as hard to understand and reconcile as it appears on the surface.

RAJEWSKY: I must say this argument doesn't satisfy me nor does Darcy's argument satisfy me, and the reason for this is that, in fact, the people who are working on the factor and, in general, people working on *Ir* gene specificity have tried to explain the differences between immunogenicity of initial recognition and the effector phase as manifested by antibody specificity by the difference in specificity of the Ir gene product and antibody. Therefore, when we now say the factor, again which is now an *I* region product, has a different specificity than the initial recognition process, we just go a step further back and we don't know anything.

BENACERRAF: Can I interject here that the truth of the matter is that there is very substantial agreement between what the factors apparently recognize and what the inducing system is, except for the HG system. Otherwise, the genetics of G-A--L and G-Pro--L behave precisely the same way as the factor's recognition. We should not lose sight of this point; moreover, if there are indeed two genes in these systems controlling the response to (T,G)-A--L and to (Phe,G)-A--L, this may explain the differences between factor specificity and genetic control alluded to by McDevitt.

MOZES: I want to clarify something. We can't compare binding experiments to T cells with the experiment on the factor specificity because we found also that the factor will trigger B cells only in the presence of the right antigen; thus we get a response to (Phe,G)-A--L with a (T,G)-A--L factor only if the (Phe,G)-A--L is present there, and I think that here we don't have any controversy.

BENACERRAF: That's a very good point because that tells you that the genetic difference observed between (T,G)-A--L and (Phe,G)-A--L then may depend, as I said earlier, on the respective B cell acceptor and not on the genetics of factor production by the T cell.

GERSHON: I have sort of an apology; I asked that question because I thought that the specificity of the ability of a factor to recognize the difference between (Phe,G)-A--L and (T,G)-A--L might place some constraints on what the nature of the factor is because of the fact that what is required to give this type of specificity would, in my opinion, require more in the molecule, and I would like some of the protein chemists to comment on that. For example, in the triggering, what you say is absolutely true. You have many, many antigen-binding cells which obviously cannot be triggered so that is a completely different controversy, but getting back to the point of just what the nature of the molecule is, we have to know the level of its specificity.

BENACERRAF: Thank you, Dick. Now I would like again to re-iterate that Edna Mozes's comment goes to the root of the controversy, because if, indeed, the B cell accept-or for the factor is responsible for the genetic dif-ference between (T,G)-A--L and (Phe,G)-A--L and the T cell helper factor in these systems has restricted spe-cificity only as far as the G-A--L is concerned, then everyone's findings fit together. In other words, the issue we have here is that the factors that have been studied by Taussig and Edna Mozes and Munro have the following properties: 1) When they are made to (T,G)-A --L, they are not absorbed by (T,G)-Pro--L but they are absorbed by (H,G)-A--L and (Phe,G)-A--L, and in fact, they are absorbed by *G-A--L*. 2) They are able to help the response of animals to (Phe,G)-A--L, if those ani-mals have B cells which are responder to (Phe,G)-A--L, but not if they are not responders to (Phe,G)-A--L. This is a statement of the facts. Now, if you consider the hypothesis that one gene is responsible for the pro-duction of factor, and the other gene controls the spe-cific acceptor Ia molecule on the B cell, as proposed

by Munro and Taussig, the genetic restriction imposed
in the system may depend on the B cell gene and then
you will find that the factor specificity will not
match phenotypically the responsiveness that we observe, and this is precisely what is happening. I believe that this is what Edna was saying.

BACH: What does that prove?

BENACERRAF: That indicates that if you accept that two
genetic defects exist, one for the production of the
factor which involves the macrophage and the T cells
and relates to the specificity of the factor, and a
different one for the acceptor or the capacity to re-
ceive the factor, which also is to some degree antigen-
specific involving the capacity of the Ia molecule to
interact with the (Phe,G)-A--L or (T,G)-A--L, then we
may say the following: If we have either one of the defects in the whole animal, the whole animal will behave
phenotypically as if restricted by both genes. If you
look at the product of one gene or another by looking
at the factor itself, or looking at the B cell itself,
then you will find that the factor specificity does not
necessarily match the genetics of the system because it
is only the product of one of the genes. The hypothesis of Munro and Taussig in their system -- one gene
determines factor production and its specificity; the
other gene determines factor acceptance -- is consistent with this interpretation; both are to some degree
antigen-specific, but not necessarily to the same extent. If I have not clarified the point, I apologize.

McDEVITT: Well, as long as you agree that your explanation
is only one way to explain the evidence, because I
think that Darcy's way, now that I think about it, is
also acceptable. In other words, if you say that there
is a product on T cells which recognizes (T,G)-A--L and
will trigger but will not recognize (Phe,G)-A--L or any
of these differences, but when you isolate that product
and see whether it will bind, it will bind to any of the
three. That doesn't mean, however, that on the cell
membrane it has the ability to trigger; that's an
equally tenable explanation.

BENACERRAF: Except that you have to have the genetic restriction of the B cell on which it works.

BACH: But I thought that the B cell acceptor for the factor that carries the Ia antigen has not been shown to recognize antigen specifically.

BENACERRAF: That is not a statement that has been made anywhere.

BACH: I'm making a negative statement. I'm saying I thought it had not been shown that the B cell factor acceptor which carries Ia antigen is antigen-specific; it may be a recognizing factor because of the kind of things that Taussig and Munro hypothesize.

BENACERRAF: The other day when these matters were discussed, I asked very specifically what do we know about the genetics of acceptors in terms of antigen specificity? The answers I got there were nil. All we know at this time are the genetic defects at the level of the B cells, and these are specific. Therefore, until proven otherwise, we must entertain the possibility that there is such specificity at the level of the B cell acceptor.

BACH: I don't disagree. I just thought you were stating that as a fact. I'm sorry.

KATZ: Baruj, in fact, almost implicit in what you said, if it is correct, is that the specificity of the gene that is coding for the acceptor molecule has almost got to be identical, if not the same, to the v region gene, because the specificity would have to match precisely with the immunoglobulin product of that cell in view of the argument that we're making about the relative differences in the specificities of the factors versus immunoglobulin products. And so, if that is true, what you're saying is that the B cell acceptor gene is the v region gene of the immunoglobulin.

BENACERRAF: No, that's not what I said. What I said is that the Ir gene which is responsible for the restriction in the system and which permits the binding of the antigen to Ia on the B cell, according to the hypothesis which I made in my introduction, functions on the B cell the way it does on the macrophage which induced the T cell -- that's what I said.

MOZES: I want to add to your explanation that the acceptor of the B cell will be triggered only in the presence of the right antigen.

BACH: I believe that we have heard very convincing evidence in this meeting that would lead one to the conclusion that the receptor on T lymphocytes uses as its variable portion the same gene product that is used by immunoglobulin. This is, of course, based on the evidence presented by Rajewsky and Wigzell. Whereas this is clearly the interpretation of choice, I would like to ask Rajewsky whether an alternative option is still worth considering, although I personally do not favor it in any way.

Is it possible that, in fact, the antigen places rather high restriction on the molecular structure on the lymphocyte surface which acts as a receptor so that for any given antigen, at least in many cases, the variable portion, thus the idiotypic determinant for the receptor, will be quite similar on T cells and B cells even though the genes used to code for these two receptors are different? This will be an example of convergent evolution, and I raise it simply for further discussions stressing that I certainly do not favor such an explanation.

BENACERRAF: I want to make the point that as far as I am concerned, I have not given up the concept that there is antigen recognition capacity in the Ir gene system and it may indeed be expressed in these factors. Now this is to be tested; and what Fritz Bach said is precisely the point.

BACH: I was just really trying to enlarge on what you said in your Introduction.

RAJEWSKY: Fritz, I think the situation is as follows: In our system of the helper cell receptor, the evidence shows very strongly that what we are detecting is coded for by a gene linked to the allotype and idiotype, that is, to the v_H gene cluster. That conclusion is based on the genetic studies which we have done, so I think this is very clear evidence and, moreover, it is not coded for by $H-2$. In the case of Hans Wigzell and Hans Binz's receptor, I think these genetic experiments are not yet available; and I think in their system at the present time, one cannot decide. It could very well be that here we are dealing really with cross-reactions. It is a bit difficult to envisage in view of the total cross-reaction which they apparently see at least in one direction, but that is certainly a possibility.

May I just say another point; and that is that I think even if the receptor sites on T lymphocytes would in certain cases, as for example in our case, be coded for by the same gene as idiotypic determinants on antibody molecules, I do not think that this will be necessarily true for all idiotypes. Even if, for example, one would have translocation of v genes from the heavy chain gene complex to the $H-2$ locus, even then it may very well be that if somatic diversification is taking place in T and B cells, and that process is different in T lymphocytes and B lymphocytes, then you would end up with completely different spectra of idiotypes in both cells. That would also be true if there were no translocation to the $H-2$ complex but just simply the antibody molecule itself which is mediating the information.

KUNKEL: I think that there is very little possibility that what Binz and Wigzell are dealing with is anything else but immunoglobulin. From all aspects whether they are dealing with an antibody to the hypervariable areas or the framework residues, it is still what we call immunoglobulin. But the other point, which unfortunately Hans is not here today to answer, which I would have liked to have raised is how much he has done in the reverse direction -- as Edna has done and Taussig and Munro have done -- that is, to see whether anti-Ia or anti-$H-2$ columns will remove his idiotype. Is the idiotype bound to the histocompatibility product at all?

[EDITOR'S NOTE: This exchange was forwarded to Hans Wigzell who was unable to attend the final session and his written reply appears below - DHK.]

WIGZELL: Anti-$Ag-B$ columns have only been tried for the 35,000 component. Only one column with high titered anti-$Ag-B$ antibodies has been used. No evidence for the presence of $Ag-B$ linked determinants on the 35,000 component was obtained by such column filtrations so far.

KUNKEL: It is a very important point to relate these two phenomena in this fashion, and I guess it just has to wait for the work to be done.

BENACERRAF: But, even if we had a situation where the
factors were owing their specificity to the immunoglobulin v region, you would then have to contend with the
fact that they carry Ia determinants and that they have
biological activities which are commanded by these Ia
determinants, and how you translocate one into the
other is a matter of some genetic engineering.

PAUL: If I understand the experiments which Binz and
Wigzell have carried out to deal with the question of
whether anti-histocompatibility antibodies of any type
will remove the factor, they have looked at the factor
that appears in urine, or the shed factor, which by
their own testimony is probably very different from the
material on the cell surface and may be only a single
chain. I think it can't yet be decisively said even if
anti-I sera don't remove this 35,000 dalton factor
that, in fact, on the cell one doesn't have an arrangement of a heavy-light chain analogue in which the heavy
chain is a variable region, such as Wigzell points out,
using a constant region different from any of the tra-
ditional immunoglobulin constant regions and the light
chain might be a Taussig-Munro-Mozes-Tada-like factor.
This is a formal possibility.

BENACERRAF: Can I ask one question to Edna Mozes which has
been burning me for the last few days, and I want to
ask it publicly. Does your antiserum which you have
prepared with David Givol to the (T,G)-A--L factor react any way at all whatsoever with anti-(T,G)-A--L antibody?

MOZES: We have not done the experiment, so I can't answer
this question.

GERSHON: I think Bill Paul's comment brings me back to a
question that I seem to find him asking very often, and
one that I often like to ask, but he gets there first;
and that is, when we deal with these factors and characterize them, and we say how we take it out and the
activity is gone, does that mean that the factor is
carrying the activity, or are there possibilities of
complementary factors that would be taken out separately by antigen and anti-Ia columns respectively? How
much work has been done by trying complementation

744

procedures to find out if it is really true that these
very small molecules show all this exquisite specificity -- they know where to go, they have all this information in them and they do all these things!

MUNRO: Edna has an answer to that because she has eluted
the factor from the (T,G)-A--L columns and finds she
gets activity afterwards.

MOZES: The eluate of the (T,G)-A--L immunoadsorbent has
the whole activity of the whole supernatant.

KATZ: Is this true even after reduction and alkylation?

MOZES: I don't know; we haven't tried that yet.

GERSHON: Well, that is a very important experiment to do to
address this question.

KUNKEL: I would like to go back to the question Baruj
asked Edna as to whether she has tested the reactivity
with antibody to (T,G)-A--L. I'd like to pursue that
further, and ask whether you have made any idiotypic
antibody to the antibody to (T,G)-A--L and determined
whether the factor reacts with the idiotypic antibody?
That should be very testable.

MOZES: No, we have not done this.

McDEVITT: Well, as long as we keep coming back to the
(T,G)-A--L factors, I would like to reiterate what I
said in the discussion in Session III about our attempts to look for complementation for an IgG response
in the (B10.M x B10.BR)F_1. The factor that Taussig and
Munro and Mozes have produced gives predominantly an
IgM response, and it has no effect on an IgG response.
In our lab, we have even used primed spleen cells and
been unable to get help for an IgG response. On the
other hand, the suppressor factors all appear to have
an effect on IgG responses, and while I think the hypothesis that Baruj put up is tenable, or Darcy's is
tenable, I would also suggest that the jury is still
out, and there is a distinct possibility that what
looks like a helper factor may be a helper factor only
for IgM or may, in fact, be a suppressor factor that
permits IgM responses to develop. This has to be
looked at very, very carefully because of the very

great similarities between the Taussig and Munro factor
and the suppressor factor story that Tomio Tada laid
out yesterday, and if I look at this from the point of
view of the tetraparental mice experiments, I don't see
a B cell defect; so that I would simply say that while
I think these issues will be solved within a year, at
the moment I am not sure all of these factors aren't
similar, and that we shouldn't immediately make the assumption that this is, in fact, the helper *Ir* gene
product.

BENACERRAF: Very good. Now I would like to have one last
comment. There are two of them. Dieter, you have a
comment.

ARMERDING: Yes, I would like to suggest a molecular model
for what these factors could really mean or represent.
You said that an I gene product consisted of two chains
and one might have specificity; however, it has not
been shown at all whether those specific factors consist of two or maybe more chains because the molecular
weight of those factors is much bigger than those of
normal Ia antigens.

BENACERRAF: Those factors have not been characterized as to
chain structure.

ARMERDING: Well, they could have even more than that, so it
could be that the part which gives those factors specificity might still be coded by completely different
genes than an *Ir* gene.

BENACERRAF: It is possible. Again, the jury is still out
on that one.

TAUSSIG: On the question of idiotypes and whether these
are really on Ia molecules, I don't think this has
been definitively analyzed. We certainly haven't done
the crucial experiment which is to pass a (T,G)-A--L
factor through an antigen column, take the effluent,
and through an anti-Ia column and mix the effluents
and see if you recombine the activity. I know Tomio
Tada has done that. I was discussing this with him
last night and he doesn't recombine the activity. So
the question is, whether the binding site of the factor
is really covalently linked to the Ia specificities.
Alternatively, another suggestion which seems to come

from Binz and Wigzell's work (if it is true that his small molecular weight product is not removed by anti-histocompatibility sera), would be that the actual receptor on the T cell consists of a new class of heavy chain, so far undefined but not identical with the known serum heavy chain types, but yet coded for in that complex on the same chromosome as the classical immunoglobulins. The T cell receptor itself might then consist of an immunoglobulin molecule with a new class of heavy chain. The effector molecules which are secreted by the T cells, on the other hand, in order to have a regulatory or cooperative or suppressor activity need then to form a non-covalent or some form of association with Ia molecules, and that is responsible for the regulatory potential, but the idiotype may actually be on another chain. I think that is still open.

BENACERRAF: Dr. Tada, I would appreciate it if you describe for the record your critical experiment in which you have demonstrated that at least one of the factors simultaneously possesses both antigen specificity and Ia specificity.

TADA: Yes, actually I have done the same experiment as performed by Edna Mozes, and we could elute the suppressive T cell factor from the antigen-coated column. The question was raised whether the suppressive T cell factor is only a single molecule or consisting of two molecules -- one antigen-specific and the other possessing Ia specificity. So we passed the KLH antigen-specific factor through the column of the KLH-immuno-adsorbent and we took the effluent, and at the same time, we passed the other part of antigen-specific factor through the anti-Ia column, and we combined the effluents together and then tested the activity. We could not find any activity in the combined effluent material, so I personally think that the antigen-specific factor is a single molecule which has both specificity for antigen and Ia specificity.

BENACERRAF: But did you study the product eluted from the antigen column to determine whether it was neutralizable by anti-Ia?

TADA: No, we have not.

HOOD: There is one other technical point. Did you reduce the molecules, because if they were disulfide-bridged together, then you would not separate the two and get the complementary results.

TADA: No, we have not reduced the factor in this particular experiment, but if we reduce the factor and co-precipitate with anti-Ia or with antigen, then the molecular weight comes out around 28,000 daltons. So I think the molecule is composed of subunits, but that is just all I know at this time.

4. SIMILARITIES AND DIFFERENCES BETWEEN HELPER AND SUPPRESSOR FACTORS

BENACERRAF: Thank you. Now the next point to which I would like you to address yourselves, which I don't think will take very long because our knowledge there is extremely slim, is what are the differences between helper and suppressor factors? From what we've heard from Dr. Tada, from Judy Kapp, from Edna Mozes and from Taussig and Munro, I cannot see any differences between the factors outside of what they do in the context of the way they do it. Does anyone else have further insights on that point?

MILLER: I'd like to first preface my comment by stating that what I will say would apply only if the phenomenology described by Taussig, Munro and Mozes can be reproduced unequivocally in different laboratories. If it can, then I suggest, as mentioned earlier by McDevitt, that the factors which they have produced are not helper factors but suppressor factors, and the reason why I say that is three-fold. 1) In the (T,G)-A--L system, it has been clearly shown by McDevitt and others that the IgM response is least or not T cell-dependent, whereas the IgG response is highly T cell-dependent. 2) The IgG response is the most susceptible to T cell-dependent suppression; and 3) I think a point which is not perhaps known to everyone is that there is a high concentration of suppressor T cells in bone marrow. Now I would suggest that why the IgM response is enhanced in the Munro-Taussig system is simply because those factors are depressing the suppressor T cells which are present in bone marrow and preventing, therefore, the switch from IgM to IgG.

TAUSSIG: You don't mean, Jacques, that the suppressors are
       suppressors of the Tada type but that they are suppres-
       sors of other suppressors?

MILLER: That's right.

TAUSSIG: Well, going back to Tomio's experiments; it was
       noticeable that although in his suppressor system the
       factors suppressed the IgG response, they never did
       anything to IgM responses; they never showed any com-
       pensatory elevation of IgM. The question of whether
       the *Ir* genes really only control the IgM versus IgG re-
       sponses and whether the IgM responses are truly thymus-
       independent in those high and low responders is, I
       think, rather more open than you suggest. In our hands,
       and also in Edna's, and I think in some of Hugh's work
       at least, the differences between high and low respond-
       ers are reflected in both IgM and IgG responses. In
       our hands, at least, they are very, very significantly,
       and in Edna's perhaps less so and in Hugh's, perhaps
       even less so, but I don't think there is any doubt that
       IgM responses are affected by *Ir* gene control. Second-
       ly, if you test the thymus-dependence by taking bone
       marrow and seeing whether this is susceptible to T cell
       help as far as IgM is concerned, you find that it, in-
       deed, follows the criteria you would expect for thymus-
       dependent responses, and that the differences in those
       helped bone marrow responses reflects the difference
       you would predict between high and low responder
       strains on the basis of their haplotypes and in an an-
       tigen-specific manner. Therefore, I think that there
       is an *Ir* control of IgM and this is because of the
       thymus-dependence. Therefore, I think it is valid to
       interpret the effects which we've seen as true *Ir* gene
       effects and that the factor and acceptor are really
       Ir-l gene products. That is our basic hypothesis.

       I think it is possible, as you suggested, that the
       similarities between the suppressor and helper factor
       are perhaps more dramatic than their differences.
       There are certain small points; for instance, whether
       suppressor factors can act across allogeneic barriers,
       and so forth. Maybe these are not really points of
       quite so great importance, but I would agree that the
       similarities between these factors does perhaps push
       one in the direction of thinking that maybe they are
       identical or that, as Michael Sela once remarked, it

would be fascinating that if once they have been fully characterized, the differences can be pinpointed to some very trivial amino acid sequence.

BENACERRAF: There is one nevertheless crucial difference that I now recall as you are talking, and that is that the helper factors are produced in the presence of antigen and excreted into the medium; whereas, there is no evidence in any system known that the antigen-specific suppressor factors are so produced -- they have to be extracted from the cell as shown in Tada's laboratory and in our own.

HÄMMERLING: There is evidence for one suppressor factor which is secreted by cells; that is in the allotype system. I guess Dick Gershon knows more about it than I do.

GERSHON: Well, for whatever this is worth. At the recent meeting in East Germany, Marc Feldmann presented evidence for an Ly-2 positive cell which secreted a suppressor factor which seemed to be in the range of all the factors we are talking about, so that may be the first example of an antigen-specific secreted suppressor factor. The other comment I wanted to make concerned what Jacques said, and that is about suppressor cells being predominantly found in the bone marrow. It is my understanding that after suppression is generated, you can then find the cells that transfer the suppression in the bone marrow and that might be quite a secondary phenomenon in that they may be in the bone marrow because that's where the action is, so to speak. In other words, the cells they are suppressing are being generated there, and that is where they are working. But I know of no evidence; we certainly have not been successful in trying to generate suppressors from the T cells in the bone marrow compared to other types of T cells.

McDEVITT: Well, I think there is some data that just ought to be cleared up again. In our hands, with (T,G)-A--L or any of these antigens, whether you immunize in aqueous form or in Freund's adjuvant, the major difference between responders and non-responders is in the IgG response. There is no question about that. I would like to be very clear about that, and that is the reason that has always given me hesitation about con-

sidering the Taussig-Munro factor as a helper factor
because we can never get it to help for an IgG response
even if we use previously primed spleen cells.

The second point is meant to clarify something that
Bill Paul raised earlier. He asked the question that if
you have an animal that is a responder to both (H,G)-A
--L and (Phe,G)-A--L, for example, and you immunize and
then test for antigen-induced tritiated thymidine uptake, do you get cross-reaction? And the answer is no.
If you have an H-2^k animal primed to (H,G)-A--L, you
cannot stimulate that animal with (Phe,G)-A--L, but you
can with (H,G)-A--L and vice-versa. We can argue about
the interpretation forever. I think the argument really is not worth going on with much longer. The phenomena are all out on the table. Some of us think that
suppression is an interesting possibility and ought to
be explored and obviously we are all going to look at
it, and in a year we will know the answer.

BENACERRAF: Edna, please come and give your last comment
and in the meantime, I think it would be useful if one
would know the Ly type of the cell which produced the
Munro and Taussig and Edna Mozes helper factor.

MOZES: I wanted to comment on the IgM response to (T,G)-
A--L in our transfer system. I think that it is not
the factor which isn't able to elicit IgG response because under the same conditions when we mixed bone marrow and thymocytes, or bone marrow and educated thymocytes, we get also mainly an IgM response. I think it
is because of the transfer system and not because of
the factor. Now, to Hugh's remark about the thymidine
incorporation, it might very well be that the two T cell
populations that we are dealing with are different, because I am not at all sure that the T cell population
which proliferates and which we measure by thymidine
incorporation are the helper T cells which produce the
factor.

BENACERRAF: Thank you, Edna. I believe this issue has
been given a very good hearing, and I think the matter
will be resolved by the next workshop.

5. BASIS FOR THE LARGE NUMBERS OF ALLOSPECIFIC T CELLS RECOGNIZING MHC ANTIGENS

BENACERRAF: Now, I think we should move on to the next point of discussion which is why are allospecific T cells directed against MHC antigens so numerous?This is a finding which has been made many years ago by many investigators and Darcy Wilson who is among us and Morten Simonsen as well, were among the first to point to this most important biological phenomenon, and it was given further weight by the fact that Binz and Wigzell's idiotypic experiments in the rat have been rendered that much more feasible by precisely the fact that the T cells bearing receptors for allo-aggressive antigens are present in a normal non-immunized rat in relatively large numbers. We must deal with the issue that if, indeed, these cells are bearing receptors which are heavy chain v regions, what mechanism has selected preferentially those heavy chain v regions to be expressed on numerous T cell clones, and furthermore, are their receptors absolutely identical? When you add them all up what is left for the other recognition systems for other T-dependent antigens? Or do you resolve this issue by combining the recognition of MHC allo-antigens with that of foreign antigens?

SIMONSEN: I feel that this is the time to bring in phylogeny because my answer to point 5 would be that they are so numerous because allo-antigens were what they were devised to recognize in the first place. I would like to show you two slides, but I would first make two very elementary points. First, that allo-aggression is phylogenetically much older than the vertebrates. I believe that in some way or another it may be demonstrated in all the phyla and classes of invertebrates. Second, if we are going to look for the evolutionary importance of the MHC it may be advisable to go to those invertebrates which are the immediate predecessors of the vertebrates, and these are believed now to be the colonial tunicates. It so happens that these are also perhaps the only invertebrates in which something like a good immunogenetic study has been performed. Actually, the history begins in California in 1903 when a gentleman named Bancroft was studying colony fusion in *Botryllus schlosseri* which I would like to show you in the first slide (Figure 1).

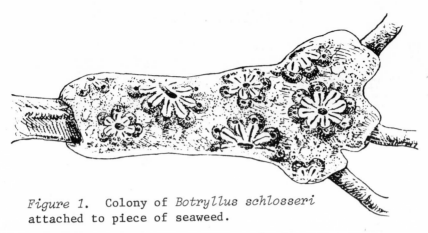

Figure 1. Colony of *Botryllus schlosseri* attached to piece of seaweed.

From J.G. Lutzen: Saekdyr. *Danmarks Fauna.* Vol. 75, 1967. Copyright by the Dansk naturvidenskabelig Forening.

What Bancroft showed was that sometimes colonies developed from sibling larvae would fuse and sometimes they would not, but this analysis was taken very much further by Oka in Japan in the 1960's (Oka, H.: Colony specificity in Compound Ascidians. *In* Profiles of Japanese Science and Scientists, H. Yutawa, ed., Tokyo 1970). Now, perhaps I should say a few words about the zoology of these animals. They have a very curious life-history. They begin as free-living larval creatures that look a bit like tadpoles, but they soon decide to fix their head to rock or seaweed, and then undergo a regressive evolution. They lose their eyes and their tails and assume a sac-like shape. They then undergo asexual divisions and form true clones of genetically identical individuals. These colonial animals are hermaphroditic; but what is very important is that they cannot fertilize their own eggs. Now, such colonies may be cut into fragments and they will then grow out into entire new colonies which will fuse happily and establish a common circulatory system. But if you take two unrelated colonies they normally will not fuse and, to cut it short, Oka describes this fusability or non-fusibility as being governed by one locus, the *F* locus, with many alleles. The next slide (Figure 2)

FUSIBILITY AND F-alleles

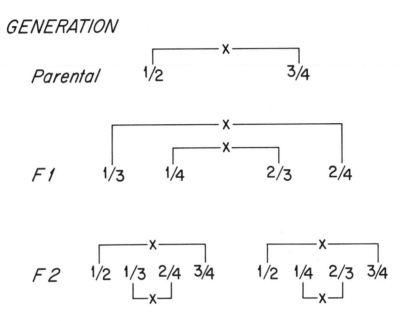

Figure 2. Colony fusion in parental, F_1, and F_2 generations. The figures signify alleles of the *F*-locus. X signifies non-fusion (rejection). It is seen that heterozygotes are fusible if they share one *F*-allele, but nonfusible if they don't.

summarizes Oka's fusion experiments in F_1 and F_2 colonies which are the off-spring of non-fusible parental colonies. It is seen that colonies will fuse which have one allele in common, whereas those which have no allele in common will not fuse. Instead, after an initial period of 24 hours or so they undergo violent rejection with necrotic reactions which separate the two colonies entirely.

Well now, this same *F*-locus is also governing fertilization in these creatures and the ground rule here is that in order to fertilize, the sperm must be *F*-locus

754

allogeneic.

It is important to know that fertilization takes place inside the animal when the ovum is surrounded by diploid layers of maternal cells. If the maternal cells carry the genes 1 and 2 on the *F*-locus, either an *F1* or *F2* sperm is unable to penetrate the diploid layers, whereas if the sperm carries *F3* or *F4* or whatever, it can penetrate. The fact that this is a discrimination mediated by the maternal diploid cells is strongly suggested by the finding that trypsinization, which removes the diploid cells, permits also syngeneic sperms to fertilize. Now, I think there are, in principle, two different ways of looking at this phenomenon. One is that the syngeneic sperm gets arrested by a sort of self-recognition in the maternal layer, but then we have to devise another mechanism to explain the rejection phenomenon in the fusion experiments. The alternative explanation, which I prefer myself, is that the allogeneic sperm is recognized and reacted against by the maternal cells; that it provokes allo-aggression and that some product of allo-aggression, an AEF, facilitates or stimulates penetration of the sperm through the maternal layers. Now, if this is so, mankind probably never was in greater need of a good AEF than then and there, because without it, evolution might not have brought us much further than the tunicates. So then, the *F*-locus seems to me to be a natural starting point for an MHC. The more mutations, the greater the chance of fertilization, hence there was a very direct selective pressure to favor mutation. Once a system was elaborated which could recognize and react to alloantigens, it is easy to imagine that it could be further developed to deal with other antigens, too.

I am now making an enormous jump to the vertebrates, and let us take the rat because that will make it a little easier to discuss Hans Wigzell's findings which to me are very, very crucial. I will suggest that some basic features of the archaic recognition system of the tunicates have been preserved in certain gene products of the vertebrate MHC, which are still particularly good at recognizing the other allo-aggression antigens of the species. I would imagine that the pertinent genes within the MHC form at least one, but more likely several multigene families such as those Lee Hood was talking about yesterday.

a)

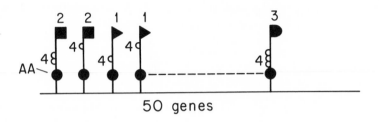

50 genes

b)

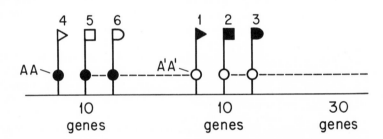

| 10 genes | 10 genes | 30 genes |

Figure 3a. AA = Major allo-aggression antigen of Lewis rats. This allotypic determinant
is on all molecules of the multigene family.
1 = the combining site recognizing the DA
allo-aggression antigen. This is also the
idiotypic determinant L-anti-DA on the T cell
receptor of Lewis rats, shared by some 6% of
the T cells. 2 & 3 = alternative combining
sites recognizing "3rd-party" strains in the
Wigzell-experiments, e.g. BN and August.
4 = different variants in the fine structure
of the gene products. Thus 2 genes which
both code for the L-anti-DA idiotype need
not yield identical products.

Figure 3b. Four kinds of determinants are depicted, 2 on each chain. AA (solid circle) = Major allo-aggression antigen of Lewis rats. A'A' (open circle) = Variant of AA representing a minor allo-aggression antigen. Both AA and A'A' are allotypic determinants shared by all products of the respective multigene families, and are expressed in all cells. 1-3 (solid symbols) = Specific combining sites (and idiotypes) recognizing major allo-aggression antigens of other strains (DA, BN and August). Only one symbol expressed per cell. 4-6 (open symbols) = Variants of 1-3 which may participate in the formation of compound receptors.

Let us consider, first, the case for a single multigene family with, say, 50 different genes. I shall depict the Lewis rat genes here (Figure 3a) by drawing their gene products which I visualize as polypeptide chains with a common allotypic determinant which is the major allo-aggression antigen of the MHC haplotype of that strain. However, the polypeptides differ in other parts of the molecule by 2 kinds of groupings, namely one kind responsible for recognition of the major allo-aggression antigens of other strains (symbols 1, 2 and 3), and another kind (symbolized by 4) which encompass all minor variants, which may be important in the formation of compound receptors recognizing antigens other than allo-aggression antigens. With 50 different recognition chains movable in the lateral plane of the membrane and being able to combine freely into compound multi-chain receptors, we could have more than 2×10^6 different receptors, considering just the number of five-chain molecules. Not all of these 50 genes could be expressed in all T cells, or else we should have nearly omnipotential T cells which we clearly have not. We could still very well have multipotential T cells, but Wigzell's data show that, if so, there must be a non-random distribution of the genes expressed. It follows from his positive selection experiments that cells which express the genes coding for symbol 1 of Figure 3a are not expressed in the same cell as genes coding for symbols 2 or 3. Still, the subpopulation of 6% of anti-DA reactive cells would be expected to be reactive to many conventional antigens also. However, a sufficient degree of multipotency to ensure that may require many more than a total of 50 genes when the simultaneous expression in one cell of several genes is restricted to those which are anti-DA.

Figure 3b depicts an alternative and more clonal model for the formation of multi-chain receptors. It is based on the very likely assumption that the single-chain molecules are products of genes belonging to several multigene families, although one among these may be dominant in terms of allo-aggression determinants. We might now play the numbers' game in such a way that 50 genes be distributed over five multigene families with 10 genes each. (For the sake of simplicity only 2 multigene families are shown in Figure 3b.) That arrangement would permit the formation of 10^5 different 5-chain receptors even if we were to assume both allelic exclusion and restriction of the genic expression to one gene per multigene family. In fact there is no evidence of allelic exclusion so far in the MHC. Therefore, if both haplotypes are, in fact, expressed in a MHC heterozygote, there would be up to 10 different gene products expressed in one cell, even assuming clonal restriction to 1 gene per multigene family. In terms of 5-chain receptors that would mean a potential of nearly 200 different compound receptors per cell. On either model, elimination of a subpopulation of 6% of DA-reactive Lewis T cells would be expected to remove also about 6% of the repertoire of multi-chain receptors to conventional antigens. The latter model may help understanding linkage disequilibrium in terms of the necessity for the products of different multigene families to cooperate in the membrane. This they may do the more efficiently if they have a common allo-aggression determinant in their origin.

BENACERRAF: What I don't understand in your system is how you are able to explain Binz and Wigzell's observations with respect to the idiotypic specificities being a heavy chain v region, whereas your receptors there appear to have all the characteristics of postulated Ir or Ia molecules.

SIMONSEN: Correct, I have not explained the apparent great similarity in Wigzell and Binz's experiments between T and B cell idiotypes. I would not expect such a high degree of similarity to be a general phenomenon. When it occurs I suggest it may be due to the fact that the antigen is being particularly restrictive in its requirements to a good receptor fit. This being so, the T and B cell receptors which do fit must have very similar geometry, hence also provoke very similar anti-idiotypes. The T and B receptors could still be quite different molecular species which is what I have envisaged.

BENACERRAF: The issue of allo-specific T cells being numerous is still open for discussion and particularly by Darcy Wilson if he wishes.

WILSON: I am not sure I can say anything very profound except maybe a few very naive things. I would envision that one of the reasons for the high frequency goes along the line of thinking adopted by Shearer and by Zinkernagel and Doherty with certain predictions that, in fact, an alloantigen is really a neoantigen, in their terminology; that self has a large proportion of cells potentially reactive to self, and that if Binz and Wigzell had not pre-absorbed their antibody on the strain that produced it, they might have found idiotype-positive cells. There is some reason to believe they may exist in the individual that makes the antibody. Now, a prediction from this is that if one were to negatively select a population of lymphocytes against the histocompatibility antigens that are going to be chemically or virally modified, then one should not be able to make the killing reaction work.

BENACERRAF: But how do you or anyone reconcile the large number of T cells specific for alloantigens with the very large number of thymus-dependent antigens against which T cells are reactive? I know, Darcy Wilson, that you are doing experiments to try to demonstrate that one class is within the other, and I wondered whether you believe it strong enough now to be able to state that it is more than a hypothesis.

WILSON: No, I don't think I believe anything on it. I think I am a man at a horse race, and I haven't put any money down, so I am just enjoying it. I do not think the experiments we have done with the sheep red cell antigen are the proper kind of experiments -- it's the proper approach, but not the appropriate antigen to

study. As to how one can account for the fine specificity for reactions to conventional antigens, I would
envision, for example, that a very simple model might
be that Binz and Wigzell's is a heavy chain idiotype
and that the fine specificity is added on to that by
associated light chains. So, for example, one might
try the trick of positively selecting in the Wigzell
sense, and in a much purer sense than we can get, I
think, and then to take some antibody, for example to
KLH, dissociate it into heavy and light chains and feed
the light chains to the T cell and see if one can generate fine specificity T helpers for KLH that way. I
mean it is a very naive experiment, but it's certainly
straightforward.

BENACERRAF: I would have preferred it if you would have
added a different set of v regions.

PAUL: The idea that the T cell system was predominantly
defined or derived to respond against alloantigens and
that the vast majority of the T cells are participating
along this line, suggests an interesting experiment
that either Shearer or Zinkernagel and Doherty might do
or, in fact, may have done. But if one immunizes an
animal with TNP-syngeneic cells and is drawing upon
this limited library of cells responsive to alloantigens, one might now test these killer cells against
every other member of the species or every other strain
one can obtain and encounter, perhaps, one that will be
killed very efficiently. That is, you have a multi-
specificity system in the sense of Frank Richards so
that you are selecting a clone which was really derived
for a quite different function and the nice part would
be to prove that. I wonder if either Gene or Rolf has
looked at that possibility?

SHEARER: We have restricted most of our target cells to
the B10 congenic lines for obvious reasons, but we have
gone to other inbred non-congenic strains and so far as
we have looked, this has not been the case.

ZINKERNAGEL: We also haven't found any gross cross-reactivity on normal or infected allogeneic targets. However, in the pox virus systems, there is a phenomenon
which occurs at the very early stage; that is 2 or 3
days after infection, a high background of killing on
uninfected target cells is observed, which may have

760

some bearing to the issue raised by Bill Paul. Now the other question is, are these 6% reactive cells one finds using several types of approaches, are these 6% really immunologically-specific cells in the terms of cytotoxic T cells, for example, or do these 6% reflect a heterogeneous population of immunologically-specific reactive cells and cells which have other functions than an immunologically-specific recognition in terms, for example, of just eliciting graft-versus-host phenomena which cannot be entirely a reflection of the aggressor cells but rather, a response of the attacked cells of the host. So, I think the situation is much more complex.

GERSHON: Again, I have to say I like the suggestion that Bill Paul put forth but I had a thought of a different way of testing it which might test the same thing; and that is, the question if you remove by negative selection, as Darcy or Hans do, the cells that can react with a given alloantigen, can you then still demonstrate using the Zinkernagel, Doherty, Shearer systems whether or not the two are different phenomena or whether the same cell carries all those fine specificities?

BACH: It is frequently stated that the system of cell-cell recognition about which we are speaking is one specifically for alloantigens. I really do not feel that the evidence supports that view. There is now ample evidence that xenogeneic MLR do take place both in normal and germ-free animals. Widmer tested 5 species in several different xenogeneic combinations and showed that in some combinations the average MLR were as great as, or greater than, in allogeneic combinations. He, Sondel and we extended these findings to germ-free animals. One might not argue that xenogeneic MLR actually reflect recognition by lymphocytes of xeno-LD antigens, that are cross-reactive with allo-LD antigens, and hence the xeno-reaction shows nothing more than allo-recognition. Kirsten Lindhal, Joanne Martinis and I have been trying to test this using lymphocytes that have been primed in a regular MLC to allogeneic LD antigens. We have then, as in our PLT method, restimulated these primed cells with xenogeneic cells to ascertain whether the latter possess cross-reactive LD antigens. In the initial experiments using human and mouse cells, we found no evidence for such cross-reactivity. More recently, Martinis obtained evidence suggesting that there may be some LD cross-reactivity between man and monkey, cows and dogs. However, the results suggest that at least part of the recognition in xeno-reactions is not due to cross-reactivity. These data do not rule out that allo-LD antigens are recognized more strongly than xeno-LD antigens. Kirsten and I have speculated that the lower xeno-reactivity is not due as much to decreased recognition as to decreased efficacy of various amplifying factors involved in such reactions which simply may not function as well across species barriers, a concept for which she has some data. Wigzell's 6% responding cell frequency for one allogeneic MHC haplotype is not inconsistent with the estimates Simonsen, Wilson and we made for the initial response frequencies. His dramatic finding is that there is no cross-recognition of other allogeneic haplotypes by those cells. I believe that this may be peculiar to the 3 rat strains he is using, and predict that if the system is extended to man or mouse, or perhaps even other rat strains, that cross-recognition will be seen. I personally cannot understand how his positive selection method would influence the results, as compared with our demonstration by PLT of extensive LD cross-reactivity in humans.

BENACERRAF: Fritz, would you be satisfied if one would not write the sentence as alloantigens but rather, antigens which are restricted to allo-aggression in one species and would be also represented in the other species. In other words, corresponding to the MHC locus.

BACH: No, because as soon as you say restricted to antigens of that species, I disagree.

BENACERRAF: Not of that species; I said restricted in any species to those molecules coded for by the MHC which we have learned only yesterday that they are so similar in amino acid sequence.

BACH: I fully accept that, then you can speak of cross-reactivity.

SACHS: As Fritz knows, Henry Winn and Paul Russell and I described exactly the same result with antibody made in xenogeneic combinations 5 or 6 years ago, and again, we were unable to detect any particular H antigen of the species in which it was made with those which we had shown were specific for the H antigens of the other species. But I don't think it really proves anything because if you have a huge amount of polymorphism as you seem to have in any of these species, the chance that with any of the available strains that you could test that you would pick up just that particular specificity, I think would become vanishingly small. So I don't think that either in your system or in our system it proves that that isn't exactly what is happening and there isn't a specific recognition system for the H antigens.

BACH: The experiments I just discussed were done by sensitizing human lymphocytes to a pool of 20 different human lymphocytes which I refer to as a standard stimulating cell. Dr. Paul Sondel, Michael Sheehy and we have shown in a number of studies that a cell sensitized to the pooled standard stimulating cell will now be restimulated markedly by essentially any cell in the population unless that cell shares LD determinants with the initial responding cell. In fact, we have proposed this as a potential histocompatibility test which we have referred to as the secondary stimulation test or SST.

Given that the cells of individual A have, in fact, been sensitized to essentially all the LD antigens within the species, we now attempt to restimulate such a sensitized responding cell in the secondary restimulation system with cells of another species such as mouse. It is in such a situation that Kirsten Lindahl and Joanne Martinis have obtained preliminary results suggesting that there are no shared LD antigens. These results are clearly preliminary, and experiments testing more directly where the sensitization to specific LD determinants will show cross-reactivity with specific mouse restimulating cells are underway.

6. THE PHENOMENON OF *CIS-TRANS* PREFERENCE IN COMPLEMENTATION OF *Ir* GENES AND ITS RELEVANCE TO LINKAGE DISEQUILIBRIUM IN THE MHC

BENACERRAF: Now I would like to go very rapidly through the next point because this is a question which is very interesting but for which there is again no explanation, and here there is probably no controversy because

763

nobody has data on this point except our laboratory and
Paul Maurer's. What is the explanation for the *cis-
trans* effects in the *Ir* gene control responses? I
would like to ask for critical comments from Lee Hood
or Jan Klein,or people who are certainly more competent
than we are in interpreting gene interactions and gene
complementation.

SIMONSEN: I would like to suggest that if we are going to
have a formation of compound receptors by preformed
building stones, then it is a great advantage if they
can recognize each other through some stretch of identity or great similarity. And those on the *cis*-posi-
tion are more like each other than those on the *trans*-
position and therefore, they are held together and that
explains the linkage disequilibrium as well as the *cis-
trans* effect.

BENACERRAF: Thank you, Morten. Martin Dorf who discovered
this phenomenon has a right to comment on it.

DORF: Well, first I think we should still be a bit cautious about the phenomenon since there are only a limited number of examples and they have only been demonstrated in one laboratory. The role of gene dosage in
the phenomena really has to be excluded in more instances. We've only really ruled it out in one, and
the data there are, I think, convincing, but the numbers aren't overwhelming. I think if we do accept this
cis-phenomena, then we certainly have to worry about
how genes are interacting and what this haplotype
preference means in terms of functional expression. I
think it represents a new area for *H-2* or *Ir* geneticists and although I have no explanation for the phenomenon mechanistically, *cis*-effects can be considered
the result of a translation of a poly-cistronic message or perhaps some sort of operon system. I am not
really convinced that *cis*-phenomena accounts for maintenance of the entire MHC in a complex; I think it can
account for the clustering of *Ir* genes within the genome but extending it to other parts of the MHC is perhaps a bit unwarranted unless we also assume that the
Ir genes show some sort of haplotype preference for *K*
or *D* or Ia MLR-type products so that the entire complex
must be maintained in the genome as an intact unit.

HOOD: My comment is just a cautionary one. I think we

should be very cautious about interpreting this phenomenon in terms of operons, because, to my knowledge, outside of a couple of very exceptional cases, there is no evidence whatsoever of operons or poly-cistronic messengers in eukaryotes. So, I think the explanation will almost certainly be something else.

BENACERRAF: I simply would like to add one point that I feel a little more confidence than Martin in the validity of the phenomenon because in *Ir* gene systems there is no example of gene dose effects in all the systems that have been investigated in the guinea pig. A small gene dose effect was demonstrated in the mouse by Hugh McDevitt in the (T,G)-A--L system. We looked for gene dose effects with Ira Green in the guinea pig system and we could not find them.

McDEVITT: I think in the (T,G)-A--L system there is definitely a gene dose effect.

SACHS: Hugh, you are talking about antibody levels, but have you observed the phenomenon when you have done it with F_1 between two congenic animals, such that you are not also getting a gene dose effect due to the allotype locus?

McDEVITT: The answer is yes, with C3H and CSW or with C3H and CWB. In fact, the data went by in a very complicated slide yesterday, but you do see a gene dose effect if you do serial dilution titrations in maximally immunized (C3H x CSW)F_1's and C3H's. There is a definate gene dose effect. Now the question is if the difference between the non-responder and the F_1 is 20-fold and then the difference between the F_1 and the homozygous high responder is another 2-fold, you are dealing with a threshold. That could still be an absolutely classical gene dose effect.

RAJEWSKY: There is also a gene dose effect at least in one combination in the response of rats to LDH$_B$ in high and low responders, as Dr. Würzburg in our lab discovered some years ago.

7. THE BASIS FOR PRESENCE OR ABSENCE OF GENETIC RESTRICTIONS IN T-B CELL COOPERATION -- ADAPTATION OR SELECTION?

BENACERRAF: Alright, there are some gene dose effects, but

not in the system which we investigated; we did not
find any. Now we move on to the last point before we
discuss the area of human application. It is a very
important issue which concerns the restriction or lack
of genetic restriction observed by different laboratories, in experiments on cooperation between helper T
cells and B cells in antibody responses, when the B and
T cells are allogeneic. A variety of hypotheses have
been offered to reconcile these differences and they
seem to me to be of two types. 1) That the cooperation
observed in those experiments where it is seen between
allogeneic T and B cells are due to T and/or B cell
adaptation, or 2) to a selection process whereby allo-
aggressive T cells have been selected out, or B cells
have been selected in.

SHEARER: I would like to comment on the point I brought up
the other day about our old experiments in which we
found allogeneic collaboration between thymocytes and
bone marrow cells for the generation of responses to
the whole series of synthetic polypeptides under *Ir*
gene control. Now, there are distinct differences between the way the experiments were designed in our case
and those in the case of David Katz and collaborators,
and these differences could be significant. They include, first of all, that we were looking at thymocytes and bone marrow cells which are certainly not as
differentiated or the same class of T and B cells that
one would find in the periphery; and the second point
is that Katz and collaborators have worked with T cell
populations which were primed in the animals before the
adoptive transfers were done. In contrast, our allogeneic transfers which appeared to cooperate were performed with thymus and marrow cells from animals which
had not been preimmunized. I would just like to raise
the possibility -- is there any chance that previous
priming could be responsible for the apparent discrepancies that we see? Especially, if one would consider
the possibility that Ia antigens may be expressed on
cells as a function of priming and that those Ia specificities may have to do with cell collaboration.

KATZ: I think that Gene Shearer has just made precisely
the point that I was trying to bring out in the discussion following my presentation on Wednesday. This
is, of course, still at the level of speculation, but
we may be able in the near future to demonstrate that

766

such differences between unprimed and previously primed lymphocytes do, indeed, account for the apparent discrepancies in the observations that he had earlier with Edna Mozes and Michael Sela, the more recent studies of Katie Bechtol, et al in tetraparental mice, and those of Harald von Boehmer and John Sprent in bone marrow chimeras as compared to our own results. The concepts of "haplotype preference" and "adaptive differentiation" that I presented are based on the presumption that cellular interactions at very early stages of lymphocyte differentiation condition, in some way, the lymphocytes involved such that upon recall stimulation -- i.e. as in a secondary response -- they interact most efficiently with lymphocytes possessing identical cell interaction (CI) structures as those with which the original interactions took place. Now whether this adaptation, if it can be shown to occur without doubt, reflects inductive or selective events and, moreover, whether there is a molecular basis for it in cell membrane-associated structures will require considerable investigation in the immediate future.

von BOEHMER: Since Darcy Wilson isn't here at this time, I would like to talk about his experiments which to my mind argue against adaptation. Because what he has simply done is to remove allo-reactive cells and then has made a mixture of unprimed T and B cells and gotten perfect cooperation. John Sprent and I have in a way similar results in a secondary response. Thus, we have used two strains primed to sheep red cells and have selected out allo-reactive cells and in two experiments we seem to get cooperation; a third experiment failed. However, the other interpretation in this case may be that the removal of the allo-reactive cells is not complete. If this is the case, then what Darcy and we are looking at is really a sort of mild allogeneic effect which mimics cooperation. On the other hand, I think that is a very unlikely explanation for the cooperation in bone marrow chimeras as we have observed and as Alan Munro has observed. So there still could be adaptation, but if Wilson and we can exclude that we are dealing with an allogeneic effect, I think it becomes very unlikely.

McDEVITT: Harald, what you were saying is that if you selected out allo-reactive cells when the cells were separated prior to immunization, they were not immun-

ized together, and then put them together, they cooperated perfectly well? It is very important because that
says that all of the effects in David's experiments
were simply due to allo-reactive cells.

von BOEHMER: Well, that may be so if Darcy Wilson is not
looking at an allogeneic effect, which he has to exclude. But we haven't done those experiments ourselves. The experiments I am quoting are experiments
of Darcy Wilson and Ellen Heber-Katz taking unprimed T
and B cells and recruiting out the allo-reactive cells
from the T cell population in an F_1 hybrid.

McDEVITT: I thought you were saying you had done that as
well, because the key problem with that experiment is
that it is only for IgM responses. If, in fact, the
predominant allo-reactive effect is on IgG responses,
then the same cooperation between cells primed separately and allo-reactive-depleted has to be shown for an
IgG response.

von BOEHMER: Well, as I said, John Sprent and I have attempted to do those experiments. The results are not
as clear as they should be, since we have positive and
negative results.

BENACERRAF: David, did you want to comment on that?

KATZ: In essence, I was just going to make the point that
Hugh has already made. I don't think that it is perhaps possible to draw correlative explanations from the
chimera experiments, and the allo-reactive filtration
experiments for the reasons that Hugh pointed out, and
Harold pointed out. What I would like to emphasize is
the fact that the similarity in the slopes of the
curves that Darcy Wilson and Ellen Heber-Katz have obtained with their filtered alloantigen-reactive cells
versus syngeneic cells, which is the predominant basis
for the conclusion that has been reached, can be misleading for the following reason: The reason is that,
although it may not be as apparent to people who have
not worked in these systems, there really is a perfectly good linear relationship between the numbers of
cells used for an allogeneic effect and those that are
used for syngeneic cooperation in terms of the mangi-
tude of response obtained. In other words, with X numbers of cells that give an allogeneic effect of X

768

magnitude, when you dilute these cells down, you also dilute down the magnitude of the response that one obtains, presumably because you are looking at a reflection of the numbers of B cells capable of being stimulated under the circumstances. Therefore, to draw a conclusion from parallel regression line plots -- that this means that you are only getting physiologic syngeneic cooperation is not, I think, a correct assumption. For this reason, I would raise a cautionary note in proving without a doubt, particularly in the filtration experiments, that one is not dealing with very small numbers of allo-reactive cells that may be causing the effect. And I should add that unfortunately in that system it is an almost impossible situation to clarify.

The data for those of you who don't know or remember are that if you use allogeneic unprimed cells, together with histoincompatible B cells *in vitro*, one gets an allogeneic effect at very low numbers of cells which reaches a plateau and falls off at higher numbers of cells because of suppression due to the allogeneic effect. This number of cells may be 1/2 log or more lower than the maximum numbers of syngeneic T cells that one can put in the system. Unfortunately, if one looks at the maximum numbers of syngeneic cells that you can put in the system and still get a response, you reach a point above which you cannot go without also suppressing the response. These are the features of *in vitro* cultures. Therefore, to do the experiments, it almost becomes impossible to definitively rule out the possibility that I was just discussing, because if you raise the numbers of filtered alloantigen-reactive cells to numbers above that which give suppression with syngeneic cells, you are also going to get suppression, and so the curves are going to be linear.

PAUL: David, I don't think, in fact, it is true that Darcy's experiment cannot be definitively tested because there is the direct prediction that if it is simply the dilution of an allo-aggressive cell to a point ten-fold lower than it previously existed, then removal of cells specific for sheep erythrocytes should have no effect whatever on the helping activity of that population. Now, on the other hand, if it truly reflects the collaborative ability of sheep cell-specific T lymphocytes, then depleting those cells will deplete the helper activity of the allogeneic cells, and that is, in fact, possible to do by the same technology that Darcy and Ellen did. I think Jacques Miller has described techniques in which you can deplete cells during a thoracic type passage.

KATZ: No, on the contrary, because as Darcy pointed out -- in fact, one of their experimental observations in that system is that if they look at the positively selected cells for reactivities against sheep erythrocytes, all of the sheep erythrocyte-reactive cell population exist in that same population; so the problem may exist that if you remove sheep-reactive T lymphocytes from the population, you may also be removing the allo-reactive cells.

HOOD: Well, let me turn a consideration of this subject around and ask, from the point of view of the chemists, David Katz or those who have some concern with the subject, what are the predictions you would make a) with regard to the adaptive model, or b) with regard to the selective model at the cell surface? What are the predictions, what are the kinds of molecular changes you would see, and are there experiments one could design to distinguish between the alternatives? Because it seems to me you are at a point where -- and it is one of the very few cases -- you can move possibly from the phenomenology to chemistry. That is one of the things I have been noticing as we try to bring together these two areas. I think there are very few bridges; maybe there is one here and I'd be curious as to whether or not you or others think there is.

KATZ: Well, ideally, it would be wonderful to be able to say that if you take cells that have adapted, if this is in fact happening, in an allogeneic environment so that they show a switch in their haplotype preference after differentiation, that one would be able to look at those cells and either by serotyping analysis or, preferably, by more direct chemical means could, indeed, show the expression of alloantigen or histocompatibility molecules which reflects this adaptation. Now, by serotype analysis which I think has been done extensively, such as the ones Harald von Boehmer has done in his chimeras, and many other people have done in chimeras in the past, there is no evidence that this is something that can be demonstrated in this way.

770

However, I think this is an impossible approach from which to draw conclusions because you may be dealing with small numbers of molecules that are being expressed on the surface of the cell representing only a minor proportion of the total histocompatibility gene products of the genome, and perhaps the ultimate answer will come from being able to demonstrate changes chemically but nevertheless, that may also be impossible for the same reason. And that goes back to the concept which you and Hugh and I have discussed privately last June about the regulator gene concept, and whether, in fact, you are manifesting expression of genetic material already present in the strain of mouse that you are dealing with that is now being expressed.

HOOD: Well, perhaps the reason it has been missed serologically again is we are dealing with v regions and the change that is relevant is in a part of the molecule that we can't see serologically, so again we get back to the chemistry.

BENACERRAF: There is also one point you must consider when we talk about this phenomenology and that is the genetic restrictions that are also seen between T and B cell cooperation, in Ir gene-restricted systems between F_1 responder T cells and non-responder B cells, using the very same experimental protocol that we found useful to demonstrate the other type of restriction. Whereas in tetraparental conditions you overcome that restriction which is one which you would not see for conventional antigens. It may be reasonable to consider that the genetic restrictions which we see with conventional antigen are simply a generalization of the phenomenon we see for the antigen under Ir gene control.

GERSHON: I'd like to suggest a new approach to this problem that is based on the ones that have been used and also on what we have learned about Ly antisera. That is, we know you can get very good cooperation against a M locus barrier, and you get a certain form of allo-aggression, in that there's a proliferative response, but what is lacking is the generation of the killer cells. Now, if the Ly-2-positive cells are the cells that are preventing the allo-aggression, the theory would be that if you depleted your cells of all Ly-2 positive cells, thus leaving only Ly-1 cells, and then got cooperation with these Ly-1 cells and, moreover, could abrogate the cooperation using Ly-1 cells from an animal tolerant to the particular antigen, I think that would answer the question. I bring this up for two reasons. One is to mention preliminary results that Harvey Cantor and I have obtained in this system which indicate that depletion of the Ly-2, 3 population produces a very nice cooperative response; however, we have none of the adequate controls to say that this is not an allogeneic effect. Secondly, I would like to ask David whether he thinks that this type of approach would answer the question.

KATZ: This sounds like a reasonable approach; but I'm not sure until I think about it very carefully.

McDEVITT: I would like to focus more on the cell type in which the adaptation is occurring. I think it may be a bit much to ask the question, right off the bat, if there is a molecular change. There may be no molecular change at all. It may be purely selection among a population of responding T cells in a chimeric situation, and that experiment can be done and I am sure Harald is going to do it and we're going to do it. You take chimeras that are tolerant, that are showing good allogeneic T-B cell interaction and then ask the question, by using the appropriate syngeneic and allogeneic cells, whether it is the T cell that has learned how to interact with allogeneic and syngeneic B cells or whether it is the B cell which has learned how to cooperate with allogeneic T cells. Then you can ask the question of which T cell population is involved. In other words, had you simply sub-selected a population of T cells there, or is there some molecular variation? I agree that if it is getting down to the question of expressing a particular v region, then it is going to be very hard to show it. To me, it is quite important because if the answer is that it is a T cell selection or adaptation, then the argument that the B cell in the particular responder - non-responder pair we used in our tetraparental studies is completely competent, gains a great deal of strength.

von BOEHMER: We have done part of the experiment you have suggested by taking primed B cells from a straight allogeneic donor -- B cells which have never been in the chimeric environment -- and they cooperated with T cells which had been in the chimeric environment; so if

adaptation occurred, it must have occurred at the level
of the T cell.

SACHS: David, in your curve that goes up and down, it is
assumed that the same cell causing the allogeneic effect is, in fact, also suppressing at the higher dose
due to whatever the allo-aggressive reaction is. But,
in fact, if the interpretation from Darcy Wilson's experiment is applied to your explanation, you have irradiated your cells to get rid of an allogeneic effect.
Now, if someone would like to say that the reason you
now find histocompatibility requirements is that the
allo-aggressive phenomenon still occurs, then it was
not sensitive to irradiation. So, wouldn't it be quite
simple to irradiate, then do the passaging of Wilson
and see if those allo-aggressive cells would still be
removed in that case?

KATZ: I think the point to which you are alluding is a
very important one; I am not confident, however, that
the approach you suggested is the proper one. There
are complexities here which are crucial to consider in
this problem.

The first point is, as you have correctly pointed out,
that we have purposely subjected our T cell populations
to X-irradiation *in situ* to limit, below detectable
levels, any possible enhancement of responses due to an
allogeneic effect. I must stress repeatedly, however,
that we have lowered any allo-reactions to *undetectable*
levels by the use of a fixed number of T cells -- this
does not mean that allo-reactions have been eliminated
totally.

A second point to remember is that we ourselves made
the unexpected observation that T cells in a heavily
irradiated recipient were nevertheless capable of exerting a potent allogeneic effect against transferred
histoincompatible donor B cells. We have also found
that even in the two-stage, double adoptive transfer
system used for the experimental observations under
debate here, we can get allogeneic effects by doubling
the numbers of T cells transferred from unprimed donors
histoincompatible with the B cells employed. I emphasize that in the latter situation the T cells are
irradiated and, moreover, the allogeneic effect is re-
producibly enhancing, *never* suppressive. These allo-

reactive cells are, therefore, not totally radioresistant, and the only way one can, without doubt, feel secure that an allogeneic effect is not occurring is to include the appropriate experimental controls. In our case, we have fastidiously done so by designing the system to 1) use numbers of cells which were below detectability of an allogeneic effect, and 2) to control every experiment with comparable numbers of normal, unprimed T cells of every haplotype employed in the experiment.

Therefore, in response to the approach you suggested, I would say that the most suitable experiment that Darcy Wilson and Ellen Heber-Katz could perform would be as follows: They should take the filtered T cells which have been depleted of allo-reactivity, prime them to sheep erythrocytes in an appropriate environment -- i.e. a histocompatible "B" rat -- recover those primed T cells, subject them to X-irradiation and then test them for their capacity to provide helper activity for primed syngeneic and allogeneic B cells *in vitro* to produce IgG anti-SRBC responses. If this is successful, with appropriate specificity controls, etc. included, then I think they have a more convincing argument than their present data supports. That is what I have been trying to say.

RELATIONSHIP OF THE MHC TO HUMAN DISEASE

BENACERRAF: I think we ought to close the discussion now and devote the rest of this morning's session to the relationship of the MHC to human disease, and I would like to ask Dr. van Rood to initiate this discussion.

van ROOD: After all these interesting and precise -- even down to the chemistry level -- discussions about the MHC, and the relationship between MHC and immune response, it is kind of hard to switch to something so vague and poorly understood as the association between the MHC of man, *HLA*, and disease. Nevertheless, there are a few points we could discuss. Before doing so there is another matter. The *HLA* people in this conference have been a "minority" group, and I am sure that I speak on behalf of all of them, that we are very grateful for the exciting information we have gathered in these last few days. The dialogue between *H-2* and *HLA* might, in the years to come, turn out to be very

774

fruitful. To start this dialogue I will formulate a few questions to those working in *H-2* concerning the points I will discuss.

Now back to disease associations. Disease association studies are a rather unsatisfactory approach to unravel the biological role of the MHC in man, for the simple reason that in all probability, disease is an expression of the price a few individuals in the population at large have to pay to retain genes of great survival value for the species as a whole. I will neither try to summarize in such a short time which disease associations have been found or what the current theories are which have been formulated to explain these associations. This has been done elsewhere (McDevitt, H.O. and Bodmer, W.F., *The Lancet*, no. 7869: 1269, 1974; *Transpl. Rev.* 22, 1975). Instead I will highlight some aspects which have received relatively little attention in the past.

The studies on associations with disease have so far failed to explain, for instance, such enigmas as the enormous polymorphism of the *HLA* system. If polymorphism is not accidental, but has a biological meaning, we would expect that heterosis or hybrid vigor would apply; in other words, that the heterozygote of the MHC would have a survival advantage over the homozygote. Assuming that this is so, the question is then: can we test this in man? Yes, we can, and as a matter of fact, it has already been done; the information is available. In our search for homozygous-typing cells, several selected groups of individuals have been studied to collect these cells, and one of them I have discussed with you already, were the cousin marriages. We can calculate which fraction of cousin marriages' offspring will be homozygous for *HLA*, and if heterosis or hybrid vigor applies, we would find less homozygous offspring than we expected. As I told you, Keuning tested the offspring of over 200 families of cousin marriages and where he expected to find 44 homozygous offspring he found 48 (Keuning, J.J. et al. *Histocompatibility Testing*, 1975, Copenhagen, Munksgaard). The conclusion appears to be that heterosis does not play a role, because the number expected and found was virtually the same. This study was done in a Dutch population in 1975. At about the same time that Keuning was collecting the cousin marriage offspring, Degos,

Colombani and others were studying the Tuaregs (Degos, L. and Colombani, J. *Nature* 249: 62, 1974). The Tuaregs are a South Sahara tribe which lives under primitive conditions and has the obligation by law of religion to marry with their cousin. A study of the Tuaregs, by the way, has the advantage that their geneology is very carefully documented because they have to know who is their cousin. Degos' study showed that the number of *HLA* homozygous offspring found was much smaller than what was expected. These two studies are thus not in agreement, and they suggest that in the Tuaregs heterosis might apply, but not in the Dutch, and this is of interest because the Tuaregs are living in a far less artificial situation than the Dutch in 1975 in Holland.

It should be pointed out, that there is another explanation for this lack of homozygotes in the Tuaregs, and that is that there might be a lethal gene in this tribe, a recessive lethal gene, which then could explain why no homozygotes were found. However, this would also imply that this recessive gene would be linked to *HLA*, and this, in itself, would be of interest. To differentiate between these two possibilities, it would be necessary to study not only the adult Tuareg population, but also the population at birth. If you would find the expected frequency of the homozygous at birth but not in the adult group, then I think you have a good argument for the heterosis theory. If, on the other hand, you have at birth no, or almost no, homozygous children, the recessive gene theory is far more likely to be true. In this connection, I wonder whether it is feasible to study the problem of heterosis also in mice. Offspring of wild mice might be even better. And I wonder whether it would be possible to do this not only in the artificial sterile condition of the animal house, but also in conditions where they are challenged by commonly occurring micro-organisms.

A second point I would like to make concerns human chimeras. There are two groups which are especially relevant; 1) the chimeras who survive after a bone marrow transplantation for instance for combined immune-deficiency. You have no need to give pretreatment here; you just infuse the bone marrow. Dooren and his colleagues have treated three such children in Leiden, two of whom are alive and well (Dooren, J.L. et al.

Sem. Hemat. <u>XI</u>: 369, 1974). One of these survivors
more than six years after the bone marrow transplantation provided us with a bit of unexpected and interesting information. It was possible to type the immunoglobulin allotypes -- the Gm factors -- before and after transplantation. Now, this child had a complete
recovery, but the interesting point was, that although
a take of the donor marrow, his sister, could be proven
to exist, the immunoglobulins were of recipient type;
in other words, there was here a block -- what type of
block we do not know -- which was relieved by the
transplantation of the bone marrow. I have no explanation for this finding, but I present it in order to
point out that these patients might be a worthwhile
group to study in more detail. If you ask the right
questions here, you might come up with some highly relevant information.

Another group which has almost been forgotten, although
most of the original work in the early days of transplantation biology was based on them, are the naturally-occurring chimeras. These naturally-occurring chimeras could tell us something about the conditions under
which a successful chimera can exist. A "successful"
chimera implies here not only the absence of GVH, but
also the presence of a normal immune response. The
relevance of this point in the context of this conference is self-evident. There are 20 chimeras known and
some have been studied. Healthy chimeras with a normal
immune response (as far as we know) can exist while the
twins are SD-different; that is, they are different for
the LA and 4 antigens. What we do not know is whether
they are identical or not for the *D*, MLC-stimulating or
LD region, and this can now be studied. Now that we
have typing cells available and now that we have the LD
serology, we can study this further. It is perhaps of
interest that in the first case we have been able to
study in this manner the data suggest that although the
twins differ for SD they carry the same LD determinants (van Rood, J.J. *Transpl. Proc.*, in press). It
would be of interest if we could study all 20 cases.
The question to those working with animal models is, of
course, what about the naturally occurring chimera in
animals? The whole thing started with the cow. Are
there other species in which natural chimerism occurs,
and from which one might we get an answer to the above
questions?

And then, as a closing point, the last thing I would like to discuss is a new area in which man can really be very useful and provide information which might be also exciting to the people who are working with *H-2*. I am referring to the complement deficiencies which were discussed by Dr. Kunkel. Just to point out one single problem: there is a linkage disequilibrium between *HLA10*, *W18* and *DW2*, the MLC factor. Now linkage disequilibrium, roughly speaking, can have two causes. One is that there has been relatively recently a mutation. Because the introduction of the mutation has been so recent, equilibrium has not yet been reached. The second, more exciting, possibility is that there might be an advantage to be heterozygous for this complement-deficient gene, just as is the case for sickle cell anemia.

BENACERRAF: Well, thank you, Jon. There are two comments before we close. One from Jean Dausset and one from Lee Hood.

DAUSSET: I just want to add some remarks about the Tuaregs. First, this is a very interesting tribe which foundered around 1750, and we have been able to know the *HLA* type of the founder because we can deduct all of the *HLA* type of the tribe; and so, the fact that there is no known homozygote is very striking, and my own explanation is, as you said, that maybe this is a gene equivalent of the *t* locus in mice, but we have not proven that. However, perhaps with the new marker of the region, we will be able to prove that. The second remark concerns another possibility of studying the importance of the MHC in man; this would be to test the newborn and to test old people. It has been done, I think in Europe, but in a population in which you have a very, very large death-life ratio. I have had this idea for years, but I have never been able to realize it because you have to be in the field and to determine the *HLA* type of the newborn in a primitive country. This could be, of course, very good information but this would suppose you have a very, very heavy selection and that maybe is unlikely. Another possibility of research is, of course, in the line of the Zinkernagel-Doherty and Shearer phenomenon, which I think is very important. In man it could be possible, in psoriasis for example, to see if the lymphocytes of this patient are killing specifically the cells of the psoriatic skin lesion.

Maybe this could be done in other diseases, but in psoriasis you have the cells readily available, and it would be very easy. What I would also like to say is that in this conference, it seems that no word has been said of the *Hh* locus, which is also in the MHC, and it could be very important in bone marrow transplantation. I think that we should not forget this because this is now, I think, a very clear immunological process, and it is probably very important in human beings.

I would like to finish by saying that I think that *HLA* in disease is a very, very important field, and the practical applications that we are expecting are fundamental because this will be nosology, a new classification of disease. This will be helpful in diagnosis, as is already the case in some circumstances; it will be valuable in prognosis as in diabetes, for example, in which those cases which are in association with *W15* are those which have the worst disease; and it will also be helpful in preventive and therapeutic medicine. At this point, I would recall that if there is a very severe disease linked to the *HLA* complex, it would be possible to determine the *HLA* type of the newborn by amniocentesis and eliminate the fetus if indicated.

Finally, I would like to thank all of you very much because we learned very much in this conference. It was for us *HLA* people very stimulating, and the most important one.

BENACERRAF: I think, as always, the last comment is to the chemist.

HOOD: As very much an outsider to this field in reading general reviews, at least in the past, I was very much struck by how people, in many ways defensively, said their systems were different, and I would like to point out the obvious. From a chemical point of view, it is clear that we are dealing with molecules that were derived from homologous genes, and I think this is very reassuring to all of us that we must certainly be dealing with gene complexes that are homologous in their general functions;   accordingly, much of what the human people have to say to the mouse people and vice versa, I think we can rest assured now that we are dealing with homologous systems. The other point I would like to make is that in all of my years of

779

dealing with immunoglobulin structure, I never ran into
a situation in which people were so generally cooperative about pooling their data together; remember, that
general discussion yesterday (Session VII) really was
from four labs, and I hope this spirit of cooperation
continues, just as I hope the Brook Lodge Symposia continue in the future.